Auto Fundamentals

How and why of the design, construction, and operation of automobiles. Applicable to all makes and models.

Martin W. Stockel
Automotive Writer

Martin T. Stockel
Automotive Writer

Chris Johanson
ASE Certified Master Automobile Technician

Publisher
The Goodheart-Willcox Company, Inc.
Tinley Park, Illinois

Copyright 2000

by

THE GOODHEART-WILLCOX COMPANY, INC.

Previous Editions Copyright 1996, 1990, 1985, 1982, 1978, 1974, 1969, 1963

All rights reserved. No part of this book may be reproduced, stored in a retrieval system, or transmitted in any form or by any means, electronic, mechanical, photocopying, recording, or otherwise, without the prior written permission of The Goodheart-Willcox Company, Inc. Manufactured in the United States of America.

Library of Congress Catalog Card Number 98-53655
International Standard Book Number 1-56637-577-0

4 5 6 7 8 9 10 00 03 02

Important Safety Notice

Proper service and repair is important to the safe, reliable operation of motor vehicles. Procedures recommended and described in this book are effective methods of performing service operations. Some require the use of tools specially designed for this purpose and should be used as recommended. Note that this book also contains various safety procedures and cautions, which should be carefully followed to minimize the risk of personal injury or the possibility that improper service methods may damage the engine or render the vehicle unsafe. It is also important to understand that these notices and cautions are not exhaustive. Those performing a given service procedure or using a particular tool must first satisfy themselves that neither their safety nor engine or vehicle safety will be jeopardized by the service method selected.

This book contains the most complete and accurate information that could be obtained from various authoritative sources at the time of publication. Goodheart-Willcox cannot assume any responsibility for any changes, errors, or omissions.

Library of Congress Cataloging-in-Publication Data

Stockel, Martin W.
    Auto fundamentals : how and why of the design, construction, and operation of automobiles : applicable to all makes of and models / by Martin W. Stockel, Martin T. Stockel, Chris Johanson.
        p.   cm.
    Includes index
    ISBN 1-56637-577-0
    1. Automobiles—Design and construction.   I. Stockel, Martin T.
II. Johanson, Chris.   III. Title.
TL240.S83   1999
629.2'31—dc21   98-53655
                                                                    CIP

Components used in the cover photograph were provided by Jack Loehman, owner of Elmhurst Auto Parts.

Introduction

CIP

Auto Fundamentals provides you with a thorough understanding of the design, construction, and operation of automotive systems. It contains information on the latest developments in the field of automotive technology. The material in this text is easy to understand and is applicable to all vehicles.

This text explains each system by starting with basic theory, then parts are added until the system is complete. By following this procedure, the function of each system is explained and its relationship to the complete vehicle is made clear.

A build-it-yourself approach is used in a number of areas. You will "build" on paper many of the systems being described. This provides a thorough understanding of the basic principles that are necessary to learning the how and why of automotive technology. Areas involving math, physics, chemistry, electricity, magnetism, and hydraulics are covered in the text where they apply.

Many of the illustrations were drawn especially for **Auto Fundamentals.** Important areas are featured in these illustrations and many are exaggerated to place emphasis on the parts being discussed. Color is used throughout to add emphasis and is coordinated with the specific needs of each illustration.

Each chapter of the textbook begins with Learning Objectives that provide focus for the chapter. Technical terms are printed in ***bold italic type*** and are defined when first used. Warnings are provided where a danger to life or limb may exist in the system being discussed. Each chapter also includes a Summary, a "Know These Terms" section, and Review Questions. A Dictionary of Automotive Terms is included in the back of this text.

A Workbook for **Auto Fundamentals** is also available. It is a convenient study guide and shop activity guide directly related to this textbook.

Martin W. Stockel
Martin T. Stockel
Chris Johanson

Contents

Chapter 11　Cooling Systems　193

Chapter 12　Lubrication Systems　211

Chapter 13　Exhaust Systems　229

Chapter 14　Emission Systems　239

Chapter 15　Computer Systems　259

Chapter 16　Charging and Starting Systems　277

Chapter 17　Chassis Electrical　303

Chapter 29   ASE Certification   555

Chapter 30   Career Opportunities   561

Conversion Tables   569

Dictionary of Automotive Terms   577

Acknowledgments   597

Index   599

Although most modern engines may seem complex, each one uses the same theories of operation. (Lexus)

1

Building an Engine

After studying this chapter, you will be able to:
- Identify the basic parts of an engine.
- Explain engine operating principles.
- Describe the function of the major parts of an engine.
- Describe the four-stroke cycle sequence.

This chapter covers the basic design and operation of an engine. This chapter is very important. To properly understand the theory and operation of the internal combustion engine, it is essential that you completely understand all the material presented in this chapter. Studying this chapter will prepare you for the chapters on engine design and construction later in this book.

What Is an Engine?

An engine is a group of related parts assembled in a specific order. In operation, it is designed to convert the energy given off by burning fuel into a useful form.

There are many parts in a modern engine, each essential to the engine's operation. For the time being, however, we may think of an engine as a device that allows us to pour fuel into one end and get power from the other, **Figure 1-1.**

Internal Combustion Engine

Before beginning to construct an engine, it would be helpful to know what the term internal combustion engine means. ***Internal combustion*** means burning within. ***Engine*** refers to the device in which the fuel is burned. ***Fuel*** indicates what is being burned. The engine converts the heat of burning fuel into useful energy.

Building an Engine on Paper

An excellent way to learn about engines is to build one on paper. Pretend that the engine has not yet been invented. You will be the inventor. You will solve the problems involved, step by step.

What to Use for Fuel

If you are going to convert fuel into useful energy, you will need a fuel that will ignite (burn) easily. It should burn cleanly, be reasonably inexpensive, and produce sufficient power. It must be available in quantity. It should also be safe to use and easy to transport. How about dynamite? No, it is expensive and burns violently. In short, it would blow up the engine, **Figure 1-2.** Kerosene? No, it is too hard to ignite and does not

Figure 1-1. An engine converts fuel into useful energy.

Figure 1-2. Dynamite will explode. Because of this, it is not useful as a fuel.

burn cleanly. Gasoline? Now you have found a fuel that will serve your purpose.

Gasoline

Gasoline is a product obtained by refining crude oil (petroleum) obtained from wells drilled into the earth. Basically, the crude oil is treated in various ways to produce gasoline, **Figure 1-3**. Gasoline is only one of the many items produced from crude oil. Gasoline used in engines is a complex mixture of basic fuels and special additives. See **Figure 1-4**. Since gasoline is a mixture of carbon and hydrogen atoms, it is termed a **hydrocarbon**.

Gasoline is usually available in three grades: regular, the lowest grade, plus or extra, the intermediate grade, and premium, the highest grade. All grades are assigned an **octane rating.** The octane rating indicates how well the gasoline will resist detonation (too rapid burning) in the cylinders. Regular gasoline usually has an octane rating of 87, plus has an octane rating of about 89, and premium has an octane rating of 92 to 94.

All gasoline sold today is **unleaded**. Unleaded gas contains no **tetraethyl lead**, which was used to raise octane. Unleaded gas must be used in late-model cars as tetraethyl lead will quickly destroy parts that help to reduce exhaust emissions (catalytic converter).

Many factors enter into the quality of any gasoline. It must pass exhaustive tests, both in the laboratory and in actual use. Basically, gasoline must burn cleanly, ignite readily, and resist freezing or boiling. It should contain a minimum number of harmful ingredients and prevent detonation.

 Warning: The following steps, which show how gasoline is prepared for use in the engine, are for purposes of illustration only and should not be tried by the student. Gasoline is dangerous. Treat it with care and respect.

Preparing the Fuel

As you know, gasoline burns readily. However, to get the most power from this fuel and, in fact, to get it to power an engine, special treatment is required.

If you were to place a small amount of gasoline in a jar and drop a match in it, it would burn, **Figure 1-5**. Such burning is fine to produce heat, but it will not give us the explosive burning effect we need to operate an engine. We must figure

Figure 1-4. Gasoline is a complex mixture of refined crude oil and other chemicals that allow it to provide maximum performance.

GAS   + MATCH = FIRE

Figure 1-5. Gasoline burns. However, it will not burn outside the presence of oxygen.

out a way to get the gas to burn fast enough to produce an explosive force?

If you examine **Figure 1-5,** you will notice that the gasoline is burning on the top side. Why is it not burning along the sides and bottom of the container? In order to burn, gasoline must combine with oxygen in the air. The sides and bottom of the gasoline in the jar are not exposed to air, so they do not burn.

OIL WELL   REFINERY   SERVICE STATION

TANKER   TANKER   AUTO

Figure 1-3. Before reaching your engine, crude oil requires much refining.

Breaking up Gasoline

For purposes of illustration, imagine that a gasoline particle is square, **Figure 1-6A.** It will burn on all sides. However, it still will not burn quickly enough for use in an engine.

To make the gasoline burn more rapidly, we can break it into smaller particles. Notice that as you divide it into smaller particles, you expose more area to the air, **Figure 1-6B.** If you ignite it now, it will burn much faster.

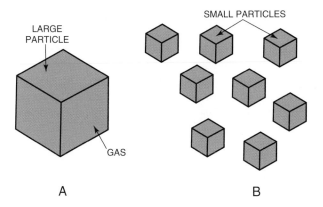

Figure 1-6. Breaking gasoline into smaller particles exposes more surface to the air, increasing the burning rate.

The Basic Force of an Engine

If you break up gasoline into very tiny particles, burning is fierce, **Figure 1-7.** Rapid burning produces a tremendous amount of heat, which in turn causes a rapid and powerful expansion. The burning gasoline gives off *energy* in the form of *heat.* You now have the necessary basic force with which to do work. The next step is to harness this force and make it work for you.

Trapping the Explosion

If you were to spray a mixture of gasoline and air into a sturdy metal container, place a lid over the top of the container, and then light the mixture, the resulting explosion would blow the lid high into the air. See **Figure 1-8.**

This is an example of using gasoline to do work. In this case, the work is blowing the lid into the air. Obviously, a flying lid will not push a car, but the flying lid does suggest a way to convert the energy of burning fuel into useful motion.

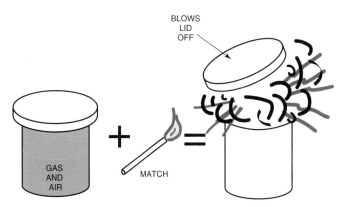

Figure 1-8. If air and fuel are mixed in a closed container and lit, it will blow the lid off of the container.

A Simple Engine

Make the same setup again, but this time use a rod to hook the lid to a shaft that is shaped like the one shown in **Figure 1-9.** Support each end of the shaft in bearings. Then, place a wheel on one end of the crankshaft, **Figure 1-10.**

Now, when the mixture explodes and the lid is blown into the air, the shaft will be given a sharp upward push, causing

Figure 1-9. A closed container containing air and fuel can be connected to a shaft to create a simple engine.

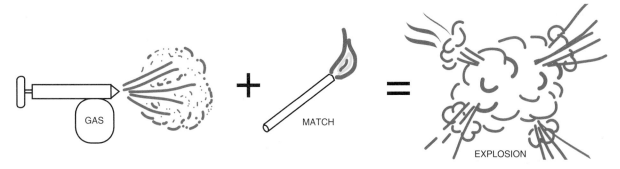

Figure 1-7. When gas particles are small enough they will explode.

the wheel to spin. You have built a very simple engine. Although this engine is not practical, it is pointing the way.

What Is Wrong With It?

What is wrong with our simple engine? Many things. Let us discuss them one at a time. The lid will fly up during the explosion. As the wheel spins, the lid will be forced down again. The lid can come down in any position, but if the engine is to work, it must come down over the container.

Instead of putting the lid over the container, cut it so that it just slips inside. Make the container longer so that the lid can push the shaft to the top of its travel and still not fly out of the container, **Figure 1-10.**

If you were to bolt the container and the shaft bearings so they could not change position, you would have an engine that would spin the wheel every time you fired a fuel mixture.

In order to cause the wheel to spin in the proper direction, you would have to fire the mixture with the crank in a

position similar to the one shown in **Figure 1-10A.** If the crank is in the position shown in **Figure 1-10B,** the lid could not fly up without pushing the crank bearing up or the container down. If it were fired with the crank in the position shown in **Figure 1-10C,** the wheel would spin backwards.

The mixture must be fired when the shaft is in the proper position. By studying **Figure 1-11**, you can see that the crankshaft changes the *reciprocating motion* (up and down) of the lid into *rotary motion* (round and round).

Name the Parts

At this time, the parts you have developed should be named. By doing so, you will learn what to call the parts in a gasoline engine that serve the same general purpose.

The container will be called the *block.* The hole in the container, or block, will be called the *cylinder.* The lid will be termed the *piston.* The shaft, with a section bent in the shape of a crank, will be called the *crankshaft.* The rod that connects the crankshaft to the piston will be called the *connecting rod.* The bearings that support the crankshaft will be called *main bearings.* The connecting rod has an upper bearing and lower bearing. The lower bearing (the one on the crankshaft) is called a *connecting rod bearing*. The wheel will be called the *flywheel.* Refer back to **Figure 1-10** and see if you can substitute the correct names for those listed.

Fastening the Parts

Since you are going to fasten the parts so the main bearing and cylinder cannot move, it would be wise to invert your engine and place the cylinder on top. Just why this is done will soon be obvious.

Make the block heavy to give it strength to withstand the fuel explosions. Bring it down to support the main bearings, **Figure 1-11A.** By bringing the block out and down around the main bearings, you now have a strong unit. In **Figure 1-11B,** the lower block end forms a case around the crankshaft. It allows you to have two main bearings. This lower block end is called the *crankcase.*

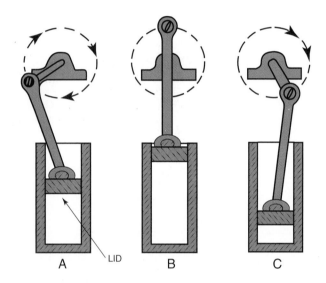

Figure 1-10. Placing the lid inside the container forms a simple engine.

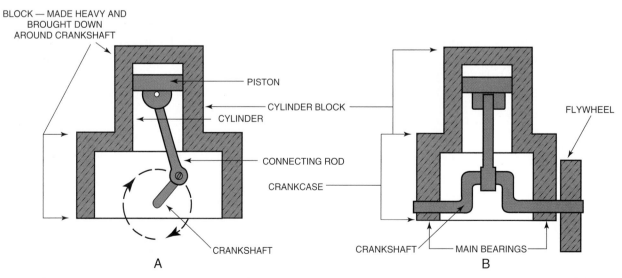

Figure 1-11. Front, side views showing how an engine is inverted, the block strengthened and brought down and around the crankshaft, forming the crankcase.

Lengthen the Piston

Now, make the piston longer. This stops it from tipping sideways in the cylinder. In order to avoid a piston that is too heavy, make it hollow. See **Figures 1-12** and **1-13.**

If the piston is to travel straight up and down and the connecting rod is to swing back and forth in order to follow the crank, it is obvious that the connecting rod must be able to move at the point where it is fastened to the piston, **Figure 1-14.**

Now, drill a hole through the upper end of the connecting rod. Also drill a hole through the piston. Line up the two holes and pass a pin through them. This pin is called a **piston pin**, or **wrist pin.** It is secured in various ways (more on this later). See **Figure 1-15.**

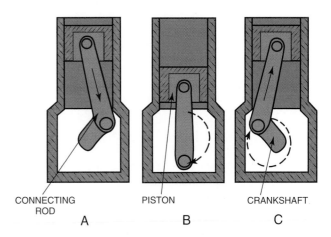

CONNECTING ROD   PISTON   CRANKSHAFT

A   B   C

Figure 1-14. To take advantage of the full piston action, the connecting rod must swing. Note position in A compared to C.

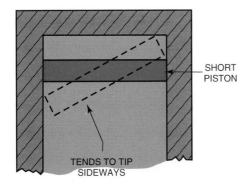

SHORT PISTON

TENDS TO TIP SIDEWAYS

Figure 1-12. Effect of a short piston. A short piston will tip from side to side.

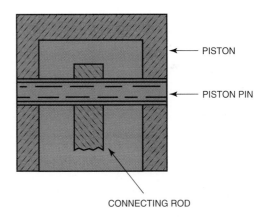

PISTON

PISTON PIN

CONNECTING ROD

Figure 1-15. A metal pin is used to secure the connecting rod to the piston.

PISTON

CYLINDER WALL

CONNECTING ROD

PISTON PIN

Figure 1-13. All automotive pistons are lengthened to avoid tipping.

Getting Fuel into the Engine

You have probably noticed that no provision has been made to get fuel into the upper cylinder area of your assembled engine. Your next step is to develop a system to admit fuel and to exhaust (blow out) the fuel after it is burned.

One opening in the upper cylinder area (called the **combustion chamber**) will not be adequate. You cannot admit fuel and exhaust the burned gases from the same opening. You need *two* openings.

Removable Cylinder Head

Redesign your cylinder block and make the top removable. You will call this removable top a **cylinder head.** It will be fastened in place with bolts or studs and nuts, **Figure 1-16.**

Fuel Intake and Exhaust Passages

Making your cylinder head removable has not yet solved all of the problems. You cannot take the head off and put it on each time the engine fires. Now, make the head of much thicker metal and make two holes, or passages, like those shown in **Figure 1-17.** This will give you one passage to take in the fuel mixture and another passage to exhaust it. These passages are called **valve ports**, **Figure 1-18.**

Figure 1-16. Cylinder head. Top of the cylinder has been removed.

Figure 1-17. The cylinder head metal is thickened and passages have been added. The passages and additional head metal will permit the installation of additional parts.

Figure 1-18. The valve ports in the cylinder head allows the air-fuel mixture to enter and exhaust gas to leave the cylinder. The space above the piston and below the valves is called the combustion chamber.

Valves

The next logical step is to provide a device to open and close the ports. If the ports are left open and fuel explodes in the combustion chamber, the forces from the explosion will blow out through the openings and fail to push the piston down.

This port control device, or **valve**, will have to be arranged so that it can be opened and closed when desired. Place a valve in each opening. This may be done as shown in **Figure 1-19.** When the valve sits on its **valve seat**, it seals the opening. The valves may be held in position by a hole bored in the head at A in **Figure 1-19.** This hole is called a **valve guide** because it guides the **valve stem** up and down in a straight line.

Figure 1-19. Valves are installed in the ports to seal the combustion chamber.

You will also install a **spring**, **spring washer,** and **keeper**. The spring is necessary to keep the valve tightly closed against its seat. When the valve is opened, the spring will close it again. Arrange your spring, spring washer, and keepers as shown in **Figure 1-20.** The valves now provide a satisfactory method of opening and closing the ports.

Four-Stroke Cycle

At this point you have an intake valve to allow fuel to enter the cylinder and an exhaust valve to let the burned fuel out. The next problem is how to get fresh fuel into the cylinder and how to get burned fuel out of the cylinder.

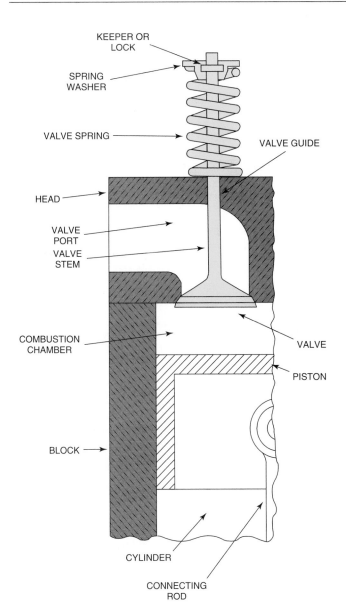

Figure 1-20. Installation of valve, spring, washer, and other valve assembly parts. This assembly closes the valves.

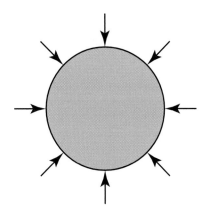

Figure 1-21. Air presses on all things with a pressure of 14.7 lb. per square inch at sea level. Air pressure varies with altitude.

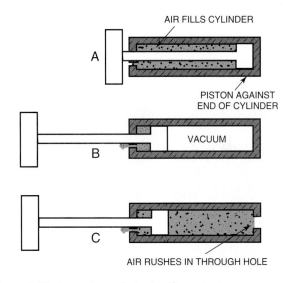

Figure 1-22. An engine cylinder is also a simple vacuum pump.

Vacuum Is the Clue

The air we live in presses on all things, **Figure 1-21**. This pressure is approximately 14.7 lb. per square inch (103 kPa) at sea level.

When we draw all the air out of a container, we form a *vacuum.* A vacuum is unnatural, and atmospheric pressure will do all it can to get into the low pressure area. If there is the slightest leak in the container, air will seep in until the pressure is the same on the inside of the container as it is on the outside. A vacuum, then, is any area in which the air pressure is lower than atmospheric pressure.

You Already Have a Vacuum Pump

Figure 1-22 illustrates a simple vacuum pump. This pump consists of a cylinder into which a snug fitting piston is placed. In **Figure 1-22A**, the piston is against the end of the cylinder. Obviously, there is no air between these two surfaces.

When you pull the piston through the cylinder, as in **Figure 1-22B**, you will have a large area between the face of the piston and the end of the cylinder. If there was no air between them before, and if the piston fits snugly against the cylinder, there still will be no air between them. This gives you a large area in which there is no air, or in other words, a vacuum.

If you were to drill a hole in the closed end of the cylinder, **Figure 1-22C**, air would immediately rush in and fill the cylinder. Any material, such as fuel, that happened to be in the surrounding air would also be drawn into the cylinder.

Where Is Your Vacuum Pump?

If the cylinder and piston in **Figure 1-22** form a vacuum, the cylinder and piston in your engine will do the same. If the piston is at the top of the cylinder (with both valves closed) and you turn the crankshaft, the piston will be drawn down into the cylinder. This will form a strong vacuum in the cylinder. If you now open the intake valve, the air will rush into the cylinder.

Stroke No. 1—The Intake Stroke

The first stroke in your engine is called the *intake stroke.* Instead of opening the intake valve after you have drawn the piston down, you will find it better to open the intake valve as the piston starts down. This allows the air to draw fuel in the entire time the piston is moving down. If you wait until the piston is down before opening the valve, the piston will be moving up before the cylinder can be filled with air, **Figure 1-23.**

Remember, the intake stroke starts with the piston at the top of the cylinder (intake valve open and exhaust valve closed) and stops with the piston at the bottom of its travel. This requires one-half turn of the crankshaft.

Figure 1-23. Engine cylinder on its intake stroke. As the piston travels down, it creates a vacuum, drawing in air and fuel.

Stroke No. 2—The Compression Stroke

You have discovered that the smaller the particles of gasoline mixed in the air, the more powerful the explosion.

As the crankshaft continues to move, the piston is forced up through the cylinder. If you keep both valves closed, the fuel mixture will be squeezed, or compressed, as the piston reaches the top. This is called the *compression stroke*, **Figure 1-24.** It, too, requires a half turn of the crankshaft.

The compression stroke serves to break up the fuel into even smaller particles. This happens due to the sudden swirling and churning of the mixture as it is compressed.

When the air-fuel mixture is subjected to a sudden sharp compression force, its temperature rises. This increase in temperature makes the mixture easier to ignite and causes it to explode with greater force. As the piston reaches the top of its travel on the compression stroke, it has returned to the proper position to be pushed back down by the explosion.

Remember, the compression stroke starts with the piston at the bottom of the cylinder (both valves closed) and

Figure 1-24. Engine cylinder compression stroke. As the piston approaches the top of the cylinder, it compresses the air and fuel.

stops with the piston at the top of the cylinder. This requires an additional half turn of the crankshaft.

Compression Ratio

The amount your engine will compress the fuel mixture depends on how small a space the mixture is squeezed into. In **Figure 1-25A,** the piston has traveled down 6" (152.4 mm) from the top of the cylinder. This is the intake stroke. In **Figure 1-25B,** the piston, which is on the compression stroke, has traveled up to within 1" (25.4 mm) of the cylinder top. It is obvious that 6" (152.4 mm) of cylinder volume has been squeezed into 1" (25.4 mm) of cylinder volume. This gives you a ratio of 6 to 1. This is called the *compression ratio*.

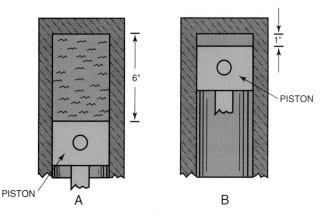

Figure 1-25. The compression ratio of an engine is the volume of a cylinder at the bottom of its stroke compared to its volume at the top of its stroke.

Stroke No. 3—The Power Stroke

As the piston reaches the top of the compression stroke, the mixture is broken into tiny particles and heated up. When ignited, it will explode with great force.

This is the right time to explode the mixture. A spark plug provides a spark inside the combustion chamber. The spark produced at the plug is formed by the ignition system. This will be discussed in Chapter 8.

Just imagine that a hot spark has been provided in the fuel mixture. The mixture will explode and, in turn, force the piston down into the cylinder. This gives the crankshaft a quick and forceful push. This is the *power stroke*. Both valves must be kept closed during the power stroke or the pressure of the burning fuel will squirt out through the valve ports. See **Figure 1-26.**

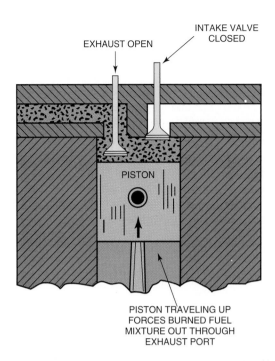

Figure 1-27. Engine cylinder exhaust stroke. As the piston travels up, it pushes the burned air and fuel exhaust gases out of the combustion chamber.

Figure 1-26. An engine's power stroke. The compressed air and fuel is ignited and the piston travels down.

Remember, the power stroke starts with the piston at the top of the cylinder (both valves closed) and stops with the piston at the bottom of the cylinder. This requires another half turn of the crankshaft.

Stroke No. 4—The Exhaust Stroke

When the piston reaches the bottom of the power stroke, the exhaust valve opens. The spinning crankshaft forces the piston up through the cylinder, pushing burned gases out, **Figure 1-27.** This is the *exhaust stroke*.

Remember, the exhaust stroke starts with the piston at the bottom of the cylinder (exhaust valve open and intake valve closed). It stops with the piston at the top of the cylinder. This requires one more half turn of the crankshaft.

Completed Cycle

If you count the number of half turns in the intake, compression, power, and exhaust strokes, you will find you have a total of four. This gives you two complete turns, or *revolutions*, of the crankshaft, **Figure 1-28.** While the crankshaft is turning around twice, it is receiving power only during one half turn, or one fourth of the time.

Cycle Repeated

As soon as the piston reaches the top of the exhaust stroke, it starts down on another intake, compression, power, and exhaust cycle. This cycle is repeated over and over. Each

Figure 1-28. Four strokes are equal to two revolutions of the crankshaft.

complete cycle consists of four strokes of the piston, hence the name **four-stroke cycle.** There is also a two-stroke cycle, which will be covered later in this text.

What Opens and Closes the Valves?

You have seen that the intake valve must be opened for the intake stroke, both valves must remain closed during the compression and power strokes, and the exhaust valve opens during the exhaust stroke. You must now design a device to open and close the valves at the proper times.

Start by placing a round shaft above the valve stem. This shaft is supported in bearings placed in the front and the rear of the cylinder head. See **Figure 1-29.**

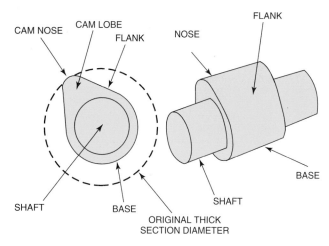

Figure 1-30. Section of a camshaft showing a cam lobe. Study the names of the various parts of the cam lobe.

Figure 1-29. Engine section showing how the camshafts are positioned.

Camshaft

The shaft will have an egg-shaped bump called a **cam lobe.** The cam lobe is machined as an integral part of the shaft. This shaft is called a **camshaft, Figure 1-30.**

The distance the valve will be raised, how long it will stay open, and how fast it opens and closes can all be controlled by the height and shape of the lobe. The lobe in this illustration is located directly over the valve stem, **Figure 1-31.** Other camshaft placements in the block and head will be discussed in later chapters.

As you will see later, it is impractical to have the cam lobe contact the end of the valve stem itself. You have placed the camshaft some distance above the end of the valve stem. When you turn the camshaft, the lobes will not even touch the valve stem.

Figure 1-31. How the cam lobe opens a valve. The valve is closed by the valve spring assembly you studied earlier.

Valve Lifter

Your next step is to construct a cylindrical unit called a cam follower, or **valve lifter.** The valve lifter in **Figure 1-32** is a solid lifter. Other lifters are hydraulic. Some lifters have an adjustment mechanism. These lifters are discussed in Chapter 2.

The lifter is installed between the cam lobe and the valve stem. The upper end rides on the lobe and the lower end almost touches the valve stem. The lifter slides up and down in a hole bored in the head metal that separates the valve stem from the camshaft. See **Figure 1-33.**

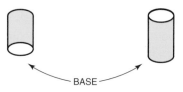

Figure 1-32. A simple valve lifter. Most valve lifters are more complex than this.

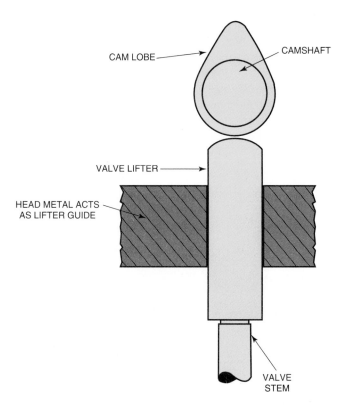

Figure 1-33. Exaggerated drawing showing valve lifter installation. The lifter is installed and moves inside the cylinder head metal. Note how the lifter would reduce wear and friction on the valve and camshaft lobe.

You have now built the essential parts of the valve system. The parts, in their proper positions, are referred to as the *valve train*. See **Figure 1-34.**

Camshaft Speed

You have developed a method of opening and closing the valves. The next problem is how and at what speed to turn the camshafts. Stop a minute and think. Each valve must be open for one stroke. The intake valve is open during the intake stroke and remains closed during the compression, power, and exhaust strokes. This would indicate that the cam lobe must turn fast enough to raise the valve every fourth stroke. See **Figure 1-35.**

You can see from **Figure 1-35** that it takes one complete revolution of the cam lobe for every four strokes of the piston. Remember that four strokes of the piston requires two revolutions of the crankshaft. You can say that for every two revolutions of the crankshaft, the camshaft must turn once. If you are speaking of the speed of the camshaft, you can say that the camshaft must turn at one-half crankshaft speed.

Turning the Camshaft

If the crankshaft is turning and the camshaft must turn at one-half crankshaft speed, it seems logical to use the spinning crankshaft to turn the camshaft. One very simple way to drive the camshaft would be by means of gears and a belt. One gear is fastened on the end of the crankshaft, and the other is fastened on the end of the camshaft. The large camshaft gear drives the smaller crankshaft gear through the belt.

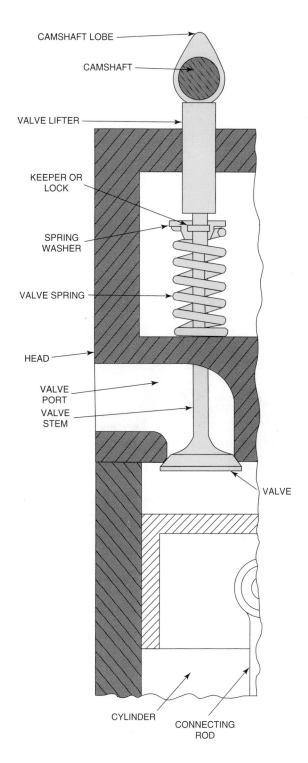

Figure 1-34. Complete valve train. Note how the cam lobe would force the valve open against valve spring pressure.

If, for instance, the small gear on the crankshaft has 10 teeth and the large gear on the camshaft has 20 teeth, the crankshaft will turn the camshaft at exactly one-half crankshaft speed. See **Figure 1-36. Figure 1-37** shows a front view of the *crankshaft gear*, both *camshaft gears*, and a *timing belt* as they would appear on the engine.

Figure 1-35. Each valve is opened once every fourth stroke. Each engine stroke turns the camshaft one-quarter turn.

Figure 1-36. The crankshaft turns the camshaft at one-half crankshaft speed. The camshaft is driven through gears or sprockets and a chain or belt.

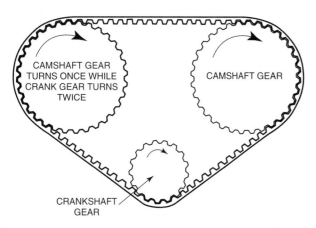

Figure 1-37. Front view. Crankshaft gear driving both camshaft gears through a belt.

Timing the Valves

You have now developed a method of turning the camshaft at the correct speed. The next problem that must be solved is how to get the valves to open at the proper time. This is called *valve timing.*

Start with the intake stroke. As you have discovered, the intake valve must open as the piston starts down in the cylinder. Place your piston at top dead center (TDC topmost point of piston travel). See **Figure 1-38.**

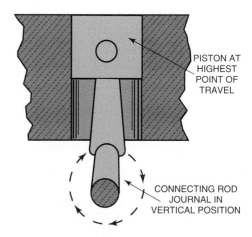

Figure 1-38. Engine piston at top dead center (TDC).

Insert the intake camshaft, then turn it in a counterclockwise direction until the flank of the cam lobe contacts the lifter. The timing gear should be connected to the crankshaft gear with a timing belt, **Figure 1-39.**

Figure 1-39. The position of the cam lobes at the start of the intake stroke. The camshafts are supported above the cylinder head surface. The lifters ride inside the cylinder head metal.

You should punch a mark on the crankshaft gear and a mark on the camshaft gear. These are called *timing marks*. See **Figure 1-40.** If the camshaft is removed, it may be reinstalled by merely lining up the timing marks. Were you to crank the engine, the crankshaft would pull the piston down on the intake stroke. The camshaft would also rotate, causing the cam lobe to turn. The turning lobe will raise and lower the valve. During this stroke, the crankshaft would make a half turn and the camshaft would make a quarter turn. See **Figure 1-41.**

Figure 1-42. Position of an intake valve's camshaft lobe at the start of each stroke.

Figure 1-40. Timing gears meshed and marked. The gears shown here are meshed to illustrate proper timing mark alignment.

Exhaust Timed the Same Way

The only difference between the intake and exhaust timing is that you start by placing the piston on bottom dead center (BDC). Turn the exhaust camshaft until the lobe contacts the lifter, then mark the gears. Use two marks on the crankshaft gear and two on the camshaft gear for the exhaust camshaft. This prevents aligning with the wrong marks.

The Flywheel

When you crank an engine, it turns through all the necessary strokes. The only time the crankshaft receives power is during the power stroke. After the power stroke is completed, the crankshaft must continue to turn to exhaust the burned gases, take in fresh air and fuel, and then compress the mixture. One power stroke is not enough to keep the crankshaft turning during the four required strokes. See **Figure 1-43.**

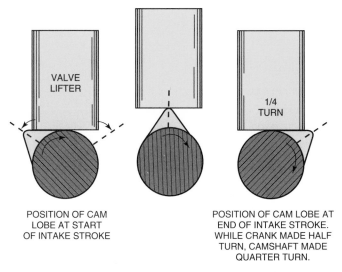

Figure 1-41. A camshaft makes one-quarter turn during each stroke.

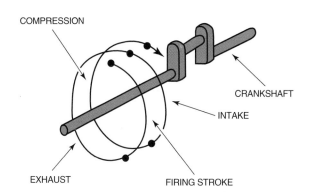

Figure 1-43. After the power stroke, the crankshaft must coast through the next three strokes.

Intake Remains Closed

As the crank continues to turn, it will push the piston up on compression, down on power, and up on exhaust. During these three strokes, the intake cam lobe continues to turn. When the piston reaches top dead center (TDC) on the exhaust stroke, the flank of the cam lobe will again be touching the intake lifter.

As your next stroke will be the intake, the piston is ready to start down and the cam lobe is ready to push on the valve lifter to provide proper timing. See **Figure 1-42.**

You will recall that one end of the crankshaft has a timing gear attached. If you will fasten a fairly large, heavy wheel to the other end, the engine will run successfully. This wheel is called a flywheel.

The flywheel, which is caused to spin by the power stroke, will continue to spin because it is heavy. In other words, the inertia built up within the flywheel will cause it to keep turning. Because it is attached to the crankshaft, the flywheel will cause the shaft to continue to turn. The shaft will now spin long enough to reach the next power stroke. See **Figure 1-44.**

HEAVY FLYWHEEL

CRANKSHAFT

Figure 1-44. Flywheel inertia helps the engine to run.

Engine Will Run Smoothly

You can see that every time the engine fires, the crank receives a hard push. This will speed it up. As the power stroke is finished, the shaft coasts. This slows it down. The alternating fast and slow speeds would make for a very rough running engine.

With the heavy flywheel in place, the power stroke cannot increase the crankshaft speed as quickly since it must also speed up the flywheel. When the crankshaft is coasting, it cannot slow down as quickly because the flywheel velocity keeps it spinning. This will cause the crankshaft speed to become more constant and will, in turn, give a smooth-running engine.

Basic Engine Completed

You have now completed a basic engine. With the addition of fuel, spark, and oil, it will run. This is a one cylinder engine, and its uses would be confined to such small tasks as powering lawn mowers, scooters, portable generators, go-carts, and chainsaws. There are many modifications and improvements that can be made to your simple engine. These will be discussed in following chapters.

Regardless of the size, number of cylinders, and horsepower, all four-stroke cycle engines will contain the same basic parts as the small engine you have just built. The parts may be arranged in different ways and their shape may change, but they will do the same job in the same way. You will not find *different* basic parts, just more of them.

Summary

An engine operates by converting the heat given off by burning fuel into motion. The most convenient and widely used fuel is gasoline. Diesel and other fuels are also used. These fuels are able to burn efficiently in internal combustion engines. To deliver the maximum amount of power, the fuel is vaporized and mixed with air before it enters the engine.

As the piston is pulled down by the crankshaft, the camshaft opens the intake valve and the air-fuel mixture is drawn into the cylinder. When the piston reaches the bottom of its stroke, the intake valve closes and the crankshaft forces the piston up through the cylinder. This compresses the air-fuel mixture in the combustion chamber.

As the piston nears the top of the compression stroke, the air-fuel mixture is ignited by a spark from the spark plug. This explodes the mixture, and the pressure of the rapidly expanding gas drives the piston down through the cylinder. Both valves are closed during this power stroke.

After reaching the bottom of the power stroke, the exhaust valve opens, and the spinning crankshaft forces the piston up through the cylinder. This time, all the burned gases are driven (exhausted) from the cylinder and combustion chamber. When the piston reaches the top of the exhaust stroke, the exhaust valve closes and the intake opens. The piston is drawn down on another intake stroke.

Once the cylinder has fired, the heavy flywheel will keep the crankshaft spinning long enough to go through the exhaust, intake and compression strokes. It will then receive power from another power stroke. This cycle is repeated over and over, and the engine will run on its own power.

Know These Terms

Internal combustion	Valve ports
Engine	Valve
Fuel	Valve seat
Gasoline	Valve guide
Hydrocarbon	Valve stem
Octane rating	Spring
Unleaded gas	Spring washer
Tetraethyl lead	Keeper
Energy	Vacuum
Heat	Intake stroke
Reciprocating motion	Compression stroke
Rotary motion	Compression ratio
Block	Power stroke
Cylinder	Exhaust stroke
Piston	Revolutions
Crankshaft	Four-stroke cycle
Connecting rod	Cam lobe
Main bearings	Camshaft
Connecting rod bearing	Valve lifter
Flywheel	Valve train
Crankcase	Crankshaft gear
Piston pin	Camshaft gear
Wrist pin	Timing belt
Combustion chamber	Valve timing
Cylinder head	Timing marks

Review Questions—Chapter 1

Do not write in this book. Write your answers on a separate sheet of paper.

1. An engine converts heat into ___A___ .

   (A) exhaust gas

   (B) noise

   (C) useful work

   (D) All of the above.

2. Gasoline is obtained from *crude oil*

3. Gasoline is a mixture of hydrogen and carbon atoms and is therefore called a ___C___ fuel.

   (A) carbon

   (B) hydrogen

(C) hydrocarbon

(D) efficient

4. In order to burn, gasoline must be mixed with ___A___ .

(A) oxygen

(B) hydrogen

(C) carbon

(D) None of the above.

5. When the gasoline explodes in the cylinder, what movable part of the engine first receives the force? *B*

(A) Crankshaft.

(B) Piston.

(C) Flywheel.

(D) Connecting rod.

6. The connecting rod must have a bearing at ___C___ .

(A) the piston end

(B) the crankshaft end

(C) both ends

(D) either end

7. On what stroke is a vacuum produced? *A*

(A) Intake.

(B) Compression.

(C) Power.

(D) Exhaust.

8. What is the purpose of valve ports? *D*

(A) To let exhaust gases out of the cylinder.

(B) To let air and gasoline into the cylinder.

(C) To allow the valves to move up and down.

(D) Both A & B.

9. The burning air-fuel mixture forces the piston down on what stroke? *C*

(A) Intake.

(B) Compression.

(C) Power.

(D) Exhaust.

10. Describe what a valve does in a valve port.

11. The position of each valve during the various strokes is important. Give the position (open or closed) of each valve for each of the following strokes.

	Intake valve	Exhaust valve
(A) Intake Stroke	O	C
(B) Compression Stroke	C	C
(C) Power Stroke	C	C
(D) Exhaust Stroke	C	O

12. The part on a camshaft that moves the lifter is called a *LOBE* .

13. The camshaft is turned by the *B* ___ .

(A) flywheel

(B) crankshaft

(C) lifter

(D) connecting rod bearing

14. What is the speed of the camshaft in relation to that of the crankshaft? *A*

(A) One-half speed.

(B) Same speed.

(C) Twice as fast.

(D) Depends on the type of engine.

15. In order to keep the engine running smoothly, it needs a large heavy _____ to keep the crankshaft turning.

FLYWHEEL

Cutaway of a 2.0 liter inline four-cylinder engine. Many of the parts in this engine are similar to those you just studied. (Ford Motor Co.)

2

Design, Construction, Application of Engine Components

After studying this chapter, you will be able to:
- Describe engine part design.
- Explain the construction of engine components.
- Define the purpose of each engine part.
- Identify engine part variations.

In Chapter 1, you designed and built an engine on paper. To give you a clear idea of how the engine works, it was necessary to move from step to step without studying the fine points of engine construction. Now that you are familiar with the general theory involved in engine design, you will be able to study the parts of the basic engine in greater detail. It is important for you to understand how these parts are built, of what materials they are constructed, why they are built the way they are, and the purpose each part serves.

The Engine Block

The *engine block*, **Figure 2-1,** serves as a rigid metal foundation for all parts of an engine. It contains the cylinders and supports the crankshaft and camshaft. In older engines, the valve seats, ports, and guides are built into the block. Accessory units and the clutch housing are bolted to it. Note in **Figure 2-1** that the crankcase is formed with the block.

Blocks are made of either cast iron or aluminum. In some small one-cylinder engines, the material is die-cast metal. Die-cast metal is a relatively light, soft metal especially suited to the die casting process.

Blocks are commonly formed in two ways. One method is to pour molten iron or aluminum into a mold made of sand. A core is placed within the mold to form the cavities and passageways within the block. See **Figure 2-2.** After the casting has cooled, it is removed from the mold and the sand core is dissolved and washed out.

The second method forces molten aluminum or die-cast metal into a metal mold under pressure. The pressure-casting process has several advantages. It produces a block that is free of air bubbles (called voids), gives sharp corners, and is extremely accurate. This keeps machining operations to a minimum. The same mold can be used over and over. All parts of the aluminum or die-cast block that are subjected to wear will have iron or steel inserts either pressed in place or cast into the block.

Figure 2-1. Typical block construction for a V-6, valve-in-head, gasoline engine. (Toyota)

The lighter the block (providing it has sufficient strength), the better. The modern thin-wall casting process controls core size and placement much more accurately than the older casting process. This permits casting the block walls much thinner, reducing the weight of the block. Since the block wall thickness is more uniform, block distortion during service is less severe.

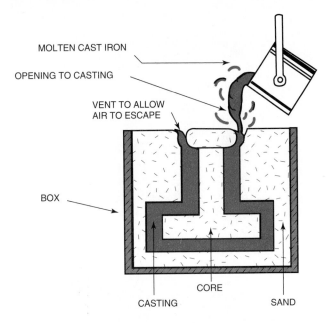

Figure 2-2. Simple mold used for block casting.

Cylinders

The cylinder is a round hole formed in the block. See **Figure 2-3.** It is first cast into the block and then bored and honed to a smooth finish. The cylinder dimensions must be extremely accurate. A good cylinder will not vary in diameter more than .0005″ (0.013 mm). The paper on which this text is printed is around .004″ (0.102 mm) thick.

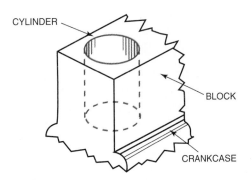

Figure 2-3. Section of an engine showing cylinder location.

The cylinder forms a guide for the piston and acts as a container for taking in, compressing, firing, and exhausting the air-fuel charge. Cylinders have been made of both steel and cast iron. Cast iron is by far the most popular.

Cylinder Sleeves

When steel cylinders are desired in an aluminum block, they are installed in the form of *cylinder sleeves* (round, pipe-like liners). These sleeves may be either cast or pressed into the block. Some engines use removable cylinder sleeves. When the cylinder becomes worn, the old sleeves can be pulled out and new sleeves can be pressed in. See **Figure 2-4.** The sleeves are pressed into oversize cylinder holes.

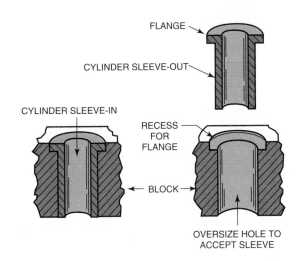

Figure 2-4. Section of a block showing typical cylinder sleeve installation.

Cylinder sleeves are widely used in heavy-duty truck and industrial engines. Sleeves can also be used to repair a worn or cracked cylinder in a cast iron block.

Cylinder sleeves are either the dry or wet type. The *dry sleeve* is pressed into a hole in the block and is surrounded over its full length by block metal, **Figure 2-5.** This type of sleeve can be quite thin because it utilizes the block metal to give it support over its full length. The *wet sleeve* is also pressed into a hole in the block. However, it is supported at the top and bottom only, **Figure 2-6.** The engine coolant is allowed to directly contact the sleeve. The wet sleeve must be heavier than the dry sleeve because it receives no central support from the block.

Securing the Sleeve

Sleeves can be secured in the block in several ways. Where a cast iron or steel sleeve is placed in an aluminum block, it can be cast into place. See **Figure 2-7.** The removable sleeve may be held in place by friction alone, **Figure 2-8.** However, this requires a very tight fit and is not dependable.

Figure 2-5. A dry sleeve in place in cylinder hole.

Figure 2-6. A wet sleeve in place in cylinder hole. Note that the sleeve is surrounded by coolant.

Figure 2-7. Some sleeves are held by the block casting. The grooves help prevent movement.

Figure 2-8. Sleeve held in place by friction between sleeve and block.

Figure 2-9. The flange on this sleeve fits a corresponding groove in the block. Sleeve is held in place by the cylinder head.

A better method is to have a flange on the top edge of the cylinder sleeve that drops into a corresponding groove in the block. See **Figure 2-9.** When the cylinder head is bolted on, it presses on the flange and holds the sleeve in place. This type of sleeve can be fitted with a greater degree of freedom. However, any cylinder sleeve must be a fairly snug fit so that heat is conducted away by the surrounding block material.

Pistons

The piston is literally a sliding plunger that rides up and down in the cylinder. It has several jobs to do in proper sequence.

The piston must move down through the cylinder to produce a vacuum to draw a fuel charge into the cylinder. It then travels up in the cylinder and compresses the mixture. When the mixture is fired, the pressure of the expanding gas is transmitted to the top of the piston. This drives the piston back down through the cylinder with great force, transmitting the energy of the expanding gas to the crankshaft. The piston then travels up through the cylinder and exhausts the burned fuel charge.

The overall job the piston performs is difficult. A piston is subjected to intense heat from the burning air-fuel mixture. It must change directions at high speed. It is subjected to friction against the cylinder walls. In addition to all this, the piston receives the tremendous thrust of power on the power stroke. Study the cross-sectional drawing of a piston in **Figure 2-10.** Learn the names of all the parts of the piston.

Piston Materials

Pistons are usually made of aluminum. Often, aluminum pistons are tin-plated to allow proper break-in when the engine is started. Aluminum pistons can be forged, but they are more commonly cast.

The aluminum piston is light. In most cases, this gives it an advantage over the cast iron type. A piston must change its direction of travel at the end of every stroke. Considering the fact that modern engines sometimes reach speeds in excess of 6000 revolutions per minute (RPM), it is obvious that lighter pistons help increase engine efficiency.

Cast iron is a good material for pistons used in a slow-speed engine. It has excellent wear characteristics and will provide good performance. Aluminum pistons that are designed to operate in aluminum cylinders are iron-plated.

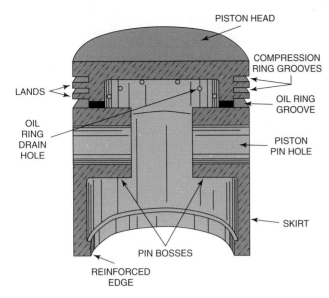

Figure 2-10. Sectional view of a piston. Note the names of each section of the piston.

Piston Expansion Problems

Pistons must be carefully fitted into engine cylinders to prevent them from tipping from side to side (slapping). They must hold the burning fuel charges above the piston heads and be tight enough against the cylinder walls to form a vacuum, compress the fuel charge, exhaust the burned gases, and prevent excess oil loss.

A piston will expand when it gets hot, so enough clearance must be left between the piston and cylinder wall to allow for this. Aluminum pistons expand more than cast iron pistons. See **Figure 2-11.** The problem of fitting an aluminum piston close enough to prevent tipping while leaving enough clearance for an oil film to separate the piston and the cylinder has been solved in several ways.

Figure 2-11. Exaggerated view shows the effect of heat on piston expansion.

Steel Strut Pistons

Steel struts and, in some cases, steel rings are cast into aluminum pistons. See **Figure 2-12.** Steel expands less than aluminum, and as a result, the steel struts tend to minimize piston expansion.

Figure 2-12. Steel rings control or minimize piston expansion.

Cam Ground Piston

The *cam ground piston*, **Figure 2-13,** is a popular type. Instead of being made round, this piston is ground so that it is elliptical, or egg-shaped. Note in **Figure 2-13** that diameter A is larger than diameter B.

Diameter A is established so that the piston has a minimum amount of clearance in the cylinder. This clearance, around .001″ (0.025 mm), is necessary to allow oil to form a lubrication film between the piston and cylinder wall. The larger diameter at A in **Figure 2-13** is always at right angles to the block (in relation to the crankshaft centerline).

As the piston heats up, diameter A will not expand as much as diameter B. This will cause the piston to become round when fully heated. See **Figure 2-14.** Cam grinding will give a minimum clearance at the thrust surfaces. The thrust surfaces are the two sides of the piston that contact the cylinder walls at right angles to the crankshaft and the piston pin. See **Figure 2-15.** These surfaces support the piston and prevent tipping.

Partial Skirt Piston

To make *partial skirt pistons*, (also called slipper skirt pistons), a large area of the *piston skirt* (the bottom section

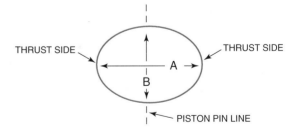

Figure 2-13. Exaggerated top view of a cam ground piston, which is designed to be wider across the thrust surfaces.

Figure 2-14. A cam ground piston becomes round when hot. Diameter A remains constant while diameter B expands.

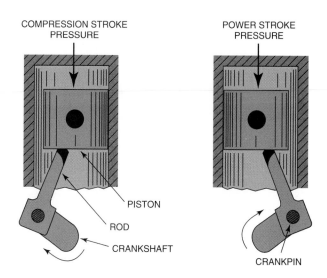

Figure 2-15. Exaggerated view shows how a loose piston is pushed from one side of the cylinder to the other. The sides that contact the cylinder wall are called thrust surfaces.

of the piston) is removed. This reduces piston weight and allows the piston to move closer to the crankshaft.

Since the non-thrust sides of the skirts are removed, the counterbalances on the crankshaft will not strike the piston, **Figure 2-16.** The non-thrust sides of a piston do not carry much of a load, and therefore, their removal is not detrimental. The partial skirt piston is also cam ground.

Figure 2-16. Non-thrust sides of the piston skirt are removed from partial skirt pistons. This allows the piston to approach the crankshaft closely without striking.

Split Skirt Piston

Some older engine designs make used of a **split skirt piston**, **Figure 2-17,** the skirt is either partially or, in some cases, completely split. When the piston warms and begins to

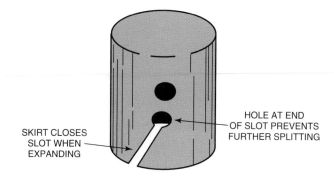

Figure 2-17. A split skirt piston is sometimes used to solve expansion problem.

expand, it cannot bind in the cylinder because the skirt merely closes the split.

T-Slot Piston

The **t-slot piston**, **Figure 2-18,** is a variation of the split skirt. The top of the T tends to retard the transfer of heat from the piston head to the skirt. The vertical slot allows the skirt to close in when heated.

Figure 2-18. A T-slot piston is another type of piston used to control expansion.

Piston Temperature

The piston head is subjected to the direct heat of the exploding fuel. This heat can raise the temperature of the piston crown (very top) to over 600°F (316°C). The temperature will be lower as you go down the piston. The bottom of the skirt will be about 300°F (149°C), **Figure 2-19.**

The temperatures will vary according to engine design and work application. Because the bottom of the skirt is the coolest, the skirt on some pistons is slightly larger in diameter at the bottom. The top area of the skirt would be smaller in diameter.

Piston Construction

It is obvious that the piston head is by far the hottest part of the piston. As a result, it expands more. In order to avoid having the piston head grow tight in the cylinder, it is turned to a smaller diameter than the skirt (not cam ground). The head

Figure 2-19. Approximate temperature range from piston head to skirt. Piston temperature can vary considerably based on engine type, design, and use.

will generally be .030″ to .040″. (0.76 to 1.02 mm) smaller than the skirt, **Figure 2-20.** The section of the piston that supports the pin must be thicker and stronger. This area is called the *pin boss*. See **Figure 2-21.**

Piston Head Shape

Some pistons have flat-topped heads. Others are designed to assist in creating a rapid swirling and to help

Figure 2-20. As the head is the hottest part of a piston, it must be ground approximately .030″-.040″ (0.76 mm to 1.02 mm) smaller than the skirt

Figure 2-21. The pin boss must be strong to withstand directional changes during each stroke of the piston.

break up gasoline particles on the compression stroke. In one design, the shape of the combustion chamber is formed in the head of the piston, allowing the use of a flat-surfaced cylinder head. See **Figure 2-22.**

Piston Rings

The piston must have some clearance in the cylinder. If the skirt has .001″ to .002″ (0.025 to 0.05 mm) clearance and the head has .030″ to .040″ (0.76 to 1.02 mm) clearance, it is obvious that the piston cannot seal the cylinder effectively. See **Figure 2-23.**

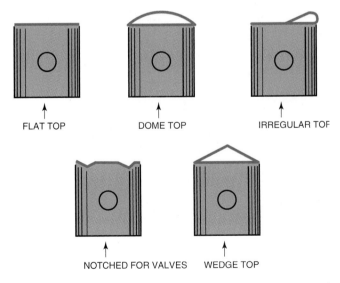

Figure 2-22. Several types of piston heads that have been used in engines. The flat top is the one most commonly used today.

To solve the leakage problem, *piston rings* are used. A properly constructed and fitted ring will rub against the cylinder wall with good contact all around the cylinder. The ring will ride in a groove that is cut into the piston head. There will be

Figure 2-23. A piston cannot seal by itself because clearance with the cylinder wall must be maintained.

a slight clearance between the sides of the ring and the edges of the groove. This clearance, which is known as side clearance, is generally around .002″ (0.05 mm).

The rings do not contact the bottom of the ring grooves. Actually, the ring will rub the cylinder wall at all times but will not be solidly fastened to the piston at any one point. See **Figure 2-24.**

Ring Gap

The ring is built so it must be squeezed together to place it in the cylinder. This will cause the ring to exert an outward pressure, which keeps it tightly against the cylinder wall. See **Figure 2-25.** The ring is not solid all the way around, but is cut through in one spot. This cut spot forms what is called the **ring gap**. See **Figure 2-26.**

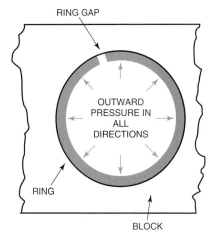

Figure 2-25. Top view of the cylinder shows the sealing action of a piston ring.

Figure 2-26. Simplified piston ring showing ring gap present on piston rings.

When the ring is in the cylinder, the cut ends must not touch. When the ring heats up, it will lengthen. Since it cannot expand outwardly, it will close the gap. See **Figure 2-27.** If there is not enough gap clearance, the ends will touch as the ring expands. As the ring continues to lengthen, it will break up into several pieces. This can quickly ruin an engine.

Figure 2-24. Piston rings are used to seal the gap between the piston and cylinder wall.

Figure 2-27. When the rings get hot, the gap closes.

A general rule for ring gap clearance is to allow .003″ to .004″ per inch (0.07 to 0.10 mm per 25.4 mm) of cylinder diameter. For example, a 4″ (101.6 mm) diameter cylinder would require from .012″ to .016″ (0.30 to 0.41 mm) clearance in the gap.

Many different types of joints have been used in an endeavor to stop leakage through the ring gap. This leakage is commonly referred to as **blow-by**. It has been found that the common butt joint is effective and is simple to adjust. **Figure 2-28** illustrates a few of the joints that have been used.

BUTT JOINT   LAP JOINT   BEVEL JOINT

Figure 2-28. Types of piston ring gap joints. Most engines use three rings on each piston, two compression rings and one oil control ring. Others use two compression rings and two oil rings. Some diesel engines use five or more rings. All rings may be above the piston pin; or a second oil control ring may be set into a groove near the bottom of the skirt. The compression rings are always used in the top grooves and the oil control rings in the lower grooves.

The ring is placed in the groove by expanding it until it will slip over the piston head and slide down and into the ring groove. **Figure 2-29** illustrates how a ring fits the piston groove. Note that there is both side clearance and back clearance.

Figure 2-29. Compression ring-to-groove fit. Note that the ring has both side and back clearance. Side clearance is actually quite small, running around .0015″ to .002″ (0.04 to 0.05 mm).

Types of Rings

There are two distinct types of rings. One is called a **compression ring,** and the other is called an **oil control ring**. Most engines have three rings: two compression rings at the top and one oil control ring at the bottom, **Figure 2-30.**

Figure 2-30. Location of compression and oil control rings. The locations and number of rings vary by application.

Compression Rings

Compression rings are designed to prevent leakage between the piston and the cylinder, **Figure 2-31.**

Various types of grooves, bevels, and chamfer shapes are used to achieve this goal. The idea is to create an internal stress within the ring. This stress will tend to cause the ring to twist in such a fashion that the lower edge of the ring is pressed against the cylinder wall on the intake stroke. This will cause the ring to act as a mild scraper. The scraping effect will assist in the removal of surplus oil that may have escaped the oil control rings, **Figure 2-32.**

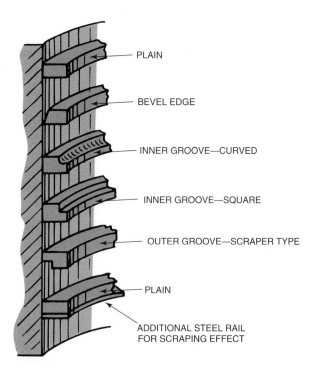

Figure 2-31. Typical compression ring shapes as they would look in a cylinder.

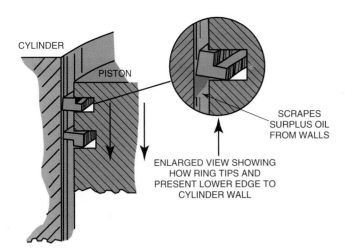

Figure 2-32. Internal stress causes the rings to tip and act as mild scrapers.

On compression and exhaust strokes, the rings will tend to slip lightly over the oil film. This will prolong the life of the ring, **Figure 2-33.** On the power stroke, pressure of the burning gases will force the top edge of the ring downward. This causes the ring to rub the wall with full face contact and provides a good seal for the enormous pressure generated by the power stroke. See **Figure 2-34.**

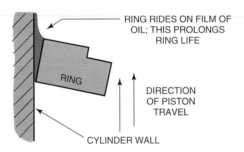

Figure 2-33. On compression and exhaust strokes, piston rings tip and slide easily on a film of oil.

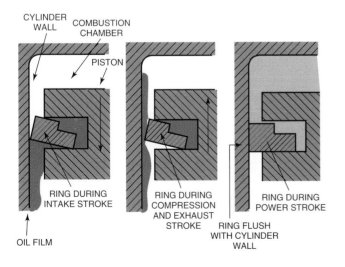

Figure 2-34. Pressure of burning gases during the power stroke force the ring down and out so that it is flush with the cylinder wall.

Heat Dam

The compression rings, especially the top ring, are subjected to intense heat. To minimize the transfer of heat from the head of the piston to the top ring, a **heat dam** is sometimes used. This is actually a thin groove cut into the head of the piston between the top ring groove and the top of the piston.

Instead of passing through the aluminum of the piston to the ring, the heat encounters the heat dam. The heat cannot move as readily through the empty space in the groove as it can through the piston metal. This helps minimize heat transfer, **Figure 2-35.**

Figure 2-35. Heat dam are used to keep the top ring cool.

Top Ring Groove Insert

Some aluminum pistons have nickel-iron or comparable metal inserts cast into the piston heads. The top ring groove is cut in this metal. Since top ring grooves in aluminum pistons tend to be pounded out of shape during engine operation, this insert will prolong the useful life of the piston and ring, **Figure 2-36.**

Figure 2-36. Top ring insert groove cast into the piston.

Oil Control Ring

The oil control ring is used to scrape the surplus oil from the cylinder walls. This prevents oil from escaping into the combustion chamber. As engine designs have changed, much research has been devoted to the design of oil rings. See **Figure 2-37.**

All oil rings are slotted and have edges that scrape the excess oil from the cylinder walls. The oil between the edges passes through slots on the ring. When two rings are used, the oil passes through slots in the bottom of the ring groove. From there, the oil drips down into the crankcase area, **Figure 2-38.**

Expander Devices

Some ring sets that are designed for worn cylinders utilize expanding springs between the bottom of the ring groove and the ring. This will force the ring outward against the cylinder wall. The top of a worn cylinder is usually wider than the bottom. When the head of the piston is on the bottom of its stroke, the rings will be squeezed in the smaller section of the cylinder. See **Figure 2-39.**

Figure 2-37. Several common types of oil control rings.

Figure 2-39. If a cylinder is badly tapered from wear, the rings are compressed in the bottom of the cylinder.

When the piston travels up the cylinder, the rings must expand outward to follow the ever-widening cylinder diameter, **Figure 2-40.** This makes it necessary for the rings to expand and contract during every stroke. If engine speed is high enough, the piston will travel up the cylinder and will be snapped back down before the rings have time to expand. This leaves the piston at the top of the stroke with the rings not touching the cylinder walls.

Expander devices used for rings designed for worn cylinders are stronger than those used for a new or rebored cylinder. **Figure 2-41** illustrates a common type of ring expander. Some expanders do not touch the bottom of the grooves. In this type, the ends butt together, and when the ring is compressed during piston installation, the expander is compressed within itself. Another type of expander is a round wire spring type. The ends butt together and even though the spring does not touch the bottom of the groove, it still pushes out on the ring, **Figure 2-42.**

Rings Must Fit the Cylinder

In addition to following the cylinder walls, rings must make perfect contact all the way around. **Figure 2-43** illustrates a ring that is poorly fitted and would do a poor job of sealing.

Even with accurately bored cylinders and new rings, it is impossible to secure an absolutely perfect fit when the rings

Figure 2-38. A—This shows the action of the oil ring as it travels down the cylinder wall. B—Note the path the oil takes through the ring.

Figure 2-40. When the piston reaches the top of the tapered cylinder, the rings expand. Note the large end gaps.

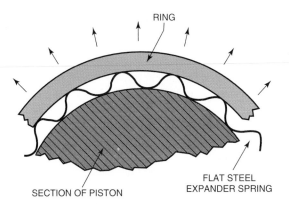

Figure 2-41. Spring expander rests on the bottom of the ring groove and forces the ring outward. This pressure will keep the ring in constant contact with the cylinder wall.

Figure 2-42. A round wire spring expander does not touch the bottom of the ring groove. When the ring is compressed to enter the cylinder, the spring is compressed within itself to keep constant tension on the ring.

are first installed. After the engine has operated for several hundred miles, the rings will wear into perfect contact with the cylinder walls.

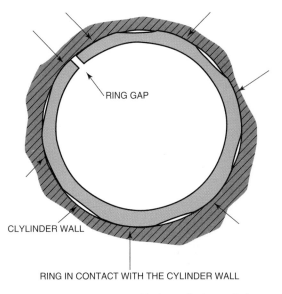

Figure 2-43. Poor ring contact with the cylinder wall. Arrows indicate high spots that touch, the area between the arrows do not touch.

Ring Break-In

To facilitate a fast job of ring break-in, the ring's outer face is left rough. Although this surface feels smooth to the touch, a close inspection will show that fine grooves are left in the ring surface. Similarly, the cylinders may look smooth, but final honing with fine stones leaves tiny surface scratches in the walls.

When the engine is started, the rings will be drawn up and down the cylinder. Since both the ring faces and the walls have fine scratches, some wear will occur. Any high spots on the ring faces will soon be worn off and the ring will fit properly, **Figure 2-44.**

The ring and wall surfaces must be designed with a degree of roughness that will cause the rings to wear in. By the time an acceptable fit is achieved, the initial roughness will be gone and excessive wear will cease.

Special Ring Coatings

To assist with a fast wearing-in period, ring faces are often coated with a soft, porous material. This material also absorbs some oil and allows a gentle wear-in. Materials such as graphite, phosphate, and molybdenum are used for this purpose. See **Figure 2-45.** Rings can also be tin coated.

All the expanding pressure of new rings is applied to the walls at the ring high spots. This can cause overheating and *scuffing* at these points. Scuffing is a roughening of the cylinder wall. It is caused when there is no oil film separating the moving parts and metal-to-metal contact is made. The porous coating wears quickly and since it holds oil, the danger of scuffing is lessened.

On some rings, the outer edge is chrome-plated. This chrome surface wears very well and stands up under severe operating conditions. Chrome-plated rings are generally finished smoother and to a higher degree of accuracy, giving fewer high points to retard wear-in. They may also have grooves to aid seating and break-in. See **Figure 2-46.**

Figure 2-44. Fine scratches in the cylinder wall and grooves in the ring face rub against each other to assist in prompt and proper wear-in. A—Here, the ring touches cylinder only on high spots. B—This shows proper ring contact after wear-in.

Figure 2-45. A porous coating on the ring face helps to ensure rapid and scuff-free break-in.

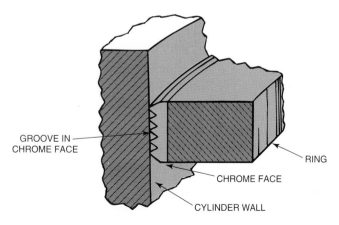

Figure 2-46. The chrome face of a chrome-plated ring is grooved to aid break-in.

Ring Material

Piston rings are made from high-quality cast iron. This material must have excellent wear properties and possess spring-like qualities that will hold it out against the walls. The installation and handling of cast iron must be done carefully to avoid breaking the brittle rings.

Thin oil ring rails are made of steel. Special expanding oil rings may also utilize steel in their construction, **Figure 2-47.** Some rings are made of stainless steel. Often, a molybdenum-filled cast iron ring is used in the top ring groove.

Figure 2-47. Side view of a three-piece oil ring. The top and bottom rails are made of steel.

Ring Types Are Numerous

Ring design is steadily improving. Many new designs are constantly appearing. All rings are designed to provide good sealing, long wear, quick break-in, excellent oil control, and freedom from breakage.

Piston Pins

Pistons are fastened to connecting rods with steel pins. These pins, called *piston pins*, pass through one side of the piston, through the upper end of the connecting rod, and then through the other side of the piston. Look at **Figure 2-48.**

The piston pin is usually hollow to reduce weight. It is also case-hardened to provide a long-wearing surface. *Case-hardening* is a process that hardens the surface of steel, but leaves the inner part fairly soft and tough to prevent brittleness. This hardness penetrates from .004″ (0.10 mm) up to any depth desired. However, there would be little advantage in making the hard shell any deeper than a few thousandths of an inch, **Figure 2-49.** Piston pins are ground to a very accurate size and are highly polished.

Pin Installation

Piston pins are installed and secured to provide a bearing action. One method has the piston pin fastened to the rod and uses the piston bosses for bearings. At times, a separate bushing is pressed into the bosses to provide a bearing surface. Current practice favors a press fit (friction holds the two pieces together) between the piston pin and the connecting rod, with the pin oscillating in the aluminum pin bosses. See **Figure 2-50.**

Another method is to secure the pin at each end with a *snap ring* that rides in a shallow groove cut in each pin boss.

Figure 2-50. Piston pin locked to rod turns in a bushing. These are sometimes used on heavy duty diesel engines.

Figure 2-48. A piston is fastened to the connecting rod with a piston pin.

Figure 2-51. The piston pin is free to turn in the rod and in the pin bosses.

Figure 2-49. Sectioned piston pin shows the thin skin of case-hardening.

The pin is free to turn in the bosses and in the rod. This is called a free-floating pin, **Figure 2-51.**

Connecting Rods

As the name implies, connecting rods are used to connect pistons to the crankshaft **Figure 2-52.** The upper end of the rod oscillates (swings back and forth), while the lower, or big end, bearing rotates (turns).

Because there is very little bearing movement in the upper end, the bearing area can be reasonably small. The lower end rotates very fast, and the crankshaft bearing journal turns inside the connecting rod. This rotational speed tends to produce heat and wear. To make the rod wear well, a larger bearing area is required.

The upper end of the rod has a hole through it for the piston pin. The bottom of the large end of the connecting rod

Figure 2-52. A typical connecting rod is made of forged steel rod. It is used in conjunction with an aluminum piston. (Jaguar)

must be removed so the rod can be installed on the crankshaft journal. The section that is removed is called the connecting rod cap.

The top of the rod and the connecting rod cap are bolted together. If removed, the rod and cap should be numbered. When installed, the numbers should be on the same side. This prevents turning the cap around when installing it on the rod.

Turning the connecting rod cap around would make the rod bearing hole out-of-round, **Figure 2-53.** When rods are manufactured, the upper and lower halves are bolted together and the holes are bored to an accurate size. The hole may be slightly off center. If the caps are crossed, the upper hole half may not line up with the lower hole.

Figure 2-53. If a connecting rod is removed, they should be numbered and the rod and cap kept together.

Connecting Rod Construction

Connecting rods are normally made of alloy steel. They are drop-forged to shape and then machined. The customary shape uses I-beam construction.

Some rods are made of aluminum. Generally, these are for small, light-duty engines. Small engines often utilize the rod material for both upper and lower bearing surfaces. Special aluminum rods for high-speed, high-performance engines are also available.

Connecting Rod Bearings

As mentioned, the upper end of the connecting rod may use a bushing for a bearing surface. If the rod is bolted or pressed to the piston pin, it will not use any special bearing. The bearings in this case would be in the piston boss holes. The lower end uses a precision insert. The rod bearing hole is bored larger than the crank journal and an *insert bearing* is placed between the rod and journal. See **Figure 2-54.**

A bearing insert does not turn in the rod. It is held in place by a locating tab (locking lip) on the insert that is placed in a corresponding notch in the rod. Look at **Figures 2-55** and **2-56.**

The insert must fit the rod snugly in order to transfer heat to the connecting rod. To ensure a proper fit, the insert will protrude a small amount above the rod bore parting surface.

Figure 2-54. Connecting rod precision insert bearing is properly fitted when the bearing parting surfaces (ends) touch before the rod halves meet. This provides what is known as bearing crush. (Sunnen)

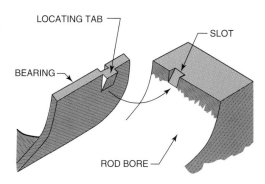

Figure 2-55. A connecting rod precision inserts are aligned and held in place by a bearing locating tab engaging a slot in the rod bore. (Clevite)

Figure 2-56. Cutaway showing construction of a precision insert bearing.

This distance (from less than .001″ to .002″ or less than 0.025 to 0.050 mm) is called *crush height*. When the rod halves are drawn together, the inserts touch before the halves, forcing the insert tightly into place, **Figure 2-54.**

Insert Construction

An insert is started as a steel shell. This gives it shape and rigidity. The inner part of the shell that contacts the journal is then coated to form a lining. Some bearings have steel shells with a thin (.002″ to .005″ or 0.05 to 0.13 mm) babbitt lining. Others use steel shells coated with a copper-lead-tin matrix followed by a very thin (.001″ or 0.025 mm) coating of pure tin. Others use an aluminum coating. **Figure 2-56** illustrates a typical bearing insert.

Bearing Characteristics

The ideal bearing is not easy to construct. For every advantage, there seems to be a disadvantage that goes with it. A good bearing must have many characteristics. Refer to **Figure 2-57** as you read the next few paragraphs.

Load Strength

The bearing is subjected to tremendous stress from the power stroke. There is pounding as the crank first pushes up and then pulls down. The bearing must not fatigue, crack, or spread out from the pounding force.

Antiscuffing

The material in the bearing should be such that in the event the oil surface skin is destroyed, the shaft journal will not be damaged by scuffing and scratching.

Corrosion Resistance

The bearing material must resist any tendency to corrode when exposed to vapors and acids in the crankcase.

Conductivity

All bearings produce heat. It is essential that the bearing material be of a type that will conduct heat to the rod. This is one reason why insert bearings must be a near-perfect fit.

Temperature Change

The bearing strength must not be lessened when the bearing reaches its operating temperature. It must have reasonable strength when cold and when hot.

Each insert must have a small hole to allow oil to enter for lubrication. See **Figure 2-56.** Some inserts have shallow grooves in the surface to allow oil to spread out across the bearing surface.

Embedability

If a small abrasive particle enters the bearing area, the bearing should allow the particle to embed itself in the bearing material so it will not scratch the journal.

Conformation

No surface is perfectly true. Even with a highly accurate shaft, a new rod, and a new insert, the bearing will not fit the journal without some minute imperfection. A good bearing is soft and ductile enough to shape to the journal after it has been used for some time.

Crankshaft

The engine crankshaft provides a constant turning force to the wheels. It has throws to which connecting rods are attached, and its function is to change the reciprocating motion of the piston to a rotary motion to drive the wheels. Crankshafts are made of alloy steel or cast iron. **Figure 2-58** shows a typical crankshaft.

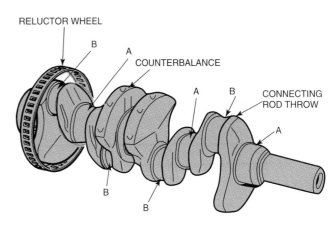

RELUCTOR WHEEL
B
A
COUNTERBALANCE
A
B
CONNECTING ROD THROW
A
B
B

Figure 2-58. A typical four-cylinder engine crankshaft. A—Main bearing journals. B—Rod bearing journals. Note the notched reluctor wheel. A crankshaft position sensor reads the reluctor wheel (crankshaft) position and sends this data to the engine's computer or electronic control module.

Main Bearings

The crankshaft is held in position by a series of main bearings. The maximum number of main bearings for a crankshaft is one more than the number of cylinders. It may have fewer main bearings than cylinders. Most engines use precision insert bearings that are constructed like the connecting rod bearings, but are somewhat larger. See **Figure 2-59.**

In addition to supporting the crankshaft, one of the main bearings must control the forward and backward movement

HAMMERING

ATTACK BY ACID

MUST CONDUCT HEAT

MUST RESIST SOFTENING FROM HEAT

MUST ALLOW ABRASIVE PARTICLES TO EMBED IN BEARING MATERIAL

MUST MOLD TO UNEVEN SHAFT SURFACE

Figure 2-57. Bearing inserts must resist many destructive forces.

(end play) of the shaft. This bearing has flanges on the edges that rub against a ground surface on the edge of the crankshaft main journal. This bearing is referred to as a **thrust bearing**. Look at the center bearing in **Figure 2-59**.

Figure 2-59. Set of main bearings. Some of these bearings use an aluminum coating, while others employ babbitt. Note the thrust flanges on thrust bearing. (Cadillac)

Crankshaft Throws

The **crankshaft throws** (part of the shaft the connecting rod fastens to) must be arranged in such a way as to bring the piston to top dead center at the proper time for the power stroke. As the pistons in a multicylinder (more than one) engine do not fire one after the other, but fire in a staggered sequence, the throw position is very important.

Figure 2-60 illustrates end views of four-, six-, and eight-cylinder crankshafts. **Figure 2-60A** and **Figure 2-60B** are for inline engines. An inline engine is one in which all the cylinders are arranged one after another in a straight row. An inline six-cylinder engine, **Figure 2-60B,** requires six connecting rod throws. A V-8 engine, **Figure 2-60C,** has four throws. Each throw services two connecting rods.

Crank Vibration

To offset the unbalanced condition caused by off-center throws, many crankshafts use counterbalances to stop vibration. They may be forged as part of the crankshaft, or they may be bolted to the crankshaft, **Figure 2-61**.

Vibration Damper

When the front cylinders fire, power is transmitted through the crankshaft. The pressure the piston applies can

Figure 2-60. A—A four-cylinder crankshaft will normally have throws spaced 180° apart with cylinders 1 and 4 on the same side. B—A right hand crankshaft for a six-cylinder engine will have throws arranged like this. C—A V-8 engine may have the crankshaft throws arranged the same as a four-cylinder engine, or the method shown here which is widely used.

Figure 2-61. All crankshafts needs counterweights to bring them into proper balance.

exceed 3000 lbs. (1350 kg). The front of the crankshaft receiving this power tends to move before the rear, causing a twisting motion. When the torque is removed from the front, the partially twisted shaft will unwind and snap back in the other direction. This unwinding, although minute, causes what is known as torsional vibration.

To stop the vibration, a damper, sometimes called a *harmonic balancer*, is attached to the front of the crankshaft. Basically the *vibration damper* is built in two pieces. These pieces may be connected by rubber plugs, spring-loaded friction discs, or a combination of the two, **Figure 2-62.**

Figure 2-62. Vibration damper utilizes a small flywheel which moves a limited amount, bending the injected rubber plugs. See A and B.

When a front cylinder fires and the shaft tries to speed up, it tries to spin the heavy section of the damper. When this occurs, the rubber connecting the two parts of the damper is twisted. The shaft does not speed up as much with the damper attached. The force necessary to twist the rubber and to speed up the heavy damper wheel tends to smooth out the crankshaft operation. When the firing pressure is removed from the shaft, the shaft cannot spring back quickly because the twisted rubber attempts to keep the damper wheel turning. The unwinding force of the crankshaft cancels out the twist in the opposite direction.

Balance Shafts

Some engines use a *balance shaft* that is geared to the crankshaft or camshaft. This balance shaft helps to counterbalance vertical and torsional vibrations from the crank and camshafts. A balance shaft has offset bob weights that rotate in opposite directions, canceling out vibrations from the crankshaft and or camshaft. **Figure 2-63** shows a balance shaft used in a inline four-cylinder engine.

Figure 2-63. Some engines use balance shafts geared to the crankshaft or camshaft, depending on the design. Note that this particular setup uses a chain. The bob weights offset the vibrations created by the crankshaft. (Pontiac)

Drilled, Ground, and Polished

The crankshaft is drilled so oil being fed to the main bearings will pass through the shaft to the connecting rod throws, **Figure 2-64.** All bearing surfaces are precision ground and are highly polished.

Timing Gear or Sprocket

A *timing gear* or a *chain sprocket* is installed on the front end of the crankshaft. A chain sprocket is usually made of steel. In the case of the timing gear, the teeth are helical in shape. A timing gear is used to turn a camshaft timing gear. Where a sprocket is used, the sprocket will drive a *timing chain* or *timing belt*, which turns a larger sprocket on the front of the camshaft, **Figure 2-65.** Some engines use a combination of chain and belt to drive the camshafts.

A timing gear or sprocket is secured with a metal key that rides in a slot cut in the crankshaft. The gear or sprocket also contains a slot or groove. See **Figure 2-66.**

Figure 2-64. This crankshaft which is partially cut away shows how oil is pumped into the center main bearing. From there it enters an oil gallery drilled through the crankshaft to each rod journal.

Figure 2-66. A steel key, which is installed in a slot in the crankshaft, passes through a similar slot in the gear to secure the gear to the shaft.

Figure 2-65. Timing gear drive on the crankshaft; also timing chain (or belt) drive sprocket on crankshaft.

Figure 2-67. On all engines, a heavy flywheel is bolted to the crankshaft flange. The flywheel helps to keep the engine running at all speeds.

The outer rim of the flywheel has a large ring attached with gear teeth cut into it. The teeth of the starter motor engage these teeth and spin the flywheel to crank the engine. When an automatic transmission is used, the torque converter assembly works with the flywheel.

Camshaft

The camshaft is used to open and close the valves. There is one cam on the camshaft for each valve in the engine. Generally only one camshaft is used in most engine. Newer engines are increasingly equipped with two or more camshafts. (On the elementary engine you designed in Chapter 1, you used two camshafts and the valves were

Flywheel

A heavy flywheel is attached to the rear of the crankshaft with bolts. The function of the flywheel is to smooth out engine speed and keep the crankshaft spinning between power strokes. In some engines, the flywheel also serves as a mounting surface for the clutch. See **Figure 2-67.**

arranged to better illustrate the action in relation to an end view of the crankshaft.) A camshaft has a series of support bearings along its length. Camshafts turn at one-half crankshaft speed.

The cam lobes are usually not flat across the top as they might appear. The bottom of the valve lifter may be slightly crowned and the cam lobe tapered. This places the lobe-to-lifter contact to one side of center, **Figure 2-68**. A gear cut into the camshaft is used to drive the distributor and oil pump.

Figure 2-68. A—Section of a camshaft showing one method of tapering cam lobes. The lifter bottom is crowned. B—Overall view of typical camshaft design.

The camshaft is kept in place using a thrust washer behind the timing gear or by using a spring-loaded plunger to push on the end of the camshaft. An additional cam may be ground on the shaft to drive the fuel pump.

The typical camshaft is made of cast or forged steel. The cam surfaces are hardened for long life. **Figure 2-69** illustrates a typical camshaft with the gear and thrust washer in place. The camshaft may be turned by a gear, timing chain, or a toothed timing belt. See **Figure 2-70** through **Figure 2-72**. The camshaft gear can be made of cast steel, aluminum, or a special pressed fiber. Chain sprockets are made of cast steel.

Valves

Each engine cylinder ordinarily has two valves. However, modern engines often use four valves per cylinder (two intake and two exhaust). A few engines used in smaller vehicles have three valves per cylinder: two intake valves and one exhaust valve.

Because the head of an exhaust valve operates at temperatures up to 1300°F (704°C), valves are made of heat-resistant metal. It is obvious that the steel used in valve construction must be of high quality. In order to prevent burning, the valve must give off heat to the valve seat and to the valve guide. The valve must make good contact with the seat and must run with minimum clearance in the guide.

Figure 2-70. Timing gear drive for camshaft also requires alignment of timing marks. (Pontiac)

Figure 2-69. A camshaft and timing gear. A—Main camshaft bearing journals. B—Cam lobes. C—Eccentric to drive fuel pump. D—Gear to drive distributor. E—Camshaft sprocket. F—Thrust washer. G—Key. H—Retaining capscrew. I—Timing chain. J—Rubbing block.

Figure 2-71. Front view of typical timing chain drive. Note the alignment of the gear timing marks. (Dodge)

Figure 2-72. Dual overhead camshaft driven by a toothed drive belt. (Toyota)

Some valves have special hard coating on the face areas to increase their useful life. Others use hollow stems filled with metallic sodium, **Figure 2-73.** At operating temperatures, the sodium becomes a liquid and splashes up into the head of the valve. This draws the heat into the stem, where it transfers to the valve guide.

STOP Warning: Sodium is extremely toxic and reacts violently with any form of water, even the moisture in the air. Never cut, drill, melt, or burn a sodium-filled valve.

Figure 2-73. A—Valve with special hardfacing to lengthen useful life. B—Special heat resistant valve utilizing a hollow stem partially filled with metallic sodium. Never drill or cut into such a valve as the sodium inside the valve is dangerous. If worn out, dispose of carefully as recommended by the manufacturer.

Valve Seats

Two angles commonly used for valve seats are 30° and 45°. Some manufacturers grind a 1° difference between the valve face and seat to permit fast seating, **Figure 2-74.** The seat may be ground to 45° and the valve to 44° or vice versa.

Figure 2-74. Common valve seat angles. 30° and 44° are the most common.

Valve seats can be cut in the cylinder head, or special, hard steel inserts can be pressed into the head, **Figure 2-75.** Seats can also be induction hardened, which is an operation that hardens the seat surface, increasing its useful service life. The valve face and seat must make perfect contact to ensure efficient operation.

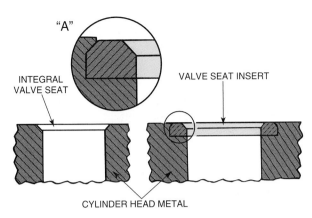

Figure 2-75. Most valve inserts are often frozen to shrink their diameter, then pressed into warm head to secure insert. The head metal, A, is sometimes peened over the edge of the insert to ensure a secure fit.

Valve Guides

The valve guide can be an integral part of the cylinder head, or it may be made as a separate unit that is pressed into a hole in the head or the block. The pressed-in type of valve guide is made of cast iron. The valve stem must fit this guide with about .002″ to .003″ (0.05 to 0.08 mm) clearance. See **Figure 2-76.**

Figure 2-76. Examples of valve guides. A—Integral (not removable). B—Pressed-in (removable).

Valve Springs

Valve springs push the valves closed when the cams lower. Since the springs are compressed and expanded over 70,000 times per hour at 50 mph (80.5 kmh), they must be made of high-quality spring steel. You have already learned how the spring is fastened to the valve using a spring washer and split keepers.

Some springs have the coils closer together at one end than at the other. In an installation of this kind, the end with the more closely spaced coils must be placed against the head. Some engines use two springs per valve, one inside of the other.

Mechanical Valve Lifters

Mechanical valve lifters are usually made of cast iron. The bottom part that contacts the camshaft is hardened. Some lifters are hollow to reduce weight. Most valve trains that contain mechanical lifters have some provision for adjusting clearance. See **Figure 2-77.** Mechanical valve lifters were used in older engines.

Figure 2-77. Mechanical valve lifters are usually solid. Some mechanical lifters are hollow, which reduces their weight.

Hydraulic Valve Lifters

Hydraulic valve lifters perform the same job as mechanical lifters. However, hydraulic lifters are self-adjusting, operate with no lifter-to-rocker arm clearance, and uses engine oil under pressure to operate. Hydraulic lifters are quiet in operation.

To operate, engine oil under pressure enters the hydraulic lifter body. The oil passes through a small opening in the bottom of an inner piston and into a cavity beneath the piston. The oil raises the piston up until it contacts the push rod (the oil pressure is not high enough to open the valve).

When the cam raises the lifter, pressure is applied to the inner piston. The piston tries to squirt the oil back through the small opening, but it cannot do so as a small check ball seals the opening.

As the cam raises, the lifter becomes solid and lifts the valve. When the cam lowers, the lifter will be pushed down by the push rod. The lifter will then automatically adjust to remove clearance. **Figure 2-78** shows one type of hydraulic valve lifter. See **Figure 2-79** for complete lifter action.

Turning Reduces Valve Wear

If the valve goes up and comes down in the same place time after time, carbon buildup between the valve face and seat may cause the valve to remain partially open. This will cause valve burning. If the valve turns even a few degrees on each opening, a wiping action between the face and seat will be developed. This keeps carbon from building up. Turning also helps to prevent localized hot spots since the valve will keep moving away from the hottest areas.

Types of Rotators

There are several methods of causing valves to rotate as they open and close. One is through the use of a release-type mechanism. This removes the spring tension from the valve while it is open and induces rotation from engine vibration. See **Figure 2-80.** Another type of rotator is the positive-type, which uses a spring or rolling action to move the valve. This rolling action causes the retainer and the valve to turn a few degrees each time the valve opens.

Roller Lifters

Some late-model engines are equipped with hydraulic *roller lifters.* The roller reduces wear on both the lifter and the camshaft, **Figure 2-81.** The roller lifter operates in the same

Figure 2-78. Typical hydraulic valve lifter. Oil enters channel (3) in the block, passes through hole (4) in the lifter body (5), then enters hole (12) in the inner piston. It fills the inner piston cavity and passes through hole (13). This pressure will push the check ball (6) off its seat. It now flows through hole (14) in the lifter cage (7). It fills the cavity under inner piston (11). The pressure raises the inner piston up until it contacts the valve push rod, or stem, whichever is used. Other parts include: 1—Push rod seat. 2—Inner piston cap. 15—Block. 8—Inner piston spring. 10—Ball check spring. 9—Camshaft. 16—Lobe.

Figure 2-80. A release-type valve rotator. (Thompson Products)

Figure 2-79. Hydraulic valve lifter operation during two stages. A—Valve closed. B—Valve open. (Cadillac)

Figure 2-81. A roller lifter is used in some heavy-duty applications.

manner as a conventional hydraulic lifter with the exception of the roller, which engages the camshaft lobe. Instead of a sliding action, the lifter rolls on the cam surface.

Valve Timing

Both the intake and exhaust valves are open longer than it takes the piston to make a stroke. The exact number of degrees that a valve will open or close before top or bottom dead center varies, depending on engine design. The degrees shown in **Figure 2-82** are for one specific engine. Note that the intake valve opens about 20° before the piston starts down on the intake stroke. It closes about 67° after the piston reaches the bottom of its stroke.

The exhaust valve opens about 69° before the piston reaches bottom dead center (BDC) on the power stroke. It does not close until about 27° after top dead center (TDC) on

the intake stroke. The early opening and late closing of both valves greatly improves the intake of fresh fuel mixture and the thorough exhausting of burned gases.

The intake and exhaust valves in **Figure 2-82** are partially open at the same time. For example, the intake valve opens 20° before TDC and the exhaust valve closes 27° after TDC on the same intake stroke. This situation is termed *valve overlap*. Overlap improves engine performance at higher speeds.

When a valve closes or opens, how fast it will rise, how long it will stay open, and how fast it will close depend on the shape of the cam lobe and the position of the camshaft in relation to the crankshaft.

The timing sprockets are generally marked to ensure correct valve timing. The camshaft is mounted to one side of the crankshaft on most inline engines (except engines using overhead camshafts), **Figure 2-83.** On V-type engines, the camshaft may be mounted above the crankshaft in the center region of the block. See **Figure 2-84.**

A few overhead cam engines have a hydraulic camshaft sprocket assembly that can vary the valve timing. These engines are said to have *variable valve timing*. The variable valve timing sprocket assembly is operated by engine oil pressure. The assembly retards valve timing at low speeds for smooth operation and advances timing at high speeds for more power. Dual overhead cam engines may have a variable valve timing sprocket assembly at each camshaft.

Engine valves are not always operated directly from a camshaft. Some engines utilize additional linkage to operate the valves. This will be discussed in Chapter 3.

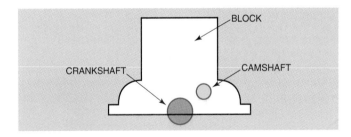

Figure 2-83. One location for the camshaft in an inline engine.

Figure 2-82. Valve timing diagram. The angles will vary widely depending upon engine design. The length of time, in degrees, that a valve is held open is referred to as valve duration.

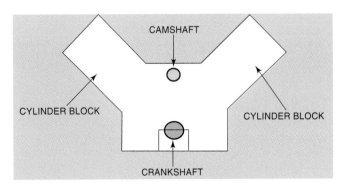

Figure 2-84. Camshaft location in a cam-in-block or valve-in-head (OHV) V-type engine.

Cylinder Head

The cylinder head serves as a cover for the cylinders and forms the top of the combustion chamber. The head also holds the spark plugs. All modern cylinder heads contain the valves. Engines with the valves located in the cylinder heads are called **valve-in-head** engines. Cylinder heads are usually made of cast iron or aluminum. They must be strong and rigid. They are bolted to the block with **head bolts**. The surfaces of the head and block that make contact must be absolutely flat. See **Figure 2-85.**

Figure 2-85. A typical overhead camshaft cylinder head arrangement. 1—Cylinder head cover. 2—Camshaft sprocket. 3—Camshaft. 4—Rocker arm assembly. 5—Semi-circular seal. 6—Cylinder head. 7—Spark plug. 8—Valve keeper. 9—Upper spring seat. 10—Spring. 11—Lower spring seat. 12—Valve seal. 13—Valve. (Mazda)

Oil Pan

The **oil pan** acts as a reservoir for oil and serves as a dust shield for the bottom of the engine. It is attached to the bottom of the block with cap screws. The pan is generally made of thin steel stamped to shape, **Figure 2-86.** Plastic and aluminum may also be used.

Timing Gear Cover

The timing gears, belts, and chains must be covered to prevent the entrance of dirt and to eliminate the loss of oil. In addition to this function, the cover often contains an oil seal that allows the crankshaft to protrude through the cover without leaking oil. Timing covers may be made of thin steel, plastic, aluminum, or cast iron. An example of a timing cover is shown in **Figure 2-87.**

Figure 2-86. Engine oil pan size and shape will vary widely. (Nissan)

Figure 2-87. One type of stamped steel timing gear cover.

Gaskets

In an engine where machined parts fit together, gaskets are used to make the joints tight and to prevent leakage of oil, water, and/or gasoline. The cylinder heads must seal in the water of the cooling system and must also contain the pressure of the exploding fuel. Thin steel, copper, and fiber **gaskets** are used between the head and engine block.

It is very difficult to machine metal parts to the degree of accuracy necessary for leakproof joints. As the engine expands and contracts during warm-up and cooling periods, there are minute shifts in the fastened parts. This, coupled with vibration, will loosen many parts to the point of leakage.

Gasket material is somewhat resilient (soft and springy) and will adapt itself to expansion and contraction. It will also conform to irregularities in the surfaces of the mating parts. Many materials are used in gasket construction, such as steel, aluminum, copper, cork, rubber (synthetic), paper, felt, and liquid silicone. **Figure 2-88** shows how the gasket material accomplishes this. **Figure 2-89** illustrates some of the common gaskets found in an engine.

Sealants

Some newer engines use chemical sealants in place of or along with a normal gasket. **Sealant**, or gasket sealer, is a liquid or semiliquid material that is sprayed, brushed, or spread on the gasket surface. Various types, having different

Figure 2-88. Gaskets are designed to compress and seal irregular surfaces. A—Note how oil is leaking out through the two areas. B—A gasket is used here to seal off leaks.

Figure 2-89. A few of the typical gaskets used in an engine.

properties, are available. Most sealants are highly resistant to oil, water, gas, diesel fuel, grease, antifreeze, mild acid, and salt solutions.

Two of the most popular are *room temperature vulcanizing* (RTV) and *anaerobic* sealants. RTV sealant hardens at room temperature and is used with gaskets or as a stand alone sealant. Anaerobic sealants are used as a stand alone replacement for a gasket. They have the capability of hardening in the absence of air.

Seals

A *seal* can be used to confine fluids, prevent the entry of foreign materials, and separate two different fluids. An oil seal is secured to one part, while the sealing lip allows the other part to rotate or reciprocate (move).

Sealing elements are usually made of synthetic rubber. Older engines used leather seals. Synthetic rubber seals are replacing leather in most applications. The rubber seal can be made to close tolerances. It can also be given special shapes and heat-resistant properties.

In the oil seal, a rubber sealing element is bonded to the case. The element rubs against the shaft. The case holds the element in place and in alignment. A garter spring forces the seal lip to conform to minor shaft runout (wobble) and maintains constant and controlled pressure on the lip.

Oil seals are used throughout the mechanical parts of the car. The engine, transmission, drive line, differential, wheels, steering, brakes, and accessories all use seals in their construction.

Other Parts

Other engine parts that are required by the various systems will be discussed in later chapters. **Figure 2-90** shows a cutaway of an engine. Note the relationship of each part to the entire engine.

Summary

The engine block forms the base on which all the other engine parts are mounted. Engine blocks are made of cast iron or aluminum. Cylinders are formed when the block is cast or cylinder sleeves are installed in the block after casting. Pistons ride up and down the length of the cylinders. The pistons must be carefully sized to prevent tipping or excessive friction. Pistons must also be constructed of rigid materials to withstand the wear associated with normal engine operation.

Cast iron rings are installed around the pistons to seal the combustion chamber from the crankcase. Piston rings are of two different types: compression and oil control. Expander devices are sometimes used with rings designed for worn cylinders. Rings are often coated with special materials to assist break-in and to give them long life.

The pistons are attached to the connecting rods through the use of piston pins. Most connecting rods use an I-beam construction. Connecting rod bearing inserts must be able to fit precisely while being rigid enough to withstand the tremendous forces in an engine. The crankshaft uses bearings similar to the connecting rod bearings. Most engines use dampers to offset vibration created by the crankshaft.

The camshaft is used to open the valves in precise time with the crankshaft. The camshaft is connected to the crankshaft through the use of timing gears or sprockets and a chain or belt. Mechanical and hydraulic lifters transfer the force from the camshaft to the valves. Valves are designed to turn in order to reduce heat and carbon build-up.

Figure 2-90. Cutaway of an 8.0 liter, V-10, fuel injected engine. Study all the parts.

The valves in most engines are housed in the cylinder head. The oil pan and timing cover house the crankcase and timing gears respectively. Gaskets, sealants, and seals are used to seal the engine and other vehicle components. They help to keep dirt and water out and vital fluids in.

Know These Terms

Engine block
Cylinder sleeves
Dry sleeve
Wet sleeve
Cam ground piston
Partial skirt piston
Piston skirt
Split skirt piston

T-slot piston
Pin boss
Piston rings
Ring gap
Blow-by
Compression ring
Oil control ring
Heat dam

Scuffing
Piston pins
Case-hardening
Snap ring
Insert bearing
Crush height
Thrust bearing
Crankshaft throws
Harmonic balancer
Vibration damper
Balance shaft
Timing gear
Chain sprocket
Timing chain
Timing belt

Mechanical valve lifters
Hydraulic valve lifters
Roller lifters
Valve overlap
Variable valve timing
Valve-in-head
Head bolts
Oil pan
Gaskets
Sealant
Room temperature
  vulcanizing
Anaerobic
Seal

Review Questions—Chapter 2

Do not write in this book. Write your answers on a separate sheet of paper.

1. All of the following statements about engine blocks are true, EXCEPT: *B*
   (A) the block forms a basic foundation for the entire engine.
   (B) the heavier the block, the better it can control heat expansion.
   (C) blocks can be made of cast iron or aluminum.
   (D) blocks contain the engine cylinders.

2. Technician A says that a dry sleeve can be thin because the block metal supports it. Technician B says that coolant in the engine directly contacts the wet sleeve. Who is right? *C*
   (A) A only.
   (B) B only.
   (C) Both A & B.
   (D) Neither A nor B.

3. The _____ the piston is, the more efficient it will be.

4. Technician A says that a cylinder that is round to within .100″ (2.54 mm) is accurate enough. Technician B says that a cylinder that is round to within .050″ (1.26 mm) is accurate enough. Who is right? *D*
   (A) A only.
   (B) B only.
   (C) Both A & B.
   (D) Neither A nor B.

5. The main advantage of using aluminum instead of cast iron in engine construction is that it is __*A*__ .
   (A) lighter
   (B) stronger
   (C) less likely to rust
   (D) cleaner

6. Name three common ways of controlling piston expansion.

7. Technician A says that the piston must fit tightly in the cylinder to prevent slapping. Technician B says that the piston must be loose enough in the cylinder to leave room for an oil film. Who is right? *C*
   (A) A only.
   (B) B only.
   (C) Both A & B.
   (D) Neither A nor B.

8. A cam ground piston becomes round when it is __*C*__ .
   (A) cold
   (B) partially heated
   (C) fully heated
   (D) None of the above.

9. The head of the piston will generally be .030″ to .040″ (0.76 to 1.02 mm) _____ than the skirt.
   SMALLER

10. Piston heads are of different shapes. What are some of the reasons for these shapes?

11. What does a piston heat dam protect? *B*
    (A) Piston.
    (B) Top ring.
    (C) Bottom ring.
    (D) Piston pin.

12. Name the two types of piston rings and state how many of each type are used on a modern piston.

13. Proper ring gap prevents ring _*BREAKAGE*_ when the engine heats up.

14. All of the following statements about piston rings are true, EXCEPT: *A*
    (A) chrome-plated rings are generally rough finished for quicker break in.
    (B) new ring and wall surfaces are designed with some roughness to cause the rings to wear in.
    (C) compression rings are made from cast iron.
    (D) oil ring rails are made of steel.

15. Ring expanders must be stronger when used on a piston installed with what type of cylinder? *D. WORN*
    (A) new
    (B) used
    (C) rebored
    (D) None of the above.

16. During the break in period, new piston rings will wear at a _*FASTER*_ rate than after the break in.

17. The bottom rings are always _*OIL*_ rings.

18. Piston pins fasten the _*ROD*_ to the _*PISTON*_.

19. Piston pins are hollow to reduce __*D*__ .
    (A) wear
    (B) heat transfer
    (C) noise
    (D) weight

20. Case-hardening hardens what part of an engine component? *A*
    (A) Outside.
    (B) Inside.
    (C) The sharp edges.
    (D) All of the component.

21. Connecting rods are used to connect the _*PISTONS*_ to the _*CRANK*_.

22. The smaller connecting rod upper end bearing is _____, but the big end bearing is _____ to facilitate installation.

23. Connecting rods use precision _*INSERT*_ for the big end bearings.

24. Name six characteristics of a good bearing material.

25. Crankshafts are usually made of __*D*__ .
    (A) aluminum
    (B) stainless steel
    (C) wrought iron
    (D) None of the above.
    ALLOY STEEL OR CAST IRON

26. Technician A says that crankshafts can vibrate from being off balance and also from twisting. Technician B says that the flow of power is smoother in a four-cylinder engine than in an eight-cylinder engine. Who is right?

    (A) A only.
    (B) B only.
    (C) Both A & B.
    (D) Neither A nor B.

27. Crankshafts have drilled passageways. What are they for?

28. Camshafts are driven in three ways. Name them.

29. Technician A says that all modern engines use one exhaust and one intake valve per cylinder. Technician B says that the exhaust valve sheds its heat into the exhaust stream leaving the cylinder.

    Who is right?   A.
    (A) A only.
    (B) B only.
    (C) Both A & B.
    (D) Neither A nor B.

30. Two common valve seat angles are __30__ degrees and __45__ degrees.

31. The camshaft lobes are usually _NOT_ .FLAT

32. Why is the valve rotated on some engines? – REDUCE WEAR

33. What are the advantages of a hydraulic lifter?

34. Which of the following parts is sometimes made of a hard metal and pressed into the head?   A
    (A) valve guide
    (B) valve seat.
    (C) valve spring
    (D) Both A & B.

35. Gaskets are used to seal _UNEVEN_ surfaces.

3

Engine Classification, Parts Identification

After studying this chapter, you will be able to:
- Compare four-stroke and two-stroke cycle engines.
- Explain the different engine classifications.
- Describe the operating principles of a rotary type engine.
- Identify the parts of various engine types.

In the first two chapters, you designed and constructed a basic engine and studied engine parts and their uses. This chapter studies the various methods in which basic engine theory and parts are utilized to produce multicylinder engines. Methods of engine classification as well as different kinds of engines will be discussed. Internal combustion engines can be classified in many ways. The most common methods used to classify engines are by cycle, valve location, cylinder arrangement, type of fuel used, cooling, and number of cylinders. This chapter will discuss each classification.

Cycle Classification

Engines are often classified according to cycle. Most internal combustion piston engines use a two- or four-stroke cycle. The basic engine which was discussed in the first two chapters is a *four-stroke cycle* engine. **Figure 3-1** illustrates that it takes two complete crankshaft revolutions to complete the cycle. As a result, each cylinder receives only one power stroke per cycle. All modern automobile engines use the four-stroke cycle engine.

Two-Stroke Cycle Engine

The *two-stroke cycle* engine performs the intake, compression, firing, and exhaust sequence in one revolution of the crankshaft. This is accomplished by eliminating the valves used in the four-stroke cycle engine. In place of the valves, two ports enter the cylinder wall. One is used for the intake of fuel and the other for exhaust.

A passage connects the intake port to the crankcase interior. The air-fuel mixture is drawn into the crankcase through a *reed valve* or a *rotary valve*. Oil is usually mixed with the gasoline to provide lubrication. Some two-stroke cycle engines use an oil injection system. Upon entry into the crankcase, the oil provides ample lubrication for the bearings.

Figure 3-1. Four-stroke cycle principle. This series of events requires two complete revolutions (720° of rotation) of the crankshaft. Note that there is one power stroke per cycle. (TRW, Inc.)

Two-stroke cycle engines are used in chain saws, lawn mowers, marine outboard motors, go-carts, and other small engine applications. Due to emission control problems, gasoline powered two-stroke cycle engines are not used in automobiles.

Two-Stroke Cycle Operation

Imagine that a charge of air and fuel is in the cylinder and that the piston is at the bottom of its stroke. As the piston travels up, it closes off both intake and exhaust ports. As it continues upward, it compresses the air-fuel charge while forming a vacuum in the airtight crankcase. The vacuum pulls open a small flap-like reed valve and a mixture of air and fuel enters the crankcase. When the piston reaches the top of its stroke, it has compressed the charge in the cylinder and filled the crankcase with an air-fuel mixture. This has all happened in one-half revolution of the crankshaft.

The spark plug fires the cylinder charge and drives the piston down. Several things happen as the piston travels downward. The air-fuel mixture in the crankcase is compressed and the reed valve closes. The piston is also performing the power stroke at this time. When the piston has traveled down the cylinder far enough to expose the exhaust port, the exhaust will flow out of the port. As the piston continues to travel down, the intake port is uncovered. As the crankcase air-fuel mixture is compressed, it is forced to flow through the now uncovered intake port into the cylinder.

The piston top is usually shaped to deflect the incoming air-fuel charge upward. This fills the top of the cylinder with a fresh charge while simultaneously scavenging (cleaning out) the remaining exhaust gases. This has all taken place in one revolution of the crankshaft. Every time the piston reaches the top of its travel, it will be driven downward by a power stroke. Study **Figure 3-2**.

Advantages of the Two-Stroke Engine

The two-stroke cycle engine has several advantages that make it popular for use in small engine applications. By eliminating the valves, it also eliminates valve springs, cam followers, camshaft, and gears. Since there are no valves to "float," two-cycle engines can operate at very high speeds. This enables the engine to be quite compact and light. Machining costs are reduced.

Because the two-stroke engine fires on every stroke, more power per pound of engine weight is available. However, it does not produce the power of a four-stroke cycle engine of comparable size. A two-stroke engine has poor volumetric efficiency (ability to intake fuel) and will lose some power through compressing the crankcase mixture. In order to completely scavenge the cylinder, some of the intake air-fuel charge also leaves the cylinder, resulting in higher emissions and less fuel economy. A two-stroke cycle engine that utilizes an exhaust valve and no mixture in the crankcase will be shown in the section on diesel engines later in this chapter.

Valve Location Classifications

Engines are also classified according to the valve location. The various valve arrangements are known as the L-head, T-head, F-head, and I-head. The names are derived

Figure 3-2. In the left-hand view, the piston is traveling upward and has almost reached the top of its stroke. It has compressed the air-fuel charge trapped above the piston. The spark plug has just fired and the mixture is starting to burn.

On its way upward, the piston has drawn a fresh fuel mixture into the crankcase through a reed valve. The fuel vapor contains suspended droplets of oil that lubricates the surfaces of moving parts.

In the right-hand view, the air-fuel mixture has fired and the piston is traveling down. It has uncovered the intake and exhaust ports, allowing burning gases to escape and fresh charge to enter. The air-fuel mixture flows through the intake port because the piston, while traveling down, compressed the mixture in the crankcase.

In two-strokes, the engine has performed all the necessary functions to enable it to receive a power stroke for every crankshaft revolution.

from the resemblance to letters of the alphabet. This will be demonstrated in forthcoming sketches. The I-head is almost universally used in cars and light trucks.

L-Head, T-Head, and F-Head Designs

These three head designs are no longer used in automotive applications, but it is possible to find them in some stationary power plants or small engine applications. The **L-head** engine has both valves in the block and on the same side of the cylinder. A line drawn through the cylinder and across to the valves will produce the letter *L* in an inverted (upside down) position. **Figure 3-3** illustrates the L-head design. This design may still be found on some small engines and forklifts.

In the **T-head** engine, both valves are in the block and on opposite sides of the cylinder, **Figure 3-4**. This design has been obsolete for many years and is no longer used. The **F-head** places one valve in the head and one in the block, **Figure 3-5**. Today, this design is only used on small air-cooled

Figure 3-3. L-head engine. Valves are in the block, both on the same side. Note letter L. (TRW, Inc.)

Figure 3-4. T-head configuration, like the L head engine, the valves are in the block. This configuration is not used anymore, but may be found on some older engines.

Figure 3-5. F-head engine. Note that there is one valve in the block and one in the head. (TRW, Inc.)

Figure 3-6. I-head engine. Both valves are located in the head. (TRW, Inc.)

engines, such as those found in most lawn mowers and garden tillers.

I-Head

In the *I-head* engine, both valves are located in the cylinder head. They may be arranged in a straight line, **Figure 3-6** or staggered, **Figure 3-7**. This is sometimes referred to as a valve-in-head engine.

Since the valves are placed in the I-head, a *valve train* must be used to operate them. **Figure 3-8** illustrates the use

of a *rocker arm* and *push rod* setup to actuate the valves. The rocker arm is mounted on a *rocker shaft*. Note how push rod force is transferred in the opposite direction by the rocker arm. **Figure 3-9** illustrates the use of a rocker arm-push rod valve train on an actual engine. **Figure 3-10** shows a different rocker arm design. Instead of oscillating on a rocker arm shaft, this type uses a *ball pivot* arrangement on which the rocker arm pivots.

Figure 3-7. Transverse cross-section of an I-head (overhead valve) engine. Both intake and exhaust valves are located in the head. (Dodge)

Figure 3-8. Schematic shows simplified valve train for one cylinder of an overhead valve engine.

Figure 3-9. Cutaway view shows a typical valve train used to operate overhead valves on a V-6 engine. (Dodge.)

Figure 3-10. Ball type rocker arm. Note the shape of the ball pivot. (TRW, Inc.)

Overhead Camshaft I-Head

Some I-head engines mount the camshaft in the head. Either one or two shafts can be used. When an **overhead camshaft** is used, push rods are not required. The rocker arm setup shown in **Figure 3-11** is operated by the camshaft lobe rubbing directly on the rocker. Zero valve stem-to-rocker clearance is maintained by a hydraulic valve lash adjuster, **Figure 3-12**, which operates in the same manner as the hydraulic

Figure 3-11. One type of overhead camshaft rocker arm arrangement. Note the hydraulic lash adjuster. (Ford)

Figure 3-13. Cutaway view of a 3.0-liter, dual overhead camshaft (DOHC), 24-valve, inline six-cylinder, gasoline engine. Note the camshaft lobes act directly on the ends of the valves. No rocker arms are used. Study carefully. (Lexus)

Figure 3-12. Cross-sectional view of an engine which incorporates a single overhead camshaft (SOHC) to operate the valves. Note the use of a hydraulic valve lash (clearance) adjuster. (Chrysler)

lifter discussed earlier in Chapter 2. The camshaft lobes can also be arranged to work directly on the valves as shown in **Figure 3-13**.

Overhead Valve Adjustment

Some overhead valve installations provide an adjusting screw in the push rod end of the rocker arm. This screw is moved in or out until the recommended clearance is obtained between the valve stem and the rocker arm. See **Figure 3-14**. Some engines use hydraulic lifters, which eliminates the need to adjust clearance. The only adjustment necessary is the initial setting to place the lifter plunger at the halfway point in its travel. Some engines make the initial setting with adjustable

Figure 3-14. Rocker arm with adjustment screw used to set proper valve clearance or "lash." (British-Leyland)

rocker arms, while others use push rods that provide the proper setting when installed. **Figure 3-15** shows such a setup. Push rods of slightly different lengths are available to make minor changes.

Figure 3-15. This non-adjustable rocker arm depends upon precise parts so that the hydraulic lifter plunger will be at midpoint of travel upon assembly. (Dodge)

Valve-to-Piston Clearance

Some engines utilize high compression, which squeezes the air-fuel charge into a smaller than normal area. In order to have this small area and still allow room for the valves to open, it is sometimes necessary for the pistons to have small indentations cut into their tops to allow the valves to clear the piston at top dead center (TDC), **Figure 3-16**. These indentations, or grooves, keep the piston head from striking the valves at the top of the exhaust stroke when both valves may be partially open. If the piston and valve(s) are allowed to make contact, extensive engine damage would result.

Detonation and Preignition

When a highly compressed air-fuel charge is fired, the flame travels from the plug in an outward direction. As the charge continues to burn, chamber pressure greatly increases. If the combustion chamber pressure increases faster in another part of the cylinder before the flame reaches it, this area will become hot enough to fire itself. This will produce two flame fronts, which increases the fuel charge burn rate. Instead of firing smoothly, there is a violent explosion that literally slams the piston down. This is called *detonation*, which is very damaging to an engine.

Detonation can be caused by an excessively high compression ratio or by a low grade of gasoline. An overheated valve or piece of carbon can ignite the remaining air-fuel mixture and cause the formation of the second flame front, **Figure 3-17**. *Preignition* is caused when a glowing piece of carbon, an overheated spark plug, or a piece of metal extending into the combustion chamber ignites the fuel charge before the spark plug fires. When preignition occurs, the premature explosion attempts to drive the piston down against the direction of rotation. Detonation and preignition can destroy an engine if it is not corrected.

Combustion Chamber Design

The size and shape of the combustion chamber is very important. A well designed chamber will allow high compression ratios without the occurrence of detonation or preignition.

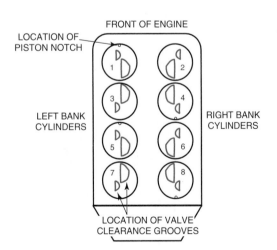

Figure 3-16. Piston indentations used for valve clearance. Each piston has two small indentations to allow the valves to clear. (Chevrolet)

Figure 3-17. Detonation. A—Proper flame travel. B—Two flame fronts increase burning rate and cause detonation.

Compression ratios of 10.5 to 1 and higher were once widely used. Modern engines have compression ratios of around 8, 8.5, or 9 to 1, which provides both good performance and emission control.

Ricardo Combustion Chamber

Many years ago a man named **Ricardo** developed a combustion chamber for L-head engines that has been modified for use in many I-head engines. He found that by causing a violent turbulence in the compressed air-fuel charge and by locating the spark plug near the center of the turbulence, flame travel through the charge was smooth and compression could be raised considerably without detonation.

Modern designs locate the combustion chamber under the valves and allow the piston to come very close to the head. As the piston travels up on compression, it forces the fuel into the area below the valves. As the piston comes close to the head, the remaining mixture is rapidly squeezed, causing it to shoot into the combustion chamber, setting up a rapid turbulence. The area between the piston top and the head is referred to as the **squish area**, **Figure 3-18**.

Figure 3-18. When the top of the piston nears the head, the trapped air-fuel mixture in the "squish" area shoots into the combustion chamber, causing turbulence. This is known as the Ricardo principle.

Hemispherical Combustion Chamber

The **hemispherical combustion chamber** is compact and allows high compression with very little detonation. By placing the valves in two planes, it is possible to use larger valves, thereby improving air-fuel intake and exhaust scavenging. The hemispherical combustion chamber was first used many years ago on high performance engines. Today, it is used on a number of modern engines. **Figure 3-19** illustrates the hemispherical combustion chamber and valve configuration.

Figure 3-19. A cutaway view of a hemispherical combustion chamber. The valves are set in two places. (TRW)

Wedge Shape Combustion Chamber

Another combustion chamber shape is the **wedge chamber**. When the wedge shape is incorporated in the head, a flat top piston will produce a desirable squish effect. When the top of the engine block is machined at an angle of around 10°, it is possible to build the cylinder head flat. The combustion chamber wedge is formed by the angled cylinder and a piston with an inverted V top. This setup will also produce a squish effect.

The spark plug is generally located at one corner of the wedge, **Figure 3-20**. This provides a smooth flame travel and loads (presses down) the piston gradually. When the charge is first ignited, it loads only a portion of the piston. This partial pressure starts the piston down smoothly. As the piston

Figure 3-20. Notice that the head in this wedge combustion chamber is flat and cylinder block is machined at an angle — approximately 10°. The valves are set in a plane.

begins to travel down, the flame front spreads across the entire piston dome, providing smooth loading.

Cylinder Classification

Cylinder placement gives rise to one of the most common methods of engine classification. Many arrangements have been used, but only those in popular use today will be covered in this text. **Figure 3-21** shows one other type. This is a *radial* engine, which has been very popular for use in propeller-driven aircraft.

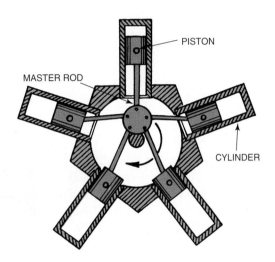

Figure 3-21. In this radial engine, all the connecting rods are fastened to the master rod. This design has been used for many years in aircraft.

Inline Engine

The *inline* engine has its cylinders arranged one after the other in a straight line. They are in a vertical, or near vertical position, **Figure 3-22**. Most modern inline engines are four cylinders. Inline six-cylinder engines were used in older vehicles and can still be found in a few modern light trucks. Until the adoption of the V-8, eight cylinder inline engines were common. A few three- and five-cylinder inline engines are now produced. A variation of the inline engine is the *slant* or *inclined engine*, **Figure 3-23**. An inclined engine is an inline engine with the cylinder block slanted to one side. This is done to fit the engine into a smaller engine compartment, allowing for a lower hood line.

V-Type Engine

A *V-type* engine places two banks or rows of cylinders at an angle to each other—generally at 60° or 90°. The V-type engine has several advantages: short length, extra block rigidity, a short, heavy crankshaft, and low profile that is conducive to low hood lines. The shorter block permits a reduction in vehicle length with no sacrifice in passenger room.

Higher compression ratios can be used in the V-type engine without block distortion under load. The short, heavy crankshaft is more resistant to torsional vibration. In the past,

Figure 3-22. Cutaway view of an inline, four-cylinder, overhead valve, electronic fuel injected engine. Note the ribbed drive and timing belts. (Ford Motor Co.)

V-12, and V-16 engines were widely used. Current production V-type engines are the V-6 and V-8, along with a few V-10 and V-12 designs, **Figure 3-24**.

Horizontal-Opposed Engines

The *horizontal opposed engine* is like a V-type engine, except that both banks lie in a horizontal plane. The advantage here is an extremely low overall height, which makes this engine ideally suited to installations where space is limited. **Figure 3-25** shows a horizontal-opposed engine. It is an air-cooled, six-cylinder engine.

Firing Order

Firing order refers to the sequence in which the cylinders fire. Firing orders are given in order from the front of the engine to the rear. The order in which the engine must fire is determined by the number of cylinders and the arrangement of the crankshaft throws. Firing order can be found in the service manual for the vehicle being serviced. Firing orders vary between engines, and must be obtained from the service manual.

Cooling Classification

As you have learned, engines are either liquid-cooled or air-cooled. Most vehicles use liquid-cooled engines. Air-cooled engines are used in limited numbers on modern vehicles, but are widely used to operate chain saws, lawn mowers, scooters, and other equipment. Both types have advantages and disadvantages.

Air cooling is simple and has no coolant to leak or freeze in cold weather. However, air cooled vehicles are very uncomfortable in cold weather, since there is no efficient or safe way to transfer engine heat to the passenger compartment.

DISTRIBUTOR

PUSH ROD

ROCKER ARM

LONG BRANCH INTAKE MANIFOLD

VALVE

HEAD

OIL FILTER

ALTERNATOR

OIL PUMP

PISTON

OIL PICKUP

CONNECTING ROD

CRANKSHAFT

OIL PAN

Figure 3-23. Cross-sectional view of an inclined four-cylinder engine. By setting the engine at an angle, overall height is reduced. This allows for a lower vehicle hood. (Toyota)

Fuel Classification

Automobile engines can use gasoline, diesel fuel, gasohol (mixture of gasoline and alcohol), alcohol, LNG (liquefied natural gas), CNG (compressed natural gas), or LPG (liquefied propane gas). Gasoline powers the majority of vehicles, but diesel fuel is used in some vehicles. Gasohol, LNG, CNG, and LPG are beginning to see wider use.

One of the principal differences in these engines is in method of fuel delivery and carburetion. Gasoline, LNG, CNG, and LPG utilize the same basic type of engine, but LNG, CNG, and LPG utilize a slightly different fuel delivery setup. Diesel engines do not use a carburetor or an ignition system. Due to the pressures and stresses involved, diesel engines are constructed very rigidly. The theory of diesel engines is covered in the diesel injection section in Chapter 9. Diesel engines are either two- or four-stroke cycle types.

Two-Stroke and Four-Stroke Cycle Diesel Engines

A two-stroke cycle diesel engine is somewhat different than the two-stroke gasoline engine discussed earlier in this chapter. The two-stroke cycle diesel engine utilizes an exhaust valve. No fuel mixture enters the crankcase. Due to the pressures involved, a supercharger is used to force air into the cylinder intake ports. **Figure 3-26** shows the two-stroke cycle operation in a diesel engine.

Notice that air rushing in through the cylinder liner ports helps scavenge the cylinder by flowing out the exhaust passage for a portion of the piston travel. Since only air enters the cylinder, there is no loss of fuel. **Figure 3-27** shows a typical four-stroke cycle, four-cylinder automotive diesel engine. Inline five-, six-, and V-8 diesels are also used, **Figure 3-28**. Diesel fuel injection system operation is discussed in Chapter 9.

Figure 3-24. Two cutaway views of one particular V-12, electronic fuel injected, gasoline engine. Study the engine construction carefully in both views. (BMW)

Figure 3-25. Cutaway view of a horizontally opposed 3.3 liter, six-cylinder, fuel injected engine. A low profile makes this engine suitable to limited spaces. (Porsche)

Figure 3-26. Two-stroke cycle diesel engine operation. Note the use of a supercharger to force the air-fuel mixture into the combustion chamber. (Detroit Diesel Engine Div.—General Motors)

Rotary Engines

The **_rotary engine_** was used on a few vehicles for many years and was not produced in large numbers. The rotary engine is very powerful for its size. This engine is often referred to as a Wankel engine, **Figure 3-29**.

The rotary engine has fewer moving parts than a piston engine. Since it has no reciprocating motion, the rotary engine produces less vibration and offers more horsepower. Drawbacks of the rotary engine included difficulty meeting emission control standards, and poor fuel economy compared to a piston engine of similar power output.

Rotary Engine Construction

Rotary engines are classified according to the number of **_rotors_** used in the engine. The remainder of the engine consists of one or more **_rotor housings_**, end housings, fixed gears, and a center housing all held rigidly together with a series of bolts.

There are just two or three moving parts in the rotary engine depending upon the number of rotors the engine has —the **_eccentric shaft_** (also called the mainshaft) and the cast iron rotor assemblies. The rotors have spring-loaded cast iron seals to close the very small running clearance between them

Figure 3-27. Four-cylinder diesel engine. Note the use of a timing belt instead of gears or chains. (VW)

Figure 3-28. Cross-section of a 6.2 liter V-8 diesel engine. Note how similar this engine is to some gasoline engines. (General Motors)

and the housing surface while providing a barrier against compression loss and oil consumption.

Rotary Engine Operation

The rotary engine performs the four distinct strokes—intake, compression, power, and exhaust, **Figure 3-30**. Each face of the triangular rotor acts like a conventional piston. Instead of a reciprocating action, however, the rotor

Figure 3-29. Cutaway view of a turbocharged rotary engine. This particular engine has a compression ratio of 8.5:1. Study the various parts. (Mazda)

continually revolves in the same direction as the eccentric shaft.

By meshing the rotor internal gear with a fixed gear attached to the end housing, it forces the rotor to "walk" around the fixed gear when the eccentric shaft turns. This walking action causes the rotor to revolve around the eccentric shaft rotor journal in the same direction as the eccentric shaft. At the same time, the walking action keeps all three rotor tips constantly close to the wall of the rotor housing.

This planetary motion of the rotor constantly changes chamber volume between each rotor face and rotor housing. The change in volume is the principle used for engine operation. Study the rotor movement in **Figure 3-30A** through **Figure 3-30E**. We will follow one rotor face through the complete cycle. Note that this face lies between rotor tips A and B.

Rotary Engine Rotor Cycle

In **Figure 3-30A**, rotor face A and B has rotated past the intake port. As tip B passed the intake port, the chamber volume increased. This action forms a vacuum, causing the fuel mixture to flow into the enlarged chamber area. In **Figure 3-30B**, the rotor has turned further to the right and in so doing, chamber size has started to reduce, compressing the fuel. When rotor face A-B has turned to the position shown in C, maximum compression is applied.

When compression is at its maximum, the spark plug ignites the fuel charge, **Figure 3-30C**. When the charge ignites, the rapidly expanding gases apply pressure to the A-B face of the rotor, forcing it to continue walking around the fixed gear. As it rotates, it transmits the power of the burning gas to the eccentric shaft rotor journal, causing the eccentric shaft to spin, **Figure 3-30D**.

Figure 3-30. Rotor action within the rotor housing. The rotor internal gear and housing gear are not shown. (NSU)

The burning gas will continue to revolve the rotor until tip B uncovers the exhaust port, causing the burning gas to rush out the exhaust port as shown in **Figure 3-30E**. Follow rotor face A-B from **Figure 3-30A** to **Figure 3-30E** and note that as the ports are uncovered and the chamber volume changes, each phase of a four-stroke cycle is performed.

Miller-Cycle Engines

In a conventional engine, the intake valve is open during the piston's intake stroke, and closes almost as soon as the piston begins to move upward on the compression stroke. However, on a *Miller-cycle* engine, the intake valve is held open for a much longer time as the piston comes up on the compression stroke. To prevent the air-fuel mixture from exiting through the intake valve, a supercharger raises the intake manifold pressure. This forces more of the air-fuel mixture into the cylinder. The Miller-cycle design is said to produce more power and economy over a wider RPM range. **Figure 3-31** shows a cutaway of a Miller-cycle engine.

Natural Gas Engines

Natural gas is piped to millions of homes, where it is burned in water heaters, furnaces, and stoves. In addition, some vehicles operate on natural gas. The vehicle holds the gas in a high pressure storage tank, since it must be under high pressure in order to stay liquid. The gas must be maintained in a liquid state, as the vehicle could not carry enough to go very far if the gas were in its vapor state. The high pressure tank gives the natural gas vehicle a cruising range similar to that of a gasoline powered engine.

A natural gas engine is an internal combustion engine similar to a gasoline engine. In fact, most natural gas engines are production gasoline engines with a modified fuel system. The fuel system is modified to allow the natural gas to vaporize and mix with the incoming air. A simple mixing valve arrangement replaces the carburetor or fuel injectors. The natural gas system can even be adapted to work with the existing computer control system.

The advantage of natural gas is that it produces much less pollution and is readily available in large quantities. The

Figure 3-31. This Miller-cycle engine design allows the intake valve to open sooner. A supercharger is used to force the air-fuel mixture into the cylinders. (Mazda)

disadvantage of natural gas is that the high pressure tank adds weight and price to the vehicle. Also, since most vehicles are gasoline powered, refueling stations are hard to find. Refueling time is slightly longer than for gasoline. If natural gas powered vehicles become more common, it may be possible in the future for homeowners to refuel their vehicles from their home gas system.

Experimental Engines

The search for better engines is never ending. Many ideas have been tried and adopted, others have failed. Currently, manufacturers are experimenting with engines that can operate on more than one type of fuel. Manufacturers are also developing vehicles driven by electricity. Whether or not these types of engines will find successful application as automobile power plants, only time will tell.

Engine Mounting

It is common practice to mount the engine on fluid-filled or rubber pads, usually called *engine mounts*. This helps isolate engine vibrations from the vehicle body. It also eases torque (twisting strain) loading of the drive line. Mounts are used to support the engine and to minimize torque deflections. Small shock absorbers are sometimes employed, especially on diesel engines, to further control vibration.

The three point suspension, used mostly on rear-wheel drive vehicles, is one of the most popular. This method uses one mount on either side of the engine near the front and one at the back, usually under the transmission. However, other setups use two, three, four, or five engine mount arrangements. This varies from each model and manufacturer. **Figure 3-32** shows a five point mounting pattern.

Identification and Classification

The remainder of this chapter is devoted to engine classification and parts identification. Study all the engine figures in this chapter very carefully, especially **Figure 3-33** through **Figure 3-38**. Make certain you know the names and uses of all parts. It is most important that you build a complete and accurate mental image of the various types of engines, and the relationship of one part to the other.

As you study each figure, ask these questions:

- Is it a four-stroke cycle or a two-stroke cycle engine?
- Is this engine air- or liquid-cooled?
- Is this a V-type, inline, or opposed engine?
- How many cylinders does it have?
- Does it burn gasoline, diesel, or other fuel?
- If gasoline, is it carbureted or fuel injected?
- What type of head is on it?
- What type of combustion chamber design is used?
- Do I know the names and uses of all the parts?
- Do I know the working relationship of one part to another?

In addition to knowing the names and uses of all parts, be certain to test your knowledge of the various systems by identifying the cooling, lubrication, ignition, and fuel systems.

Summary

Engines can be classified in many ways. The most commonly used classifications are by cycle, valve location, cylinder arrangement, fuel used, cooling and number of cylinders. The vast majority of auto engines are of the four-stroke cycle type. The two-stroke cycle is generally used in small engines. Both have advantages and disadvantages. The I-head (overhead valve or valve-in-head) engine is in almost universal use today.

The most commonly used combustion chamber shapes are the wedge and the hemispherical. Detonation during the compression stroke can be stopped by proper fuel and com-

Figure 3-32. One type of front-wheel drive engine mount. The fluid sealed in the mount absorbs low speed vibrations. (Toyota)

bustion chamber design. Ricardo, in early experiments, set forth some basic principles of combustion chamber design that are still incorporated in modern engines. He found that by providing turbulence in the compressed charge, compression could be raised without detonation.

The V-8, V-6, and inline four-cylinder engines dominate the field of engine design and use. Some inline six-cylinder, V-10 and V-12, and four- or six-cylinder horizontal-opposed engines, are occasionally found. The diesel two-stroke cycle engine differs from the small gasoline engine of the same type. The diesel engine incorporates an exhaust valve, a supercharger and a conventional crankcase. The Wankel rotary piston engine uses a triangular shaped rotor that revolves inside a housing. It operates on the four-cycle principle. It has no reciprocating action and as a result, is very

Figure 3-33. An exploded view of an inline six-cylinder engine. Study the construction. (Ford Motor Company)

Figure 3-34. Cross-sectional view of a slant V-6 engine. By slanting the engine, overall height is reduced. This allows for a lower vehicle hood. (Saab)

Figure 3-35. A cutaway view of an all-aluminum, low maintenance 2.5 liter dual overhead camshaft (DOHC) V-6 electronic fuel injected gasoline engine. This engine will not need a tune-up for 100,000 miles (160 000 km) under normal conditions. It produces 170 horsepower. (Ford Motor Company)

Figure 3-36. A cross-sectional view of a 3.8 liter V-6, split port induction (SPI) gasoline engine. Study the construction. (Ford Motor Company)

Figure 3-37. Overall view of a fuel injected, 6.0 liter V-12 gasoline engine. (Mercedes-Benz)

Figure 3-38. A cross-sectional view of an inline, four-cylinder, 2.7 liter (164.4 cu. in.), 16-valve, dual overhead camshaft, electronic fuel injected gasoline engine. The engine has a compression ratio of 9.5:1, and produces 150 horsepower at 4800 RPM and 177 lbs. ft of torque at 4000 RPM. (Toyota Motor Corp.)

smooth running. The rotary is a simple engine with very few moving parts (rotor and eccentric shaft) in the basic engine.

Experiments with new and different types of engines are always in progress. Further development of existing engines is also taking place. Considerable research is being done on natural gas and electric drive autos. Engines are mounted on rubber, generally using the three point suspension system, but some vehicles can utilize up to five mounts.

Know These Terms

Four-stroke cycle	Hemispherical combustion chamber
Two-stroke cycle	Wedge chamber
Reed valve	Radial
Rotary valve	Inline
L-head	Slant engine
T-head	Inclined engine
F-head	V-type
I-head	Horizontal-opposed engine
Valve train	Firing order
Rocker arm	Rotary engine
Push rod	Rotor
Rocker shaft	Rotor housing
Ball pivot	Eccentric shaft
Overhead camshaft	Miller-cycle
Detonation	Natural gas
Preignition	Engine mounts
Ricardo	
Squish area	

Review Questions—Chapter 3

Do not write in this book. Write your answers on a separate sheet of paper.

1. List the strokes in a four-cycle engine in their proper order.

2. The strokes of a four-cycle engine take place during how many revolutions of the crankshaft?

3. The two-strokes of a two-cycle engine take place during how many revolutions of the crankshaft?

4. What type of valves does the two-cycle gasoline engine have?

5. In a two-cycle engine, what opens and closes the reed valve(s)?
   (A) Air pressure and vacuum.
   (B) A camshaft lobe.
   (C) A crankshaft lobe.
   (D) All of the above, depending on the manufacturer.

6. Explain where the valves are located in the following engines.
   I-head
   F-head
   L-head
   T-head

7. Using cylinder arrangement, list the three most popular engines in use today.

8. A horizontally opposed engine has _____ banks of cylinders.

9. Where are the valves located in an overhead camshaft I-head engine?

10. Valve-to-piston clearance is most important on _____ compression engines.

11. Additional compression can be obtained without causing detonation if the air-fuel _____ is increased inside of the combustion chamber.

12. What is detonation and how is it caused?

13. All of the following could cause preignition, EXCEPT:

    (A) glowing carbon.
    (B) overheated spark plug.
    (C) burned valve.
    (D) piece of metal extending into the combustion chamber.

14. What determines an engine's firing order?

15. Which valve does a supercharged two-cycle diesel engine use?

    (A) Intake.
    (B) Exhaust.
    (C) Reed.
    (D) None.

16. Technician A says that engine mounts are used to reduce noise in the engine compartment. Technician B says that engine mounts can be made of solid rubber or fluid filled.

    Who is right?

    (A) A only.
    (B) B only.
    (C) Both A & B.
    (D) Neither A nor B.

17. Name two advantages of natural gas as a vehicle fuel.

18. In fuel classification, what are the three principal fuels used today?

19. In the rotary engine, the rotor turns _____ to every _____ turns of the eccentric shaft.

20. Technician A says that rotary engines have fewer moving parts than piston engines. Technician B says that piston engines operate more smoothly than rotary engines.

    Who is right?

    (A) A only.
    (B) B only.
    (C) A and B.
    (D) Neither A nor B.

4

Safety, Lab Procedures

Upon completion of this chapter you will be able to:
- Identify the major types of accidents and their causes.
- Identify the consequences of accidents.
- Explain how to dress safely in the shop.
- Identify personal protective equipment.
- Explain how to identify and correct unsafe conditions in the shop.
- Identify unsafe work procedures.

This chapter covers the importance of safety. You will learn how to dress safely, work safely, and maintain a safe shop. The safety precautions given here are intended to help you avoid accidents as you perform laboratory jobs under your instructor's supervision. Learning good safety practices now will give you the safety habit at all jobs in the future. This chapter examines various types of unsafe shop conditions and work practices, and discusses ways to correct or avoid them.

Preventing Accidents

Safe working conditions and safety procedures protect the automotive technician, the vehicle, and the shop. *Accidents* are unplanned events that can occur without anyone intending for them to happen. Also unintended are the consequences of accidents, such as property damage or injury. The following sections show how a little foresight and common sense can eliminate the causes of most accidents.

Kinds of Accidents

There are many kinds of accidents. The most common accidents in the automotive shop include:
- *Falls* from slipping on a wet or oily floor.
- *Fires* and *explosions* caused by flammable substances contacting a heat source.
- *Asphyxiation* caused by exhaust fumes or refrigerants building up in a closed space.
- *Injury to body parts*, such as hands, arms, face, head, or feet from moving parts, or from being caught under heavy parts.
- *Strains and sprains* from lifting heavy parts improperly.
- *Burns* from contacting hot coolant, oil, or metal.

- *Chemical burns* from battery acid or parts cleaner.
- *Electrical shocks* from ungrounded electrical tools or outlets.

In addition to the above accidents, the careless technician can be exposed to substances which cause long-term health problems including:
- *Emphysema* and *lung cancer* from inhaling brake dust over a period of years.
- *Skin cancer* from prolonged exposure to used motor oil and some cleaners.

As you can see, there are many ways to be injured or killed when working in an automotive shop. Therefore, it is good practice to find out how accidents happen and how to avoid them.

How Accidents Happen

Some of the accidents described earlier are caused when technicians try to take shortcuts instead of following proper repair procedures. Other accidents are caused when shop personnel fail to correct dangerous conditions in the work area. Accidents are often caused by a series of *unsafe acts* or *unsafe conditions*, which lead to other actions. An example of an unsafe act is leaving spilled gasoline on the shop floor.

In some shops, this spill would remain unattended indefinitely because everybody is too busy to clean it up. Another unsafe act is using a standard light bulb in a drop light, which many technicians do because it is too much trouble to obtain a rough service bulb. Neither of these unsafe acts becomes an accident until someone drops the light to the shop floor. It breaks, and the spark ignites the gasoline. This causes a large fire, which could result in severe damage to the shop and any vehicles in the shop. It may also severely burn, or even kill someone in the shop. In this example, no one deliberately set out to cause an accident. Instead, it was just a series of things that were too much trouble to do correctly. The end result of this chain or series of unsafe acts was a fire, **Figure 4-1**.

Results of Accidents

An accident may result in injuries that keep you from working or enjoying your time off. Some accidents can kill. Even slight injuries are painful and annoying, and may impair

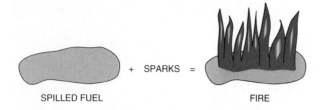

Figure 4-1. Spilled fuel and a stray spark or flame can cause a fire. Never leave spilled fuel or any other substance for someone else to clean. Clean it up immediately.

your ability to work and play. Even if an accident causes no personal injury, it can result in property damage. Damage to vehicles or shop equipment can be expensive and time consuming to fix, and could even cost you your job.

No mature and competent automotive technician wants to be injured or cause property damage. Even if immediate problems do not occur, remember that carelessness in the shop can also lead to long-term bodily harm, such as emphysema and cancer from prolonged contact with harmful liquids, vapors, and dust.

Keep Safety in Mind

The most experienced technician can become rushed and careless when they are under pressure. Pressure to complete a job on time eventually occurs in every shop. Falls, fires, injuries to hands and feet, explosions, electric shocks, and asphyxiation occur in auto repair shops every day. For these reasons, the technician must keep safety in mind at all times. This is especially true when pressure to complete a job tends to make safety the last thing on his or her mind.

Reducing the Possibility of Accidents

While it is true that some accidents are unavoidable, it makes sense to reduce the possibility of their occurrence as much as possible. Most accidents occur because of the following reasons:

- Wearing improper clothing.
- Not using protective equipment.
- Failure to keep the shop neat.
- Improper service procedures.
- A combination of all of these.

Prevent accidents by maintaining a neat work place, using safe methods and common sense when making repairs, and wearing protective equipment when needed. The following sections give some suggestions for reducing the possibility of accidents.

Dressing Safely for Work

The technician who keeps himself neat and clean is usually a safe worker. However, the most basic way to dress safely is to dress appropriately and avoid dangerous clothing. Do not wear open jackets or sweaters, scarves, or shirts with long, loose sleeves. They can get caught in the moving parts of an engine or machine and pull you in. Ties, belts, and suspenders, if they must be worn, should be kept away from moving parts. If you wear your hair long, keep it away from moving parts by tying it up or securing it under a hat.

Remove any rings, watches, or other jewelry. Jewelry can get caught in moving parts, resulting in a severe injury to your hands or fingers. If the jewelry should contact a short circuit, or is caught between a positive terminal and ground, severe burns will result.

Safety shoes, preferably with steel toe inserts, should be worn at all times. Most good quality safety shoes are constructed using materials which are oil and chemical resistant, giving the shoe a longer life expectancy in a harsh shop environment. Safety shoes have soles that are not only slip resistant, but also provide support and comfort. This is an important feature, since most technicians must stand on a concrete floor for an entire work day. In any shop, there is a constant danger of falling parts or tools. Since such an incident can occur at any time, it is a good idea to wear safety shoes whenever you are in the shop.

Personal Protective Equipment

Some ***personal protective equipment*** must be used in certain situations. This equipment protects you from personal injury, and if used regularly, also protects you from long-term illnesses, such as cancer. Long-term exposure to some common shop byproducts such as brake dust or oil fumes can cause diseases such as skin and lung cancer, and emphysema.

Eye protection is vital when working in any situation that could result in dirt, metal, or liquids being thrown into your face. This includes working around running engines; when using drills, saws, welders, or grinders; and when working around batteries and hot cooling system parts, **Figure 4-2**.

Figure 4-2. Always wear eye protection when working with grinders, air tools, hammers, chisels, etc. Remember, you can replace safety glasses, but not your eyesight. (Deere & Co.)

Respiratory protection, such as face masks, should be worn whenever you are working on brake systems or clutches. The dust from the friction lining materials used in these devices contain **asbestos**, which can cause lung damage or cancer, **Figure 4-3**. Respiratory protection is also a good idea when working around any equipment that gives off fumes, such as a hot tank or steam cleaner. **Figure 4-4** shows a special brake washer tool, which should be used to clean brakes before service work begins.

Figure 4-3. A typical asbestos warning label. Follow all safety rules when working with parts containing asbestos. Do not inhale the dust. (Sterling & Author)

Rubber gloves are necessary whenever you are working with chemicals such as parts cleaning solvents or carburetor cleaner. If you spill oil, gasoline, cleaning solvents, or any other substance on your skin, clean it off immediately. Prolonged exposure to even mild solvents or petroleum products can cause severe skin rashes or chemical burns. Material Safety Data Sheets, which are discussed later in this chapter, should be located and read before handling any chemical that is unknown to you.

Keep a Neat Shop

Neatness is the number one accident preventer. Whenever you are assigned projects in the school shop or lab, clean and return all tools and equipment to their proper places when the job is completed. Do not allow dirt, oil, old parts, boxes, or other refuse to pile up.

Keep all workbenches clean. This reduces the chance of tools or parts falling from the bench, where they could be lost, damaged, or possibly land on your foot. A clean workbench also reduces the possibility that critical parts will be lost in the clutter. It also reduces the chance of a fire from oily debris.

Return all tools and equipment to their proper storage places. This saves time in the long run, as well as reducing the chance of accidents and theft. Do not leave any pieces of equipment out where others could trip on them. If tools are dirty or oily, clean them before you put them away. This will not only extend the life of the tool, but is also a courtesy to others who use them.

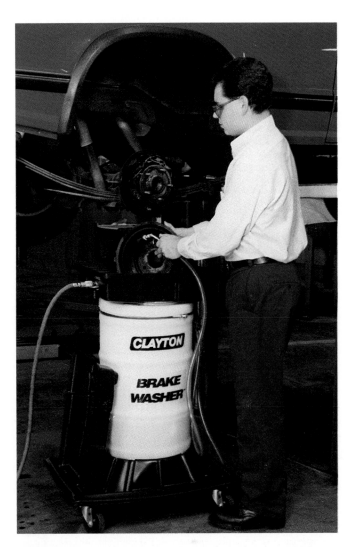

Figure 4-4. Use an approved brake washing tool in a well ventilated area of the shop. Note the safety glasses and protective shoes worn by the technician. (Clayton Mfg. Co.)

Clean up spills immediately, before they get tracked all over the shop. Many people are injured when they slip on floors coated with oil, antifreeze, or water. Gasoline spills can be extremely dangerous, since a flame or the smallest spark can ignite the vapors, causing a major explosion and fire. Do not leave open containers of any chemical in the shop or outside. Antifreeze, for example, contains ethylene glycol. While ethylene glycol is not flammable, it is harmful to the environment and will poison any animal (or person) who accidentally drinks it.

Fire Extinguishers

Although a shop fire is one of the most frightening things that you may encounter, it is important to keep your head and not panic. If you are familiar with the layout of your shop, you should be able to quickly locate and use the nearest **fire extinguisher**. The correct fire extinguisher will quickly smother a fire by cutting off its supply of oxygen. Fire extinguishers are identified by the type of fire that they will put out. See **Figure 4-5.**

Fire Extinguishers and Fire Classifications

Fires	Type	Use		Operation
Class A Fires Ordinary Combustibles (Materials such as wood, paper, textiles.) *Requires... cooling-quenching*	**Soda-acid** Bicarbonate of soda solution and sulfuric acid	Okay for use on **A**		Direct stream at base of flame.
		Not for use on **B** **C** **D**		
Class B Fires Flammable Liquids (Liquids such as grease, gasoline, oils, and paints.) *Requires...blanketing or smothering*	**Pressurized Water** Water under pressure	Okay for use on **A**		Direct stream at base of flame.
		Not for use on **B** **C** **D**		
	Carbon Dioxide (CO$_2$) Carbon dioxide (CO$_2$) gas under pressure	Okay for use on **B** **C**		Direct discharge as close to fire as possible, first at edge of flames and gradually forward and upward.
		Not for use on **A** **D**		
Class C Fires Electrical Equipment (Motors, switches, and so forth.) *Requires... a nonconducting agent.*	**Foam** Solution of aluminum sulfate and bicarbonate of soda	Okay for use on **A** **B**		Direct stream into the burning material or liquid. Allow foam to fall lightly on tire.
		Not for use on **C** **D**		
	Dry Chemical	Multi-purpose type	Ordinary BC type	Direct stream at base of flames. Use rapid left-to-right motion toward flames.
		Okay for **A** **B** **C**	Okay for **B** **C**	
		Not okay for **D**	Not okay for **A** **D**	
Class D Fires Combustible Metals (Flammable metals such as magnesium and lithium.) *Requires...blanketing or smothering.*	**Dry Chemical** *Granular type material*	Okay for use on **D**		Smother flames by scooping granular material from bucket onto burning metal.
		Not for use on **A** **B** **C**		

Figure 4-5. This chart illustrates the various fire classifications and fire extinguisher types. In the automotive repair shop, extinguishers designed for chemical and electrical fires (multi-purpose or BC types) should be used.

The three basic classes of fire extinguisher are:

- Class A: Will put out fires from ordinary combustibles, such as wood and paper.
- Class B: Will extinguish fires caused by flammable liquids, such as gasoline and oil.
- Class C: Designed to put out electrical fires.

The uses of these various types of fire extinguishers are clearly marked on the tank. Today, most shops have multi-purpose (A, B, and C class) dry chemical fire extinguishers, which will put out all of the fires described earlier. A fourth class of fire extinguisher is used on flammable metals, but this type is not encountered in the average automotive shop.

Never use water to put out a fire. If gasoline is involved, it will float on the water and spread the fire. Never depend on a fire extinguisher to any more than slow down the spread of the fire. Call the fire department first and then attempt to extinguish the fire. Stay low to avoid inhaling the smoke. If the fire begins to spread or if there is too much smoke or heat, *get out.* Do not open doors or windows as this will give the fire more oxygen. Never go back into a burning building for any reason.

Identifying Unsafe Conditions

In addition to keeping the shop neat, the student should identify and take steps to correct other unsafe conditions which may develop in the shop. Many of the statements below will seem to be just a matter of common sense, but they are often disregarded.

If you detect a problem in any shop equipment or tools, notify your instructor immediately. Assist your instructor in tool repair and maintenance. This may involve such things as replacing damaged leads on test equipment, checking and adding oil to hydraulic jacks, and regrinding the tips on chisels.

When servicing any shop equipment, be sure that the equipment is turned off and unplugged. Read the equipmentís service literature before beginning any repairs. Ensure that all shop equipment, such as grinders and drill presses, are equipped with safety guards. All of these devices are installed with guards by the manufacturer. These guards should never be removed, except for service operations such as changing the grinding wheels.

Know what type of chemicals are stored on the shop premises. Chemicals include carburetor cleaners, hot tank solutions, parts cleaner, and even motor oil and antifreeze. Chemical manufacturers provide **Material Safety Data Sheets**, often called **MSDS**, for every chemical that they produce. These sheets list all of the known dangers of the chemical, as well as first aid procedures for skin or respiratory system contact. There should be an MSDS for every type of chemical present in the shop. Locate the MSDS and read it before working with any unfamiliar chemical.

Ensure that the shop is well ventilated. A sealed shop, or a room in the shop, can permit the buildup of exhaust fumes or chemical vapors which can be fatal. Even a relatively harmless gas like air conditioner refrigerant can kill if it displaces all of the oxygen in a closed room.

Make sure that the shop is well lighted. Poor lighting makes it hard to see what you are doing. Not only does it make the job more time-consuming, it can lead to accidental contact with moving parts or hot surfaces. Overhead lights should be bright and centrally located. Portable trouble lights or "drop" lights, which are usually small and easy to use, should be used in close operating conditions.

Always use a rough service bulb in drop lights. These bulbs are more rugged than normal light bulbs and will not shatter if they are dropped. Do not use a high wattage bulb in a drop light. Light bulbs get very hot and can melt the light socket or burn anyone who touches the light safety cover.

Do not overload electrical outlets or extension cords by operating several electrical devices from one outlet. Do not pair up high current electrical devices, or operate them through extension cords. Examples of high current drawing electrical devices are drills, grinders, and electric heaters. Do not, under any circumstances, cut or break off the ground prong of a three-prong plug.

Waste Chemical Disposal

Probably the most common way in which auto shops cause environmental damage is the methods by which they dispose of used oil and other chemicals. These used chemicals are classified as hazardous waste. Pouring motor oil, transmission or brake fluid, antifreeze, and used cleaning solutions on the ground immediately contaminates the soil. These liquids sink further into the ground with every rainstorm. Eventually, it could contaminate your local source for drinking water. Another common way in which liquids can contaminate the ground and water is through leaking storage tanks. Although this problem is usually confined to underground gasoline tanks, any kind of tank can begin leaking. The shop is responsible for their safe disposal.

While the shop is using these chemicals, they are only subject to safety regulations concerning employee exposure to toxic chemicals. One the shop is done with them, however, they must be disposed of in a manner approved by federal, state, and local guidelines. Liquid waste should never be disposed of by pouring them into the local drainage system. Municipal waste treatment plants cannot handle the petroleum products, or their many additives, nor the heavy metals absorbed from the vehicle during their use. The Environmental Protection Agency has established strict guidelines for disposing of toxic waste. In some cases, you may be liable for cleaning up a contaminated area years after the actual violation occurred.

In many areas, local companies will recycle toxic wastes. These companies will accept used oil and antifreeze for recycling. The used oil and antifreeze is then refined and reused. Some shops use heaters that burn used oil as a fuel, eliminating the oil. Some used oil is burned by power plants to produce electricity. Additional information on waste disposal and vehicle emissions can be obtained from the Environmental Protection Agency. For more information you can write to:

Automotive/Emissions Division
United States Environmental Protection Agency
401 M Street SW
Washington, DC 29460

Follow Proper Work Procedures

Work procedures are the actual diagnosis and repair operations. You may be called on to do all sorts of procedures in your shop classes or labs. It is vital that you do them safely and correctly. Improper procedures include using the wrong tools or methods to perform repairs, using defective or otherwise inappropriate tools, not wearing protective equipment when necessary, and not paying close attention while performing the job. Whenever any work is performed, it should be performed in a safe manner, before any other considerations. The following safe work procedures may seem to be simple. However, they are often disregarded, with tragic results.

- Wear proper clothing and use protective equipment when called for.
- Study work procedures before beginning any job that is unfamiliar to you. Do not assume that the procedure you have used in the past will work with a different type of vehicle.
- Always work carefully. Speed is not nearly as important as doing the job right and avoiding injury. Avoid people who will not work carefully.
- Use the right tool for the job. For example, using a screwdriver as a chisel or a wrench as a hammer, is asking for an accident, or at least a broken tool.
- Inspect electrical cords and compressed air lines to ensure that they are in good condition. Do not run over, or close vehicle doors on, electric cords or air lines. Do not run electrical cords through water puddles or use them outside when it is raining.
- Learn how to use new equipment properly before using it. This is especially true of air-operated tools, such as impact wrenches or chisels, and large electrical devices such as drill presses, boring bars, and flywheel surfacers. These tools are very powerful and can hurt you if they are used improperly. A good way to start learning about new equipment is by reading the manufacturer's instructions.
- When working on electrical systems, avoid creating a short circuit with a jumper wire or metal tool. Not only will this damage the vehicle components or wiring, it will develop enough heat to cause a severe burn or start a fire.
- Lift safely. Make sure that you are strong enough to lift the object to be moved. Always lift with your legs, not your back. If an object is too heavy to lift by yourself, get someone to help you or use a jack.
- Do not smoke in the shop. You may accidentally ignite an unnoticed gasoline leak. A burning cigarette may also ignite oily rags or paper cartons.
- Do not attempt to raise a vehicle with an unsafe or undercapacity jack. Always support a raised vehicle with good quality jackstands. Never use boards or cement blocks to support a vehicle.
- Do not run any type of engine, even for a short time, in a closed area without good ventilation. **Carbon monoxide**, which cannot be seen or smelled, can build up very quickly. This is true even of lawn mowers and other small engines.
- When working on or near a running engine, keep away from all moving parts. Never reach between moving engine parts for any reason. A seemingly harmless part such as the drive belts and fan can seriously injure you.
- Do not leave a running vehicle unattended. The vehicle may slip into gear, or overheat while you are away. Whenever you must work on a running vehicle, shift the transmission into park or neutral and set the parking brake.
- When road testing a vehicle, be alert and obey all traffic laws. Do not become so absorbed in diagnosing a problem that you forget to watch the road. Be alert for the actions of other drivers.

Do the Job Right

It is important to correctly perform repairs to the vehicle and to make sure that your repairs are not the cause of an accident. For example, if you follow every shop safety procedure when doing a brake job, but allow the vehicle to leave the shop with a leaking brake hose, an accident is sure to occur when all the brake fluid leaks out. The driver, along with any passengers, could be injured or killed. Making sure that the vehicle leaves the shop in a safe condition is just as important as working safely in the shop.

After all other factors have been figured in, it is still up to you to notice and correct safety hazards, work safely, and prevent accidents. Always use common sense when working on vehicles. Avoid people who do not follow good work and safety practices.

Summary

Each unsafe act may not cause an accident, but a combination of two or more unsafe acts may result in a severe accident. Not taking the time to do things correctly almost always results in an accident. Many accidents are caused when technicians try to take shortcuts instead of following proper repair procedures. Another common cause of accidents is failing to correct dangerous conditions in the work area, such as defects in equipment or oil spills. An accident may result in damage to equipment or property, personal injuries, long-term bodily harm, or death. No mature and competent automotive technician wants to be injured or cause property damage.

Always dress for the shop with an eye toward safety. Avoid loose clothing, dangling hair, and jewelry. Various types of protective equipment are needed to protect the eyes, feet, lungs, and skin. Protective equipment should protect against immediate injury and the long-term effects of exposure to toxic substances.

The best way to prevent accidents is to maintain a neat work place, use proper repair methods, and use protective equipment when needed. It is up to the technician to study the job beforehand, to work safely, and to prevent accidents. Do not allow a vehicle to leave the shop in unsafe condition. Always use common sense when working on vehicles, and avoid people who do not.

Know These Terms

Accident	Lung cancer
Falls	Skin cancer
Fires	Unsafe act
Explosions	Unsafe condition
Asphyxiation	Personal protective
Injury to body parts	equipment
Strains and sprains	Asbestos
Burns	Fire extinguisher
Chemical burns	Material Safety Data Sheets
Electrical shocks	(MSDS)
Emphysema	Carbon monoxide

Review Questions—Chapter 4

Do not write in this book. Write your answers on a separate sheet of paper.

1. An accident is an _____ event.
2. What two kinds of accidents could occur when a flammable substance contacts a heat source?
3. What kind of injury could be caused by battery acid or parts cleaner? _____ .
4. Accidents are often caused by a series of unsafe _____ which could be avoided.
   (A) conditions
   (B) acts
   (C) vehicles
   (D) Both A & B.
5. Name the five major causes of accidents.
6. Technician A says that, since air conditioner refrigerant is not poisonous, it cannot cause asphyxiation, no matter how much of it is present. Technician B says that it is OK to run an engine in a closed shop, as long as it is not run for more than 10 minutes.
   Who is right?
   (A) A only.
   (B) B only.
   (C) Both A & B.
   (D) Neither A nor B.
7. You should always wear respiratory protection when working on what two vehicle components?
8. Each shop electrical outlet should be used to operate how many high current draw tools?
   (A) 1
   (B) 2
   (C) 3
   (D) 4 or more

9. Material Safety Data Sheets are provided for all dangerous _____ .
   (A) procedures
   (B) tools
   (C) chemicals
   (D) working conditions
10. If the safety guards have been removed from a grinder, what should you do?
    (A) Be very careful when using the grinder.
    (B) Let someone else do the grinding.
    (C) Do not use the grinder until the guards are replaced.
    (D) Wear eye protection.
11. Always use a "rough service" bulb in _____ .
    (A) fluorescent drop lights
    (B) incandescent drop lights
    (C) every light in the shop
    (D) the ceiling lights
12. A high wattage bulb in a drop light can cause what type of personal injury?
    (A) Blindness.
    (B) Burns.
    (C) Electric shock.
    (D) All of the above.
13. Spilled ethylene glycol antifreeze can cause all of the following, EXCEPT:
    (A) slipping.
    (B) poisoning.
    (C) fires.
    (D) environmental damage.
14. The technician should wear eye protection when _____ .
    (A) working around running engines
    (B) using drills, saws, or grinders
    (C) working around batteries
    (D) all of the above
15. Improperly fixing a vehicle could result in _____ .
    (A) repeat business for the technician
    (B) an accident
    (C) injury to the driver
    (D) Both B & C.

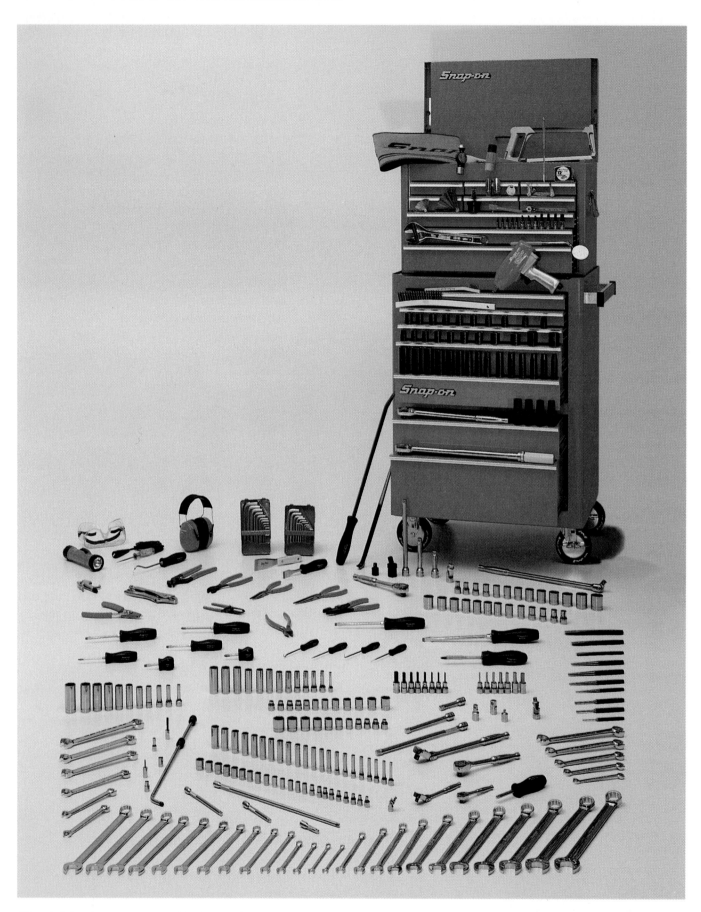

All technicians must own a good basic set of tools and a tool chest to keep them in. Many of the tools shown here are discussed in this chapter. (Snap-on Tools)

5

Tool Identification and Use

After studying this chapter, you will be able to:
- Identify the most common automotive tools.
- Describe commonly used measuring tools.
- Describe commonly used test equipment.
- Select the correct tool for a given job.

Today's technician must be familiar with a large number of tools. Proper tool selection and use will improve both the quality and speed of any repair operation. Many repair jobs are extremely difficult to perform without the right tools. Good technicians own a wide selection of quality tools. They constantly strive to add to their collection and take great pride in keeping their tools clean and in order.

What to Look for in a Tool

Some technicians prefer one certain brand of tools, while others prefer more than one brand. You will find, however, that technicians agree on several important features that are found in quality tools.

Tool Material

Quality tools are made of high-strength alloy steel. Consequently, they can be made without a great deal of bulk. These tools are light and easy to use in tight quarters. Heavy, "fat" tools are useless on many jobs. The alloy steel gives the tool great strength. Its working areas will withstand abuse, greatly extending its useful life.

Tool Construction

Quality tools receive superior heat treating. Their working surfaces are held to tight tolerances and sharp edges are removed. Additionally, quality tools are carefully polished. Polishing produces a finish that is easy to clean and comfortable to handle.

Tools worthy of consideration will be slim, strong, easy to clean, and a pleasure to use. Quality material and construction makes it possible for the manufacturer to offer a good (often a lifetime) guarantee on the tool. Efficient service should also be offered. In the case of some tools, replacement parts should be readily available. This can be an important feature. Usable tools often have to be discarded due to the loss or failure of some minor part that is no longer available.

Remember: When buying tools, you get what you pay for. Fine quality tools are a good investment.

Tool Handling and Storage

Use tools designed for the job at hand. Keep your tools orderly and clean. Store them in a good, roll-type cabinet tool chest and tote tray (a small tray that can be carried to the job to keep a few selected tools close at hand). Proper storage will help keep tools in good shape and readily available. All tools should have your name, initials, or a number that is unique to you engraved on the tool body. This will allow you to identify that a specific tool is your property.

Any tool subject to rust should be cleaned and lightly oiled. Separate cutting tools, such as files and chisels, to preserve their cutting edges. Place delicate measuring tools and electronic tools in protective containers. Store heavy tools by themselves and arrange tools so that those most often used are handy.

Remember to keep your tools clean. You cannot hope to successfully assemble a fine piece of machinery with dirty tools. The slightest bit of dirt or abrasive material that finds its way into moving parts can cause damage when the tool is used. Tools are a good indication of a technician's worth. If a technician uses dirty, worn, or disorganized tools, the quality of this technician's work is likely to be as poor as the tools.

Types of Tools

This chapter does not attempt to cover all the tools used in the automotive trade. Large shops and technicians that specialize in certain areas of repair will often utilize hundreds of special tools designed for specific jobs, models, and units. Therefore, the basic tools common to automotive shops and owned by every technician will be discussed in this chapter.

Hammers

Technicians frequently use *ball peen, brass-tipped,* and *plastic-tipped* **hammers.** The ball peen hammer is used for general striking work and is available in weights ranging from a couple of ounces to several pounds. Brass- and plastic-tipped hammers are used when there is danger of the steel ball peen marring the work surface. Some plastic-tipped hammers have their heads filled with lead shot. This prevents the hammer from rebounding when striking a hard object. See **Figure 5-1.** The handles should be kept clean and dry.

Figure 5-1. Several types of hammers. Each hammer is designed to perform a specific task.

Figure 5-2. A—A chisel and punch assortment. B—A chisel holder. By holding the punch or chisel with this holder, it protects the hand when striking with a hammer. (Snap-on Tools)

heads have been cut off. Once a pin has been started, the starting punch can no longer be used (because of its taper). A *drift punch,* which has the same diameter for most of its length, is used to complete the job. See **Figure 5-3.** A *pin punch* is similar to a drift punch, but it is smaller in diameter.

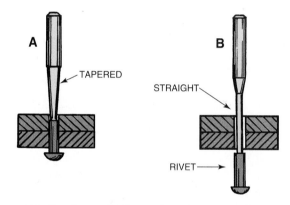

Figure 5-3. Starting and drift punches. A—The starting punch is used to start the rivet from the hole. B—The drift punch is used to drive the rivet from the hole.

Chisels

Several sizes and types of **chisels** are essential for cutting bolts or rivets, **Figure 5-2A.** Chisels can be held in your hand or secured in a holder. The holder will allow the use of large hammers and greater striking force without the chance of injuring your fingers or hand. One type of chisel holder is shown in **Figure 5-2B.** The *flat cold chisel* is used for general cutting. Special chisels, such as *cape, half-round,* and *diamond-point chisels,* are used when their shapes fit a definite need.

Punches

A variety of **punches** are used when servicing automobiles. A starting punch tapers to a flat tip. It is used when starting to punch out pins and when driving out rivets after the

An *aligning punch,* which has a long, gradual taper, is used to shift parts and bring corresponding holes into alignment, **Figure 5-4.** A *center punch* is used to mark materials before drilling. It leaves a small, V-shaped impression that assists in aligning the drill bit. A center punch may also be used to mark parts so they can be assembled in the correct positions. See **Figure 5-5.**

Files

Commonly used **files** include the *flat mill, half-round, round, square,* and *triangular files.* All come in different sizes and with cutting edges that range from fine to coarse. Some files have one or more cutting edges. Some files have one or more safe sides (surface with no cutting edges).

Figure 5-4. Aligning punch. A—This punch is pushed through the holes and then is pulled upright and pushed deeper into the holes. B—This lines up the two holes.

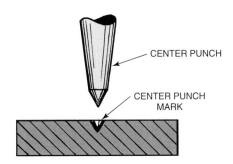

Figure 5-5. A center punch is used for marking parts and starting drill bits.

A file should have a handle firmly affixed to the tang. The handle gives a firm grip and eliminates the danger of the sharp tang piercing the hand. A typical mill file and nomenclature is shown in **Figure 5-6.**

File Cut and Shape

When a file has a single series of cutting edges that are parallel to each other, the file is referred to as a *single-cut file*. A file with two sets of cutting edges that cross at an angle is called a *double-cut file*. See **Figure 5-7.**

File cut—from rough to smooth—depends on the number and size of the cutting edges. **Figure 5-8** illustrates several classifications of cut for both single- and double-cut files. Common file shapes are illustrated in **Figure 5-9.**

Rotary Files

A selection of *rotary files* is often found in the technician's toolbox. These files are designed to be chucked in an hand drill or hand-held air grinder. They are useful in working in "blind" holes, where a normal file is useless. See **Figure 5-10.**

Drills

Most drilling today is done with power operated hand **drills**. Power drills are operated by compressed air or electric motors. Either type of power drill has a chuck, which is tightened to securely hold the **drill bit.** See **Figure 5-11.**

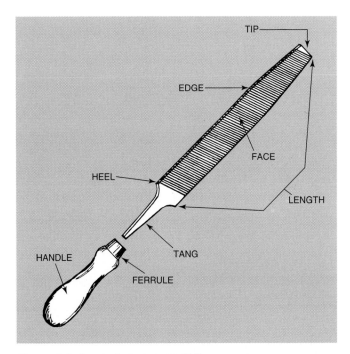

Figure 5-6. A typical single-cut mill file.

Figure 5-7. Single- and double-cut files.

The most common hand drill sizes are 3/8″ and 1/2″. The drill size refers to the largest drill bit that the chuck can handle. 3/8″ hand drills are the most common and are used for drilling light metals, light honing, and operating wire brushes. 1/2″ drills are used for drilling through thick or hard metals and for turning engine cylinder hones. Both electric and air drills are common. The compressed air drill is used, however, in situations where a long drilling session would overheat an electric motor.

Cordless Drills

Cordless drills are beginning to see greater use in the modern shop. These compact and powerful tools can fit into

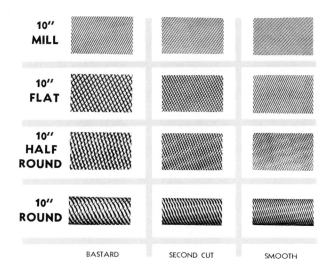

Figure 5-8. Three different file cuts: bastard, second-cut and smooth. (Simonds File Co.)

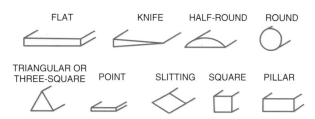

Figure 5-9. Nine common file shapes that are handy for the technician.

Figure 5-10. A rotary file. These come in a variety of sizes and shapes.

tight spots where the power cord or air hose to a conventional drill cannot go. By adding adapters, they can be used as power screw and nut drivers. This setup can make short work of removing a component that has many screws or bolts retaining it. Otherwise, this would normally be a very time consuming task.

Drill Press

Another type of drill is the drill press. The drill motor and chuck are mounted on a stand and are able to move up and down on a central shaft. The work to be drilled is mounted on a table directly under the drill motor. The drill bit, chuck, and motor are lowered by turning a lever to contact the work to be drilled.

The drill press eliminates the need to hold the drill and ensures that the drill bit will produce a properly aligned and

Figure 5-11. A heavy-duty electric drill. (Black & Decker)

sized hole. Drill presses can only be used on parts that will fit on the mounting table and cannot be taken to the vehicle for drilling any part that cannot be removed.

Drill Bits

A drill bit is chucked in a hand or power drill and does the actual cutting when drilling holes. Drill bits are available in fractional inch and metric sizes. For general auto shop use, a set of fractional size bits (from 1/16″ to 1/2″ or 1.5 to 13.0 mm) is sufficient to start. Other size drill bits may be purchased as needed.

Drill bits with a straight shank are used in hand drills and portable power drills. For heavy duty power drills, the taper shank bit is sometimes used. See **Figure 5-12.** Bits are commonly furnished in carbon steel and high-speed steel. Carbon bits will require more frequent sharpening, and they will not last nearly as long as high-speed steel drills. Cobalt drill bits, which are designed for heavy duty drilling, are also available.

Reamers

Reamers are used to enlarge or shape holes. They produce holes that are more accurate in size and smoother than those produced by drill bits. The reamer should not be used to make deep cuts in metal. A cut of a few thousandths of an inch at a time is all that should be attempted.

Some reamers are adjustable in size, while others are of a fixed size. Tapered reamers are handy for removing burrs and assisting in tap starting. Several different types of reamers are shown in **Figures 5-13** and **5-14.**

Impact Wrench

A power **impact wrench** is a must for fast work. Most impact wrenches are air operated, though electric impact tools are available. Parts can be removed and replaced in a fraction of the time required with hand wrenches. Although the impact wrench in no way replaces hand wrenches, it can be used often and should be included in the tool collection.

Heavy-duty impact sockets should always be used with an impact wrench. These sockets are much stronger than

Figure 5-12. Technicians use a variety of drill bit sizes and types.

Figure 5-13. Reamers. A—Adjustable. B and C—Adjustable with a pilot to aid in reamer alignment. D—Kingpin reamer. E—Valve guide reamer. (Snap-on Tools)

Figure 5-14. Tapered reamers. (Snap-on Tools)

standard sockets. When used with an impact wrench, standard sockets may break. **Figure 5-15** shows a pneumatic (air-operated) impact wrench. Sizes run from 1/4″ to 1″. Power ratchets, drills, chisels, hand-held grinders, sanders, and shears in a variety of designs are also available.

Figure 5-15. An impact (power) wrench is a must for every technician. They are available in a variety of sizes and shapes. (Snap-on Tools)

Hacksaws

The hand *hacksaw* is a much-used tool. It is excellent for cutting bolts, tubing, or light metal. Hacksaw blades are generally furnished with 14, 18, 24, or 32 teeth per inch. The 14-tooth blade is handy for cutting fairly thick articles. The 18-tooth blade handles work of medium thickness. The 24-tooth blade is best used on brass, copper, heavy sheet metal, and medium tubing. For thin sheet metal, use a 32-tooth blade. **Figure 5-16** illustrates typical work for each type of blade.

Hacksaw blades are made of various materials. Some blades are hardened across the full blade width; others are hardened only along the edge of the teeth. When cutting alloy steels, select one of the better quality blades, such as a high-speed (tungsten) steel blade. A conventional hacksaw is shown in **Figure 5-17**.

Special Hacksaws

The automotive technician will sometimes find use for a special hacksaw that allows cutting in restricted quarters. A hole saw, which is operated by a drill, is also handy for drilling large holes in thin sheet metal, **Figure 5-18**.

Figure 5-16. The type of work to be cut determines the blade selection. These are typical. (Crescent Tools)

Figure 5-18. Hole saws are handy for cutting openings in thin metal and for making large diameter holes.

Figure 5-17. One type of hacksaw with an adjustable frame. This allows the saw to handle blades of different lengths. (Easco Tools)

Figure 5-19. A typical bench vise.

Vise

A **vise** is a holding device. A typical bench vise is shown in **Figure 5-19.** If the work is easily marred, place special copper or nylon covers over the serrated steel jaws. Keep the vise clean. Oil all working parts. Do not use a vise for an anvil and do not hammer the handle to tighten the jaws on the workpiece.

Taps

Taps are used for cutting internal threads, **Figure 5-20.** For general use, a set of *taper, plug, bottom,* and *machine screw taps* should be available. Each type of tap will have to be provided in both National Fine and National Coarse threads, as well as common metric sizes.

The taper tap is used to tap completely through the hole. Notice that this tap has a long, gradual taper that allows it to start easily. The bottoming tap is used to cut threads all the way to the bottom of a blind hole. The plug tap should be used

Figure 5-20. Four different types of taps.

before using the bottoming tap because the bottoming tap will not start well. The plug tap is the most widely used tap. It will work satisfactorily in most cases. However, it cannot be used to run threads completely to the bottom of a blind hole. The machine screw tap is used for small diameter holes with fine threads. **Figure 5-21** shows tap nomenclature.

Dies

Dies are used to cut external threads. A die of the correct size is placed in a diestock (handle) and turned. In some

Figure 5-21. Tap nomenclature. (Winter Brothers)

cases, dies are adjustable in size, so you can enlarge or reduce (slightly) the outside diameter of a threaded area. Both taps and dies should be cleaned, lightly oiled, and placed in a protective box after each use.

Cleaning Tools

Various cleaning tools are illustrated in **Figure 5-22.** These tools provide valuable assistance in the thorough cleaning of parts. A wire wheel that can be used on a grinder mandrel is shown in **Figure 5-23.** Carbon cleaning brushes that can be operated in a 3/8″ drill are also available.

Figure 5-22. Cleaning tools. A—Rigid scrapers. B—Gasket scraper. C—Flexible carbon scraper. D—General purpose scrapers. E—Putty knives. (Snap-on tools)

Pliers

A technician needs a variety of ***pliers***. Study the pliers shown in **Figures 5-24** to **5-26.** Never use pliers in place of a wrench. Use pliers designed for the job at hand. Avoid cutting hardened parts with lineman, diagonal, or other cutting pliers. Needle nose pliers are delicate; use them carefully.

Figure 5-23. A power driven wire wheel. Wear eye protection.

Screwdrivers

Screwdrivers of various lengths and types are required. *Standard, Phillips, Reed and Prince, Clutch,* and *Torx®* screwdrivers will cover the various types of jobs ordinarily encountered by the automotive technician. It is wise to have several large screwdrivers that will stand some prying and hammering. The various types of screw head shapes used in most vehicles are shown in **Figure 5-27**.

A

B

C

D

Figure 5-24. Different types of pliers. A—Slip joint. B—Rib joint. C—Needle nose. D—Diagonal cutting.

Figure 5-25. Locking pliers, or Vise grips

Figure 5-26. Two pairs of snap ring pliers. (Snap-on Tools)

The standard, or slotted, screwdriver can have a round or square shank. A set of slotted and Phillips screwdrivers is shown in **Figure 5-28.** Reed and Prince tip screwdrivers are similar to Phillips screwdrivers. A Pozidrive® screwdriver and

Figure 5-27. Configurations for screw heads used in the typical automobile.

screw head are shown in **Figure 5-29A.** A Torx® screw head and driver are illustrated in **Figure 5-29B.** Some Torx® screw heads have a stud protruding from their center and are tamper resistant. An assortment of offset screwdrivers makes it easy to remove and drive screws in difficult areas. Another essential screwdriver is the magnetic type designed to hold screws while they are being installed.

Figure 5-28. Screwdrivers are often best purchased in sets. (Cooper Tools)

Figure 5-29. A—Similar to the Phillips design, the engagement tip of a pozidrive screwdriver is narrower and longer. A pozidrive fastener is identified by lines between the openings. B—Torx bits and screw head. (Vaco Tools)

Wrenches

All technicians must have a wide variety of both standard and metric **wrenches** at their disposal. A technician should have wrench sizes from 1/4″ to 1 1/8″ for standard and 5 mm to 24 mm for metric. A few of the wide variety of wrenches are discussed here.

Box-End Wrenches

The *box-end wrench* is an excellent tool because it grips the nut or bolt head on all sides. This reduces the chances of slipping, with resultant damage to the fastener and possibly the hand.

A box-end wrench is designed with either a 6- or 12-point opening. For general use, the 12-point opening works well. It allows the wrench to be removed and replaced without moving the handle over a long arc. When removing stubborn or damaged nuts, or when there is a danger of collapsing the nut, the 6-point will do a better job. It grips the nut across each flat, minimizing slippage and fastener damage.

The box-end wrench is available in either a double offset or a 15° offset. Sets in standard size openings, as well as standard lengths, will handle most jobs. Sets are available in midget lengths for work in cramped areas. Each end on the box-end wrench is a different size.

> **STOP** **Warning: When using a wrench, pull on the handle whenever possible. If you must push on the wrench, push with the palm of the hand with the fingers outspread to avoid smashing them if the wrench slips.**

Figure 5-30 shows two box-end wrenches. Both wrenches have an extra deep offset for additional clearance. Can you see why the wrench with the six-point opening will grasp the nut or cap screw more securely? These are standard length box-ends. Short and longer length wrenches are of the same design.

Figure 5-30. 10° offset box-end wrench in six- and twelve-point openings (Snap-on Tools)

Open-End Wrenches

Open-end wrenches are handy, but they are not as dependable as box-end wrenches. They grasp the nut or bolt head on only two of its flats and are subject to slipping under a heavy pull. There are tight places, however, where they must be used. One example would be a threaded adjusting nut on a shaft or closed-end cable, such as a brake cable. See **Figure 5-31.**

Figure 5-31. This set of open-end wrenches contains both standard and metric sizes. (Snap-on Tools)

The head of an open-end wrench is generally offset at an angle of 10-15°. When the wrench has traveled as far as allowable, it can be flipped over and placed on the nut in an arc of 30°. Open-end wrenches are also available with the heads offset more than 15°. Each end of an open-end wrench has a different size opening.

Combination Wrench

The *combination wrench* has a box-end head on one end and an open-end on the other. Generally, the open-end is offset 15° from the wrench centerline. Both ends are the same size.

The combination wrench is a very convenient tool since the box-end can be used for both breaking loose and final tightening. The open-end is for faster fastener removal or installation. See **Figure 5-32.** Some combination wrenches have flare-nut heads.

Figure 5-32. A combination wrench set in a roll-up tool pouch. (Proto Tool Division of Ingersoll-Rand Co.)

Flare-nut Wrench

All tube fittings should be removed and replaced with special *flare-nut wrenches.* See **Figure 5-33.** These wrenches are designed to provide a maximum amount of contact. They can also be used to remove soft fasteners without damage.

Figure 5-33. Flare-nut wrenches. A and B—Six-point openings C—Twelve point opening.

Adjustable Wrenches

The *adjustable wrench* is handy in that it can be adjusted for size. However, it tends to slip, so it is a poor wrench to use when other tools are available for a given job. When an adjustable wrench is used, adjust the jaws firmly. Also, make certain the wrench is placed so the pull on the handle is toward the bottom side. This relieves heavy pressure on the adjustable jaw. Some adjustable wrenches are spring-loaded and adjust themselves to the work.

Other Useful Wrenches

The flexible head socket wrench, **Figure 5-34A,** and the ratcheting box-end wrench, **Figure 5-34B,** are useful additions to the technician's toolbox. Allen and fluted wrenches are often used in tightening or removing setscrews and cap screws. They are strong and provide a good grip. See **Figure 5-35.**

A

B

Figure 5-34. Flex head socket and ratchet box-end wrenches. A—Flex head socket. B—Ratchet box.

Figure 5-35. Allen, or hex, wrenches.

Torque Wrenches

The *torque wrench* allows technicians to tighten fasteners to exact torque (tightness) specifications supplied by the manufacturer. It is of utmost importance that bolts be tightened to specifications. Improper and varying torque on units or assemblies may cause distortion.

A torque wrench is shown in **Figure 5-36.** Torque wrenches are available in both foot-pound and inch-pound types. The inch-pound wrench is used for delicate, low-torque applications. Some torque wrenches are available with dual scales on the same wrench. One scale is for foot-pounds and the other is for inch-pounds. Still others with dual scales can have one scale for foot-pounds and one scale for metric values (Newton-meters). Torque wrenches are available in special shapes and sizes.

Figure 5-36. A click type interchangeable torque wrench. The assortment of heads permits ratcheting and open-end use. (Snap-on Tools)

Figure 5-38. A set of deep six-point sockets in standard and metric sizes. Sockets should be stored on rails to prevent loss. (Snap-on Tools)

Sockets and Ratchets

Sockets and ratchets are very convenient and, in most instances, faster than normal wrenches. Both sockets and ratchets are available in a variety of sizes and types.

Sockets

Most *sockets* are available with 6-point, 12-point, and a variety of other openings and driver shapes. The 1/4″, 3/8″, 1/2″, 3/4″, and 1″ drive sizes will cover a wide range of jobs. The drive size refers to the size of the square hole into which the socket handle fits. The larger the drive, the heavier and bulkier the socket.

The 1/4″ drive is for small work in difficult areas. The 3/8″ drive will handle most general work where the torque (tightness) requirements are not too high. The 1/2″ drive is for all-around service. The 3/4″ and 1″ drives are for heavy duty work with high torque settings.

Standard-length sockets are available for general work, **Figure 5-37.** Deep sockets, **Figure 5-38,** are available for work requiring a longer than ordinary reach, such as spark plug removal and installation. Swivel sockets are also available for angle work.

Socket Handles and Ratchets

Various handles are available for sockets. See **Figure 5-39.** The speed handle is used for fast operation because it can be turned rapidly. Flex handles in varying lengths allow the socket to be turned with great force and at odd angles. *Extension bars* of different lengths allow the technician to lengthen the socket setup to reach difficult areas. The sliding T-handle varies the handle length.

The *ratchet* is versatile. It allows the user to either tighten or remove a nut or bolt without removing the socket from the fastener. On the backstroke, the handle ratchets. See **Figure 5-40.**

Figure 5-37. Six-point sockets. These sockets are slightly longer than the normal standard socket, which allows them to access recessed bolts or bolts with protruding studs. (Snap-on Tools)

Figure 5-39. Accessory handles and extensions. A—Breaker bar. B—Sliding T-handle. C—Speed handle. D—Short extension. E—Long extension. F—Flexible extension. G—Socket drivers. (Snap-on Tools)

Figure 5-40. A selection of socket ratchet handles. A—Bent handle ratchet. B—Straight handle with flex head. C—Straight handle ratchet with 360° swivel head. D—Straight handle with fixed head. E—Short handle straight fixed head ratchet. (S-K Tools)

Figure 5-41. Pullers are available in various styles and sizes.

Socket Attachments

Many socket attachments are available. Such items as screwdriver heads, drag link sockets, pan screw sockets, crowfoot attachments, and Allen wrench heads combine to make a socket set a fine tool.

Pullers

Automotive technicians will find use for a wide variety of *pullers.* These tools are used for pulling gears, bearings, hubs, and many other parts. An assortment of pullers is shown in **Figure 5-41.** Note the various sizes.

Another excellent puller is the slide hammer type. The puller jaws grasp the work, and the weighted slide is shoved forcefully against the stop. This type of puller is fast and efficient on many types of jobs, **Figure 5-42.**

Soldering Equipment

Electric *soldering irons* are used for most automotive soldering jobs, such as soldering wires. Modern 35 to 100 watt irons will handle most wire soldering jobs. The tip of an electric soldering iron will quickly reach soldering heat after it is plugged in. Soldering irons should be large enough for the job. An iron that is too small will require excess time to heat the work and may never heat it properly. A proper size iron will bring the metal up to the correct soldering heat quickly and result in a good soldering job.

Multitemperature *soldering guns* are also available. These tools allow the user to hold and use them easily. Their tips heat the work very quickly, ensuring a good solder job. Small lights are sometimes built into the body to provide additional light on the work. A typical soldering gun is shown in **Figure 5-43.**

For large soldering jobs such as radiator tanks, a large soldering iron, sometimes called a *copper* is used. These irons are heavy and must be placed in a gas flame or in an electric furnace for heating. They are too cumbersome and heavy for wire soldering.

Figure 5-42. A slide hammer puller. The slide is "hammered" against the stop, developing a powerful pulling force.

Solder

For soldering all automotive wiring, use rosin-core solder only. Acid-core solder leaves a residue that will cause corrosion in electrical units and should never be used for wiring. Acid-core solder is satisfactory for radiator work.

Measuring Tools

Technicians are often called on to make precision measurements. To do this, they must be able to use an outside micrometer, an inside micrometer, dial gauges, calipers, depth gauges, and a combination square. In addition, technicians must often measure electrical properties, various pressures, and vacuum.

Micrometers

Outside and inside *micrometers* are used to make linear measurements that are accurate to a fraction of a thousandth of an inch. See **Figures 5-44** and **5-45.** Outside

Figure 5-43. A pistol grip type soldering gun. These develop heat quickly, easily heating the work for good soldering. (Cooper Tools)

Figure 5-44. Typical outside ball anvil micrometer. This tool is handy for measuring curved surfaces. Handle with care. (Central Tools)

micrometers are used to measure outside diameters and thicknesses. Inside micrometers are used to measure internal dimensions, such as the inside diameter of a cylinder. Micrometers are available in a variety of sizes. Both standard and metric micrometers are available. The metric micrometer is graduated in millimeters instead of thousandths of an inch.

Inside and Outside Calipers

Calipers are useful tools for rough measurements. **Figure 5-46** illustrates a pair of outside calipers being used to measure the diameter of a shaft. **Figure 5-47** shows how the inside calipers can be used to measure the size of a hole. To determine the reading, hold the calipers on an accurate steel rule.

Figure 5-45. Using an inside micrometer to check cylinder bore size.

Figure 5-46. Using an outside caliper to measure the diameter of a shaft. (South Bend Lathe)

Figure 5-47. Using an inside caliper to measure the diameter of a counterbore.

Dividers

Dividers are made somewhat like calipers, but have straight shanks and pointed ends. They are handy for marking circles and making surface measurements. **Figure 5-48** shows dividers being used to find the center of a steel shaft.

Dial Indicator

A *dial indicator* is used to read movement in thousandths of an inch. Common uses are checking end play in shafts, backlash in gear teeth, valve lift, shaft runout, wheel runout, and taper in cylinders. **Figure 5-49** shows how a dial

Figure 5-48. Dividers being used to find the center of a steel shaft. (South Bend Lathe)

Figure 5-49. Checking ring gear runout with a dial indicator.

Figure 5-50. Two types of dial calipers. A—Standard dial indicator. B—Electronic digital caliper. Handle with care. (Starrett)

Figure 5-51. Feeler gauges. A—Wire gauges and standard flat blades. B—Wire gauges and stepped blades. (L.S. Starrett)

indicator is used to check a ring gear for runout. As the ring gear revolves in the V-block stand, any runout (wobble) of the gear will cause the dial needle to move. This movement is read in thousandths of an inch.

Dial Calipers

A **dial caliper** is a very handy and useful measuring tool. It is capable of taking inside, outside, and depth measurements. These instruments are highly accurate and should be handled with care.

The dial caliper shown in **Figure 5-50A** is capable of measuring objects up to 6″ (152.4 mm). Each graduation on the bar scale (body) is equal to .100″ (2.54 mm). The dial is calibrated in .001″ (0.025 mm). One full revolution of the dial needle equals .100″ on the bar scale. A thumb-operated roll knob is used to make fine adjustments. Any given adjustment can be secured by turning the lockscrew. This prevents the caliper from opening or closing. An electronic dial caliper is shown in **Figure 5-50B.**

Feeler Gauges

Feeler gauges are thin strips of specially hardened and ground steel. The thickness of each strip is marked in thousandths of an inch. Feeler gauges are used to check clearances between two parts or surfaces. See **Figure 5-51.**

Electrical Testers

To troubleshoot modern electrical systems, the technician must be familiar with many pieces of electrical test equipment. The test light, voltmeter, ammeter, ohmmeter, and tachometer are all very important to proper diagnosis, service, and repair.

Some electrical testers have a needle or pointer to indicate the electrical reading. These are called analog gauges. Many modern electrical testers are digital meters, which display a number to indicate the reading.

Test Light

A **test light** is a simple electrical tester composed of a 12-volt light bulb, two terminals, and connecting wiring, as shown in **Figure 5-52.** Using a test light is a quick way to check an electrical device or circuit. However, test lights cannot be used to measure exact electrical units—they only tell if electricity is or is not present. Test lights should not be used to check computers or other solid-state devices, since these units can be ruined by the current flowing through the light.

There are two types of test lights: powered test lights and non-powered test lights. The powered test light contains a battery and is used to check for a complete circuit when no current is flowing in the circuit. The non-powered test light is connected between a powered circuit and ground. It will light up if power is present in the circuit.

Figure 5-52. Phantom view of a 12-volt test lamp with an internal light bulb. The sharp probe will fit into tiny circuit connectors. Never use it to pierce wire insulation. (General Motors)

Ohmmeter

Ohmmeters are used to measure electrical resistance. Resistance, which exists in any electrical circuit or device, is the opposition to current flow. This resistance is measured in ohms. Resistance is discussed in more detail in Chapter 7. Ohmmeters can only be used to check an electrical circuit when no current is flowing in the circuit.

An ohmmeter has two leads, which are connected to each side of the unit or circuit to be tested. Polarity (direction of current flow) is not important when checking resistance, except when checking computer circuits and certain electronic components. Most ohmmeters have selector knobs for checking various ranges of resistance values. Analog ohmmeters have a special knob to adjust the needle to zero before checking resistance.

Voltmeter

Voltmeters are used to check voltage between two points in an energized circuit. On some voltmeters, different scales can be selected, depending on the voltage level to be measured. Always observe proper polarity when attaching voltmeter leads. When a voltmeter is used on a modern vehicle with a negative ground, the negative lead (usually black) should always be connected to the frame or other ground and the positive lead (usually red) should be attached to the positive part of the circuit.

Ammeter

An **ammeter** is used to check the amperage (current) flow in a circuit. The ammeter is used to check the amperage draw of starters or other motors and when checking battery condition. Ammeters can also be used to check the amperage draw of ignition coils, solenoids, and other electrical devices.

Multimeter

A **multimeter** is essentially a voltmeter, an ammeter, an ohmmeter, and other testers housed in one unit. Multimeters usually have at least one positive (red) lead and one negative (black) lead. Some multimeters are equipped with other leads for special functions. Polarity should be carefully noted when making certain tests with multimeters. A typical multimeter is shown in **Figure 5-53.**

Tachometer

Tachometers are used to measure engine speed. Modern tachometers are available in either analog or digital versions. Tachometers have at least two leads. One lead is connected to the distributor side of the ignition coil and the other lead is connected to ground. Some tachometers have an inductive clamp-on pickup that is placed around a plug wire to obtain the speed reading. Others use an electric "eye" setup.

The tachometer may have a low range to check idle speeds and a high speed range for making various tests at

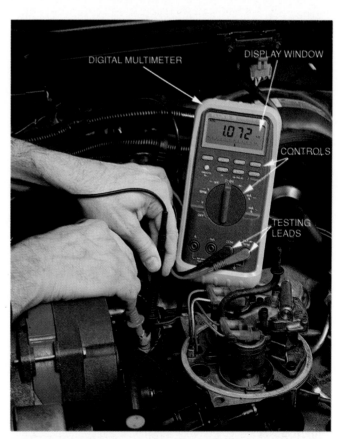

Figure 5-53. This technician is using a digital multimeter to test an electrical connection. Multimeters are precision instruments. They must be handled with care. Note the red and black leads. (Fluke)

high engine speeds. The ranges may be selected with a control knob, or they may automatically switch as engine speed varies. Some tachometers have a provision for checking distributor dwell (the amount of time that primary current is flowing in the ignition coil). This is useful when working on older vehicles with point-type ignition systems, and it has other applications as well. Some multimeters have a provision for a tachometer.

Pressure Gauges

The automotive technician must often measure pressures when diagnosing various problems. The technician needs several pressure gauges. These gauges measure air pressure or the pressure of several automotive liquids, including engine oil, transmission fluid, power steering fluid, and fuel. The most common pressure gauges are discussed below.

Compression Gauge

The *compression gauge,* **Figure 5-54,** measures the pressure developed in the engine cylinder when the piston comes up on the compression stroke. The compression gauge measures this compression in pounds per square inch (PSI) or kilopascals (kPa). By using a compression gauge to check the condition of each cylinder, the technician can identify many engine problems. The gauge is connected to the cylinder through a high-pressure hose threaded into the spark plug hole of a gasoline engine or the fuel injector hole of a diesel engine.

Figure 5-54. One type of engine compression gauge and connecting hose. Note the pressure relief valve. This valve allows relief of compression pressure so that a second reading can be obtained without disconnecting the gauge. It also aids in gauge removal from the engine. (Lisle Tools)

Vacuum Gauge

Vacuum gauges, **Figure 5-55,** measure negative air pressure, or vacuum. In an engine, vacuum is the difference in air pressure between the engine intake manifold and the outside atmosphere. Vacuum is a reliable indicator of engine load and condition. The vacuum gauge is connected by a length of hose to a port on the intake manifold. Variations in vacuum readings indicate various engine problems. Vacuum gauges can also be used to test for proper vacuum to and from vacuum-operated components, such as heater doors, brake boosters, etc.

The vacuum gauge may also be used with a hand vacuum pump to test various vacuum-operated devices. The pump creates a vacuum on the device to be tested while the gauge measures the vacuum and indicates whether or not the unit can hold the vacuum. The technician may also be able to observe the action of the vacuum device as the vacuum is applied.

Figure 5-55. A standard vacuum gauge with one particular hookup to test the vacuum for a brake booster. This instrument will provide vacuum or pressure readings. (Dodge)

Oil Pressure Gauge

An *oil pressure gauge* measures the pressure developed by the engine oil pump, automatic transmission pump, brake fluid, or power steering pump. The oil pressure test gauge is used to determine whether the pump is providing the specified pressure. The pressure gauge is attached to the unit to be tested through a high-pressure hose that threads into a pressure port, **Figure 5-56.**

The pressure gauge scale is calibrated according to the output of the system being tested. Engine oil pressure seldom exceeds 80 PSI (552 kPa), while automatic transmission pressures are in the hundreds of PSI (or kPa), and brake and power steering pressures may reach over 2000 PSI (13 789 kPa).

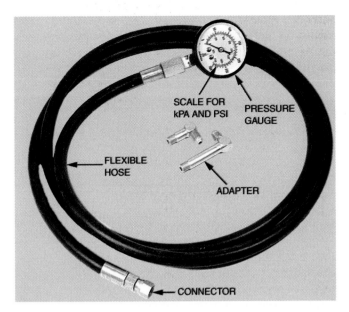

Figure 5-56. One type of engine oil pressure gauge with a flexible connection hose and adapters. (Kent-Moore Tools)

Fuel Pressure Tester

The **fuel pressure gauge** measures the pressure developed by the fuel pump. It is used to determine whether the pump is providing enough pressure and flow to keep the engine supplied with fuel. It can also be used to detect clogged fuel filters or other fuel system problems. Pressure testers can be used on both carbureted and fuel-injected engines. A typical fuel pressure tester for a fuel-injected engine is shown in **Figure 5-57.**

Figure 5-57. A fuel pressure gauge and connection to one type of electronic fuel injection fuel rail. Use caution when working with fuel. (Dodge)

Other Diagnostic Equipment

There are several other pieces of diagnostic equipment commonly used in the automotive repair shop.

A **scan tool** is a hand-held electronic device that can communicate with a vehicle's computer, **Figure 5-58.** The scan tool is connected to the computer through a special electrical connector known as the **data link connector.**

Early scan tools could only be used to retrieve diagnostic trouble codes from the computer. Modern scan tools can also be used to check input sensor signals and verify the operation of the output devices. Some scan tools can be used to reprogram the computer on late-model vehicles.

Figure 5-58. A hand-held diagnostic scan tool with related adapters and equipment. Such a tool is useful for diagnosing computer-controlled vehicles. (Snap-on Tools)

Although they are expensive, scan tools are widely used because they save diagnostic time. They also reduce the chance of misdiagnosis. On most vehicles made after 1996, the proper scan tool *must* be used to retrieve trouble codes.

The **exhaust gas analyzer** is used to measure the amount of various chemicals in the vehicle's exhaust. To use an exhaust gas analyzer, a hose is inserted into the vehicle's tailpipe. A small blower motor draws an exhaust gas sample from the tailpipe as the vehicle operates.

Early exhaust gas analyzers were able to measure carbon monoxide (CO) and unburned hydrocarbons (HC) only. In addition to CO and HC, the newest exhaust gas analyzers can measure oxides of nitrogen (NO_x), free oxygen (O_2), and carbon dioxide (CO_2).

Another commonly used tester is the **oscilloscope.** The most obvious component of the oscilloscope is the display screen, which resembles a television screen. The oscilloscope uses this screen to display a picture of the electrical activity in the vehicle's ignition system and other electrical systems. The picture is usually called a **scope pattern.**

A *vehicle analyzer* combines the functions of many of the smaller testers previously discussed, including a multimeter, an oscilloscope, an exhaust gas analyzer, and a scan tool. In many cases, these testers are mounted in a large, roll-around cabinet. Using an analyzer eliminates the need for separate pieces of test equipment. See **Figure 5-59.**

Figure 5-59. This engine analyzer incorporates a digital oscilloscope and can act as a database for technical information. This analyzer can interface with hand-held scan tools to download information gathered during a test drive. (Ford Motor Co.)

Summary

Good quality tools are necessary for working on today's vehicles. Quality tools are also the sign of technicians who takes pride in their work. You get what you pay for, so only purchase quality tools. Take good care of your tools by keeping them clean and dry and by storing them in a tool cabinet.

A good set of quality tools not only makes the job easier, but it will also make the job go faster. Hammers, screwdrivers, chisels, punches, wrenches, pliers, and a socket set are a few of the basic tools common to every technician's tool collection. Other tools can be added as your experience and the need for them arises.

Measuring tools are important in making precision measurements and diagnosing problems. calipers, dial indicators, and micrometers are used by technicians to measure engine and other parts to diagnose problems or to ensure proper clearances during assembly. Scan tools, multimeters, test lights, and pressure gauges help the technician to properly diagnose the problem the first time.

Know These Terms

Hammer	Micrometer
Chisel	Calipers
Punch	Dividers
File	Dial indicator
Drill	Dial caliper
Drill bit	Feeler gauge
Reamer	Scan tool
Impact wrench	Test light
Hacksaw	Ohmmeter
Vise	Voltmeter
Tap	Ammeter
Die	Multimeter
Pliers	Tachometer
Screwdriver	Compression gauge
Wrenches	Vacuum gauge
Torque wrench	Oil pressure gauge
Socket	Fuel pressure gauge
Extension bar	Scan tool
Ratchet	Data link connector
Puller	Exhaust gas analyzer
Soldering iron	Oscilloscope
Soldering gun	Vehicle analyzer

Review Questions—Chapter 5

Do not write in this book. Write your answers on a separate sheet of paper.

1. All of the following statements about good quality tools are true, EXCEPT:
   (A) they are heavy and thick.
   (B) they are easy to use in tight quarters.
   (C) they are made of high-strength alloy steel.
   (D) they are guaranteed.

2. Any tool subjected to rust should be cleaned and _____.

3. Keep _____ tools by themselves.

4. You should arrange your tools in a tool box so that the tools that are the most often used are _____ .
   (A) in precise order according to size
   (B) at the top
   (C) easy to get to
   (D) securely locked up

5. How are the following punches shaped?
   starting punch   _____
   drift punch   _____
   aligning punch   _____

6. A file with two sets of cutting edges at angles to each other is referred to as a _____ file.

7. A hammer handles should be _____ and _____ .

8. Technician A says that carbon steel drill bits will last longer than high-speed steel drill bits. Technician B says that carbon steel drill bits will require more frequent sharpening. Who is right?
   (A) A only.
   (B) B only.
   (C) Both A & B.
   (D) Neither A nor B.

9. A 24-tooth hacksaw blade is best for cutting all of the following, EXCEPT:
   (A) heavy sheet metal.
   (B) brass.
   (C) thinwall tubing.
   (D) copper.

10. Technician A says that reamers are used for drilling large holes. Technician B says that a husky vise is useful as an anvil. Who is right?
    (A) A only.
    (B) B only.
    (C) Both A & B.
    (D) Neither A nor B.

11. If you wish to cut internal threads in a hole, you would use a _____ .

12. If you wish to cut threads on a bolt, you would use a _____ .

13. Pliers can be used for all of the following, EXCEPT:
    (A) tightening tubing fittings.
    (B) bending cotter pins.
    (C) cutting wire.
    (D) crimping connections.

14. Briefly describe the following items:
    Box-end wrench.
    Open-end wrench.
    Adjustable wrench.

15. What advantage does a 6-point opening have over a 12-point opening?

16. What advantage does a 12-point opening have over a 6-point opening?

17. Technician A says that using an impact wrench will reduce the amount of time that a job takes. Technician B says that impact sockets should always be used with an impact wrench. Who is right?
    (A) A only.
    (B) B only.
    (C) Both A & B.
    (D) Neither A nor B.

18. Technician A says that a box-end wrench is preferred to an open-end wrench in most cases. Technician B says that combination box-end and open-end wrenches have a different size opening on each end. Who is right?
    (A) A only.
    (B) B only.
    (C) Both A & B.
    (D) Neither A nor B.

19. To remove a spark plug, the technician would need a _____ socket.

20. Standard size screwdrivers can be used for which of the following purposes?
    (A) Removing and installing screws.
    (B) Prying of oil pans.
    (C) Hammering on tight parts.
    (D) All of the above.

21. Technician A says that an adjustable wrench can be used to turn a crankshaft journal. Technician B says that a torque wrench should be used to tighten head bolts. Who is right?
    (A) A only.
    (B) B only.
    (C) Both A & B.
    (D) Neither A nor B.

22. Gears are usually removed by using a _____ .

23. Technician A says that an ohmmeter measures resistance to the flow of electricity. Technician B says that a multimeter can measure many kinds of electrical properties. Who is right?
    (A) A only.
    (B) B only.
    (C) Both A & B.
    (D) Neither A nor B.

24. Technician A says that a vacuum gauge measures negative air pressure. Technician B says that engine compression is measured with a vacuum gauge. Who is right?
    (A) A only.
    (B) B only.
    (C) Both A & B.
    (D) Neither A nor B.

25. Name three vehicle systems where an oil pressure tester could be used

26. Technician A says a fuel pessure gauge can be used to check for clogged fuel filters. Technician B says a fuel pressure gauge should not be used when testing carburated fuel systems. Who is right?
    (A) A only.
    (B) B only.
    (C) Both A & B.
    (D) Neither A nor B.

Environmental test chambers are used to test the entire vehicle as well as engines for proper operation in all kinds of weather conditions. (Chrysler)

27. A scan tool is connected to a vehicle's computer system through the _____ _____ connector.

28. A scan tool can be used for each of the following, EXCEPT:
    (A) retrieving trouble codes.
    (B) checking input sensor signals.
    (C) reprogramming the computer.
    (D) measuring exhaust emissions.

29. Technician A says exhaust gas analyzers can measure the amount of carbon monoxide in a vehicle's exhaust gases. Technician B says some exhaust gas analyzers can measure the amount of carbon dioxide in a vehicle's exhaust gases. Who is right?
    (A) A only.
    (B) B only.
    (C) Both A & B.
    (D) Neither A nor B.

30. A(n) _____ can be used to display a picture of the electrical activity in a vehicle's ignition system.

6

Engine Tests and Measurements

After studying this chapter, you will be able to:
- Recall engine measurement formulas.
- Solve basic engine measurement problems.
- Develop an understanding of engine ratings.

Everyone has heard the word horsepower, but very few people, including many technicians, understand exactly what it means and how it is computed. The science of engine testing and measurement is very complicated and, in its true sense, lies in the realm of engineering. Nevertheless, it is important that the student of automotive technology be familiar with basic formulas, terms, and how they are computed.

What Is Horsepower?

Many years ago, people recognized the need for a yardstick with which to measure the work-producing ability of an engine. Since horses had been used to do the work for so long, it was natural to compare the power developed by the early engine to that produced by a horse.

The work ability of an average draft horse measured in foot-pounds had long been the standard unit of work. **Work** can be defined as a force applied to a body that causes the body to move. The amount of work done can be computed by multiplying the distance the body is moved by the weight of the body. This answer would be in **foot-pounds**.

It was found, for example, that the average draft horse could lift 100 pounds 330 feet in one minute. If one pound is lifted one foot in one minute, one foot-pound of work would be done. The horse lifted 100 pounds (lb.) 330 feet (ft.) in one minute. The amount of work performed can be found by using the formula:

Rate of work = Distance moved x Force weight

=33,000ft.-lb.=330ft.x100lb.

We find the horse performed work at the rate of 33,000 foot-pounds per minute. This became the standard measure for one **horsepower**, **Figure 6-1**. The **rate** at which work is performed is called **power**. Horsepower is sometimes called brake horsepower. This term stems from an early method of measuring horsepower.

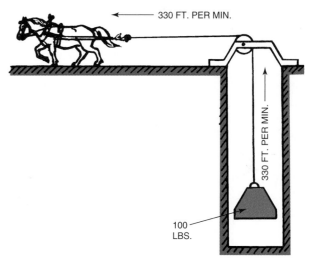

Figure 6-1. Horsepower is a measure of the rate at which work is performed. The ability to perform work at a rate of 33,000 ft.-lb. per min. is equal to 1 horsepower.

Horsepower Formula

To find engine horsepower, the total rate of work accomplished (in foot-pounds) is divided by 33,000. If a machine lifts 100 lb. 660 ft. per minute, its total rate of work would be 66,000 ft.-lb. Dividing this by 33,000 ft.-lb. (1 horsepower), you will find that the machine is rated as 2 horsepower (hp). Your formula would be:

$$\frac{\text{Rate of work in ft.-lbs.}}{233,000(1\text{hp})} = \frac{\text{Distance moved x force}}{33,000} = \frac{D \times W}{33,000} = hp$$

This formula may also be used to determine the horsepower required to perform a specific task. Let us assume that you want to lift buckets of earth from an excavation site. The loaded bucket weight is 5000 lb., and you want to raise it 15 ft. per minute. Using the formula:

$$hp = \frac{D \times W}{33,000} = \frac{15 \times 5000}{33,000} = \frac{75,000}{33,000} = 2.27 \text{ hp}$$

The minimum amount of horsepower (disregarding friction) required would be 2.27.

Potential Horsepower

If a certain engine burns a specific fuel at a certain rate, and if all the heat of the burning fuel could be converted into useful power, you would have the ideal engine. Unfortunately, engines have not reached this level of efficiency. In fact, even the best engines are relatively inefficient in that the usable power falls far short of the potential.

Engine efficiency can be broken down into two groups: *thermal efficiency* and *mechanical efficiency*. Any comparison between different engines on an efficiency basis must be conducted under identical situations. Weather, altitude, temperature, engine speed, and humidity all affect the test results.

Thermal Efficiency

Engine thermal efficiency (heat efficiency) is based on how much of the energy (ability to do work) of the burning fuel is converted into useful horsepower.

The heat generated by the burning fuel drives the piston down during the power stroke. Much of this heat is lost to the cooling system, some to the lubrication system, and a great deal to the exhaust system. The thermal efficiency of an average engine is around 25%. This means that the engine is losing approximately 75% of the fuel's heat energy, **Figure 6-2.**

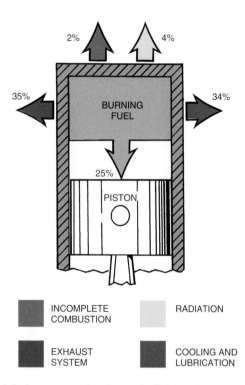

Figure 6-2. Average engine thermal efficiency is around 25%. Note the losses due to incomplete combustion, exhaust, radiation, cooling, and lubrication.

The generally accepted formula for computing brake thermal efficiency is:

$$\frac{\text{Brake}}{\text{Thermal}} = \frac{\text{Brake Horsepower (bhp)} \times 33{,}000}{778 \times \frac{\text{Fuel Heat}}{\text{Value}} \times \frac{\text{Weight of Fuel}}{\text{Burned per Minute}}}$$

The fuel heat value is rated in Btus (British thermal units) per pound (the number 778 is a constant).

Mechanical Efficiency

Mechanical efficiency is based on the relationship between the power developed within the engine and actual brake horsepower delivered at the crankshaft. Fortunately, mechanical efficiency is better than thermal efficiency—generally around 90%. This means that 10% is lost to friction within the engine. Engine friction increases with speed.

The formula for mechanical efficiency is:

$$\text{Mechanical Efficiency} = \frac{\text{Brake Horsepower}}{\text{Indicated Horsepower}} = \frac{\text{bhp}}{\text{ihp}}$$

Practical Efficiency

When dealing with vehicle engines, you are primarily interested in horsepower delivered at the drive wheels.

Every pound of gasoline that enters the engine has the ability to do a certain amount of work. The capacity of any material to do work is called its energy. However, there are many factors that rob energy before it gets to the drive wheels. As little as 15% of the potential energy in the fuel is actually delivered to the drive wheels, **Figure 6-3** illustrates some typical energy losses.

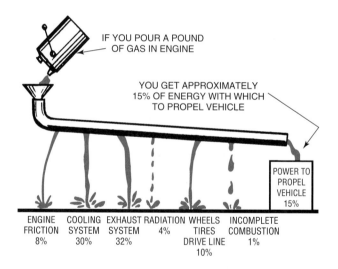

Figure 6-3. Practical engine efficiency. Energy is lost between the engine and the drive wheels. The percentages shown are approximate and depend on engine design and the conditions under which engine is operated.

Indicated Horsepower

Indicated horsepower (ihp) is a measure of the power developed by the burning fuel in the cylinders. In order to compute ihp, it is necessary to find the pressures within the cylinder during the intake, compression, power, and exhaust strokes. A measuring device gives a constant reading of the pressures. These pressures are placed on an indicator graph.

The next step is to establish a mean effective pressure (mep). This is done by taking the average pressure during the power stroke and subtracting the average pressure during the other three strokes. Once the mep is determined, the following formula is used to determine the indicated horsepower:

$$\text{Indicated Horsepower} = \frac{\text{PLANK}}{33,000}$$

P - mep in lb. per sq. in.

L - length of the stroke in feet

A - cylinder area in sq. in.

N - power strokes per min. $\frac{\text{rpm}}{2}$

K - number of cylinders

Indicated horsepower ratings do not reflect losses from friction.

Brake Horsepower

Brake horsepower (bhp) is a measure of actual usable horsepower delivered at the engine crankshaft. Brake horsepower is not constant: it increases with speed. An early method of measuring crankshaft horsepower made use of a device called a Prony brake, **Figure 6-4.**

Figure 6-4. The Prony brake is used to measure brake horsepower (bhp). A clamping device grasps the spinning flywheel. The clamp is tightened until a specific rpm is reached with the throttle wide open. At this point, a weight reading on the scale is taken. By knowing the scale reading (W), the distance from the center of the crank to the arm support (L), and the rpm of the flywheel (R), it is possible to compute bhp.

The formula for determining brake horsepower on a Prony Brake is:

$$\text{bph} = \frac{2\pi \times R \times L \times W}{33,000}$$

$$\text{bph} = \frac{R \times L \times W}{5252}$$

R = Engine rpm.

L = Length from the center of the drive shaft to the point where the beam presses on the scale.

W = Weight as registered on the scale.

The modern method of testing and determining brake horsepower is by using an **engine dynamometer** or a **chassis dynamometer**.

In one type of engine dynamometer setup, the engine drives a large generator (dynamo). By placing an electrical load in the circuit, bhp at various rpm can be determined. See **Figure 6-5.** An engine dynamometer that attaches directly to the engine is shown in **Figure 6-6.**

Figure 6-5. This schematic demonstrates the general idea of an engine dynamometer. The generator dynamo can be loaded until the engine rpm is at a certain point with the throttle wide open. By using instrument readings, horsepower can be calculated.

Figure 6-6. This engine dynamometer is located inside an altitude simulation chamber. This particular setup allows engineers to measure engine horsepower at different altitudes. The engine is operated at various atmospheric conditions and throttle positions, including wide open throttle. (Chrysler)

The chassis dynamometer is used to measure bhp at the drive wheels. The vehicle's drive wheels are placed on rollers, and the engine is engaged. As the wheels turn the rollers, the rollers are loaded (made increasingly difficult to turn). By computing the amount of loading the wheels can handle, it is possible to determine bhp at the drive wheels. This is practical efficiency that is meaningful to the average motorist. Chassis dynamometers are installed in some larger shops for use in engine tuning and testing, **Figure 6-7.**

Figure 6-7. Schematic showing the operation of a typical chassis dynamometer. This unit measures the horsepower delivered to the drive wheels. (Clayton)

Gross and Net Horsepower Ratings

Under **SAE** (Society of Automotive Engineers) specifications, a **gross horsepower** rating is the maximum horsepower developed by an engine equipped with only the basic accessories needed for its operation. This would include the built-in emission controls, oil pump, coolant pump, and fuel pump. The fan, alternator, air cleaner, catalytic converter, and muffler are removed. Other engine-driven accessories, such as the power steering pump and air conditioner compressor, are also left off.

The **net horsepower** rating is the maximum horsepower developed by the engine when equipped with all the accessories it would have when installed in the vehicle, such as the fan, alternator, catalytic converter, muffler, air pump, air cleaner, fuel pump, and coolant pump. The net horsepower rating is a more informative figure for the consumer because it shows the horsepower that will actually be produced in normal usage.

The specified test conditions (29.38″ Hg. or 99.01 kPa barometric pressure, 85°F (29.46°C) ambient air temperature, 0.38″ Hg. or 1.28 kPa water vapor pressure or humidity) are the same for both gross and net horsepower ratings.

Some other nations use a **din** horsepower rating. This is a net rating measured under slightly different conditions and specifications. Therefore, it will vary from ratings used in the United States.

Frictional Horsepower

Frictional horsepower (fhp) is a measurement of the amount of horsepower lost to engine friction. It is computed by this formula:

$$fhp = ihp - bhp$$

As mentioned, frictional horsepower increases with engine speed. See **Figure 6-8.**

Torque

Engine torque (twisting action) is the ability of the crankshaft to impart a twisting or turning force. It is measured in pound-feet (Newton-meters). If a pipe wrench is placed on a pipe and a pressure of one pound is exerted one foot from the center of the pipe, the torque (torque = force x distance) applied to the pipe would be one pound-foot. See **Figure 6-9.** Actually, when measuring torque, the reading is given in lb.-ft. When measuring *work,* the reading is given in ft.-lb.

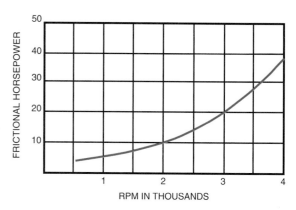

Figure 6-8. Graph showing frictional horsepower. Notice how an increase in engine rpm causes more friction.

Figure 6-9. The torque, or twist, applied to this pipe would be one pound-foot. This is torque in excess of wrench weight.

Torque and Brake Horsepower Are Not the Same

Engine brake horsepower increases with engine speed. Engine torque increases with engine speed up to the point where the engine is drawing in the maximum amount of fuel mixture, after all factors are considered. Torque is greatest at this point, and any additional increase in rpm will cause torque to diminish. **Figure 6-10** compares torque and brake horsepower.

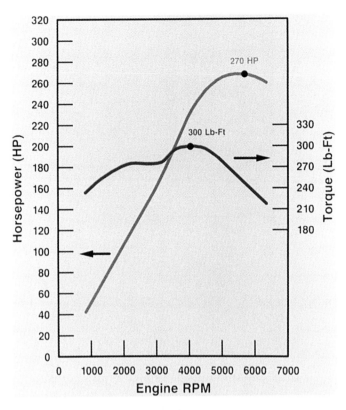

Figure 6-10. This graph shows brake horsepower and torque for one specific engine. Notice how horsepower increases almost to maximum speed, while torque drops off at a much lower rpm. The relationship between torque and bhp will vary depending on engine design. (Cadillac)

Volumetric Efficiency

Volumetric efficiency (sometimes referred to as breathing ability) is the measure of an engine's ability to draw the fuel mixture into the cylinders. It is determined by the ratio between what is actually drawn in and what could be drawn in if all cylinders were completely filled.

As engine speed increases beyond a certain point, the piston speed becomes so fast that the intake stroke is of such short duration that less and less fuel mixture is drawn in. As torque is greatest when the cylinders receive the largest amount of fuel mixture, torque will drop off as volumetric efficiency decreases.

Many factors influence volumetric efficiency, including engine speed, temperature, throttle position, intake system design, valve size and position, exhaust system configuration, and atmospheric pressure.

Volumetric efficiency can be improved by adding a supercharger; a straighter, smoother, and ram-length intake manifold (sometimes called a tuned intake manifold); larger intake valves; a more efficient exhaust system, and other modifications to the induction and exhaust systems.

A formula used to determine volumetric efficiency is:

$$\text{Volumetric Efficiency} = \frac{\text{Total Volume of the Charge}}{\text{Total Cylinder Volume (displacement)}}$$

All tests between engines must be under identical conditions. See **Figure 6-11** and **Figure 6-12**.

Engine Size (Displacement)

Engine size (not physical dimensions) is related to piston displacement. Piston displacement refers to the total number of cubic inches of space (liters) in a cylinder when the piston moves from the top of its stroke (TDC) to the bottom (BDC), **Figure 6-13**.

All related factors (such as compression, head design, and fuel system) being equal, the greater the engine displacement, the more power produced. To calculate displacement, find the area of the cylinder ($0.7854 \times D^2$). Multiply the area by the total piston travel (stroke) from TDC to BDC. This answer is then multiplied by the number of cylinders to calculate the total engine displacement in cubic inches. The formula for total displacement is:

VOLUME THAT
COULD BE HELD—
CYLINDER VOLUME

VOLUME OF FUEL
MIX ACTUALLY
DRAWN IN

Figure 6-11. Comparison of volumetric efficiency. A—This shows the volume that the cylinder can actually hold if it were completely filled. B—This shows the volume of air-fuel mixture actually drawn in by vacuum.

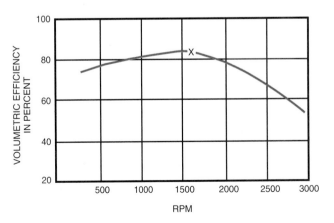

Figure 6-12. This graph shows volumetric efficiency at various speeds. The graph is only approximate as volumetric efficiency will vary from engine to engine. The X marks the point of highest efficiency and highest torque.

Figure 6-13. Measurement of piston displacement. If you were to fill the cylinder with water when the piston is at TDC (A), move the piston to BDC (B), and measure the additional water required to fill the cylinder (C), you would be able to determine the cylinder displacement in cubic inches. When the piston is at TDC, the space from the top of the piston to the cylinder head is called clearance volume. This space is occupied by the water in A.

$$\begin{array}{l}\text{Total} \\ \text{Engine} \\ \text{Displacement}\end{array} = 0.7854 \times D^2 \times \text{Travel} \times \text{Number of Cylinders}$$

To find the displacement of a V-8 engine having a cylinder diameter (bore) of 4.000 inches and a piston travel (stroke) of 3.000 inches, use the formula as follows.

$$0.7854 \times D^2 \ (4^2 = 16 \ in^2) \times \text{Travel } (3'') \times \text{Number of Cylinders (8)}$$
$$= 301.5936 \text{ cu. in,}$$

This is close enough to 302 cu. in. to tell you that you have a 302, or 5 liter, engine.

This formula can also be used to find out how many cubic inches an engine gained when it was bored out. If a 173 cubic inch (2.8 liter) V-6 was bored .030 over, add .030 to the original bore (3.503 inches) to get a new bore of 3.533. The travel is 2.992, so you can use the formula as described earlier:

$$0.7854 \times D^2 \ (3.503^2 = 12.48 \text{ square inches}) \times \text{Travel}$$
$$(2.992 \text{ inches}) \times \text{Number of Cylinders (6)} = 175.99 \text{ cu. in,}$$

This makes the bored 173 cubic inch (2.8 liter) engine a 176 cubic inch (2.9 liter) engine.

Cylinder Bore and Piston Stroke

As you noticed in the previous section, displacement hinges on the cylinder **bore** (diameter) and the piston **stroke**. The bore is the diameter of the cylinder. The stroke is the distance the piston moves from TDC to BDC, **Figure 6-14**.

When bore and stroke are equal, the engine is referred to as being **square**. Modern engines use a stroke that is shorter than bore diameter. This is referred to as an **over square** engine. By reducing the stroke, piston speed is decreased. This prolongs the life of the cylinders, pistons, and rings.

For example, say that you want to compute the distance a piston ring slides up and down during one mile of driving.

Figure 6-14. Engine bore (cylinder diameter) and stroke (distance the piston moves in traveling from top dead center to bottom dead center). The connecting rod journal offset, or throw, determines the length of the stroke.

Your hypothetical (make believe) car will have a tire diameter of 30′, the engine drives 1 to 1 through the transmission (standard transmission with no overdrive), and the differential (rear end) reduces driveline speed by a ratio of 4 to 1 (driveline turns four times for each revolution of the wheels).

The circumference of the tire (6.283 x radius) would be 94.245″. Converting this circumference to feet, you would have 7.85′. If the tire rolls 7.85′ per revolution, it will make 672.61 revolutions per mile.

The engine rpm would be four times the wheel rpm. This would give 2690.44 engine rpm per mile. The rings slide 3″ during each piston stroke, or 6″ per engine revolution. With 2690.44 rpm per mile, the rings would slide 1345.22′ for every mile traveled.

If the engine had a 6″ stroke, the rings would slide twice as far. This shows that the short stroke decreases wear. Not only is the sliding distance decreased, but the speed at which the rings slide is greatly reduced.

Compression Ratio

The **compression ratio** is the relationship between the cylinder volume (clearance volume) when the piston is on TDC and the cylinder volume when the piston is on BDC, **Figure 6-15**.

Compression ratios range from 5:1 to slightly over 11:1 for gasoline engines (8.5:1 is about average). Diesel engine compression ratios range from 17.5:1 to 22.5:1. To a certain degree, the higher the compression ratio, the more power the engine will develop. Such being the case, you may wonder why the compression ratio is not increased a great deal on all engines.

Figure 6-15. To determine engine compression ratio, the volume of the cylinder at both BDC and TDC is measured. A—When the piston is at BDC, the cylinder volume is 8. B—When the piston is at TDC, the cylinder volume is 1. therefore, the compression ration is 8:1.

One reason is that modern fuels will not allow increased compression beyond a certain point. When a fuel mixture is compressed, heat energy is developed. The temperature at which the air-fuel mixture will ignite itself limits the amount it can be satisfactorily compressed. Another problem is that when the compression ratio of an engine is too high, detonation, or knocking, will occur in the engine. Additionally, effective emission control has required that compression ratios be lowered from 10 or 11:1 down to about 8:1.

Summary

Horsepower is a measure of the rate at which work is performed. One horsepower is the ability to perform work at the rate of 33,000 foot-pounds per minute.

Engines are relatively inefficient. Efficiency is based on thermal and mechanical efficiency. Most engines are about 25% efficient on a thermal basis and about 90% efficient on a mechanical basis. On a practical efficiency basis, only about 15% of the total potential energy of the fuel is used to drive the wheels. Energy is lost to the cooling, lubrication, and exhaust systems, as well as to engine, driveline, and wheel friction.

Indicated horsepower is a measure of the power developed by the burning fuel within the cylinders. Ihp is not the power delivered by the crankshaft. Crankshaft horsepower is called brake horsepower and is measured with a dynamometer. Frictional horsepower is a measure of the horsepower lost to engine friction. Net brake horsepower ratings are taken with all normal accessories on the engine. Gross brake horsepower figures are calculated with accessories such as the fan, air cleaner, and alternator removed.

Engine brake horsepower and torque are not the same. Brake horsepower increases with engine speed until maximum rpm is reached. Torque increases to the point where volumetric efficiency is greatest, and any additional speed will cause it to diminish. Torque is a measure of the engine's turning force at the crankshaft.

Volumetric efficiency refers to how well the engine is able to draw in the air-fuel mixture. It is influenced by engine design, engine speed, and a number of other factors.

Engine size is usually given in cubic inches or liters. The number of cubic inches or liters of cylinder space is the total displacement of the engine cylinders. Cylinder bore and stroke are determining factors in cubic inch or liter computations. Compression ratios are important. High compression ratios improve power and economy. However, current ratios have been lowered somewhat to reduce emissions.

Know These Terms

Work	Gross horsepower
Foot-pounds	Net horsepower
Horsepower	Din
Rate	Frictional horsepower
Power	Engine torque
Thermal efficiency	Volumetric efficiency
Mechanical efficiency	Bore
Indicated horsepower	Stroke
Brake horsepower	Square
Engine dynamometer	Over square
Chassis dynamometer	Compression ratio
SAE	

Review Questions—Chapter 6

Do not write in this book. Write your answers on a separate sheet of paper.

1. What is horsepower?
2. Give the formula for computing horsepower.
3. Engine efficiency can be classified as _____ .
   (A) thermal
   (B) mechanical
   (C) volumetric
   (D) Both A & B.
4. What is indicated horsepower?
5. How thermally efficient is the average internal combustion engine?
   (A) 10%
   (B) 25%
   (C) 90%
   (D) 100%
6. How much mechanical efficiency does the average internal combustion engine lose to internal friction?
   (A) 10%
   (B) 25%
   (C) 90%
   (D) 100%
7. The _____ is now used to determine brake horsepower.
   (A) Prony brake
   (B) engine dynamometer
   (C) chassis dynamometer
   (D) Both A & B.

8. If the potential energy in a pound of fuel is 100%, how much of this energy lost before reaching the drive wheels?

(A) 10%

(B) 35%

(C) 85%

(D) 95%

9. Technician A says that horsepower increases with speed. Technician B says that torque decreases beyond a certain speed. Who is right?

(A) A only.

(B) B only.

(C) Both A & B.

(D) Neither A nor B.

10. The din horsepower rating is used in other countries. It is a _____ .

(A) net rating with metric outputs

(B) net rating determined under different operating conditions

(C) gross rating with metric outputs

(D) gross rating determined different operating conditions

11. The difference between indicated horsepower and brake horsepower is classified as _____ horsepower.

12. Torque is a _____ motion.

13. Technician A says that horsepower and torque are the same. Technician B says that volumetric efficiency and cubic inch displacement are the same. Who is right?

(A) A only.

(B) B only.

(C) Both A & B.

(D) Neither A nor B.

14. Torque will drop off with a decrease in _____ .

15. Piston area can be found by squaring the _____ and multiplying this value by _____ .

16. If a cylinder is bored out, the amount of oversize is added to the original _____ to determine the new displacement.

(A) bore

(B) stroke

(C) compression ratio

(D) number of cylinders

17. Compression ratio is figured by comparing the volume in the cylinder at _____ with the volume at _____ .

18. What is meant by the cubic inch or cubic liter rating of an engine?

19. What is energy?

20. Explain the difference between *gross* brake horsepower and *net* brake horsepower.

7

Electrical System Fundamentals

After studying this chapter, you will be able to:
- Explain the principles of electricity and electronics.
- Name the values used to measure electricity.
- List the basic types of electrical circuits.
- Explain the effects of magnetism.
- Explain how diodes work.
- Explain how transistors work.
- Explain the construction of an integrated circuit.

The field of electricity and electronics covers a wide and complicated range. We know much about electricity, however, much more remains to be discovered. A thorough coverage of electricity and electronics is not within the scope of this text. However, a basic understanding of electrical and electronic fundamentals and their application to the vehicle is a must for all students of automotive technology.

Basic Electricity

We have learned to control electricity, predict its actions, and harness it in many ways. No person has literally seen electricity flow through a wire or a device. For many years no one was even sure of the direction it moved or what, if anything, actually did move. There are two theories of how current flows through a circuit.

The Electron Theory

The accepted theory regarding electricity is termed the **electron theory**. This theory has explained many of the strange behavior patterns as well as opening the way to many new discoveries, not only in electricity, but in other fields as well.

The electron theory is based on the assumption that the operation of all electrical equipment is produced by a flow of electrons from one area to another. It also states that the flow of electrons is caused by having an excess number in one area, and a shortage in the other. The area with the surplus electrons is referred to as the **negative** and the area in short supply, the **positive**.

Conventional Theory

The conventional theory says that electrons flow from the positive to the negative. Electrons leave the positive terminal and flow to the negative. It is the opposite of the electron theory. Some believe that this is how electricity actually works, however, the electron theory described earlier is more widely accepted.

Matter

Anything that takes up space and has mass is considered **matter**. Everything on Earth is composed of matter. Matter can be a solid, a liquid, or a gas. Matter is made up of different combinations of atoms which are called **molecules**. Some substances, such as water can exist as a solid (ice), liquid, or gas (steam). Other substances will remain in the same state under the normal range of Earth temperatures.

Atoms

There are over one hundred different types of known **atoms**. Various combinations of these atoms will produce different kinds of matter. Some atoms exist in their pure state (uncombined with other kinds of atoms), and are called **elements**. A molecule of water is made up of one atom of oxygen and two atoms of hydrogen. Both oxygen and hydrogen are gases. All matter is made up of different atoms, or the same type of atoms. **Figure 7-1** illustrates a progressive breakdown of matter.

Structure of the Atom

The atom itself is made up of small subatomic particles called **electrons**, **protons**, and **neutrons**. The electron is a negatively (-) charged particle. The proton is a positively (+) charged particle. The neutron is a neutral particle with no electrical charge. Protons and neutrons form the center, or nucleus, of the atom. The electrons rotate rapidly around this nucleus. As unlike charges attract each other, the electrons are held in their orbital path. They will not draw in any closer, because the centrifugal force built up by their orbital flight counterbalances the mutual attraction force, **Figure 7-2**.

There can be many different atoms, each with a different number of protons, neutrons, and electrons. Every atom has the same number of electrons as it has protons. Protons and neutrons are alike in any type of atom. The number of neutrons, protons, and electrons, and their arrangement produce different types of matter. A simple atom is that of hydrogen. The hydrogen atom consists of a single neutron and a single proton. A more complex atom is that of copper. This atom consists of 34 neutrons, 29 protons, and 29 electrons, **Figure 7-3**.

Figure 7-1. Breakdown of matter. This can be applied to any substance, solid, liquid, or gas.

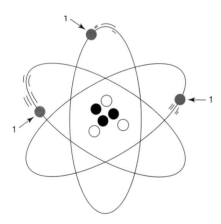

Figure 7-2. Structure of an atom. Electrons, 1, are whirling about the nucleus. Solid dots in the nucleus represent neutrons; white dots are photons.

Positive and Negative Charge Atoms

You will notice in **Figure 7-4** that the electrons move in different size orbits. The inner orbits contain what is referred to as **bound electrons**. The outer orbits contain the **free electrons**. The bound electrons are so named because it is difficult to force them from their orbits. The outer free electrons can be more readily moved from their orbits.

If some of the free electrons are moved out of their orbits, the atom will have more protons than electrons. This will give

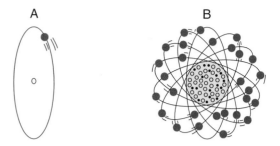

Figure 7-3. Two different atoms. A—A simple hydrogen atom consisting of one proton and one electron. B—The more complex copper atom has 34 neutrons, 29 protons, and 29 electrons.

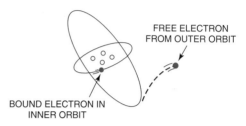

Figure 7-4. Free and bound electrons. A free electron has been knocked from its outer orbit.

the atom a positive charge. If the electrons are returned until they equal the number of protons, the atom will become electrically neutral. If a surplus of electrons are present, the atom is negatively charged. A negatively charged body will repel electrons, while the positively charged body will attract electrons, **Figure 7-5**.

Figure 7-5. Negative and positive charge atoms. Atoms with a negative charge repel electrons. Positive charged atoms attract electrons.

Electrical Current

An electrical **current** is a movement of electrons through a **conductor**, such as a wire. Electrical current may be likened to water flowing through a pipe. The amount of electrons passing any given point in the circuit in one second determines the amount of current flowing. The amount of current flow is measured in **amperes**. Before current will flow, there must be a surplus of electrons at one end of the conductor and a scarcity at the other end.

Current Flow

Figure 7-6 illustrates a schematic of a simple circuit utilizing a battery as the source. Note that the electron flow is from negative to positive. The battery, through chemical action (which will be covered in Chapter 16), has built up a surplus of electrons at the negative post and a lack of electrons at the positive post. As soon as the copper wire conductor is connected to both posts, current will flow from the negative to the positive post.

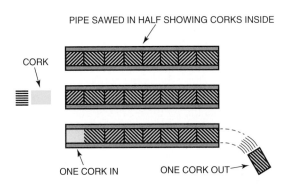

PIPE SAWED IN HALF SHOWING CORKS INSIDE

CORK

ONE CORK IN   ONE CORK OUT

Figure 7-7. Cork (electron) in a pipe (conductor). Even though the cork has just entered the pipe, it causes a chain of pressure that results in a different cork being forced out of the pipe's opposite end.

CONDUCTOR

NEG.   POS.

ELECTROLYTE

⊖ ELECTRON   ⊕ ATOM MINUS ELECTRON   ● NEUTRAL ATOM

Figure 7-6. Current flow in a simple circuit. Electrons move from the negative post through a conductor and on to positive post.

ELECTRON FLOW IN CONDUCTOR

CONDUCTOR

NEG.   POS.

−   +

BATTERY

−   +

A   B

● NEUTRAL ATOM
⊖ ELECTRON
⊕ ATOM MINUS ELECTRONS

Figure 7-8. A—This battery is completely discharged. There is no voltage or current flow. B—Once the battery is charged, normal voltage returns and electrons are massed on the negative side. Current (electrons) flow through the conductor.

On their way from the negative post, the electrons will pass through the lightbulb. As the filament in the bulb creates a resistance to the flow of electrons, it will heat up until it is white hot and glows. After passing through the filament, the electrons continue on to the positive post. When an electron leaves the negative source, this single electron does not speed through the conductor. It strikes an adjacent electron and knocks it from its orbit. This electron strikes its neighbor and knocks another electron from orbit.

To help illustrate this action, imagine placing enough corks in a pipe to fill it from end to end. If you push one cork (electron) into one end of the pipe (conductor), one cork (electron) will pop out the other. As soon as one cork presses on the column of corks, its movement is transmitted through the column. Even though it enters only a small distance, its influence is felt at the other end almost at once. See **Figure 7-7**. In the circuit in **Figure 7-8**, as one electron knocks another out of its orbit, it replaces the one it knocked out.

All automotive electricity is known as **direct current**. Direct current always flows in the same direction. Some automotive systems use **alternating current**. This type of current is normally used in homes and has the ability to change direction.

Voltage

As mentioned earlier, current flow is produced by having a difference in electrical potential, or pressure, at each end of a conductor (one end with a surplus of electrons and other lacking electrons). This pressure differential causes the current to flow. To keep the current flowing, it is necessary to maintain the electrical pressure or, as it is commonly called, **voltage**. This pressure is sometimes called **electromotive force**, or **EMF**.

In the automotive electrical system, initial voltage is produced by a battery, which uses electrochemical action. Operating voltage is produced by an alternator, which uses electromagnetic action. The amount of pressure or voltage is measured in **volts**. The higher the voltage, the more current flow it can create. Modern vehicles use a 12-volt system. Some large trucks have 24-volt systems. Very old cars have 6-volt systems, while some farm and construction equipment use 8-volt systems.

The battery in **Figure 7-8A** is discharged (dead). Both the negative and positive sides have a balanced electron condition. There is no voltage or pressure difference. In **Figure 7-8B**, the battery is charged. The negative side has a great number of surplus electrons, while the positive side has a deficiency. When a wire is connected across the terminals, the voltage will cause current to flow from negative to positive.

Electrical Resistance

When current flows through a conductor, it meets **resistance**. A relatively poor conductor offers greater resistance than a good conductor. As the electrons attempt to flow, they bump into other atoms in the conductor. See **Figure 7-9**. This causes a heating effect. As the conductor heats up, the movement of the atoms becomes more agitated. This further increases the number of collisions. If current flow is increased, the conductor will become hotter and hotter until it will literally burn up.

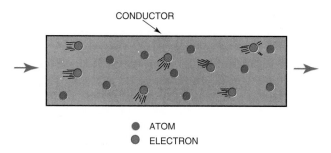

Figure 7-9. As electrons attempt to move through a conductor, they strike atoms. This deflects them and in effect resists their efforts to pass through the conductor.

This heating action is one of the great uses for electricity. Such things as lights, electric burners, and heaters make use of the resistance found in conductors. In order for the wire to reach a specific desired heat, the size and type of conductor and amount of voltage and current flow must be carefully balanced. A large diameter conductor of a given material will offer less resistance than a smaller one. The longer the conductor, the greater its resistance. The amount of resistance in a conductor is measured in **ohms**.

Test Meters

There are several tools which can be used to measure the flow of electricity. You studied the test light in Chapter 5, which can be used to check for the presence of electricity. To measure the rate of current flow in amperes, a gauge called an **ammeter** is used. The ammeter is connected in series with the circuit, **Figure 7-10**. Voltage is determined by using a **voltmeter**. The voltmeter is connected in parallel across the circuit. See **Figure 7-11**. Resistance in ohms is calculated by using an **ohmmeter**. The ohmmeter test leads are connected across the resistance being measured, **Figure 7-12**. These meters are often combined into one tool called a **multimeter**.

Materials Used for Conductors

In order for electrons to flow, they must have a path or conductor. If more than one path is available, current will flow in the path with the least resistance. Because it has a great number of free electrons and is relatively inexpensive, copper is widely used as a conductor. Aluminum has also been used

Figure 7-10. Using an ammeter to check current flow. The ammeter must be connected in series with a circuit.

Figure 7-11. Using a voltmeter to check circuit voltage. Voltmeter is connected in parallel with a circuit.

Figure 7-12. Using an ohmmeter to check load resistance. Note that the circuit is open to prevent damage to the ohmmeter. The ohmmeter has its own source of current and is hooked directly to the load.

as a conductor. The air itself will act as a conductor when voltage is high enough. There are other materials, such as gold and platinum, that are better conductors than copper. Since they are expensive, their use in vehicles is limited. To make certain current flows where desired, the conductors in the vehicle electrical system must be insulated.

Insulators

Any material in which the atoms have more than four electrons in their outer orbit will make a good *insulator*. Since the electrons in the insulator's atoms tend to be bound and will resist being knocked from their orbits, current cannot flow. Glass, ceramics, plastics, rubber, fiber, and paper are excellent insulators. All are used in automotive electrical systems. The wiring itself uses a rubber or plastic coating to prevent the escape of electrons to adjacent metal parts or to other wires. Spark plugs use ceramic insulators. Switches and relays use fiber, rubber, and glass for specific points where insulation is required.

Electrical Circuits

An *electrical circuit* consists of a power source, a unit to be operated, and the necessary wiring to provide a path for electron flow. The circuit must be complete (connected to create a path for current) in order to function. In a **complete circuit**, all of the components and wiring are electrically connected.

A very basic circuit, **Figure 7-13**, consists of a power source (battery), a single unit to be operated (bulb) and connecting wires. The current flows from the negative terminal through the conductor, through the unit, and then on through the second conductor to the positive terminal of the battery. It then passes from the positive terminal to the negative terminal through the inside of the battery.

Figure 7-13. A simple circuit. Current flows from negative to positive through the lamp.

Series Circuit

A **series circuit** consists of one or more electrical devices (sometimes called resistance units or loads) that are wired so that current has but one path to follow. To complete the circuit, the current must pass through each device. As each electrical device impedes the rate of current flow, the total amount of resistance offered by all devices in the circuit will determine the amperage flow. The more units added to a specific circuit, the greater the resistance, with a corresponding reduction in current flow. If amperage flow is checked at several points in a series circuit, all readings will be the same.

Voltage Drop in a Series Circuit

As the available voltage is lowered by each resistance unit, the voltage will drop as the units occur. The voltage may be up to a full rated 12 volts at the battery, but will become progressively lower farther out on the circuit. Study **Figure 7-14**. Notice that the current must pass through one unit to get to another. Also note that the voltage is dropping while the current flow is the same throughout, and that if any one resistance unit is broken or burned out (wire severed), the current cannot flow.

Any type of circuit will have a certain amount of normal *voltage drop*. Even the conductor itself can somewhat impede electron flow. When voltage drop becomes excessive, poor unit operation will result. Voltage drop is controlled by using the proper size wires, ample source voltage, proper insulation, and clean connections.

Figure 7-14. A series circuit. If an ammeter were inserted in the circuit at points B, C, D, and E, all readings would be the same. If a voltmeter were installed across or between points B and A, it would show a voltage drop (less voltage). If connected between points B and D, it would show still more voltage drop.

Parallel Circuit

The **parallel circuit** consists of two or more electrical devices connected in such a way as to allow current flow to pass through all of the devices simultaneously. This eliminates the necessity of the current going through one before reaching the other. Also, if one device burns out, the others will still function.

If you measure the total resistance in a parallel circuit, you would find it to be less than any one device's resistance. You will recall that in the series circuit, the current has to pass through all of the electrical devices, one after the other. This gave a resistance to current movement that was equal to the sum of all the devices. In a parallel circuit, the current has several devices that it can pass through, actually reducing the total resistance in relation to any one device's resistance value.

Equal voltage is applied to all electrical devices in a parallel circuit. The amount of current flow through each device will vary according to its individual resistance, but the total current flowing will equal the sum of the current flowing through all the devices. See **Figure 7-15**.

Figure 7-15. A parallel circuit. Voltage across 1-1, 2-2, and 3-3 would be equal. Current flow in amperes at A, B, and C would depend upon the resistance unit. Current flow at D would equal the sum of current flowing through A, B, and C. Total resistance of A, B, and C would be less than any single one.

Series-Parallel Circuit

In many automotive systems, series and parallel circuits are combined to form a ***series-parallel circuit***. It requires the connecting of three or more electrical devices in a combination series and parallel hookup. To determine the resistance of this circuit, the total resistance of the parallel circuit is added to that of the series portion. Current flow will be determined by the total resistance. Voltage drop will be the drop across the parallel circuit, plus that of any series resistance unit. See **Figure 7-16**.

Figure 7-16. A series-parallel circuit. Units A and D are in series. Units B and C are in parallel.

Vehicle Chassis Can Act as a Ground Wire

A complete circuit requires one wire from the source to the unit and one wire from the unit back to the source. In a vehicle where the body, engine, and/or drive train are made of iron and steel, it is not necessary to have a two wire circuit. The metal structure of the vehicle can act as one of the wires. The battery's negative post is connected to the steel framework of the vehicle. The positive terminal is connected to the various electrical units with an insulated wire. **Figure 7-17** illustrates the frame being used in place of a wire.

Figure 7-17. Using a vehicle frame as one wire in a circuit. The battery and electrical units are grounded to the frame. Electron flow is from the negative (–) battery terminal to the frame, to the headlamp, and back to the battery through the closed switch.

Some older vehicles used positive ground. However, most vehicleís today are negatively grounded. When looking at wiring diagrams, you will see a ***ground*** symbol where the circuit is connected to the vehicle's chassis. This symbol usually indicates that the circuit is grounded to the chassis, and is not physically connected by a separate wire to the battery. See **Figure 7-18**.

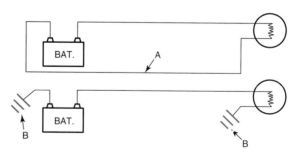

Figure 7-18. Schematic symbol for ground. In the top circuit, wire A, (indicating steel structure of car) has been drawn in. In the lower circuit, ground symbols B have eliminated drawing wire A portion of circuit.

Ohm's Law

All electrical theory is based on ***Ohm's law***. Ohm's Law can be expressed in three different ways:

Amperes equals volts divided by ohms (I = E ÷ R).
Volts equals amperes multiplied by ohms (E = I x R).
Ohms equals volts divided by amperes (R = E ÷ I).

Ohm's law can be used to find any one unknown factor when the other two are known. A handy form in which to remember Ohm's law in its three applications is illustrated in **Figure 7-19**. To use the table in **Figure 7-19**, cover the unknown value and do the appropriate math using the other two values. This will give you the unknown value.

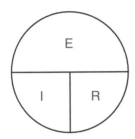

Figure 7-19. Handy form of Ohm's law. Try three combinations using this form. Simply cover the unknown value and compute using the known values.

Magnetism

A great deal remains to be learned about the strange force termed **magnetism**. It is probably best understood by observing some of its effects and powers. One theory regarding magnetism states that electrons rotating about the nucleus contain the essentials of magnetism. These electrons not only rotate about the nucleus, but also spin on their own axes. Even though each electron creates a very weak magnetic field, the electrons are orbiting in so many directions that the fields tend to cancel each other out.

Magnetic Domains

In an unmagnetized material, there are many minute sections in which the atoms line up to produce a magnetic field. As these magnetic domains are scattered through the material in all directions, one domain tends to cancel out the force of the next one.

To magnetize materials such as steel, it is necessary to orient or line up these domains so that most of them point in the same direction. This is done by placing the steel in a strong magnetic field produced by a current passing through a coil of wire (covered later). The domains will grow in size as they move into alignment. This growth involves lining up neighboring atoms so the magnetic effect is increased. Look at **Figure 7-20**.

Lines of Force

The first thing to remember about the term **magnetic lines of force** is that it is used to describe the invisible force involved in magnetism. If a simple bar magnet is placed under a sheet of glass, and fine iron filings are sprinkled on the surface of the glass, the filings will arrange themselves in accordance with the lines of force, **Figure 7-21**.

Figure 7-20. A—Magnetic domains are small and are surrounded by atoms that are not aligned. B—When metal is magnetized, it enlarges the domains and causes them to line up. The combined force creates a strong magnetic field. Note that N and S poles are aligned.

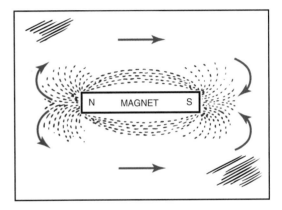

Figure 7-21. Lines of force around a bar magnet. Lines of force leave the N pole and travel along the magnet, then enter the S pole.

The lines of force leave the north pole of the magnet and enter the south pole. They then pass from the south to the north pole through the body of the magnet. All magnetized objects will have north and south **magnetic poles**. Notice the effect produced on the iron filings when a horseshoe magnet is placed under the glass. The glass should be tapped to allow the filings to line up, **Figure 7-22**. You will note that these fine lines of force do not cross. The lines tend to be drawn in as nearly a straight line as possible, but push each other apart at the same time.

Principles of Magnetism

If two bar magnets are shoved together with unlike poles on the approaching ends, they will snap together. If the approaching ends have similar poles, they will repel each other. If forced together, they will snap apart when released. Therefore, we can say that unlike poles attract and like poles repel.

By studying **Figure 7-23**, you will see that the magnetic force lines are leaving the north pole. Remember that these lines tend to draw into as straight a line as possible, yet they will not cross as the lines repel each other. As the two magnets near each other, the force lines leaving the north pole of

Figure 7-22. Lines of force around a horseshoe magnet.

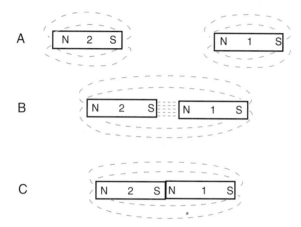

Figure 7-23. Remember that unlike magnetic poles attract. A—Both magnets are apart and the lines of force assume their normal state. B—The magnets have approached each other, causing the lines of force from N pole of magnet No. 1 to enter S pole of magnet No. 2. This draws them together, as in C, and the two magnets act as one long bar magnet.

magnet number one, instead of swinging up and back to its own south pole, leap across the gap to the other closer south pole of magnet number two. The lines leaving the north pole of magnet number two will now swing along both magnets to reach the south pole of magnet number one. As the lines stretch as tightly as possible, the magnets cling tightly to each other. They have, in effect, become one long bar magnet.

When like poles near each other, the magnetic lines entering each pole will repel each other and refuse to cross. This causes each magnet to push away from the other, until the magnetic fields are far enough apart to become too weak to cause further movement. Magnetic lines of force will follow metal more readily than air. If a metal bar is placed across the ends of a horseshoe magnet, the force lines follow the bar from the north pole to the south pole.

Electromagnetism

In the previous sections, you have studied both electricity and magnetism. This section will explain how electricity and

magnetism interact. The relationship of electricity to magnetism must be explained to better understand almost any type of automotive electrical equipment.

Magnetism can be used to create electricity. If a bar magnet is moved in the vicinity of a wire, the magnetic field causes movement of the electrons in the wire. An electric current is created, or **induced**, in the wire. If the wire is wound into a coil and the bar magnet is then moved repeatedly through it, a great amount of electricity can be produced. This is the basic principle of the vehicle alternator.

On the other hand, electricity can be used to create magnetism. If an electric current is moving in a wire, the electrons flowing in the wire create a magnetic field by energizing the electrons around the wire. If the wire is wound into a coil around a metal bar, a much stronger field is created. This device is known as an **electromagnet**. When current is passing through the electromagnet, it is said to be energized. The energized electromagnet will attract any iron or steel objects placed near it. Automotive applications of electromagnets include solenoids, relays, and ignition coils.

Like a bar magnet, the electromagnet has both north and south poles. Unlike the bar magnet, however, the polarity of the magnet can be changed by reversing the direction of current flow. Polarity is important when installing ignition coils, as a coil with reversed polarity will produce a weaker spark.

Basic Automotive Electronics

The following sections provide an explanation of electronic devices as they are applied to automobiles and light trucks. All modern automotive electronics depend on the use of **semiconductors**. Semiconductors are substances that are sometimes conductors and sometimes insulators. Semiconductors make this change at the atomic level; in other words, the atoms themselves change between conducting and insulating. Semiconductor materials are used to make diodes and transistors, which are explained below. Semiconductor devices are small and durable, making them ideal for use in vehicles.

Diodes

Diodes are made of a semiconductor material specially designed to allow current to flow in one direction only. When the current flow reverses and attempts to flow through the diode in the opposite direction, it is stopped. A diode is essentially a one-way check valve for electricity, turning off or on as the semiconductor material changes between being a conductor and an insulator, depending on which way the current tries to flow.

Diode Construction and Operation

The diode is made up of two layers of semiconductor material. One layer is positive, or P material, while the other layer is negative, or N material. See **Figure 7-24**. When current tries to flow in one direction, the boundary layer between the P and N materials changes to act like an insulator and no current can flow. When current tries to flow in the other direction, the boundary layer changes into a conductor and current flows.

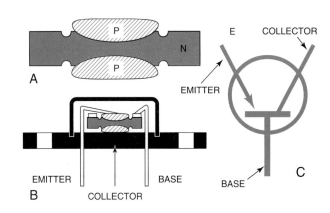

remember is to think of the transistor as two diodes sandwiched around a common base material. The method of combining the two materials determines the polarity of the transistor. The one shown in **Figure 7-25A** would be a PNP type. **Figure 7-25B** illustrates how the transistor connections are made and **Figure 7-25C** shows the conventional wiring symbol.

Figure 7-24. A diode is an electrical unit which will allow electric current to travel through itself in one direction only. A—Diode symbol. B—Diode construction.

Figure 7-25. A—PNP transistor construction. B—Typical transistor connections. C—Wiring schematic symbol for a transistor. (Delco-Remy)

Diodes are used where alternating current (ac) must be rectified (changed) to direct current (dc). They are used in alternators, which charges the battery and operates other vehicle systems. Alternator diodes are arranged to permit the current to leave the alternator in one direction only. Modern alternators contain six diodes to allow all of the alternator output to be processed into direct current. Diodes are also used in air conditioning compressor and other vehicle circuits.

Another type of diode is the **Zener diode**, which will not allow current to flow until a certain voltage is reached. When the triggering voltage is reached, the diode will become a conductor, allowing current to pass. Zener diodes are often used in electronic voltage regulators.

Transistors

A **transistor** is a solid state electronic switching device. A transistor is operated by very low current flows, but can carry heavy current. Transistors are used in almost every part of the modern vehicle. Common parts that have been replaced by the transistor include mechanical relays and switches. Unlike mechanical devices, transistors have no moving parts to wear out, go out of adjustment, or contact points to pit or corrode.

Transistor Construction and Operation

Many modern transistors are so small that they cannot be seen. The thickness of the parts shown is exaggerated for clarity. The transistor is made up of two outer layers of P material with a center section of N material. Other transistors have a center of P material, between two pieces of N material. The three materials are fused together. An easy way to

By connecting wires to the transistor, as shown in **Figure 7-26** and **Figure 7-27**, we find that when a battery is placed in the circuit, current will flow through the transistor in two ways. A small **base** current (about 2% of the total) will pass through the base circuit. When the base current is flowing, the transistor will allow a much heavier **collector** current (98% of the total) to pass through the collector circuit. The two circuits combine, and 100% of the current leaves through the **emitter** circuit. When the base circuit is broken, collector current instantly stops. Most of the transistors in use today require extremely small amounts of current to operate.

By making and breaking the primary circuit with a transistor instead of distributor breaker points, it is possible to increase primary current flow and thus produce higher available voltage at the coil. In addition, there are no physical parts, such as contact points, that can wear out or go out of adjustment. This makes the transistor an excellent switch for operating the ignition system primary circuit, the voltage regulator, and performing other tasks that were formerly done by mechanical relays. Transistors which are designed to carry heavy current loads are called **power transistors**. Some provision is usually made for cooling a power transistor.

Integrated Circuits

Many small transistors can be combined onto a large complex electronic circuit by etching the transistor circuitry on a single piece of semiconductor material. A circuit made in this manner is called an **integrated circuit**, or **IC**. The IC contains resistors, diodes, Zener diodes, and other electronic devices all in a device the size of a dime. A single IC can operate an entire system, such as controlling alternator voltage, making

Figure 7-26. Since no voltage is applied to the transistor's base, current does not flow and the light bulb remains off.

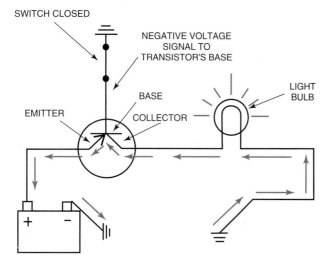

Figure 7-27. Colored arrows indicate current flow through a PNP transistor and circuit when negative voltage is applied to its base. When the transistor is turned on, the circuit is complete, which causes the lightbulb to turn on.

and breaking the ignition primary circuit, or adjusting fuel injector opening. A series of ICs can control the operation of the entire engine and vehicle electrical system.

All modern vehicles have integrated circuits as part of the engine control module. IC's are also used in the vehicle radio and tape/CD player, air bag systems, anti-lock brake system, traction control systems, automatic ride controllers, and any other place where electronic circuitry is used to monitor and control vehicle operation. An IC is often called a **chip**. Chips are used in many electronic devices. The use of integrated circuits is discussed in more detail in Chapter 15.

Summary

The electron theory states that electricity is caused by a flow of electrons through a conductor. There is a shortage of electrons at one end of the conductor and a surplus at the other. Whenever this condition is present, current will flow.

An atom is made of neutrons, protons, and electrons. The electron is a negative charge of electricity, while the proton is positively charged. The neutron is electrically neutral. The free electrons in an atom are those that are relatively easy to take out of orbit. The free electrons are those that cause the current flow.

The pressure that causes current to flow is voltage. The amount of current flowing is measured in amperes. Every conductor will have some resistance to the movement of electrons. The amount of resistance is measured in ohms. Insulators are made of materials containing atoms with very few free electrons. The bound electrons resist current flow.

In order for electricity to flow, it must have a circuit or path that is complete. Three circuits are series, parallel, and series-parallel. The lining up or orienting of the magnetic domains in a material is what causes the material to become magnetized. A magnet is surrounded by lines of force. They leave the magnet at the north pole, and enter the south pole. Like poles repel while unlike poles attract.

Semiconductors are substances that can be conductors or insulators, depending on current flow through them. Semiconductors make this change at the atomic level. A diode is made of two layers of semiconductor material, one positive, one negative. Diodes are one-way check valves for electricity. A transistor is an electronic switching device composed of two layers of P material with one piece of N material in the center. Other transistors have a center of P material, between two pieces of N material. The transistor is operated by changes in current flow through its layers.

An integrated circuit (IC) contains many small transistors, resistors, diodes, Zener diodes, and other electronic devices in a single piece of semiconductor material. An IC can operate a system in a vehicle and a series of ICs can operate the entire vehicle.

Know These Terms

Electron theory	EMF
Negative	Volts
Positive	Resistance
Matter	Ohms
Molecule	Ammeter
Atoms	Voltmeter
Elements	Ohmmeter
Electron	Multimeter
Proton	Insulator
Neutron	Electrical circuit
Bound electrons	Complete circuit
Free electrons	Series circuit
Current	Voltage drop
Conductor	Parallel circuit
Ampere	Series-parallel circuit
Direct current	Ground
Alternating current	Ohm's law
Voltage	Magnetism
Electromotive force	Magnetic lines of force

Magnetic poles

Induced

Electromagnet

Semiconductor

Diode

Zener diode

Transistor

Base

Collector

Emitter

Power transistor

Integrated circuit

IC

Chip

Review Questions—Chapter 7

Do not write in this book. Write your answers on a separate sheet of paper.

1. According to the electron theory, what causes the operation of electrical devices?

2. What causes the action described in the answer to question 1?

3. Atoms can combine to form _____ .

4. What two subatomic particles are at the center of the atom?

5. Technician A says that the electron revolves around the center of the atom. Technician B says that bound electrons are loosely held to the atom.
   Who is right?
   (A) A only.
   (B) B only.
   (C) Both A & B.
   (D) Neither A nor B.

6. If a surplus of electrons are present, the atom becomes _____ charged.

7. Electrical current is a mass movement of electrons through a _____ .

8. Current flow is measured in _____ .
   (A) volts
   (B) amperes
   (C) ohms
   (D) watts

9. Technician A says that current flows from negative to positive. Technician B says that an excess of electrons on one side of a complete circuit will cause current to flow.
   Who is right?
   (A) A only.
   (B) B only.
   (C) Both A & B.
   (D) Neither A nor B.

10. List the voltages of the following systems.
    Modern vehicles:
    Large trucks:
    Very old cars:
    Farm equipment:

11. What is another name for voltage?

12. Resistance to the flow of electricity is measured in _____.

13. Name the instrument used to check each of the following:
    (A) Voltage.
    (B) Amperage.
    (C) Resistance.

14. What material is widely used as a conductor in vehicle electrical systems?
    (A) Copper.
    (B) Lead.
    (C) Glass.
    (D) Gold.

15. In a series circuit, the current must pass through _____ .
    (A) a portion of the electrical devices
    (B) the high resistance electrical devices
    (C) every electrical device in the circuit
    (D) the light units only

16. The total resistance in a parallel circuit is _____ than any one of the electrical devices in the circuit.

17. A series parallel circuit requires at least _____ electrical devices in a combination series and parallel hookup.

18. If a 12-volt circuit is drawing 6 amperes, what is the resistance in the circuit?

19. If a circuit has 3 ohms of resistance, and the system is operated on 12 volts, what is the amperage draw?

20. If a circuit with 12 ohms of resistance is drawing .5 amperes, what is the voltage of the circuit?

21. Unlike magnetic poles _____, like poles _____ .

22. All of the following statements about semiconductors are true, EXCEPT:
    (A) semiconductors are sometimes conductors, and sometimes insulators.
    (B) semiconductors change at the atomic level.
    (C) semiconductors are being replaced with mechanical relays.
    (D) semiconductors are used in diodes and transistors.

23. A Zener diode will permit current to flow when _____ .
    (A) amperage reaches a certain level
    (B) voltage reaches a certain level
    (C) resistance heat reaches a certain level
    (D) Either A or B.

24. All of the transistor current flows through the _____ .
    (A) base
    (B) collector
    (C) emitter
    (D) Both A & C.

25. An integrated circuit contains many small _____ .
    (A) transistors
    (B) diodes
    (C) resistors
    (D) All of the above.

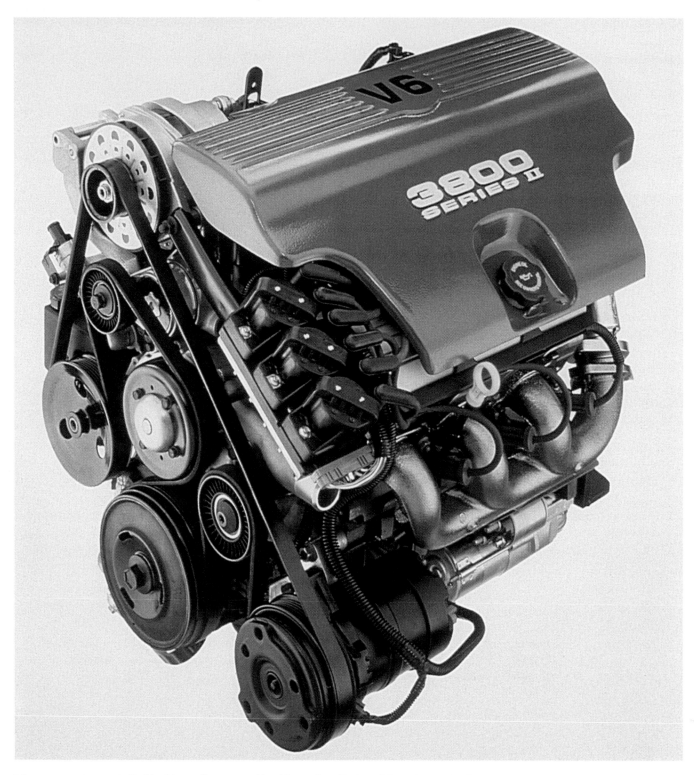

Three computer-controlled ignition coils are used by this engine. Each coil fires the spark plugs in two opposing cylinders. This engine is part of the same family as the one shown at the top of the next page. (General Motors)

8

Ignition Systems

After studying this chapter, you will be able to:
- Explain why battery voltage must be increased.
- Describe the primary circuits of an ignition system.
- Describe the secondary circuits of an ignition system.
- Describe the construction of ignition system components.
- Summarize the basic function and operating principles of ignition system parts.
- List the differences between a contact point and an electronic ignition system.
- Explain the action of spark advance mechanisms.
- Explain how a distributorless ignition system operates.

Chapters 1, 2, and 3 made frequent reference to the use of a spark to ignite the air-fuel mixture. This chapter will provide you with a clear and concise description of the various units in the ignition system. The theory, design, and construction of the parts will be discussed. You will also learn how they are combined to produce, control, and distribute the spark. Before beginning this chapter, be sure that you are familiar with the material in Chapter 7. This will provide you with a basic introduction to electricity and electronics. Such knowledge is essential to understanding ignition systems.

High Voltage Is Necessary

Jumping a spark plug gap requires thousands of volts. However, the vehicle's battery can produce only 12 volts. Since this is not enough voltage to jump across the electrodes of a spark plug in the combustion chamber, a way to raise the voltage must be found. In modern vehicles, the voltage needed at the spark plugs can exceed 60,000 volts. This means that the battery's 12 volts is increased many times. However, if you touch a plug and are shocked, there is little real danger involved. Current, which is the part of electricity that does the actual damage, is very low in an automotive ignition system.

STOP **Warning: Do not confuse vehicle electrical system voltage with the voltage in your home electrical system. Household current at 120 or 240 volts can, and often does, electrocute people. Always treat electricity with caution and respect.**

The ignition system is divided into two separate circuits, which are called the primary and secondary circuits. As you read this chapter, refer to this and other illustrations to learn the names of the various units and where they are used in the primary and secondary circuits, which are shown in **Figure 8-1**. The primary circuit will be covered first.

Figure 8-1. Two different types of ignition systems. A—A conventional contact or breaker point type. B—An electronic ignition system which incorporates a breakerless style distributor. (Sun, Geo)

Primary Circuit

The **primary circuit** consists of the battery, ignition switch, resistor (where used), ignition module or contact points, and coil primary wiring. They are covered in the order that electricity flows through them. The primary circuit voltage is low, operating on the battery's 12 volts. The wiring in this circuit is covered with a thin layer of insulation to prevent short circuits.

Battery

To better understand the operation of the ignition system's primary circuits, we will start at the battery and trace the flow of electricity through the system. The **battery**, **Figure 8-2**, is the source of electrical energy needed to operate the ignition system. The battery stores and produces electricity through chemical action. When it is being charged, it converts electricity into chemical energy. When it is discharging (producing current), the battery converts chemical energy into electricity. See Chapter 16 for more information about batteries. To function properly, the battery must be in condition or **charged**, to produce the highest output of electricity.

Figure 8-2. Typical maintenance free battery construction. Note the use of a charge indicator. (Delco Remy)

Ignition Switch

The primary circuit starts at the battery and flows to the **ignition switch**. The ignition switch is operated by the ignition key. It controls the flow of electricity across the terminals. The ignition switch may have additional terminals that supply electricity to other vehicle systems when the key is turned on. Most ignition switches are installed on the steering column, **Figure 8-3**.

Resistors

Some ignition systems include a **resistor** in their primary circuits. Electricity flows from the ignition switch to the resistor. A simple resistor is shown in **Figure 8-4**. The resistor controls

Figure 8-3. One type of ignition switch mounted on the steering column. Note the various wire connections. (Ford)

Figure 8-4. Simple resistor used in the primary circuit of an ignition system.

the amount of current reaching the coil. The resistor may be either the calibrated resistance wire or the ballast type.

Most resistors simply consist of a calibrated resistance wire built into the wiring harness between the ignition switch and coil. The resistance wire lowers battery voltage to around 9.5 volts during normal engine operation. However, when the engine is started, the coil receives full battery voltage from a bypass wire. The bypass wire supplies the coil with full battery voltage from the ignition switch or starter solenoid while the engine is cranking. When the key is released, the circuit receives its power through the resistance wire.

The ballast resistor, which is used on some vehicles, is a temperature sensitive, variable resistance unit. A ballast resistor is designed to heat up at low engine speeds as more current attempts to flow through the coil. As it heats up, its resistance value increases, causing lower voltage to pass into the coil. As engine speed increases, the duration of current flow lessens. This causes a lowering of temperature. As the temperature drops, the resistor allows the voltage to the coil to increase.

At high speeds, when a hotter spark is needed, the coil receives full battery voltage. The ballast resistor is a coil of nickel-chrome or nichrome wire. The nichrome wire's properties tend to increase or decrease the voltage in direct proportion to the heat of the wire, **Figure 8-5**. Some early transistor ignition systems use two ballast resistors to control coil voltage. From the resistor, the current travels to the coil. Most modern vehicles with electronic ignition do not use a resistor in the ignition circuit. The majority of modern electronic ignition systems use full battery voltage at all times.

Figure 8-5. Ballast resistor principle. A—This Illustrates long pulsations of current passing through a special ballast resistor wire at slow engine speeds. The current heats the special wire and lowers amount of current reaching coil. B—This illustration shows short pulsations at high speeds. This allows wire to cool, and a heavier current to flow to the coil.

Ignition Coil

The primary circuit leads from the ignition switch or resistor to the *ignition coil*. An ignition coil is actually a transformer that is capable of increasing battery voltage to as much as 100,000 volts, although most coils produce about 50,000-60,000 volts. Coils vary in size and shape to meet the demands of different vehicles.

Coil Construction

The coil is constructed with a special laminated iron *core*. Around this central core, many thousands of turns of very fine copper wire are wound. This fine wire is covered by a thin coating of high temperature insulating varnish. One end of the fine wire is connected to the high tension terminal and the other is connected to the primary circuit wire within the coil. All these turns of fine wire form what is called the *secondary winding*.

Several hundred turns of heavier copper wire are wrapped around the secondary coil windings. Each end is connected to a primary circuit terminal on the coil. These windings are also insulated. The turns of heavier wire form the *primary winding*. Study the winding connections in the cutaways shown in **Figure 8-6**.

The core, with both the secondary and primary windings attached, is placed inside a laminated iron shell. The job of the shell is to help concentrate the magnetic lines of force that will be developed by the windings. This entire unit is then placed inside a steel, aluminum, or Bakelite case. In some coil designs, the case is filled with oil or a paraffin-like material. In other designs, the coil windings are encased in heavy plastic.

The coil is sealed to prevent the entrance of dirt or moisture. The primary and secondary coil terminals are carefully sealed to withstand vibration, heat, moisture, and the stresses of high induced voltages. **Figure 8-7** shows some types of coils found on modern vehicles. Although their shapes are different, they all work in the same way.

Figure 8-6. Cutaways of two ignition coils. A—1-High voltage terminal. 2-Winding layers with insulating paper. 3-Coil cap. 4-High voltage connection via spring. 5-Coil case. 6-Mounting bracket. 7-Metal plate jacketing (magnetic). 8-Primary winding, (heavy wire). 9-Secondary winding, (fine wire). 10-Sealing compound. 11-Insulation. 12-Laminated iron core. B—1-Secondary output (+). 2-Secondary output (–). 3-Iron core. 4-Primary winding. 5-Secondary winding. (Mercedes-Benz, Deere & Co.)

Figure 8-7. Several different ignition coils and their construction, A—Remote mounted high energy ignition (HEI) coil. B—Cutaway view of HEI coil construction. C—Cutaway view of a conventional style coil showing its construction. (AC-Delco)

Coil Operation

When the ignition switch is turned on, the current flows through the primary windings of the coil to ground. See **Figure 8-8**. As you learned from Chapter 7, when a current flows through a wire, a *magnetic field* is built up around the conductor. Since there are several hundred turns of wire in the primary windings, a strong magnetic field is produced. This magnetic field surrounds the secondary as well as the primary windings. See **Figure 8-8B**. If there is a quick and clean interruption of current flow on its way to ground after passing through the coil, the magnetic field will *collapse* into the laminated iron core, **Figure 8-8B**.

As the field collapses through the primary winding, the voltage in the primary windings will be increased. This is called *self-induction*, since the primary windings produce its own voltage increase. The voltage induced in the primary windings is about 200 volts, since it consists of only several hundred turns of wire. Self-induction does not affect secondary winding operation, but can cause point arcing on contact point systems.

As the magnetic field collapses, it passes through the secondary winding, producing a tiny current in each turn. The secondary windings possess thousands of turns of wire. Since they are in series, the voltage of each turn of wire is multiplied by the number of turns. This can produce a voltage exceeding 100,000 volts. This is known as *induction*. The high voltage produced by the secondary windings exits the high tension coil terminal and is directed to the spark plugs.

Most coils have primary terminals marked with a (+) and (–). The plus sign indicates positive and the minus indicates negative. The coil must be installed in the primary circuit according to the way the battery is grounded. This alignment of the positive and negative terminals is called *polarity*. If the battery's negative terminal is grounded, the negative terminal of the coil must be connected through the ignition module or distributor to ground as applicable. This is done to ensure the correct polarity at the spark plug.

Actual Coil Output

Even though the voltage output of some coils can exceed 100,000 volts, the coil will only build up enough voltage to produce a spark. This may be as low as 2000 volts at idle on an older vehicle without emission controls, or as high as 60,000 volts on a new vehicle with the leanest possible mixture and under a load. See **Figure 8-9**.

To control the coil's output, most engines have a *distributor*. The job of the distributor it to trigger the coil and to distribute the high voltage current to the right spark plug at the right time.

Methods of Current Interruption

To cause the coil's magnetic field to collapse, the current flow through the primary windings must be interrupted instantly and cleanly with no *flashover* (current jumps or arcs across space) at the point of disconnection. For about 75

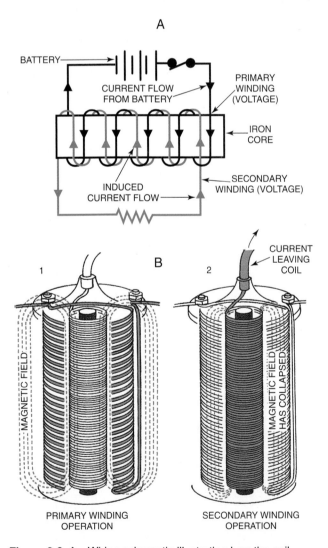

Figure 8-8. A—Wiring schematic illustrating how the coil induces current flow in a secondary coil. B—Ignition coil operaiton. 1-Primary winding. 2-Secondary winding. Current is now leaving the coil on its way to the spark plugs via the distributor. (Deere and Sun Electric)

Figure 8-9. Collapse of primary field. When the primary circuit is broken, the magnetic field will collapse through secondary winding to the core.

years, the primary current flow was controlled by using a set of contact points to break current flow and collapse the coil primary field. Over the last 20 years, contact point systems have been replaced by electronic ignition systems, which uses transistors to operate the primary circuit. Transistor construction and operation were covered in Chapter 7.

Electronic ignitions can produce the high voltage spark needed to fire the leaner mixtures used on modern vehicles. While the old contact point system could produce no more than 20,000 or 30,000 volts, electronic ignition systems allow as much as 100,000 volts to be used. All modern vehicles use ignition systems with electronic primary circuit control. The basic difference between contact point ignition systems and electronic ignition systems is the method employed to interrupt the coil primary circuit.

Contact Points

The **contact points** used on older vehicles were a simple mechanical way of making and breaking the coil primary circuit. Note the contact point set in **Figure 8-10**. The stationary piece is grounded through the distributor contact point mounting plate. This section does not move other than for an initial point adjustment.

The second piece is the movable contact point. It is pivoted on a steel post. A fiber bushing is used as a bearing on the pivot post. A thin steel spring presses the movable contact arm against the stationary unit, causing the two contact points to touch each other. The movable arm is pushed outward by the **distributor cam lobes**, which are turned by the distributor shaft. The cam lobe on the distributor shaft opens and closes the points as it revolves. The number of lobes corresponds to the number of cylinders in the engine.

The cam moves the contact arm through a fiber rubbing block. This block is fastened to the contact arm and rubs against the cam. High temperature lubricant is used on the block to reduce wear. The movable contact arm is insulated so that when the primary lead from the coil is attached to it, the primary circuit will not be grounded unless the contact points are touching, **Figure 8-10**.

Contact Point Dwell

The number of degrees the distributor cam rotates from the time the points close until they open again is called **dwell**, and is sometimes referred to as cam angle. See **Figure 8-11**. Dwell is important as it affects the magnetic buildup of the primary windings. The longer the points are closed, the greater the magnetic buildup. However, too much dwell can result in point arcing and burning. If the dwell is too small, the points will open and collapse the field before it has built up enough voltage to produce a satisfactory spark.

When setting contact point gaps, as the gap is reduced, dwell is increased. When the gap is enlarged, dwell is decreased. The dwell cannot be adjusted on electronic ignition systems, but can be measured as an aid to diagnosis. Always check the manufacturer's specifications for dwell when setting points.

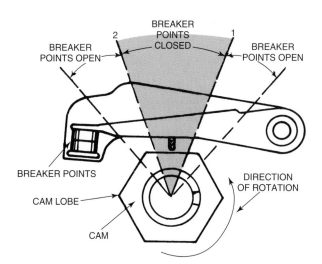

Figure 8-11. These ignition points close at 1 and remain closed as cam rotates to 2. The number of degrees formed by this angle determines dwell.

Condenser

The **condenser**, sometimes called a capacitor, absorbs excess primary current when the contact points are opened. The condenser prevents point arcing and resulting overheating, pitting, and excessive wear. In addition to increasing contact point service life, the condenser allows the coil's magnetic field to collapse quickly, producing a strong, instant spark.

Most condensers are constructed of two sheets of very thin foil separated by two or three layers of insulation. The foil and insulation are wound together into a cylindrical shape.

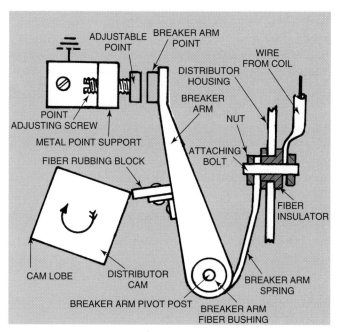

Figure 8-10. Typical contact point construction. Most incorporate the adjustable point into an adjustable support base. Average point gap specifications run around .018″ to .022″ (0.457 mm to 0.559 mm).

The cylinder is then placed in a small metal case and sealed to prevent the entrance of moisture. **Figure 8-12** illustrates the construction of the typical condenser. The close placement of the foil strips creates **capacitance**, or the ability to attract electrons.

When the points are closed, the condenser is inactive as the coil's magnetic field begins to build in strength. When the points open, the magnetic field begins to collapse and voltage in the primary windings increase due to self induction. If a condenser was not used, the voltage in the primary circuit would arc across the points, consuming the coil's energy before the magnetic field passes through the secondary windings.

However, the condenser attracts the excess primary voltage, preventing an arc across the points. By the time the condenser has become fully charged, the points have opened too far for the current to arc. The magnetic field collapses through the secondary windings, producing a quick, strong spark.

Figure 8-12. This condenser unit is hermetically sealed in a metal case. Note how the condenser is attached in the distributor. (AC Delco, Deere & Co.)

Electronic Ignition

The schematic in **Figure 8-13** is a simple electronic ignition circuit. Note that there are no mechanical devices to make and break the circuit. The entire process is done electronically. Current flows from the ignition switch, through the **ignition module**, to the coil. The ignition module contains the electronic components which cause the coil to produce a high voltage spark. Ignition modules process the inputs from other ignition components.

Ignition modules are sometimes installed on the engine firewall or inner fender to protect them from excessive engine heat. Other modules are located in the distributor, installed outside on the distributor body, or as part of the coil assembly. Some typical electronic ignition modules are shown in **Figure 8-14**. Current from the ignition switch enters the mod-

Figure 8-13. Schematic showing power flow through one type of electronic ignition circuit. (Sun Electric Corporation)

ule and passes through a power transistor before reaching the coil, as in **Figure 8-14C**. The power transistor acts like a conductor, allowing full current to flow in the circuit. This begins the build up of the magnetic field in the coil.

When the power transistor is signaled by the triggering device (explained below) and other module circuitry, it becomes an insulator. Since current cannot flow through an insulator, this stops current flow through the coil primary circuit. When current flow stops, the magnetic field collapses, creating the high voltage current in the secondary windings. After the coil collapse is complete, the process is repeated as current flow through the power transistor begins again.

Electronic Triggering Devices

Electronic **triggering devices** send a signal current to the ignition module, which then breaks the primary circuit. The parts of the triggering device do not wear, which gives them a much longer life expectancy than contact points. Since the triggering device does not wear, engine timing does not change. This improves engine performance, emissions output, and reliability. There are three types of triggering devices currently in use:

- Magnetic
- Hall effect
- Optical

Most of the triggering devices are operated by rotation of the distributor shaft. Some triggering devices are installed into or on the engine block and are operated by the rotation of the crankshaft and/or camshaft.

Figure 8-14. A & B—Exploded views of distributor assemblies which house electronic ignition modules. C—Ignition system schematic showing an electronic ignition module. (General Motors & Ford)

Magnetic Pickup

The **magnetic pickup** shown in **Figure 8-15A** is mounted in the distributor and reacts to distributor speed, which is one half of crankshaft speed. This sensor generates alternating current, **Figure 8-15B**. The current produced is small, (about 250 millivolts) but can be read easily by the ignition module. The rotating tooth assembly is called a **reluctor**, or **trigger wheel**. The stationary assembly is called the pickup coil or stator.

An air gap between the rotating and stationary teeth prevents physical contact and eliminates wear. When a tooth of the reluctor aligns with the tooth of the pick-up coil, a voltage signal is sent to the ignition module, which turns the power transistor off and interrupts primary current to the ignition coil, causing it to fire a spark plug.

Some sensors are mounted near the crankshaft, as shown in **Figure 8-15C**. A reluctor wheel is part of the crankshaft and is placed at its midpoint. An air gap also exists

Figure 8-15. Several different magnetic crankshaft position sensors. A—An air gap exists between the reluctor and pickup coil mounted on the distributor. B—An alternating current pattern is produced by this sensor. C—A position sensor and reluctor located at the crankshaft. (Chrysler, Toyota, and Oldsmobile)

between this sensor and the reluctor. When the sensor is in the middle of each slot, the transistor is turned off and interrupts current flow to the ignition coil, causing a spark plug to fire. The air gap is critical on all magnetic sensors and must be set to specifications.

Hall-Effect Switch

The **Hall-effect switch** can be mounted in the distributor or at the crankshaft, **Figure 8-16**. The Hall-effect sensor is a thin wafer of semiconductor material with voltage applied to it constantly. A magnet is located opposite the sensor. There is an air gap between the sensor and magnet.

The magnetic field acts on the sensor until a metal tab, usually called a **shutter**, is placed between the sensor and magnet. This metal tab does not touch the magnet or sensor. When contact between the magnetic field and sensor is interrupted, it causes its output voltage to be reduced. This signals the ignition module to turn the power transistor off. This interrupts primary current to the ignition coil, causing it to fire.

Optical Sensor

The **optical sensor** is usually located in the distributor, as shown in **Figure 8-17A**. The rotor plate, **Figure 8-17B**, has many slits in it through which light passes from the **light emitting diode** (LED) to the **photo sensitive diode** (light receiving). As the rotor plate turns, it interrupts the light beam from the LED to the photo diode. When the photo diode does not detect light, it sends a voltage signal to the ignition module, causing it to fire the coil.

Distributorless Ignition System

The **distributorless ignition system** has no distributor, as seen in the schematic in **Figure 8-18**. It uses a **crankshaft position sensor**, which is a magnetic pickup or Hall-effect switch. The crankshaft sensor is mounted on or in the engine block. Some distributorless systems have a second sensor on the camshaft. The sensor performs the same job that the pickup coil or Hall-effect switch does in the distributor, matching the firing of the spark plug to the piston compression stroke. The advantage of this system is the elimination of the distributor assembly, rotor, and distributor cap.

An electrical signal is generated whenever the crankshaft is rotating and the signal is sent to the ignition module and/or on-board computer. This signal allows the computer to determine the position of each piston in the engine. On systems with crankshaft and camshaft sensors, both sensor readings are used to determine piston position. The sensor input may also be used by the computer to determine engine RPM and the amount of ignition timing advance.

The distributorless ignition creates a high voltage spark using multiple ignition coils. There is one ignition coil for every two cylinders. A four-cylinder version has two coils, a six-cylinder has three coils, and a V-8 uses four coils. Multiple coils must be used since there is no distributor cap and rotor to distribute the spark.

All distributorless ignition coils have two discharge terminals. These terminals are connected to two of the engine spark plugs through conventional resistor plug wires. When

Figure 8-16. A—A magnetic field can act on a Hall-effect sensor. B—When the metal tab, attached to the distributor shaft rotates between the magnet and Hall-effect sensor, the magnetic field is interrupted. The ignition coil sends high voltage to the distributor any time the magnetic field is interrupted. (Robert Bosch)

Figure 8-17. A—An optical crankshaft position sensor uses an LED to send a beam of light to a photo diode through slits in a rotor plate. B—A rotor plate used with the optical sensor. Notice the spacing of the slits. (Nissan)

the coil fires, the spark exits one terminal, travels through the plug wire to fire the plug, and returns to the other coil terminal through the engine block, the other spark plug, and the other plug wire. In effect, the coil fires both plugs at the same time.

The coil wires are arranged so that the coil fires one plug on the top of the compression stroke and the other plug on the top of the exhaust stroke. The plug firing on the top of the exhaust stroke has no effect on the operation of the engine and is often called a **waste spark**. Since it takes very little voltage to jump the spark plug gap on the exhaust stroke, the coil is powerful enough to fire both plugs.

An **integrated direct ignition system** is a variation of the distributorless ignition system. This system uses conductor strips instead of spark plug wires to transfer electricity from the coils to the spark plugs. As in all distributorless systems, each coil serves two spark plugs. See **Figure 8-19**.

Direct Ignition System

A **direct ignition system** is similar to a distributorless ignition system. However, there is one coil for each spark plug in a direct ignition system. Spark plug wires or other conductors are not used between the coils and the plugs. Instead, the coil towers are connected directly to the spark plugs. See **Figure 8-20**.

Primary Circuit Complete

You have now traced the flow of current through the primary system. After going through the control module or contact points, it returns to the battery through the metal parts of the vehicle to which it is grounded. Be sure you understand how each unit works and its relationship to the other parts.

Secondary Circuit

You have seen how the coil produces high voltage current. The job of the **secondary circuit** is to send this current to the proper spark plug at the proper time. The current jumps from the center electrode of the plug to the side, or ground electrode. When it jumps across, it produces a hot spark that ignites the air-fuel mixture. This section explains how this is accomplished.

Spark Plug Construction

All internal combustion gasoline engines have one thing in common: they use spark plugs. The **spark plug** is made up of three major parts: the electrodes, insulator, and shell. See **Figure 8-21**.

Spark Plug Electrodes

The typical modern spark plug may be expected to last from 15,000-30,000 miles (24 000-48 000 km) or more. Some spark plugs can last as long as 100,000 miles (160 000 km). To accomplish this, the plug **electrodes** must be constructed of material that will be resistant to heat, oxidization, and burning. Typical materials used to make spark plug center electrodes include copper and nickel alloy. Platinum, although expensive, is sometimes used. The center electrode is insulated from the rest of the plug by a ceramic insulator. The top terminates in a push-on terminal to which the plug wire may be attached, **Figure 8-21**.

Figure 8-18. A—An electronic distributorless ignition system schematic. B—One possible arrangement of components for a distributorless ignition system. (AC-Delco)

In a modern spark plug there are two electrodes, the center electrode and the side electrode. The space between the two is called the plug *gap*. On older vehicles, the plug gap may be as small as .025″ (0.63 mm). The spark plugs in newer vehicles may require gaps of as much as .095″ (2.41 mm). The majority of plug gaps are between .045″ to .065″ (1.1 to 1.65 mm). Always check the service manual for the exact plug gap.

Electrons will flow more easily from a hot surface to a cooler one. As the center electrode of a spark plug is always

hotter than its side electrode, the plug's center electrode has negative polarity. This ensures a better flow of current from the center electrode. Air is more easily ionized (broken down from a nonconductor to a conductor) near the hotter center electrode. As a result, less voltage is needed to create a spark, which lightens the load on the coil.

In distributorless ignition systems, the waste spark travels from the side electrode to the center electrode. Since the cylinder is not under compression, an extra load is not placed on the coil. However, reverse firing can cause electrode

Figure 8-19. Exploded view of a direct ignition system. This two-coil setup is for use with a four-cylinder engine. (Oldsmobile)

Figure 8-20. Exploded view showing the coil and spark plug arrangement for one cylinder of a V-8 engine with direct ignition. Each plug in this engine has its own coil. (Ford)

damage to certain types of spark plugs. The technician must always make sure that the replacement plugs are designed for use in a distributorless system.

Spark Plug Insulators

Spark plug **insulators** must have special properties. They must resist heat, cold, chemical corrosion, and sudden voltage changes. Insulators must also be resistant to vibration and physical shock. A common material used for making spark plug insulators is aluminum oxide. The aluminum oxide is fired at high temperature to produce a glassy smooth,

dense, and very hard insulator. The length, diameter, and location of the insulator has a direct bearing on the heat range of the particular plug, which is covered later in this chapter. The top end of the insulator is often ribbed, or grooved, to prevent flashover, **Figure 8-21**.

Spark Plug Shells

The center electrode, surrounded by the insulator, is placed in a steel **shell**. The steel shell top is generally crimped over to bear against a seal. The crimping process grips the insulator tightly and also forms a pressure seal at both the top and bottom of the insulator. This prevents combustion leaks and arcing.

Figure 8-21. Cutaway of a spark plug. Study and learn the names of all the parts. (Bosch)

The side electrode is welded to the steel shell. The shell is threaded so it will screw into a threaded hole in the cylinder head. The shell's threaded area will vary in length and thread pattern to conform to the cylinder head in which it is installed. The shell forms a seal with the head by means of a copper or aluminum gasket, or by a beveled edge that wedges against a similar bevel in the cylinder head, **Figure 8-22**. The thread seal is important since this is an area through which a great deal of the plug's heat is transferred to the head metal. The insulator is subjected to tremendous temperatures. In order to prevent burning, it must get rid of surplus heat.

Spark Plug Heat Range

Spark plugs are designed to operate at a certain temperature, neither too hot nor too cold. If a plug runs too cold, it will collect deposits and become **fouled**. If it runs too hot (much above 1,700°F or 967°C), it will cause **preignition** from hot carbon deposits igniting the fuel charge before the plug fires. It is important that the plug extend into the combustion

Figure 8-22. Spark plug thread seals. Not all spark plugs use a gasket for sealing purposes.

chamber just the right amount. The **heat range** is determined by the diameter and length of the insulator as measured from the sealing ring down to the tip, **Figure 8-23**.

Notice in **Figure 8-23** that the heat generated in the insulator must travel up until it can escape through the seal to the shell and then to the head. The longer and thinner the insulator tip, the less efficiently it can transfer heat. As a result, it will run hotter (hot plug). The short, heavy insulator carries heat well and will operate much cooler (cold plug). All engine manufacturers specify heat ranges for the plugs to be used in their engines.

Projected Nose Plugs

One spark plug design extends the electrode tip and insulator further down into the combustion chamber. This **projected nose** places the insulator more directly in the path of the incoming fuel charge, which cools the tip. See **Figure 8-24**. The projected nose plug, due to its long tip, tends to run hot at low engine speeds because the incoming fuel charge is moving slowly and provides little cooling effect. This prevents low speed fouling and assists in producing a spark without excessive voltage from the coil.

At high engine speeds, the insulator temperature is kept from exceeding acceptable limits by the rapid flow of the incoming fuel mixture. The washing effect of the hot escaping exhaust tends to keep the plug clean. The projected nose plug will perform satisfactorily within acceptable temperature limits over a wider vehicle speed and load range. See **Figure 8-25**.

Figure 8-23. A—Cold-to-hot spark plug heat range. B—A cold type, short heat path and a hot type, longer heat path. Study the heat flow through both types. (Champion Spark Plug Company)

Figure 8-24. Projected core nose plug. Not all spark plugs use this type of nose plug.

Resistor Spark Plugs

The spark at the plug electrodes is delivered in two stages. The voltage at the plug's center electrode will rise rapidly until the voltage is sufficient to ionize the gap and cause the plug to fire. This is the first stage. The second stage is longer and follows the first. It is produced by the remaining residual voltage in the coil.

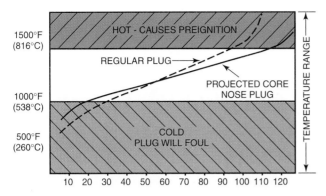

Figure 8-25. Speed/temperature range performance graph.

Figure 8-26. A cutaway view of one type of resistor spark plug. (AC-Delco)

The combustion process takes place during the first stage. The second stage causes radio interference and can cause the plug electrodes to wear. To shorten the second stage, a **resistor** of around 10,000 ohms is placed in the ceramic insulator. The resistor shortens both the stages. It does not require any higher voltage and will lengthen electrode life as well as suppress radio interference. A resistor plug is shown In **Figure 8-26**. **Figure 8-27** illustrates the difference between the spark produced by a standard plug and a resistor type plug. No additional voltage is required for the resistor plug. You have seen how the necessary voltage is produced. How this voltage is delivered to each plug at the proper time will now be covered.

Distributor Cap

High voltage from the coil is carried by an insulated wire to the center terminal of a **distributor cap**. On some vehicles, the coil is installed in the distributor cap. Additional terminals, one per cylinder, will be arranged in a circle around the center terminal. Each one of these will have a heavily insulated wire connecting it with a spark plug. The distributor cap is made of a plastic material, sometimes mica-filled to reduce flashover tendency. The materials used must provide excellent insulation. **Figure 8-28** shows the relation of the distributor cap to the other distributor components.

On the inside of the cup-like cap, the plug terminals have metal (aluminum, brass, etc.) lugs extended down past the cap material. Note the fixed carbon rod used in **Figure 8-29**. The distributor cap shown in **Figure 8-30** contains the coil terminal and a small metal connector or brush which forms the connection between the coil and rotor.

Rotor

To carry the secondary voltage from the center cap terminal to any one side terminal requires what is known as a **rotor**. In cases where the coil is installed in the distributor cap, voltage is discharged directly to the rotor through a metal connector in the cap. The rotor body is made of an insulating material, usually plastic. It is attached to the top of the distributor shaft. Its outer edge has a brass terminal that passes, as it turns, very close to the side terminals. This outer edge terminal is connected to a spring that rubs against the center coil terminal carbon post.

Figure 8-27. Spark plug discharge graph. Notice how the resistor plug reduces undesirable inductive portion of spark.

When current from the coil arrives at the center terminal, it travels down the carbon rod, through the spring, and out to the rotor's outer edge terminal. From this point, it jumps the small gap between the rotor and side terminal and goes on to the plug. A typical rotor is shown in **Figure 8-30**. Jumping the gap between the rotor and distributor cap terminal requires about 3000 extra volts, well within the coil's capacity.

Figure 8-28. A distributor cap for a four-cylinder engine. (Geo)

Figure 8-30. Cutaway view of a distributor cap and rotor. The rotor transfers current from the center terminal to the outer terminal. (Oldsmobile)

Figure 8-29. Cross-sectional view of a distributor cap. Note the carbon rod.

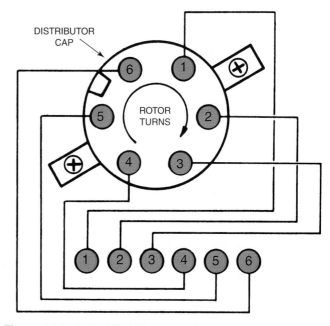

Figure 8-31. A simplified firing order for a six-cylinder engine: 1,2,3,4,5,6. Notice how the plug wires are arranged in the distributor cap to produce this firing order. (Chevrolet)

Spark Plug Wires

The **spark plug wires** carry the high voltage current from the distributor cap to the spark plugs. Spark plug wires are covered with a thick layer of insulation to protect the wire and to reduce the possibility of arcing. Original equipment plug wires contain a built-in resistance to reduce radio interference. Most replacement wires are also resistor types. Resistor wires should always be used in late model vehicles to prevent radio and computer system interference. The plug wires are arranged in distributor cap in that order. Direction of rotor rotation dictates whether a clockwise or counterclockwise order is required, **Figure 8-31**.

The cap, rotor, and wires distribute the spark to each plug at the proper time. It is essential that the plug wires be arranged in the proper sequence. The firing sequence in

Figure 8-31 is never used. An example of a typical firing order (order in which pistons reach TDC on the compression stroke) in a six-cylinder engine is 1, 6, 5, 2, 4, 3.

Ignition Timing and Advance

For correct *ignition timing*, each cylinder should receive a spark at the plug electrodes as the piston nears the top of its compression stroke (a few degrees before TDC). This is made possible by driving the distributor shaft so that it turns at one-half crankshaft speed. The distributor shaft may be turned by one-to-one gearing with the camshaft, which is already turning at one-half of the engine's rotational speed. On some engines using a timing belt, the distributor is driven by the belt.

The distributor shaft gear is timed so that the spark is produced when the cylinder is ready to fire. The rotor will then point toward the cylinder's cap plug terminal. A plug wire is attached to this terminal. The wires are attached to the cap starting at the number one cylinder and following the firing order in the direction of distributor shaft rotation.

As the engine turns, the distributor shaft revolves. Each time the distributor shaft has turned enough to cause the rotor to point to a plug terminal, the ignition system produces a spark. This cycle is repeated over and over. The engine manufacturer specifies timing in regard to the number of degrees before top dead center (TDC) that the number one cylinder should fire. All other cylinders will fire at the same number of degrees before TDC. If the plug fires later than the specified setting, the timing is said to be **retarded**. If the plug fires earlier than specified, the timing is referred to as **advanced**.

Setting Basic Timing

Most older engines, and many newer ones, have timing marks in the form of a line marked on the rim of the vibration damper. Some engines in front-wheel drive vehicles have timing marks on the flywheel. A pointer is attached to the timing cover. When the mark is exactly under the pointer, as in **Figure 8-32**, the engine is ready to fire number one cylinder. The spark will occur with the rotor pointing to the number one cap terminal. The timing is generally set by using a strobe lamp, which is a light that is operated by high voltage surges

from the spark plug wire. See **Figure 8-33**. The strobe lamp is usually referred to simply as a **timing light**.

To time the engine, the timing light pickup is clamped over the number one (or other cylinder as may be specified) plug wire. On most engines, special steps must be taken before setting the initial timing, such as disconnecting the vacuum line to the distributor, or grounding an electrical connector to the computer. On older engines with contact points, the point gap should be set before timing the engine. The engine is then started and operated at idle. Many modern vehicles do not have a provision for setting timing. Check the emissions sticker in the engine compartment before looking for the timing marks.

Figure 8-33. Using a strobe light to time the ignition. Every time the No. 1 plug fires, the strobe light will illuminate timing marks. (General Motors)

Using a Timing Light

The timing light will illuminate the pointer over the vibration damper. The timing is checked by pointing the light at the timing marks. Every time the number one plug fires, the strobe lamp lights. Each time it fires with the damper in the same position in relation to the pointer, the damper timing mark looks as though it were standing still.

To adjust the timing, the distributor clamp is loosened and the distributor is turned by hand. As it is turned, the timing mark will move. When turned in the proper direction, the mark will line up with the pointer. When the two are aligned, the engine is properly timed and the distributor clamp can be tightened. Remember to reconnect any vacuum lines or electrical connectors as applicable.

Magnetic Timing Meter

Many late model engines can be timed with a **magnetic timing meter**. This meter has a timing probe which is installed in a magnetic timing receptacle near the conventional timing marks, such as the one shown in **Figure 8-32**. The timing meter also uses an inductive pickup which clamps over the number one spark plug. Once all connections are made, the engine is started, and timing can be read directly from the meter dial.

Figure 8-32. Typical ignition timing marks have degrees marked before and after top dead center. This setup also incorporates a magnetic timing probe receptacle. (Chrysler)

Timing Advance Mechanisms

As engine speed increases, it is necessary to fire the mixture sooner. If this is not done, the piston would reach TDC and start down before the air-fuel mixture can be properly ignited. To properly fire the air-fuel charge, a device is needed to advance the engine timing (firing more degrees before TDC) as the engine speed increases. It is also necessary to retard the timing to control exhaust emissions and prevent spark knock.

When the engine is at idle, very little advance is necessary. At higher engine speeds, it is necessary to fire the mixture somewhat sooner. To see this concept, look at **Figure 8-34**. In this example, the pressure of a burning fuel charge will end when the piston reaches 23° after TDC. Notice in **Figure 8-34A**, that the combustion cycle must start at 18° before TDC in order to be complete by 23° after TDC. In **Figure 8-34B**, engine speed has tripled. It is now necessary to ignite the charge at 40° before TDC in order to complete combustion by 23° after TDC. The three common methods of advancing the ignition timing are centrifugal advance, vacuum advance, and electronic advance.

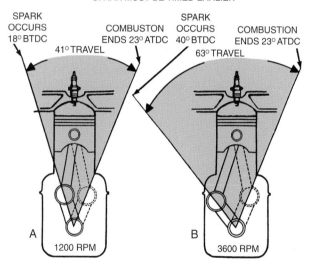

Figure 8-34. As engine speed increases, the spark must be timed sooner. Notice in A that only 41(of crankshaft travel is required while in B, at 3,600 RPM, 63° (is necessary. (Ford)

Centrifugal Advance

One method of advancing the timing is through the use of a **centrifugal advance mechanism**, which is assembled in the distributor shaft. In effect, the distributor shaft is divided into upper and lower parts, with the upper part able to advance in relation to the lower part, **Figures 8-35** and **8-36**. When the distributor shaft turns, it turns the centrifugal unit which turns either the cam (contact point ignition) or the reluctor or shutter (electronic ignition). Centrifugal advance will advance engine timing in relation to engine speed.

Figure 8-35. Two different types of distributor centrifugal advance mechanisms. (Automotive Electric Association)

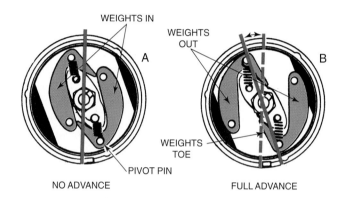

Figure 8-36. Distributor centrifugal advance unit in action. A—The engine is idling and the springs have drawn the weights in. Timing has no advance. B—The engine is running at high speed. Centrifugal force has drawn the weights outward. As they pivot, the weight toe ends force the cam plate to turn, advancing the timing.

When the engine is idling, spring pressure keeps the two weights drawn together and the shaft remains at the position for low speed timing. As the engine speeds up, the weights are drawn out by centrifugal force. As the weights move apart, they force the upper part of the shaft to move in an advance direction in relation to the lower part of the shaft. As the upper part of the shaft is advanced, it causes the triggering device to fire the coil sooner, causing the plugs to fire more degrees before TDC. The faster the engine turns, the farther apart the weights move, until they finally reach the limit of their travel.

As engine speed is decreased, the centrifugal pull on the weights is lessened and the springs pull the weights together, retarding the timing. By calculating the pull of the springs and the size of the weights, it is possible to properly advance the timing over a long RPM range. **Figure 8-36** illustrates how the weights control advance. It is possible to change the amount of centrifugal advance by changing the weights and springs. This should be done very carefully to reduce the chance of engine damage.

Vacuum Advance

It has been found that at the partial throttle open position, additional advance over and above that provided by a centrifugal mechanism is desirable. This is due to the fact that there is high vacuum in the intake manifold when the throttle valve is partially open. This high vacuum draws in less air and fuel. The smaller air-fuel mixture will be compressed less and will burn slower.

To maximize economy from this part of the fuel charge, it is necessary to advance the timing beyond that provided by centrifugal weights. This is provided by the *vacuum advance mechanism*, **Figure 8-37**. Vacuum advance is used to advance the timing in relation to engine load. Any benefit from additional advance applies only to the partial open throttle position. During hard acceleration or wide open throttle operation, there is no manifold vacuum to operate the vacuum advance mechanism.

Figure 8-37. A vacuum advance chart. Notice that part throttle vacuum advance is in addition to regular centrifugal advance.

Vacuum Advance Operation

The electronic pickup or contact points are mounted on a movable plate. This plate can revolve either on a center bushing, or on ball bearings on its outer edge. With either type of plate, an advance in timing may be obtained by turning the plate against distributor shaft rotation. See **Figure 8-38**.

The plate is rotated by means of a vacuum advance diaphragm. This is a stamped steel container with a neoprene-coated cloth diaphragm stretched across the center. One end is airtight and is connected to the carburetor, below or slightly above the closed position of the throttle valve. The other end is open to the atmosphere. The diaphragm has a lever rod attached to its center. The lever rod is connected to the moveable plate. See **Figure 8-38**.

When the throttle valve is partially open, as shown in **Figure 8-38A**, there is high vacuum in the intake manifold. The vacuum pulls the diaphragm back toward the vacuum side. This in turn pulls the plate around and advances the timing. When the throttle is opened, the vacuum drops and the spring draws the diaphragm back toward the distributor. This rotates the moveable plate in the retard direction, **Figure 8-38B**. When the engine is idling, the throttle valve closes below the vacuum advance opening. This removes vacuum pull and the spark will be retarded for idling. The vacuum advance mechanism is constantly moving as vacuum varies with the movement of the throttle valve.

Figure 8-38. Vacuum advance mechanism operation. A—The carburetor throttle valve is in the part throttle position, drawing a heavy vacuum. With a vacuum on the left side, atmospheric pressure forces the diaphragm to the left. The diaphragm link will pull the cam contact plate around and advance the timing. B—When the throttle is opened and vacuum is lowered, the contact plate primary spring will pull the contact plate back and retard the timing. The vacuum spring also controls the limits of advance. (Ford)

The vacuum advance is adjustable on some vehicles. If the vacuum advance is not operating, it can affect engine performance and fuel mileage. On some older vehicles, the vacuum may be ported, or not activated until the throttle is partially opened. See **Figure 8-39**. This is covered in more detail in Chapter 14.

Computer-Controlled Ignition

The triggering device for electronic ignition may be inside the distributor, or it may be a camshaft or crankshaft position sensor. Since the entire spark production process is performed electronically, it follows that the spark timing can also be modified electronically. While many older electronic ignitions use a centrifugal and vacuum advance, most modern systems use the on-board engine control computer to create *electronic advance*.

The latest on-board computers monitor all engine and external variables, such as engine RPM and temperature, engine accessory operation, manifold vacuum, barometric pressure, airflow rate, air temperature, throttle opening, exhaust gas oxygen, transmission gear, vehicle speed, system voltage, and whether the engine is knocking. The computer advances or retards the timing to exactly match the needs of the engine and vehicle. There are no vacuum or

Figure 8-39. This distributor vacuum advance unit utilizes engine vacuum to move the distributor contact plate. (Buick)

centrifugal advance mechanisms on computerized ignition systems. This will be covered in more detail in Chapter 15.

On some systems, the computer contains the ignition module, and controls the coil directly. On other systems the ignition control module is separate, and interacts with the engine control computer. In either case, the amount of advance is set by the computer, and cannot be adjusted.

Summary

Current from the battery flows to the ignition switch. When the switch is turned on, current flows through a resistor to the primary windings in the coil. From the primary coil windings, the current travels to the ignition module or contact points and on to ground where it returns to the battery via the metal parts of the vehicle.

Current flow through the primary windings builds up a magnetic field that surrounds the secondary windings. When the primary ignition control system breaks the primary circuit, the magnetic field around the secondary windings collapses and induces a high voltage in the secondary circuit. The primary circuit can be broken by an ignition module or by contact points. The electronic ignition module is signaled by one of three types of triggering devices.

Direct and integrated direct ignition systems do not use a distributor. Sensors are located on the crankshaft and/or camshaft. These systems use multiple coils. The secondary system consists of the coil secondary winding, distributor cap,

rotor, plug wires, and spark plugs. The plugs must last at least 15,000-30,000 miles and sometimes up to 100,000 miles. Most spark plugs contain a resistor for radio static suppression. The cap and rotor distribute the spark to the right plug. Plug wires are usually resistor types for radio interference suppression.

Initial timing is set by the use of a timing light or timing advance meter. The timing is advanced by vacuum, centrifugal, or electronic means. Computerized ignition has the computer advance the spark after measuring all possible engine and vehicle variables.

Know These Terms

Primary circuit
Battery
Charged
Ignition switch
Resistor
Ignition coil
Core
Secondary winding
Primary winding
Magnetic field
Field Collapse
Self-induction
Induction
Polarity
Distributor
Flashover
Contact points
Distributor cam lobes
Dwell
Condenser
Capacitance
Ignition module
Triggering device
Magnetic pickup
Reluctor
Trigger wheel
Hall-effect switch
Shutter
Optical sensor
Light emitting diode
Photo sensitive diode

Distributorless ignition
    system
Crankshaft position sensor
Waste spark
Integrated direct ignition
    system
Direct ignition system
Secondary circuit
Spark plug
Electrodes
Gap
Insulator
Shell
Fouled
Preignition
Heat range
Projected nose
Resistor
Distributor cap
Rotor
Spark plug wires
Ignition timing
Retarded
Advanced
Timing light
Magnetic timing meter
Centrifugal advance
    mechanism
Vacuum advance
    mechanism
Electronic advance

Review Questions—Chapter 8

Do not write in this book. Write your answers on a separate sheet of paper.

1. What is the maximum voltage that some modern electronic ignition systems can produce?
    (A) 20,000
    (B) 50,000
    (C) 60,000
    (D) 100,000

2. Normal voltage requirements for successful plug firing can range from _____ volts to _____ volts.

3. What is the major difference between electronic and contact point ignition systems?

4. What is the primary job of the ignition coil?
   (A) Convert low voltage to high voltage.
   (B) Convert high voltage to low voltage.
   (C) Reduce primary voltage.
   (D) Reduce secondary voltage.

5. Optical sensors rely on the use of _____ .

6. What causes the electronic ignition module to stop the flow of primary current?
   (A) A signal from the contact points.
   (B) A signal from the triggering device.
   (C) Coil self-induction.
   (D) Coil over-voltage.

7. Dwell is controlled by the _____ .
   (A) vacuum advance
   (B) centrifugal advance
   (C) distributor cap
   (D) None of the above.

8. The magnetic crankshaft sensor generates a(n) _____ that is sent to the ignition module or computer.

9. The ignition control module contains _____ so small that they cannot be seen without a microscope.

10. Where is the power transistor located?
    (A) Pickup coil assembly.
    (B) Ignition module.
    (C) Coil.
    (D) Ignition switch.

11. Triggering devices are operated by rotation of the _____.
    (A) distributor shaft
    (B) crankshaft
    (C) camshaft
    (D) All of the above, depending on the design.

12. What opens and closes the contact points?

13. When the contact point gap is increased, the dwell is _____ .

14. Contact point arcing is prevented by using a _____ .

15. What are the three major parts of the spark plug?

16. If the spark plug heat range is too cold, what could happen?
    (A) Fouling.
    (B) Preignition.
    (C) Detonation.
    (D) Weak spark.

17. A spark plug gap of .025″ (.635 mm) would be found on _____ .
    (A) the newest vehicles
    (B) vehicles with electronic ignition
    (C) older vehicles
    (D) Both A & B.

18. The most common spark plug gaps used today are about _____ .
    (A) .025″ (.635 mm) to .045″ (1.1 mm)
    (B) .045″ (1.1 mm) to .065″ (1.65 mm)
    (C) .065″ (1.65 mm) to .095″ (2.413 mm)
    (D) .095″ (2.413 mm) to .120″ (3.04 mm)

19. Using a resistor spark plug reduces what undesirable condition?
    (A) Static.
    (B) Radio interference.
    (C) Electrode overheating.
    (D) Both A & B.

20. What two components does the center tower of the distributor cap connect?

21. Name the two common methods of advancing the timing in a non-computer controlled ignition system while the engine is operating.

22. All transistor ignition systems use mechanical vacuum and centrifugal advance units. True or False?

23. A six cylinder engine with direct ignition has how many ignition coils?
    (A) 1
    (B) 2
    (C) 3
    (D) 6

24. Take a blank sheet of paper and sketch an electronic ignition system with a magnetic pickup.

25. Take a blank piece of paper and sketch an entire battery ignition (conventional contact point) system on it.

This fuel injected engine uses individual intake ports to channel air to each cylinder. (Ford Motor Co.)

9

Fuel Injection Systems

After studying this chapter, you will be able to:

- Describe the major parts of a gasoline fuel injection system.
- Describe the major parts of a diesel injection system.
- Identify the parts of gasoline and diesel injection systems.
- Summarize the operating principles of gasoline and diesel injection systems.
- Compare the different types of gasoline and diesel injection systems.
- Identify the parts of superchargers and turbochargers.
- Compare supercharger and turbocharger operation.

This chapter covers the principles of gasoline and diesel engine fuel injection. Operating principles and major components of the various types of fuel injection are discussed. Differences and similarities between the major types of fuel injection systems are covered. Studying this chapter will give you the basic information that you need to recognize the different types of fuel injection systems and begin to troubleshoot them.

Providing the Correct Air-Fuel Mixture

As you have learned in the preceding chapters, an engine uses a mixture of air and gasoline or other fuel. This mixture is drawn into the engine by the vacuum formed during the intake stroke. It is then compressed, fired, and exhausted. This cycle is repeated over and over with each crankshaft revolution.

The proportion of air and fuel necessary for proper combustion will vary according to engine speed, load, temperature, and design of the engine. An average mixture for a moderate cruising speed could be 14 to 16 parts of air to 1 part of fuel by weight. For a mixture that produces more power, 12 to 13 parts of air to 1 of fuel might be needed.

Gasoline is 600 times heavier than air. Therefore, if we consider the air-fuel ratio in terms of volume instead of weight, one gallon of gasoline would require around 8999 gallons (34 061 L) of air at an air-fuel ratio of 15 to 1. The relative proportions of gasoline and air by volume are shown in **Figure 9-1**. It is the job of the fuel system to constantly deliver the proper air-fuel mixture to the engine. The mixture and amount must be variable to meet the everchanging needs of the

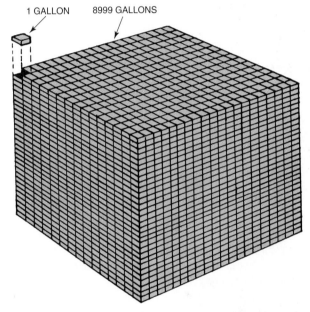

Figure 9-1. The ratio of gasoline to air, by volume. If this were 9000 one gallon cans, 8999 would be filled with air and 1 with gasoline. This is an average fuel mixture ratio.

engine, as well as government requirements for mileage and emissions.

Fuel Injection

Fuel injection is the process of spraying fuel directly into the engine. Fuel is sprayed in a *cone shaped-pattern* for maximum distribution and atomization, **Figure 9-2**. The fuel is always pressurized. The fuel injection system controls the air-fuel mixture by modifying either the system pressure or the opening of the injectors. The spraying action of the injectors *atomizes* the fuel, allowing it to better mix with the air. Although the fuel injection system does not use a carburetor, the system does have a throttle body to control airflow. A throttle body or plate is used on all fuel injection systems.

Direct and Indirect Injection

The pressurized fuel is sprayed through the injector nozzles. Placement of the nozzles is what determines the type of injection. The fuel may be sprayed directly into the cylinder.

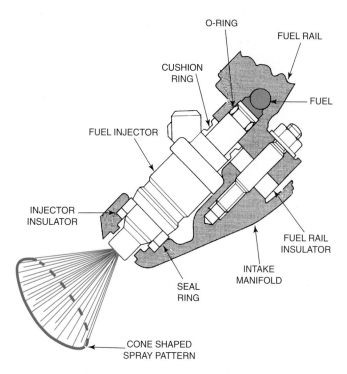

Figure 9-2. An electronic fuel injector produces a "cone" shaped fuel spray pattern in the intake manifold. (Honda Motor Co.)

This is called *direct fuel injection*, and is used in diesel engines and a few older gasoline engines.

The fuel may also be sprayed into the intake manifold just ahead of the intake valve, or into the throttle body at the entrance to the intake manifold. This is called *indirect fuel injection*. Modern gasoline injection systems use the indirect injection method. **Figure 9-3** shows one indirect setup. Note how fuel enters the intake manifold just ahead of the intake valve.

Figure 9-3. Schematic of a computer-controlled electronic fuel injection system. Study the various components and their relationship to the overall system. (AC-Delco)

Mechanical and Electronic Injection

Mechanical fuel injection systems were the first, and, for many years, the only type of fuel injection. These systems used an engine-driven injector pump that distributed pressurized fuel to the injection nozzles. The fuel was then sprayed into the cylinder or into the intake manifold. The pump was precisely timed to the engine intake strokes, in a manner similar to timing an ignition distributor.

The amount of fuel delivered was controlled by the position of the accelerator linkage that in turn actuated a valve or other mechanism within the pump body used to control the amount of fuel injected. A similar system using a fuel rail is discussed in the diesel fuel injection section.

The *electronic fuel injection* system was made possible by the introduction of compact, durable, and inexpensive electronic components and computers for automotive use. Like the mechanical type, the electronic fuel injection system delivers fuel, under pressure, to the injectors. Unlike the mechanical type, however, the electronic system does not use an injector pump. An electric fuel pump provides sufficient pressure to produce the proper injector spray pattern. This pressure can vary with the type of system, from about 7 psi (48.27 kPa) up to around 65 psi (448.1 kPa) for others. The computer controls when the fuel is sprayed into the engine.

Computer-Controlled Electronic Fuel Injection System

The operation of most modern fuel injection systems is sensitive to the oxygen content of the exhaust. The system determines the proper air-fuel ratio and then constantly monitors the engine exhaust to verify the accuracy of the mixture setting. Whenever the exhaust sensor determines the oxygen content is off, the system corrects itself to bring the oxygen content back to proper levels.

The system tries to maintain as nearly a perfect air-fuel mixture as possible. A *stoichiometric* air-fuel mixture will burn very cleanly with a minimum of pollutants. The ideal mixture is 14.7 parts of air to 1 part of fuel by weight. The computer receives signals from sensors that monitor such things as:

- Throttle position.
- Engine RPM.
- Intake air temperature.
- Coolant temperature.
- Intake airflow.
- Intake manifold vacuum.
- Barometric pressure.
- Exhaust gas oxygen.
- Vehicle speed.

Based on the sensor inputs, the computer determines exactly how much fuel is needed. Changes in sensor signals allow the computer to instantly change injector operation to correspond with engine fuel needs. **Figure 9-3** is a schematic of a computer-controlled fuel injection system. Operation of the computer is covered in detail in Chapter 15.

Pulse and Continuous Electronic Fuel Injection

In the electronic injection system, the air-fuel mixture is controlled in one of two ways. The injector may be opened and closed by electrical signals. This is a *pulse fuel injection* system. In the other type of system, the injector is forced open by fuel pressure. Fuel pressure is controlled by an electronic control device, or by an airflow metering valve, depending on the system. This is the *continuous fuel injection* system.

Pulse Fuel Injection

In pulse injection systems, the rate of fuel flow through the injectors remains constant. The total amount of fuel delivered is determined by the length of time the injectors are held open. Systems are classified by the type of timing sequence used and the location of the injectors.

Timed and Non-Timed Pulse Fuel Injection

Some pulse fuel injection systems inject fuel ahead of each valve just before and/or during the intake stroke. Each injector is open for only several milliseconds and is carefully timed to each cylinder intake stroke. This is the *timed fuel injection* system.

The injector is opened by means of an electric solenoid (magnetic winding). When an electrical current is passed through the solenoid winding, it forms a magnetic field that draws the sealing needle off its seat. This admits a stream of fuel for as long as the injector remains energized. The injector must emit an even, smooth stream. Remember, the injector is only open while energized.

Many pulse fuel injection systems do not attempt to precisely time each injector to a specific cylinder intake stroke. Some systems energize half of the injectors all at once, then the other half on an alternating basis. Other systems use two injectors at the entrance to the intake manifold and operate them either at the same time or on an alternating basis. These are called *non-timed fuel injection* systems.

These non-timed injection systems spray fuel into the manifold where it will remain until the intake stroke draws it into the cylinder. The injector sprays fuel at regular intervals. Although such systems might appear poorly designed, in actual use, they work very well.

Injector Pulse Width

Injector *pulse width* refers to the amount of time during which the injector electronic solenoid is energized, causing the injector to open. Pulse width is a measurement of how long the injector is kept open; the wider the pulse width, the longer the injector stays open. The amount of fuel delivered by a given injector depends upon the pulse width. Pulse width is controlled by the computer.

Types of Pulse Fuel Injection Systems

The next section will discuss common fuel injection systems which are typical of the pulse systems now in use. The pulse injection system is usually electronically controlled. Although there are a number of design differences between various pulse fuel injection systems, the operating principles are very similar.

Throttle Body Injection System

The *throttle body injection* system uses an assembly containing one or two fuel injectors. The assembly is mounted at the entrance to the intake manifold and injects fuel ahead of the throttle valve. These systems are also called single-point injection or central fuel injection. A typical throttle body injection system is shown in **Figure 9-4**.

Figure 9-4. This unit will regulate fuel pressure to the injector. Excess pressure opens the regulator valve and extra fuel flows back to the tank. (Cadillac)

The throttle body injection system shown in **Figure 9-5** employs two injectors. Both injectors are mounted on the throttle body directly above the throttle valves. When the engine is running, the injectors are energized alternately. The throttle body mounts on top of the intake manifold much like a carburetor and contains both injectors, throttle valves, idle air control valve, throttle position sensor, and pressure regulator.

In this system, the pump supplies fuel flow. Fuel pressure to the injectors in this system is approximately 10 psi (68.9 kPa). Fuel pressure is controlled by a vacuum-operated regulator. Any excess fuel is returned to the tank. The throttle valves, actuated by the accelerator, determines airflow. The computer, acting on signals from the sensors, determines and constantly adjusts injector pulse width and energizes the injector solenoids accordingly.

Multiport Fuel Injection

When the system uses one injector per cylinder, the individual injector nozzles are located inside the intake manifold or in the cylinder head, close to the intake valve. These systems are called *multiport fuel injection*. Some other names for these systems include multipoint fuel injection, sequential fuel injection (timed), and port fuel injection. Typical multiport injectors are shown in **Figure 9-6**.

A version of the multiport injector system uses one central fuel injector with lines connecting it to outlet nozzles at each intake passage. This system, shown in **Figure 9-7**, combines the simplicity of the single injector with the more precise fuel control of the multiport system.

Figure 9-5. Throttle body with injectors. The injectors are energized at the same time during cranking and alternately during normal engine operation. (Cadillac)

Figure 9-6. One particular multiport fuel injector system arrangement for a four-cylinder engine. Each individual injector is connected to the fuel rail. (Chevrolet)

Control of the multiport system resembles the throttle body fuel injection system. The electric fuel pump supplies fuel and creates fuel system pressure. The fuel pressure regulator controls the system pressure. Movement of the throttle valve determines airflow. The computer receives signals from the sensors and determines proper injector pulse width. The computer constantly controls the injector pulse width to maintain the proper air-fuel ratio.

Pulse Fuel Injection System Components

The typical pulse system can be broken into four basic parts:

- Air induction system.
- Fuel delivery system.
- Engine control computer.
- Electronic sensors.

Figure 9-7. A central, multiport fuel injector layout with individual fuel lines to the poppet nozzles. (Chevrolet)

Air Induction System

The air induction system consists of an *air cleaner assembly*, *throttle body*, and *intake manifold*. Some systems may have a thermostatic air cleaner, which is covered in Chapter 14. The throttle body section contains the *throttle valve*, which is opened and closed by the driver to control the amount of air entering the intake manifold.

On throttle body fuel injection systems, the throttle body also contains the fuel injection components as discussed earlier. The intake manifold forms a closed passageway between the throttle body and the cylinder head. One type of intake manifold, air cleaner, and throttle body is shown in **Figure 9-8**.

Fuel Delivery System

The fuel delivery system provides the fuel which mixes with the air. Pressure is provided by an electric fuel pump. Some systems use two pumps: a low-pressure fuel pump that delivers fuel to another pump, which develops the pressure

Figure 9-8. A dual-injector, throttle body assembly mounted on an intake manifold for a V-8 engine. (General Motors)

needed at the injectors. However, most systems use only one pump.

The fuel delivery system also contains at least one *filter* and in the case of diesel systems, a *water trap* which removes any water from the fuel. A fuel delivery system using a single in-tank pump is shown in **Figure 9-9**. The in-tank electric pump forces fuel from the tank, through a filter, and into the fuel rail.

A

B

Figure 9-9. A—An electronic fuel injection system which uses a fuel pump located in the fuel tank. B—Exploded view of the in-tank, electric fuel pump from illustration A. This pump is a twin turbine, low pressure type. (AC-Delco)

Fuel Injection Pressure Regulators

Pressure in some throttle body fuel injection systems is as low as 7 psi, while some multiport systems can reach 60 psi (55 kPa to 380 kPa) or more. Injection system pressure is controlled by a *pressure regulator*. The regulator controls pressure by bleeding excess fuel back into the fuel inlet line or the fuel tank.

Pressure regulators on multiport fuel injection systems are usually connected by a hose to the intake manifold. A typical pressure regulator is shown in **Figure 9-10**. Note that regulator pressure is controlled by a spring.

Changes in engine load affect intake manifold vacuum, which is then used to modify the fuel pressure setting. High vacuum caused by low engine load allows fuel pressure to unseat the spring easily, keeping fuel pressures low. Low vacuum caused by high engine loads allows the spring to apply full pressure to the fuel return valve, and keep fuel pressures high.

1. COVER ASSEMBLY
2. PRESSURE REGULATOR SPRING
3. VACUUM CONNECTION
4. PRESSURE REGULATOR DIAGPHRAGM
5. BASE
6. FUEL INLET
7. FUEL RETURN
8. PRESSURE REGULATOR SEAT
9. PRESSURE REGULATOR VALVE

Figure 9-10. A small pressure regulator used with a fuel rail setup. (Chevrolet)

Figure 9-11. Fuel injector pressure regulator action with a non-vacuum assist regulator. Note that this unit is factory adjusted and is sealed with a tamper-proof plug. This regulator, like the vacuum assist type in Figure 9-10, will maintain a constant pressure drop across the injectors, regardless of changes in engine speed, load, etc. (OTC Tools)

The pressure regulators used on most throttle body fuel injection systems are operated by spring pressure, **Figure 9-11**. The purpose of all fuel pressure regulators is to maintain a constant fuel pressure at the injectors at all times by controlling fuel flow.

Returnless Fuel Injection Systems

Returnless fuel injection systems do not use a fuel return line between the engine and the tank. Instead, the vehicle's computer adjusts pressure at the injectors by increasing or reducing the output of the electric fuel pump. The computer receives inputs from a fuel pressure sensor located at fuel rail. Based on this input, as well as input from other sensors, the computer applies more or less current to the pump motor. Some returnless systems use a conventional electric fuel pump with a pressure sensor mounted on or near the pump assembly. In these systems, a constant voltage is applied to the fuel pump and the regulator bypasses fuel back to the tank when pressure exceeds specifications. Again, a separate return line is not needed.

Fuel Injectors

The fuel injectors receive fuel from the pump or pumps and pressure regulator and spray it into the intake manifold. Injectors can be part of a throttle body, **Figure 9-12**, or installed in the intake manifold and connected to the fuel system through a *fuel rail*, as in **Figure 9-13**. The fuel rail is a rigid piece of steel tubing that feeds fuel to the injectors. Some systems use flexible hoses to connect the injectors to the fuel rail.

One type of electronic fuel injector is illustrated in **Figure 9-14**. Fuel passes from the fuel rail to the injector. Filter (A) is built into the injector. The fuel moves down through the injector until stopped at the *nozzle* (injector outlet) by the *sealing pintle* (needle) (B). When the injector is energized by the computer, the *solenoid winding* (C) forms a strong magnetic field that attracts the sealing needle armature (D) and draws it upward against spring pressure (E). In this injector, the sealing pintle (B) is lifted about .006″ (0.15 mm.), allowing fuel to spray out. When de-energized, *spring pressure* forces the needle closed. The length of time that the injector remains

Figure 9-13. A—Manifold mounted fuel injectors that are connected to the fuel rail with high pressure fuel hose and clamps. B—Manifold mounted fuel injector that is attached directly to the fuel rail. Note the O-ring seal. (Geo & Buick)

open is very short, usually measured in thousandths of a second.

Cold Start Aids

In addition to the sensors described, the system can incorporate other units for special functions, such as cold starts. Some systems use a *cold start valve* to add extra fuel to the intake manifold when starting a cold engine. The cold start valve is an extra injector which sprays extra fuel into the intake manifold for a temperature controlled period of time.

Figure 9-12. Central fuel system injector setup. Study the layout very carefully. (General Motors)

Figure 9-14. Cutaway view of an electronic fuel injector with an internal integral fuel filter. Study the various parts. Note the intake manifold O-ring seal.

The amount of fuel injected is controlled by a thermal switch which regulates the amount of time that the valve is energized (opened), depending on the engine temperature. The valve will be energized for the maximum amount of time when the engine temperature is below -5°F (-21°C). As ambient temperatures increase, the amount of time that the valve is energized will decrease until an engine temperature of 95°F (35°C) is reached. Above this point, the cold start valve will not be energized.

During cold startup on some systems, an *auxiliary air regulator* admits additional air into the intake manifold to increase the idle speed. The auxiliary air regulator is controlled by a thermostatic switch located in the engine water jacket. At a coolant temperature of -13°F (-25°C), the thermostatic switch allows maximum airflow through the air regulator. As the coolant warms up, the air regulator flow is gradually decreased. When the temperature reaches 140°F (60°C), airflow is completely shut off.

Engine Control Computer

Engine control computers, such as the one shown in **Figure 9-15**, are constructed using many different electronic circuits and components. Size and complexity varies depending upon the system. Modern computers control many other engine systems in addition to the fuel injectors, as shown in **Figure 9-16**. The computer is usually located in a protected area away from engine vibration and heat, and is connected

to the rest of the injection system by means of a sealed wiring harness plug.

The computer receives signals from a number of sensors whenever the engine is running. From this input, the computer evaluates engine fuel needs and adjusts injector pulse width accordingly. Some computers also energize the fuel pump or pumps for 2-5 seconds to pressurize the fuel system before a cold start. Many fuel injection systems do this in place of a cold start valve.

Figure 9-15. A—An ECM (electronic control module) with its PROM chip access cover removed. B—A 30 power magnification of an ECM integrated circuit (IC). (Bosch & AC-Delco)

Electronic Sensors

The electronic *sensors* monitor (check) various engine functions and feed this information to the computer. The number and types of sensors vary with the system. **Figure 9-16** illustrates some of the sensors used by one system. Note that information from the sensors enters the computer where it is processed into commands to the fuel injectors and other engine devices as well as the transmission. Operation of these sensors is discussed in Chapter 15.

Oxygen Sensor

The *oxygen sensor* monitors the amount of oxygen in the engine's exhaust gases. As the oxygen content in the exhaust gases changes, the voltage signal produced by the sensor also changes. The computer uses signals from the oxygen sensor to control the air-fuel mixture. The oxygen sensor is generally mounted in the exhaust manifold. Most electronic fuel injection systems rely on this sensor for much of the engine's operating information, **Figure 9-17**.

Most computer-controlled engines made after 1994 have a second O_2 sensor installed behind the catalytic converter. The purpose of this sensor is to monitor the operation of the catalytic converter. Input from this O_2 sensor, along with the input from other sensors, provides the computer with information about vehicle emissions and the condition of the converter. Computer controls are discussed in more detail in later chapters.

Engine Speed Sensor

The *engine speed sensor* monitors engine RPM. Many speed sensors are mounted in the distributor, **Figure 9-18**, where they obtain a signal from the rotating distributor shaft. In some cases, the ignition coil or Hall-effect switch provides

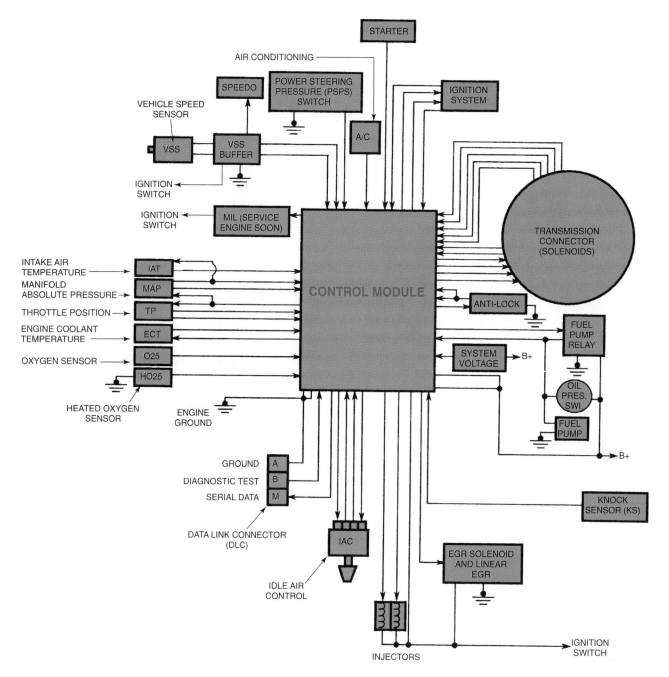

Figure 9-16. An electronic control module (ECM) schematic with various sensors, switches, solenoids, etc., for one particular vehicle. (Chevrolet)

A

Figure 9-17. A—A cutaway view of a non-heated oxygen sensor assembly. The oxygen sensor produces a low voltage signal which sends information on the oxygen content in the exhaust gas to the electronic control module (ECM). B—This shows the oxygen sensor element. The element begins to produce a signal voltage at an operating temperature of 600°F (315°C). The amount of voltage produced depends on the oxygen content in the exhaust gas. (Chevrolet)

the signal to the computer. In other systems, the speed sensor is mounted so that it can monitor crankshaft or camshaft rotation.

These speed sensors also indicate the crankshaft and camshaft position so that the computer can open the injector before the intake valve opens. This information is utilized by the computer (along with other sensor inputs) to help determine injector pulse timing and pulse width.

Throttle Position Sensor

Throttle position is relayed to the computer by the ***throttle position sensor***. Throttle position sensors are installed on

Figure 9-18. A schematic showing an alternating current (AC) signal generator (triggering device) as used with a distributor. Types and construction vary. (OTC Tools)

the throttle body, and are used to monitor the movement of the throttle valve. They can be resistance types, **Figure 9-19**, or transducers, **Figure 9-20**. Resistance sensors contain variable resistance units which send a varying signal to the computer, depending on throttle position. Transducers vary the input signal by creating a magnetic field which is then modified by movement of a metal rod attached to the throttle linkage.

Manifold Vacuum Sensor

Engine load is transmitted to the computer by means of an intake ***manifold vacuum sensor.*** The sensor shown in **Figure 9-21** converts manifold vacuum into a small electrical signal. This input allows the computer to increase fuel supply when the engine is under load and needs a richer mixture, and decrease fuel supply when engine load is light.

Figure 9-19. Throttle position sensor. The throttle shaft is attached to and operates the switch. (Toyota)

Figure 9-20. A cross-sectional view of a transducer type, throttle position sensor (TPS).

1. OUTPUT VOLTAGE
2. REFERENCE VOLTAGE
3. GROUND
4. SEMICONDUCTOR TYPE PRESSURE CONVERTING ELEMENT
5. FILTER
6. INTAKE MANIFOLD PRESSURE (VACUUM)

Figure 9-21. A—This graph illustrates intake manifold pressure (low to high vacuum) in relation to the sensor output voltage. B—A cutaway of a manifold vacuum sensor assembly. (Geo)

Barometric Pressure Sensor

Many injection systems have a sensor to measure the pressure of the outside air, usually called atmospheric or **barometric pressure.** Barometric pressure is compared with manifold vacuum by the computer to more closely monitor engine load. The input of this sensor is important when the vehicle is driven to higher and lower altitudes. This sensor is sometimes combined with the manifold vacuum sensor into a single unit, as in **Figure 9-22.**

Temperature Sensor

Temperature has a great effect on the operation of the fuel injection system. To overcome the tendency of cold fuel to condense into an noncombustible liquid, cold engines must have a richer mixture if they are to run properly. Every injection system has a temperature sensor to measure engine coolant temperature. Many injection systems have an additional sensor to measure the temperature of the incoming air. A typical temperature sensor is shown in **Figure 9-23**.

Airflow Sensor

Some late model fuel injection systems monitor the amount of air entering the engine by using an **airflow sensor**. The computer takes this input and compares it with engine RPM and manifold vacuum to determine the amount of fuel to inject. There are three types of airflow sensors, the heated wire, **Figure 9-24A**, the air valve, **Figure 9-24B**, and the Karmann vortex.

The heated wire sensor uses a resistance wire which extends into the incoming airstream. As the wire heats up, its resistance increases, and the amount of current which flows through it decreases. More airflow carries away more heat, reducing the wire's resistance. Less airflow causes the wire to heat up, increasing resistance and reducing current flow. The computer can read this change in current as changes in airflow. A heated film is sometimes used in place of the wire.

The Karmann vortex system uses a restrictor placed in the air stream. The turbulence caused by this restriction can be translated into a signal to the computer.

The air valve consists of a flap which extends into the incoming airstream. Changes in air movement cause the flap to move, moving the contacts in an electrical resistance unit. Changes in current flow through the resistance unit are read by the computer as changes in airflow.

Speed Density

Most throttle body and some multiport injection systems do not use an airflow sensor. Instead, these systems use a combination of the other sensors described earlier to determine air flow. This method is referred to as **speed density**. The computer receives information from these sensors and controls the injector pulse width, timing and other outputs based on a calculated airflow.

Overall System

The complete electronic fuel injection system is shown in **Figure 9-25**. This is a schematic showing the overall system including sensors, controls, and other components similar to those just discussed. Study **Figure 9-25** and become familiar with the units and the part they play in the overall operation.

Continuous Fuel Injection System

On the continuous injection system, the injectors are always open and fuel pressure is varied to match the fuel flow with the airflow. These systems contain a mechanically operated pressure control valve. This valve increases pressure based on the amount of air flowing into the engine. On later versions of these systems, the fuel pressure is electronically controlled and bases its pressure decisions on inputs from various sensors, **Figure 9-26**.

Figure 9-22. A—A combination atmospheric pressure and manifold absolute pressure sensor. B—An atmospheric pressure sensor. This unit converts atmospheric pressure (air density) into electric signals which are sent to and used by the electronic control module. The ECM processes the signals and adjusts the engine fuel mixture according to altitude. C—This table illustrates how barometric pressure changes will alter the frequency range. (Sun Electric Co. & Ford Motor Co.)

Figure 9-23. One particular type of engine coolant temperature sensor and its electrical schematic. The sensor is a thermistor (a resistor which changes its electrical resistance values in response to heat). Cold engine coolant creates a high resistance, while hot coolant produces a low resistance. (General Motors)

1 Printed board
2 Hybrid circuit. In addition to the resistors of the bridge circuit, it also contains the control circuit for maintaining a constant temperature and the self-cleaning circuit.
3 Inner tube
4 Precision resistor
5 Hot-wire element
6 Temperature-compensation resistor
7 Guard
8 Housing

Figure 9-24. A—An exploded view of a heated (hot) wire airflow meter. B—Potentiometer action as an air meter hinged plate is forced open by airflow. Study the various parts (Robert Bosch)

Figure 9-25. Overall cutaway view of one particular complete electronic fuel (gasoline) injection system schematic. Study it very carefully. 1–Fuel tank. 2–Electric fuel pump. 3–Fuel filter. 4–Fuel rail (distributor pipe). 5–Pressure regulator. 6–Electronic control unit (ECU). 7–Fuel injector. 8–Cold start injector. 9–Idle speed adjusting screw. 10–Throttle position sensor. 11–Throttle plate. 12–Airflow sensor. 13–Relay. 14–Oxygen sensor. 15–Coolant temperature sensor. 16–Thermal time switch. 17–Distributor. 18–Auxiliary air valve. 19–Idle mixture adjustment screw. 20–Battery. 21–Ignition switch. (Bosch)

During engine operation, the continuous fuel injection system feeds atomized fuel from the injectors at all times. The amount will vary to suit engine needs. In most systems, the injectors have a valve or check ball, which is closed by a spring when there is no pressure in the injection system. This keeps fuel from dripping out of the nozzles and causing hard starting conditions when the engine is hot. The continuous system injectors do not use a solenoid to open or close them. Fuel pump pressure forces the spring-loaded injector valve open, allowing fuel to spray into the intake manifold.

The injector is opened at minimum fuel pressure. The injectors in **Figure 9-26** open at 47 psi (324 kPa). As long as the engine is operating, pressure will exceed this amount and fuel will flow continuously from the injector nozzles. The amount of fuel will vary, depending upon system pressure. The injector is designed to atomize fuel properly at any pressure or flow rate. A continuous injector is shown in **Figure 9-27**.

Fuel Flow Control

Air passing into the intake manifold flows through a mechanical airflow sensor, **Figure 9-28**. The sensor utilizes a hinged lever that pivots on a pivot rod. An airflow sensor plate attached to one end of the lever rides up and down in the center of the air venturi, **Figure 9-28A**. A balance weight is used to balance the lever and plate assembly, which allows the sensor plate to "float" in the venturi.

During part load operation, **Figure 9-28B**, airflow has forced the sensor plate to rise a small amount. Note that the fuel distributor control valve installed in the distributor block has been raised somewhat by the lever. The airflow sensor controls the fuel distributor valve. As the engine is accelerated, more and more air flows through the venturi, raising the sensor plate higher and higher. At full load, the sensor plate is raised to its highest position, **Figure 9-28C**. The lever has moved the fuel distributor control valve to the wide open position, permitting maximum fuel flow to the injectors.

Figure 9-26. Schematic of a typical mechanically controlled continuous fuel injection system. Main controls are the airflow sensor and fuel distributor. (Saab)

Figure 9-27. Fuel injector used on a continuous injection system. (Volvo)

In order to provide a constant pressure drop through the fuel distributor metering slots, a pressure regulating valve is used for each injector outlet. The valves are built into the *fuel distributor* housing. The constant pressure drop is needed to keep the amount of fuel injected directly proportional to the size of the metering slot opening. See **Figure 9-29**.

Complete Air-Fuel Control Unit

Figure 9-30 shows the operation of the fuel control plunger. Note that there is pressure in the control chamber above the control plunger. This controlled pressure (around 52.2 psi or 360 kPa) is needed to dampen the sensor plate lever movement so that it will not be overly sensitive to sudden acceleration.

Control Pressure Temperature Regulator

The control pressure temperature regulator maintains a steady pressure in the chamber above the control plunger when the engine is at normal operating temperature. If the engine is started cold, a heating coil causes a bimetallic spring to alter the pressure on the diaphragm valve spring. This changes spring pressure on the diaphragm valve, causing a lowering of control pressure. This allows the sensor plate lever to shove the control plunger farther up, allowing extra fuel to

Figure 9-28. Airflow sensor plate action. As airflow increases through the venturi, the plate is forced upward. The lever arm will raise the control plunger, increasing fuel flow. (Volvo)

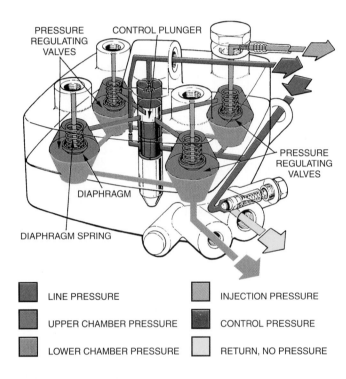

Figure 9-29. Fuel distributor for a mechanically controlled continuous injection system. There is a pressure regulating valve for each injector. (Saab)

flow through the metering slots. As the engine warms, normal fuel pressure is resumed.

Diesel Fuel Injection

Diesel engines are used on some cars and light trucks. The diesel engine uses the heat of compression, instead of a spark plug, to ignite the fuel. **Diesel fuel injection** is similar to gasoline injection, but requires higher injection pressures. Air is drawn into the cylinder and highly compressed. The compression is so high that the compressed air will reach temperatures of 1000°F (538.2°C). At the precise time the piston has completed the compression stroke, diesel fuel is sprayed into the combustion chamber, or an offset **prechamber**, **Figure 9-31**. The intense heat of the compressed air ignites the fuel, and the power stroke follows.

Diesel Fuel

The two common types of diesel fuel are grades 1-D and 2-D. 2-D fuel is specified for most engines operating under normal conditions and within normal temperature ranges. 1-D fuel is used only for extreme cold weather (below 9°F or -7°C) or in very special cases of frequent stop and start driving. Automotive diesel fuel is the same as diesel used in boat engines and construction equipment. However, diesel fuel made for non-highway use is dyed red to prevent its use in automotive diesel engines.

Diesel fuel has a **cetane number**. The cetane number is determined by comparing the burning characteristics of a sample of diesel fuel against a test fuel called cetane. It should not be confused with the **octane** (resistance to knocking) rating of gasoline. It is very important that only clean, fresh, water free diesel fuel be used.

Overall Diesel Fuel System

A schematic of a diesel fuel system layout is shown in **Figure 9-32**. Typical diesel system components include the tank, fuel pump, filter, injection pump, injectors, and the necessary fuel lines. The system in **Figure 9-32** is typical of newer systems that utilize a computer-controlled electronic fuel injection pump.

Water In Fuel Sensor

Some vehicles are equipped with a **water in fuel sensor** that will alert the driver to the fact that water is present in the fuel, **Figure 9-33**. The water may then be drawn off through a valve in the bottom of a water separator. Water is extremely damaging to the injection system.

Fuel Filter

Diesel fuel must be kept clean to avoid injector system trouble. Very small particles are enough to clog injector nozzles or jam the injector. Diesel fuel systems typically use one or more filters to trap dirt and other deposits. One type of diesel fuel filter is shown in **Figure 9-34**.

Diesel Injection Pump

Diesel fuel is injected directly into the cylinder at the top of the compression stroke. Due to the high compression (around 22:1) used in diesel engines, the **diesel injection pump** must be capable of producing high pressures. Injector pump pressures vary greatly depending on the pump and

A

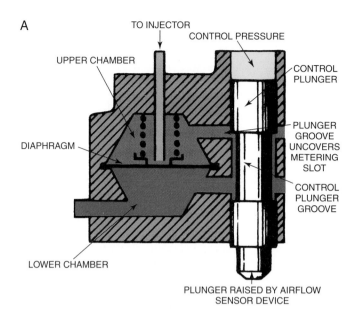

PLUNGER RAISED BY AIRFLOW
SENSOR DEVICE

B

PLUNGER RAISED BY
AIRFLOW SENSOR

PRESSURE REGULATING VALVE, FULL LOAD

LINE PRESSURE

INJECTION PRESSURE

LINE PRESSURE-
0.1 BAR (1.4 PSI)

CONTROL PRESSURE

Figure 9-30. A—Control plunger action-partial engine load condition. The diaphragm has flexed downward increasing fuel flow to the injector. B—Control plunger action-heavy engine load. Diaphragms forced down, increasing fuel flow to injector. (Saab)

Figure 9-31. This Illustration compares diesel fuel direct injection to indirect injection. Note the pre-chamber on the indirect injection engine. (Cummins Engine Co.)

Figure 9-32. An overall view of one particular diesel fuel injection system as used with a V-8 engine. This system incorporates an electronic fuel injection pump equipped with various sensors and solenoids which are controlled by the powertrain control module (PCM). (General Motors)

engine. Pressures can range from 3000-15,000 psi (20 685-103 425 kPa).

How the Injector Pump Produces Pressure

By using a plunger operating in a cylinder, the pump traps fuel ahead of the plunger. When the plunger is forced up, it builds pressure on the fuel. Pressure will be increased to the point at which the injector will open and spray fuel into the engine. **Figure 9-35** shows the essential parts. Note that the shape of the cam influences the timing, quantity of fuel, and the rate of injection—all very important to proper operation. Pumps can use a single plunger for each injector or a single pump (often consisting of two or more opposing plungers) to serve all injectors.

Injector Pump Types

There are a number of injector pump designs. The most commonly used automobile and light truck diesel injector pumps are classified as inline or distributor. Both are mechanical pumps that pressurize the fuel and deliver it to the cylinders at the proper time for each.

Inline Injector Pump

The *inline injector pump* uses a separate cylinder plunger-cam for each cylinder. They are contained in a

Figure 9-33. A—An electronic water in fuel sensor assembly. B—Water in fuel electrical circuit schematic. As the water reaches the sensor probe it closes a switch. This completes an electrical circuit path, which turns on the "water in fuel" lamp on the vehicle instrument panel. (Stanadyne & General Motors)

Figure 9-34. An exploded view of one type of diesel fuel filter assembly. Note the water in fuel sensor and the fuel heater. (General Motors)

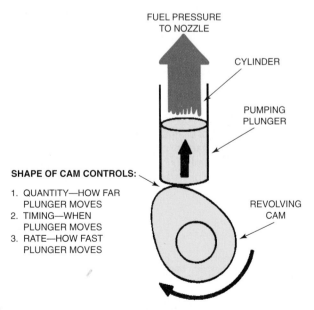

Figure 9-35. The cam operated plunger working in a cylinder, is used to produce pressure in a diesel injector pump. (Deere & Co.)

straight row in a common housing. The cams are part of a common camshaft driven by the engine at one-half engine speed. Drive may be by chain, belt, or gear. Fuel from the fuel pump is fed to all of the plunger assemblies. As the camshaft rotates, each of the plungers are moved up and down in their cylinders.

A single control rack or rail with gear teeth along one side is meshed with each plunger assembly. By moving the control rack, the effective pump action (amount of fuel pumped) of all plungers can be adjusted. A typical inline pump is illustrated in **Figure 9-36**. Study it carefully and note the location of all parts.

Inline Injector Pump Metering Control

Each plunger operates in a separate cylinder or barrel. The top section of the plunger has a wide band or groove cutaway. One edge of the cut forms a helix (spiral shape). The plunger also has a vertical slot reaching from the top of the plunger down into the cutaway area.

The bottom of the plunger is connected, by means of a flange, to the toothed control sleeve that meshes with the **control rack** teeth. When the control rack is moved back and forth, the plunger will rotate in the cylinder. Study the arrangement in **Figure 9-37**. Plunger action during the entire pumping cycle is shown in **Figure 9-38**. Note how fuel is trapped above the plunger in **Figure 9-38B**, forced out of cylinder in **Figure 9-38C**, and how the helix uncovers the port in **Figure 9-38D**, stopping pump action.

Injector Pump Delivery Valve

Fuel flowing from the pump cylinder is forced through a delivery valve on its way to the injector. The fuel flow forces the delivery valve from its seat in **Figure 9-39**. When the helix uncovers the cylinder ports, fuel pressure in the pump cylinder drops instantly. This causes the delivery valve plunger to quickly return to its seat. In so doing, the volume in the delivery line (injector housing, line to injector and delivery valve spring chamber) is suddenly increased by the amount of the delivery valve plunger travel. This increase in volume causes a sudden reduction in delivery line pressure that allows the injector nozzle valve to snap shut quickly and cleanly without dripping. A delivery valve is used on both inline and distributor type pumps.

1. Pressure pipe (injection pipe)	12. Tappet spring	22. Tappet guide screw	33. Setting lever
2. Cap nut	13. Plunger vane	23. Injection pump housing	34. Setting lever stop, also adjustment
3. Pipe union	14. Roller tappet	24. Fuel feed union	screw with full load stop
4. Valve spring	15. Clamping jaws (to grip the pipe	25. Control rod guide bearing and start-	35. Guide lever
5. Seal between pipe union and	unions)	metering stop	36. Diaphragm pin with pressure pin
injection pump housing	16. Suction chamber	26. Camshaft (drive side)	and compensator spring
6. Pressure valve with pressure valve	17. Control bore (feed and return bore)	27. Link stud	37. Diaphragm assembly
holder	18. Control rod	28. Bearing base-plate with gasket and	38. Vacuum line
7. Pressure chamber	19. Pin on control sleeve rotating lever	centering adjustment	39. Diaphragm
8. Plunger ⎫ = forming pump	20. Adjustable clamping piece with	29. Fuel feed pump	40. Guide pin
9. Cylinder ⎬ element	guide groove	30. Journal bearing	41. Air cleaner and oil filler bore
10. Seal	21. Clamp screw	31. Rocker arm	
11. Governor sleeve with steering arm		32. Stop pin for full load stop	

Figure 9-36. Typical diesel engine inline injection pump. Study the cutaway carefully and learn part names. (Mercedes-Benz)

Figure 9-37. Pump plunger construction. When the control rack is moved, the plunger will be forced to rotate by the segmented gear sleeve acting on the plunger flange. (Bosch)

Distributor Type Injection Pump

The *distributor injection pump* is shown in **Figure 9-40**. You will note that a single, double-plunger type pump serves all injector outlets. A single delivery valve is located in the rotor. Study the pump thoroughly and learn all part names.

Pump Charging Cycle

Fuel enters the transfer pump from the inline fuel pump. From the transfer pump, fuel moves through the rotor pas-

sages into the pumping chamber and fuel metering valve area. Excess fuel flows through the transfer pump pressure regulator back to the inlet side.

For fuel to flow through the rotor passages, the rotor must turn far enough to align the rotor passages with the fuel

Figure 9-39. Injector pump fuel delivery valve. This valve produces a sudden drop in injector line pressure as soon as fuel delivery ceases. This helps the injector nozzle valve to close without dripping. (Oldsmobile)

Figure 9-38. Pump plunger action during its entire pumping cycle. Note how the helix has uncovered port in D, stopping fuel delivery even though full plunger lift travel may raise it still higher. (Deere & Co.)

Figure 9-40. Cutaway view of a distributor type injection pump. This pump creates pressure and distributes fuel from a single rotary pump to all injectors. Learn the part names and their relationship to overall pump operation. (Ford)

charging ports. The cam ring is positioned to permit the pump plungers to be forced apart by the fuel entering the chamber. The distance the pump plungers move apart determines how much fuel is delivered. The distance the plungers move apart is controlled by the governor operated metering valve.

Pump Discharge Cycle

When the angled inlet passages no longer line up with the charging ports, fuel is trapped in the pumping chamber. The cam ring rollers have been squeezed inward, forcing the two plungers toward each other. As the plungers are forced together, the trapped fuel is forced past the delivery valve, into the injector line which opens the injector nozzle, spraying fuel into the cylinder.

Pump Fuel Return Circuit

Transfer pump pressure forces fuel through a vent passage in the hydraulic head. Flow through the passage is partially blocked by a wire to prevent excessive flow and pressure loss. Any air from the transfer pump flows, with some fuel, through the vent into the governor linkage compartment and then back to the fuel tank.

Electrical Fuel Shutoff

An electrical *fuel shutoff*, **Figure 9-41**, is used on diesel engines to stop the engine. It rotates the metering valve to the closed position when the shutoff solenoid is de-energized. This stops fuel flow.

Other Pump Features

The pump can also offer a *viscosity compensating valve* that tends to keep the injector pump functioning the same with either light or heavy (or cold) fuels. Fuel delivery timing can be automatically advanced or retarded to compensate for engine speed and/or load changes. A fuel automatic *delivery advance mechanism* is shown in **Figure 9-40**.

Figure 9-41. A—An electrical schematic for a fuel shutoff circuit. B—A distributor type fuel injection pump showing the location of one particular fuel shutoff solenoid. This solenoid is controlled by the powertrain control module (PCM). When energized, it is designed to completely stop the fuel flow into the injection pump. (Chevrolet)

A schematic of the entire fuel system is shown in **Figure 9-42**. Start at the fuel tank and study the various components and their relationship to the overall system.

Diesel Injector Types

Fuel pressure, fuel viscosity, nozzle design, and nozzle condition must all be correct so that a proper spray pattern is formed. There are many different injector designs, but all are a variation of two basic types—*inward opening* and *outward opening*. Study the action of the two nozzle designs in **Figure 9-43**. Diesel spray patterns will vary depending upon engine design.

One type of inward opening injector nozzle is illustrated in **Figure 9-44**. Note the heavy spring (10), keeping the jet needle (12), against its seat. Injection pressure will force fuel down canal (1), to pressure passage (4) where it will act against the shoulder of the jet needle. When fuel pressure reaches a point high enough to overcome spring pressure, the needle will lift off its seat and fuel will be sprayed into the cylinder.

METERING VALVE

GOVERNOR SPRING

HOUSING PRESSURE REGULATOR

VENT WIRE ASSEMBLY

HEAD PRESSURE

CAM RING

TRANSFER PRESSURE TAP HOLE PLUG

BALL CHECK ASSEMBLY

AUTOMATIC ADVANCE MECHANISM

GOVERNOR HOUSING LINE

CHARGING PASSAGE

ROTOR

DELIVERY VALVE

PRESSURE REGULATOR

FILTER

FUEL PUMP

FUEL TANK

TRANSFER PUMP

FILTER

NOZZLE

HIGH PRESSURE DISCHARGE CIRCUIT

TRANSFER PUMP PRESSURE CIRCUIT

HOUSING PRESSURE CIRCUIT

INLET PRESSURE AND RETURN OIL CIRCUIT

Figure 9-42. A schematic of a diesel fuel system employing a rotary type injector pump. (General Motors)

Glow Plugs and Intake Air Heaters

To aid in igniting the compressed air-fuel mix during cold starting, diesel engines use **glow plugs** and **intake air heaters**. The glow plug is an electrically operated device that protrudes into the precombustion chamber. When energized, the glow plug tip heats to a dull red. The swirling, highly compressed air-fuel mixture is heated by the glow plug tip. This additional heat helps the engine to start by causing the mixture to ignite more readily.

On older vehicles, the glow plugs must be turned on by the vehicle operator and allowed to heat the combustion chamber for several seconds before the engine can be started. On later engines, the glow plugs are turned on and off automatically. Under most starting conditions, the plugs are energized for a very short period. The engine can be started in seconds after the key is turned on, **Figure 9-45**. The glow plugs may still be energized for a very short while following engine startup.

Intake air heaters warm the air as it passes through on its way to the intake manifold. The heater element is a wire mesh that is electrically heated. The computer energizes the heater element before cranking, **Figure 9-46**.

Superchargers and Turbochargers

The purpose of superchargers and turbochargers is to force more of the air-fuel mixture into the engine cylinders. This extra air and fuel results in more power output. Superchargers are driven by a belt or chain from the engine crankshaft. Turbochargers are a type of supercharger that is driven by the engine exhaust.

Superchargers

A **supercharger** assembly is shown in **Figure 9-47**. It consists of a drive belt, drive and driven gears, and a centrifugal **compressor wheel**. The belt drives the gear and compressor wheel. The compressor wheel pumps air into the engine. Superchargers are installed on top of the intake manifold on V-type engines, and on the side of inline engines.

Supercharger speed is dependent on engine speed and is most efficient at higher engine speeds. Another type of

Figure 9-43 Diesel fuel injector nozzles are of either inward opening or outward opening design. (Deere & Co.)

NOZZLE HOLDER WITH PINTLE NOZZLE.

1 Fuel from injection pump
2 Filter
3 Valve-holder body
4 Pressure passage
5 Intermediate sleeve
6 Nozzle retaining nut

7 Union nut for pressure line
8 Leakage-fuel connection
9 Pressure adjusting shim
10 Pressure spring
11 Pressure spindle
12 Pintle nozzle

Figure 9-44. Cutaway view of an inward opening, diesel fuel injector. (Robert Bosch)

Figure 9-45. Diesel engine glow plug. The glow plug heats the air-fuel mixture in a precombustion chamber to assist in cold engine startup and initial driveaway. Note how the glow plug tip protrudes into the precombustion chamber. Injector spray enters this area. (Mazda)

Figure 9-46. An electrical schematic for an intake air heater circuit. This unit takes the place of glow plugs to aid in cold starting. (Dodge)

supercharger is a positive displacement vane type and works like a vane oil pump. Its operational speed is also dependent on engine speed.

Turbochargers

Turbochargers use the exhaust gases to drive a *turbine wheel*. It is connected to the compressor wheel by a shaft, **Figure 9-48**. Shaft speeds may approach 150,000 RPM. The shaft is supported by ball or tapered roller bearings that are pressure lubricated and cooled by the engine oiling system.

The turbine wheel is installed after the exhaust manifold. Exhaust gases leave the engine at high speed, and spin the turbine wheel. The turbine wheel spins the compressor wheel, which is connected to the intake manifold passages after the air cleaner and before the intake valve. The compressor wheel forces more of the air-fuel mixture into the engine.

Turbocharger Boost Control

If turbocharger **boost pressure** (pressure delivered to the intake manifold) becomes too high, it can cause detonation and other engine damage. Boost pressure is controlled by a **waste gate**, **Figure 9-49**. The waste gate controls the engine exhaust gas flow.

Figure 9-47. A—A V-6 engine that uses a belt-driven, positive displacement supercharger. The supercharger contains two counter-rotating rotors that are connected by spur gears. They produce a boost pressure of 7 psi -11 psi (48.3 kPa - 75.8 kPa). The unit is lubricated with its own supply of synthetic oil. It is sealed for life, and does not require service. B—Supercharger rotor positions. 1–Taking air in. 2, 3 and 4–Compressing the air. 5–Forcing the air out. The air is pumped out four times per rotor revolution. (Pontiac and Toyota)

Figure 9-49. A cross-sectional view of a turbocharger which incorporates a mechanically operated waste gate. When a preset boost pressure is reached and exceeded by the turbocharger, the waste gate valve will overcome spring pressure in the actuator, allowing it to open and vent off excessive exhaust gas pressure. Study the air and exhaust flow paths.

Figure 9-48. An exhaust gas driven turbocharger. A—Cutaway view of an exhaust gas driven turbocharger unit. B—A cutaway view of the turbocharger bearings, oil, and coolant passages. An intercooler is used to cool the incoming air, helping to create a denser air/fuel mixture. (Toyota)

The waste gate is operated mechanically or by a vacuum diaphragm, which will move when the intake manifold pressure rises above a set level. When the pressure exceeds this level, the diaphragm opens the waste gate. When the waste gate is open, exhaust gas is permitted to bypass the turbine wheel. This causes the wheel to slow down, reducing the turbocharger boost pressure to a more suitable level.

Due to the increased air-fuel mixture delivered to the engine (with a corresponding increase in pressure), it is essential that the engine compression be lower than that of a non-supercharged engine. Modern supercharged and turbocharged engines have electronic controls which can adjust the ignition timing to prevent detonation.

Summary

Gasoline fuel injection systems, both electronic and mechanically controlled systems, have completely replaced the carburetor on the newest vehicles. Some systems use pulse injection while others employ continuous injection. The major types of pulsed injection systems are the throttle body injection system, which takes the place formerly occupied by the carburetor; and the multiport injection system which uses one injector per cylinder. Fuel injection systems provide extremely accurate control of the air-fuel mixture thus increasing engine efficiency while at the same time reducing emission levels.

Older fuel injection systems were controlled by mechanical linkage. The new injection systems are controlled by the engine control computer based on inputs from sensors.

Diesel engines are highly efficient and are available in trucks and some cars. They use high pressure injector pumps and inject fuel directly into the precombustion chamber.

Superchargers and turbochargers are simply air pumps which force more of the air-fuel mixture into the engine cylinders to create extra power. Superchargers are driven by a belt or chain from the engine crankshaft and are always turning in relation to engine speed.

Turbochargers are a type of supercharger that is driven by the engine exhaust. The turbocharger has no effect until engine speed provides enough exhaust flow to spin the turbine. A waste gate prevents excessive boost pressure in the intake manifold.

Know These Terms

Fuel injection	Pulse width
Cone shaped pattern	Throttle body fuel injection
Atomizes	Multiport fuel injection
Direct fuel injection	Air cleaner assembly
Indirect fuel injection	Throttle body
Mechanical fuel injection	Intake manifold
Electronic fuel injection	Throttle valve
Stoichiometric	Filter
Pulse fuel injection	Water trap
Continuous fuel injection	Pressure regulator
Timed fuel injection	Returnless fuel injection
Non-timed fuel injection	systems

Fuel rail	Octane
Nozzle	Water in fuel sensor
Sealing pintle	Diesel injection pump
Solenoid winding	Inline injector pump
Spring pressure	Control rack
Cold start valve	Distributor injection pump
Auxiliary air regulator	Fuel shutoff
Engine control computer	Viscosity compensator valve
Sensors	Delivery advance
Oxygen sensor	mechanism
Engine speed sensor	Inward opening injectors
Throttle position sensor	Outward opening injectors
Manifold vacuum sensor	Glow plugs
Barometric pressure	Intake air heaters
Airflow sensor	Supercharger
Speed density	Compressor wheel
Fuel distributor	Turbocharger
Diesel fuel injection	Turbine wheel
Prechamber	Boost pressure
Cetane number	Waste gate

Review Questions—Chapter 9

Do not write in this book. Write your answers on a separate sheet of paper.

1. Technician A says that most gasoline fuel injection systems inject the fuel directly into the cylinders. Technician B says that most gasoline injection systems are continuous flow types.

   Who is right?

   (A)   A only.

   (B)   B only.

   (C)   Both A & B.

   (D)   Neither A nor B.

2. Gasoline fuel injection systems employing a mechanical pump operate on the _____ flow principle.

   (A)   continuous

   (B)   pulse

   (C)   rotating

   (D)   timed

3. The fuel injector solenoid is energized by the _____ .

   (A)   ignition switch

   (B)   computer

   (C)   airflow sensor

   (D)   ignition module

4. The two kinds of electronic gasoline injection systems are _____ and _____ .

5. Technician A says that central fuel injection systems have one injector for each cylinder. Technician B says that electronic injection systems use an electric fuel pump to produce the needed injector pressure. Who is right?

(A) A only.

(B) B only.

(C) Both A & B.

(D) Neither A nor B.

6. Mechanical injection system injectors are opened by _____ .

(A) electric solenoids

(B) airflow

(C) fuel pressure

(D) compression pressure

7. In the continuous flow fuel injection system, basic air-fuel ratio control is provided by a(n) _____ sensor.

(A) pressure

(B) engine speed

(C) manifold vacuum

(D) airflow

8. List the four basic parts of the pulse fuel injection system.

9. Electronic fuel injection systems can use either:

(A) one injector per cylinder.

(B) two injectors for the entire engine.

(C) one injector for the entire engine.

(D) All of the above.

10. On some fuel pressure regulators, the spring loaded valve is assisted by _____.

11. The cold start injector supplies _____ for cold starts.

12. All of the following statements about gasoline fuel injectors are true, EXCEPT:

(A) injectors spray gasoline into the intake manifold.

(B) injectors can be part of a central fuel system assembly.

(C) injectors are operated by manifold vacuum.

(D) injectors can be installed in the intake manifold.

13. Multiport injectors are connected to the fuel pump by a _____ .

14. Technician A says that all gasoline injection systems use higher pressures than diesel injection systems. Technician B says that some gasoline injection systems use higher pressures than diesel injection systems. Who is right?

(A) A only.

(B) B only.

(C) Both A & B.

(D) Neither A nor B.

15. All of the following statements about diesel injectors are true, EXCEPT:

(A) diesel injectors are operated by fuel pressure.

(B) diesel injectors inject fuel directly into the cylinder.

(C) diesel injectors are closed electrically.

(D) diesel injectors are closed by spring pressure.

16. Glow plugs are used to _____ .

(A) open the injectors

(B) heat the injectors

(C) assist in cold starting

(D) assist in hot starting

17. Diesel injection pumps are of two general types. Name them.

18. Technician A says that diesel injection systems feed some fuel from the injector nozzle at all times. Technician B says that some diesel injection pumps inject fuel at any time.

Who is right?

(A) A only.

(B) B only.

(C) Both A & B.

(D) Neither A nor B.

19. Some diesel injection pumps use a control rack to adjust fuel flow. The rack is used to rotate the _____ .

20. Rewrite the following sentence, leaving out the wrong words. "Diesel engines use a glow plug that protrudes into the cylinder, precombustion chamber, crankcase."

21. The function of the delivery valve is to _____ .

(A) prevent system leaks

(B) regulate system pressure

(C) inject fuel into the hollow control rack

(D) None of the above.

22. Diesel injector nozzle designs are of two general types. Name them.

23. Superchargers are driven by the crankshaft through _____ .

(A) a chain

(B) a belt

(C) gears

(D) Both A & B.

24. Maximum turbocharger speed is around _____ RPM.

(A) 5000

(B) 150,000

(C) 20,000

(D) 2000

25. The turbocharger waste gate is operated by _____ .

(A) a diaphragm

(B) manifold pressure

(C) a detonation sensor

(D) Both A & B.

10

Fuel Supply and Carburetors

After studying this chapter, you will be able to:
- Describe the components of the fuel supply system.
- Explain the basic function of the fuel pump.
- Describe the major parts of the fuel pump.
- Identify the basic parts of a carburetor.
- Summarize carburetor operating principles.
- List the seven basic carburetor circuits.

This chapter will cover the methods by which fuel is transferred from the fuel tank to the engine, and the principles of carburetion. Modern engines must be provided with an air-fuel mixture in the right proportions for proper engine operation, and to meet mileage and emission requirements. In Chapter 9 we discussed the need to atomize and mix gasoline for proper combustion and how this was accomplished by the fuel injection system. This chapter will describe how gasoline is atomized and mixed with air by the carburetor. The fuel supply system will also be discussed in this chapter.

Fuel Supply System

If fuel does not reach the carburetor and fuel injection system, the vehicle will not run. Therefore, the fuel supply system is vitally important to the operation of the vehicle.

Fuel Tank

The *fuel tank* has been located in just about every conceivable spot on a vehicle—in the rear, behind the seats, even in the front. An ideal location is a spot where the tank is protected from flying stones and debris, where it will not bottom on the road, and where it will not easily rupture in the event of an accident. The overall design features of a car often dictate the location of the tank.

The tank is usually constructed of thin sheet steel and coated with a lead-tin alloy to protect against rusting. Tanks can also be made of aluminum or plastic such as polyethylene. Capacity can be anywhere from 9 to 26 gallons (34 to 98 L). Internal baffles are arranged to prevent sloshing, **Figure 10-1**. A filler neck, reaching to a convenient spot, is attached either directly or by a neoprene hose. The filler cap normally seals the tank, but does have a vacuum and pressure relief valve to allow air to either enter or leave the tank, in the event the emission control vent lines were to become inoperative.

Figure 10-1. Construction of a typical fuel tank.

The tank is vented to a charcoal canister (covered in Chapter 14) which traps gasoline vapors before they enter the atmosphere. The tank must be vented to allow fuel to be drawn out. The tank is securely strapped into place. It is often protected on the outside by an application of undercoating material.

 Warning: A fuel tank, even when apparently empty, is as dangerous as a bomb! Keep all sparks, heat, and open flames away from the tank.

Gasoline Pickup Tube

A *pickup tube* enters the tank to draw off fuel for the engine. This tube can enter from the top, side, or bottom. The tube end is generally located about one-half inch from the tank bottom. This allows considerable water and sediment to form before being drawn into the pickup tube.

Several types of filters are used on the ends of pickup tubes, including plastic, metal mesh, and fiberglass. An effort is made to design screens that will not clog while filtering out sediment and most water, **Figure 10-2**.

Water Forms in Tank

When a fuel tank is only partially full, water tends to form within the tank. Any moisture within the tank condenses on the

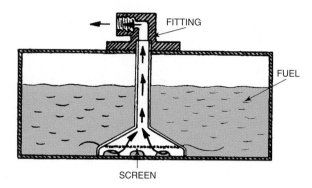

Figure 10-2. Fuel pickup pipe. Notice that the pickup screen is above the bottom of the tank.

tank wall, then runs under the fuel. Since water is heavier than gasoline or diesel fuel, it will remain at the bottom where it will fail to evaporate as it is not exposed to the air. Water buildup is a slow process, but can eventually be drawn into other parts of the fuel system or can cause the tank to rust out, **Figure 10-3**. In cold weather, water in the fuel system can cause the fuel lines to freeze.

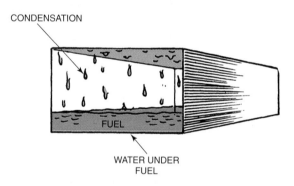

Figure 10-3. Fuel tank showing condensation when the fuel level is low.

Tank Gauge Unit

The fuel tank contains a float that is attached to a resistance device similar to that used in an electric oil pressure sender. In this case, the up-and-down travel of the float causes the resistance to vary, depending on the depth to which the tank is filled. This is the *tank gauge unit*.

Most gauges are designed to read empty when one or two gallons of fuel are left in the tank. This is a concession to human nature as some people are inclined to drive until the gauge does read empty. **Figure 10-4** illustrates a typical tank sender and bimetallic receiver. When the float drops, current flow to ground through the bimetal wire coil will be less, because it must travel through more resistance wire. This cools the bimetallic hairpin and pulls it together. When the tank is filled, the contact slides up, cutting out resistance and current flow increases. This heats the hairpin and causes it to separate.

Figure 10-4 A—Fuel gauge operation with tank empty. When the tank is empty, the hairpin expands, causing the needle to move toward the full mark. B—Fuel gauge operation with the tank full. (Plymouth)

How Gasoline Leaves the Tank

Fuel tanks usually are lower than the rest of the fuel system, so gravity must be overcome before the fuel will reach the engine. The fuel must be drawn from the tank and delivered to the rest of the fuel system. This is accomplished by the vehicle fuel pump. Fuel pumps can be operated mechanically or electrically.

Mechanical Fuel Pump

Mechanical fuel pumps are mounted on the engine and operated by the camshaft. The pump consists of an air chamber divided in the center by a flexible *diaphragm* made of gasoline-resistant material. The diaphragm is pinched between the halves, either by a series of screws that hold the pump halves together, **Figure 10-5**, or by crimping the halves together (on modern pumps).

Figure 10-5. An air chamber and diaphragm typical of a basic fuel pump.

Check Valves

Two **check valves**, one inlet and one outlet, are added to the top chamber. The inlet is connected to the fuel tank and the outlet to the carburetor via copper, steel, or plastic tubing. These check valves use flat washer valves held closed by spring pressure, **Figure 10-6**. The purpose of the check valves is to ensure that the fuel flows in one direction only.

Figure 10-6. Check valves added to the top chamber. Small springs hold the valves shut until vacuum or pressure overcomes spring tension.

Pull Rod and Return Spring

A **pull rod** is now fastened to the center of the diaphragm and a strong **return spring** pushes the diaphragm in an upward direction. If you were to connect the inlet of this fuel pump to a container of gasoline, then run the outlet to another container, the pump could be worked by pulling down

on the pull rod by hand. Fuel pump operation is shown in **Figure 10-7**.

Rocker Arm

In order to pull the diaphragm down, it is necessary to install a **rocker arm**. The rocker arm hooks in the slotted end of the pull rod and extends out where it rides on a cam on or is attached to the front of the camshaft. Note that the cam lobe used for this is different from the cam lobes used to operate the valves. When the cam lobe pushes up on the rocker arm, it pulls the pull rod down. When the cam turns, the rocker follows the lobe down.

Figure 10-7 A—Fuel pump intake stroke. When the pull rod is drawn down, diaphragm is flexed downward. This forms a vacuum in the air chamber. The intake check valve will open and gasoline will be drawn into the pump. B—Fuel pump outlet stroke. When the pull rod is released, the diaphragm is pushed up by the return spring. This creates pressure, forcing the inlet check valve shut and opening the outlet check valve. Gasoline will be forced from the outlet.

The pull rod is raised by the spring, not the rocker arm. A small spring keeps the rocker firmly against the cam lobe. The rocker arm is contained in a housing which also forms the mounting flange. This flange, along with a gasket and/or sealer prevents engine oil from leaking out where the rocker arm enters the engine. A complete pump assembly is shown in **Figure 10-8**.

Figure 10-8. Lower housing, rocker and link added. Notice that the cam lobe has raised the rocker arm, pulling diaphragm (4) down. This opens the inlet check valve, pulling in fuel. When the cam lobe turns, spring (3) will force the rocker arm to follow. The diaphragm spring will push the diaphragm up, close the inlet, and expel gasoline through the outlet. Vent (2) is provided so the diaphragm can flex without compressing air in the lower chamber. A seal keeps engine oil from entering the lower chamber. All link and rocker rubbing surfaces are hardened to retard wear.

The seal around the pull rod keeps engine oil and fumes from entering the lower chamber and prevents any gasoline, which leaks from the diaphragm, from entering the engine. A vent is provided in the lower chamber so the diaphragm can be pulled down without compressing the air in the chamber. Note that when the diaphragm is held down by fuel pressure in the carburetor, the rocker arm can slide up and down on the diaphragm pull rod. Study the parts and learn their names and functions. As illustrated, this fuel pump will move gasoline efficiently, but will not filter nor dampen the pulsating movement of gasoline leaving the outlet.

Fuel Pulsation Damper

Fuel pressure rises and falls, or pulsates, as the fuel pump operates. This pulsation can create a slamming effect against the carburetor float needle valve, causing it to come off its seat and flood the carburetor. **Figure 10-9** illustrates this effect.

Figure 10-9. Pulsation effect. A—Notice how float pressure controls the flow of gasoline. B—Here, fuel is being delivered in a jerky manner, called pulsation. See how it slams against the scale and upsets needle pressure.

To smooth out the flow of fuel, many systems are equipped with a *pulsation damper*. A pulsation damper is a flexible diaphragm stretched across an air compartment. The trapped air acts as a spring against which the diaphragm can flex. The damper can be built into the pump, mounted on the outlet of the pump, or line as a separate unit.

When the pump injects fuel into the line, the pulsation bulges the diaphragm outward, absorbing the shock. While the pump is in its intake stroke, the diaphragm will return to its normal position, **Figure 10-10**.

Figure 10-10. Pulsation damper principle. A—When the pump injects fuel, the diaphragm pushes up against the trapped air inside the air chamber. This absorbs the slamming effect. B—No fuel from the pump. Trapped air pushes the diaphragm down, continuing some fuel pressure during the lull. C—When the pump ejects more fuel, it is absorbed again by the diaphragm.

Mechanical Fuel Pump Efficiency Measurements

The amount of pressure the mechanical fuel pump exerts on the fuel line to the carburetor depends on the strength of the diaphragm spring. Pump pressures can be designed into the pump by the manufacturer according to need. An average would be around 4 to 10 psi (28 to 41 kPa). The normal pump can discharge over a quart per minute.

Serviceable and Non-Serviceable Fuel Pumps

The majority of modern mechanical fuel pumps are non-repairable, and must be replaced as a unit. If the pump is defective, it is discarded. A repairable fuel pump is shown in **Figure 10-11**. Note the various parts making up the pump.

Electric Fuel Pump

An *electric fuel pump* is always used with fuel injection and on some carbureted engines. The electric pump will fill the fuel lines merely by turning on the key. Another feature is the electric pump's adaptability to almost any location. This allows the pump to be mounted away from the heat of the engine to reduce the chance of vapor lock. Some electric pumps are submerged inside the fuel tank. A few fuel injected vehicles have two fuel pumps. A low pressure transfer pump feeds the high pressure pump for the fuel injectors.

Older electric fuel pumps used an electromagnet (a magnet produced by electricity flowing through a coil) to operate a metal bellows that alternately formed a vacuum and then pressure. It resembled a mechanical fuel pump, complete with one-way check valves. When the key was turned on, the electromagnet was energized and attracted a metal armature that was attached to the bellows. This stretched the bellows and formed a vacuum, which drew in gasoline through the inlet check valve.

As the armature continued downward, it would strike a pair of contact points, opening them. This would break the circuit to the electromagnet and it would release its pull on the bellows. A return spring shoved the armature and bellows up. As the bellows closed, gasoline was forced out the outlet check valve. When the armature traveled all the way up, the points closed and it would be drawn down again. When the carburetor's float bowl was full, the return spring could not collapse the bellows and the pump would be inoperative until some of the gasoline was drawn from the bowl.

Other electric fuel pumps use a small electric motor to drive a rotating pump. Modern rotating pumps are one-piece units. The motor is usually surrounded by the incoming gasoline for cooling. These fuel pumps can be the *positive displacement* type, which delivers a certain amount of fuel every time the pump makes one revolution. Or they may be a *non-positive displacement* type, which can vary the output on each revolution. Electric fuel pumps can use positive displacement vanes or rotors to pump the fuel, or a non-positive impeller. **Figure 10-12** shows a cutaway of one type of electric rotating pump.

Fuel Filter

The tank pickup screen will not filter out small particles. It is necessary to have an additional *fuel filter* either between the tank and the pump or between the pump and the carburetor (or fuel rail). Some pumps have a filter built into the pump assembly.

Types of Fuel Filters

Filters can be sealed units which are replaced as a unit, or may have a replaceable element inside of a reusable housing. The filter element may be a fine screen, or be made of ceramic, treated paper, or sintered bronze. All filters need periodic replacement. **Figure 10-13** illustrates an inline (placed in the fuel line) filter. All fuel must pass through the cleaning element. A special pleated paper is widely used for cleaning elements.

Fuel Lines

Gasoline is carried from the tank to the carburetor in plated steel, neoprene, or plastic *fuel lines*. When plastic is

COVER SCREW
LOCKWASHER
PULSATOR DIAPHRAGM
VALVE BODY
TUBING FITTING
GASKET
CHECK VALVE
VALVE RETAINER
PUMP DIAPHRAGM
PULL ROD
DIAPHRAGM SPRING
ROCKER ARM
SEAL
LOWER HOUSING
SPRING
PIN
SPACER
GASKET

Figure 10-11. Typical serviceable fuel pump construction. Learn the part names. (Nissan)

A

FUEL LINE TUBE

ELECTRICAL CONNECTIONS

FUEL PUMP

FUEL FILTER

FUEL PUMP BRACKET

B—FUEL PUMP CROSS-SECTION (SIDE VIEW)

ELECTRICAL CONNECTION

FUEL PUMP COVER

IMPELLERS

FUEL IN

FUEL OUT

CHECK VALVE

ARMATURE COIL

FUEL PUMP CASING

C—FUEL PUMP ASSEMBLY CROSS-SECTION (TOP VIEW)

DISCHARGE PORT   INLET PORT

CASING

IMPELLER

GROOVES

Figure 10-12. A—An in-tank electric impeller type fuel pump assembly. B—Cross-sectional view of a dc (direct current) fuel pump. C—Cross-section top view of an in-tank pump. When the engine is started, the computer main relay turns on the pump—turning the impellers. Fuel pressure is produced by the many grooves around the impellers. Fuel entering the inlet port travels inside the motor from the pumping chamber and is forced out the discharge port check valve. If the fuel flow is obstructed at the discharge side, the relief valve will open and bypass fuel to the inlet port to prevent excessive fuel pressure. When the engine is turned off, the fuel pump will stop automatically. A check valve closes by gravity to help retain residual line pressure. This aids in restarting the engine.

PLEATED PAPER ELEMENT

FUEL FILTER ELEMENT

FUEL OUTLET

FUEL INLET

Figure 10-13. Cutaway view of a paper or throwaway fuel filter. (Chevrolet)

used, it often runs from the pump to the carburetor. All lines and joints must be tight and secure to prevent destructive vibration and rubbing.

STOP **Warning: Fire is a constant hazard around any fuel system. A loose connection or unsecured fuel line can break or leak. If this happens, fuel can be sprayed over the engine, which will cause a dangerous fire if ignited.**

Vapor Lock Eliminators

It is important to shield fuel lines, pump, and carburetor from excessive heat. When gasoline reaches a certain temperature, it will turn to a vapor. Since the fuel pump is not designed to pump vapor, the fuel flow can either be reduced or completely stopped. This condition is called *vapor lock*. Upon cooling, fuel flow will resume at the normal rate.

Metal plates, heat shields, and heat resistant line covers are used to prevent vapor lock. Chemical additives are blended into gasoline to raise its boiling point to eliminate this tendency as much as possible. A fuel pump vapor discharge (return) valve can be incorporated to prevent vapor lock when underhood temperatures are high. The vapors return, via a separate line, to the fuel tank where they condense and rejoin the liquid fuel. Cars equipped with air conditioning often utilize vapor return devices to offset the danger of vapor lock due to increased underhood temperatures.

Carburetors

The job of the fuel system is to constantly deliver an **air-fuel ratio** of the proper proportions to the engine. The proportion must be variable to meet the ever changing needs of the engine. For many years this was effectively accomplished by the **carburetor**.

While the carburetor has been replaced by fuel injection on late model vehicles, there are still millions of vehicles with carburetors on the road. The latest carburetors are highly developed, complex systems. There are many types and sizes, however, they all share the same basic concepts.

Build a Carburetor

As you have done with an engine, you will now build a basic carburetor on paper. In Chapter 1, you learned that gasoline must be mixed with air to burn. The proportions of gasoline and air can vary, depending on engine temperature, speed, load, and design. A rapidly moving stream of air enters each cylinder on the intake stroke. You will use this airstream to make your carburetor work. Each intake port feeds into the intake manifold. The intake manifold runs from the ports to the carburetor.

Air Horn

Start with a plain round metal tube. This tube is called the **air horn**. The air enters the engine through the air horn. The tube has a flange that bolts to the intake manifold, **Figure 10-14**.

Fuel Bowl

A **fuel bowl** is attached to the air horn to hold a supply of gasoline. Inside of the bowl, a **float** is hinged. The float controls a tapered pin called a **needle valve** that will open and close in relation to its **needle seat** to admit gasoline. When the bowl fills, the float will rise and shove the needle valve against its seat to stop the flow of gasoline. When the fuel level drops, the float releases its pressure, the needle valve lifts from the seat and more gasoline enters. The float and needle valve will keep the fuel level constant.

The fuel level in the bowl is vital for maintaining the proper air-fuel ratio. A high float level in the carburetor will make the engine run **rich** (too much gasoline reaching the engine). A low float level in the carburetor will make the engine run **lean** (too little gasoline reaching the engine). The float level can be adjusted to maintain the proper level. The bowl must have a hole (vent) to allow air to enter or leave as the fuel level changes. The bowl may be vented to the air horn as in **Figure 10-15**, to the atmosphere, or to both.

Figure 10-14. Air horn. Arrows indicate flow of air through the horn into the intake manifold and on into the cylinders.

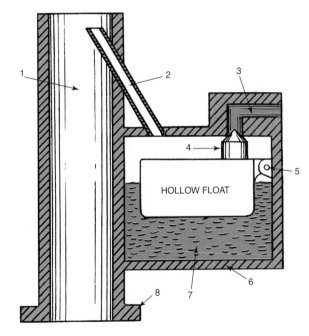

Figure 10-15. Float bowl, float, needle valve and bowl vent added to the carburetor air horn. Notice how the float has pushed the needle valve into its seat to shut off the flow of gasoline. 1—Air horn. 2—Bowl vent or balance tube. 3—Fuel inlet. 4—Needle valve. 5—Hinge. 6—Float bowl. 7—Gasoline. 8—Flange.

Fuel Bowl Vent

If the air cleaner becomes clogged, a stronger vacuum will result in the air horn. This tends to draw in more fuel. To prevent an overly rich mixture, a **bowl vent** is made between the bowl and air horn, **Figure 10-15**. If it is vented, the pressure on the fuel in the bowl will decrease in the same proportion and fuel intake will tend to remain constant.

A common setup employs the internal bowl vent plus an external vent that opens during periods of engine idle. This type of external vent helps prevent hot (engine overheated) starting problems by venting fuel vapors that would otherwise be forced into the carburetor air horn. The external vents are channeled to the emission control charcoal canister, which absorbs the fuel vapor. The operation of the canister will be covered in Chapter 14.

Main Discharge Tube

In order to allow the gasoline to be drawn into the air horn, it is necessary to connect the fuel bowl and horn with a small tube. This tube is called the **main discharge tube**, **Figure 10-16**.

Notice in **Figure 10-16** that the gasoline level in the discharge tube is slightly below the nozzle. In order to get the gasoline to flow out the nozzle and mix with the airstream, a vacuum is necessary. Some vacuum is created by the moving air, but it is not strong enough.

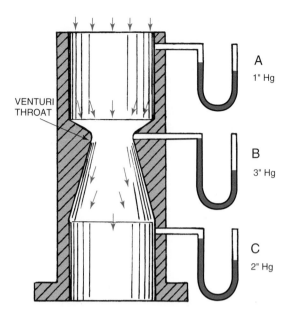

Figure 10-17. A venturi increases the speed of vacuum. A—Air rushing into the air horn near the top produces some vacuum. B—As it travels down into the venturi throat, it speeds up. This causes an increase in vacuum. C—After leaving the venturi throat, the air expands and slows down somewhat. This reduces vacuum.

Figure 10-16. Main discharge tube. Note the fuel level in discharge tube.

Creating Venturi Vacuum

By building a restriction, or **venturi**, in the air horn, the air will be forced to speed up where it strikes the venturi. As the air suddenly speeds up, it tends to be "stretched." In other words, a vacuum is created. The more the air speeds up, the stronger the vacuum. This **venturi vacuum** will be strongest in the throat of the venturi, but will still exist for a short distance below it.

Figure 10-17 illustrates an air horn with a venturi. Imagine three tubes containing mercury enter through the horn at different points. Notice the variations in vacuum at dif-

ferent spots in the horn. The higher the air velocity, the more vacuum formed. This is evident by examining the distance the atmospheric pressure has pushed the mercury up the tube.

Secondary Venturi

The vacuum can still be increased even more by constructing a smaller venturi in the center of the air horn and positioning it so that its outlet end is even with the throat of the main, or primary venturi. The primary venturi forms a vacuum at the outlet of the secondary venturi, causing the air to flow quickly through the secondary venturi. This produces a sizable increase in vacuum.

The main discharge tube nozzle enters the secondary venturi. When the engine starts, rushing air draws off drops of gasoline that join the passing air. See **Figure 10-18**. One carburetor uses a venturi valve that can change size in relation to engine vacuum and throttle position.

Air Bleed

The setup so far would add gasoline to the passing air, but the drops would be rather large and would tend to stick to the nozzle. Adding a tiny stream of air to the fuel as it travels through the nozzle causes the drops to combine with the air and break up. The smaller particles will move quickly and vaporize easily. The tube through which the air travels is called an **air bleed**. See **Figure 10-19**.

Jets

The carburetor must be able to control the amount of gasoline that can travel through a passageway. The carburetor uses **jets** to accomplish this task. The jets form a restriction to certain passageways. Jet sizes are very carefully

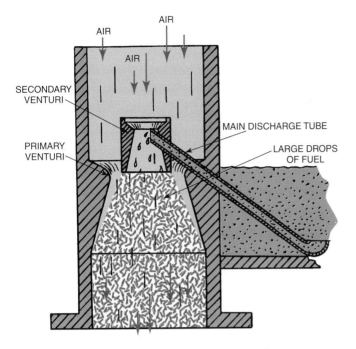

Figure 10-18. A secondary venturi can increase the vacuum speed. Note large drops of fuel being drawn from the nozzle.

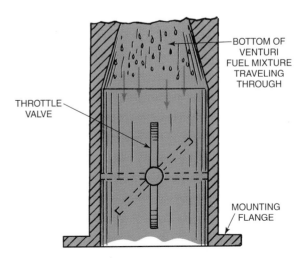

Figure 10-19. An air bleed is used to break up the large drops. A—If no air bleed is used, large fuel drops result. B—An air bleed mixes air into fuel by breaking the gasoline into small droplets.

calculated to control the amount of gasoline that can travel to these passageways.

Jets are constructed of brass and screw into the ends of the various passageways in the carburetor. Some jets are pressed into place and are not removed for routine maintenance. A jet is placed at the lower end of the main discharge tube to control the amount of gasoline that can pass through the tube. See **Figure 10-20**.

Figure 10-20. Main discharge jet. This jet controls the amount of fuel entering the discharge tube.

Throttle Valve

An engine could start and run with the carburetor described above, but would run wild or wide open. We have not provided a way to control the speed. A valve of some sort is needed to control the idle speed. The **_throttle valve_** is a circular metal plate placed between the bottom of the primary venturi and the mounting flange. In the closed position, it will almost completely seal off the air horn.

Moving the throttle valve will give us control of the amount of air-fuel mixture reaching the cylinders. It is controlled by linkage connected to the accelerator pedal. **Figure 10-21** illustrates a throttle valve, and **Figure 10-22** shows the necessary linkage.

Figure 10-21. Throttle valve. Throttle valve controls the flow of air-fuel mixture. Shown in wide open, half open, and closed positions.

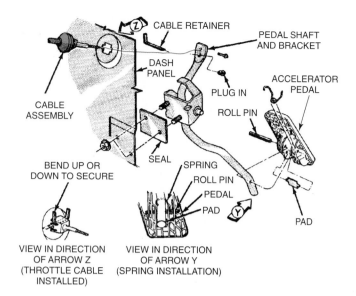

Figure 10-22. One type of carburetor throttle control, cable linkage. Linkage types and arrangements vary widely. (Chrysler)

Basic Carburetor Is Complete

Study the basic carburetor in **Figure 10-23**. Notice the position of the air horn, float bowl, float, needle and seat, fuel passages, and throttle valve. Study the venturi design and notice the relationship of the secondary to the primary venturi.

A basic carburetor as shown could be used to operate an engine. The throttle is opened to about one-half speed and the main discharge nozzle meters fuel into the airstream. If the main discharge jet is the correct size, the engine will run efficiently as long as this certain engine speed was maintained. The system designed so far is called the **main metering system** and is used in all carburetors for cruising at highway speeds. The **float system** is also in place for maintaining the proper level in the fuel bowl.

Correcting the Remaining Faults

This basic carburetor, however, has many faults. The engine will not idle without stalling and will have little power at low speed. Whenever the throttle valve is quickly opened to full throttle, the engine will have a flat spot (engine will seem to die, power fades, and for a brief second there will be no response) until the main metering system begins working.

The engine will not get enough gasoline to operate under a heavy load. There must be some provision for adding extra fuel when the engine is cold. The carburetor would be subject to vapor lock. This basic carburetor seems rather hopeless, but it is the foundation upon which all carburetors are built. By adding a few more components, we can make it operate very well.

Carburetor Circuits

The job of the various **carburetor circuits** is to produce the proper air-fuel ratio to meet all possible engine needs. The

Figure 10-23. A cutaway view of a basic single-barrel carburetor.

ideal ratio for fuel economy and emission control is 14.7:1. However, ratios must vary for other conditions. When starting a cold engine, the ratio can be a low as 8:1 for a brief period. When accelerating from a stop, and when the engine is under a heavy load, the mixture might be around 12:1. When cruising at highway speed, the mixture might be as high as 15:1. These ratios are averages and will vary from engine to engine.

We have already covered the float circuit and high speed, or main metering circuit as we built our basic carburetor. The other basic circuits (often called systems) which most carburetors have can be listed as:

- Idle circuit.
- Low speed circuit.
- High speed full power circuit.
- Acceleration circuit.
- Choke circuit.
- A secondary circuit (on some carburetors).

There are other devices that are used in the construction of carburetors, but they are not classified as circuits. We will now see how each circuit overcomes a specific problem or fault. The problem will be given first, followed by the manner in which a particular circuit functions.

Problem—Engine Will Not Idle Properly

When the throttle valve is closed to slow the engine to idle speed, the main discharge nozzle stops supplying fuel, and the engine will stall. The nozzle fails to feed gasoline because the rush of air through the air horn is cut off when the throttle is closed.

Solution—Idle Circuit

Notice in **Figure 10-24** that a passage branches off of the main discharge tube, and leads to the idle mixture screw. This is the *idle circuit*. Since there is no vacuum above the throttle but a strong vacuum below, the vacuum will draw fuel from the bowl in through the passageway to the area underneath the throttle plate. The vacuum is also drawing air in at the idle air bleed openings. The fuel is thoroughly mixed with this air and travels to the mixture screw.

The amount of the mixture that can be drawn into the engine is determined by the position of the *idle mixture adjustment screw*. Turning it in reduces the amount and turning it out increases the amount. In the past the screw could be adjusted to produce the smoothest idle. Today, mixture adjustment procedures must be followed exactly to produce the lowest possible exhaust emissions. Note that the idle adjustment screw illustrated in **Figure 10-24** is set at the factory and is sealed to prevent anyone from changing the setting.

To maintain the proper idle speed, an idle speed screw is installed at the base of the carburetor, and touches a piece of linkage attached to the throttle shaft. Turning this screw adjusts the idle speed.

Problem—Engine Will Not Operate at Part Throttle

As soon as the throttle valve is opened past the idle position, more fuel mixture is necessary. The idle screw port will

Figure 10-24. Carburetor idle circuit. Follow the flow of fuel from the metering jet to the idle screw port. This idle circuit uses a factory set idle adjustment needle. The access hole to the needle is plugged. (Ford)

not furnish enough fuel mixture and airflow through the main metering system is not strong enough to cause the fuel to be drawn from the main discharge nozzle. The engine will not operate properly in this range.

Solution—Low Speed Circuit

Going back to **Figure 10-24**, you will see a slot-shaped opening just above the throttle. This is called the idle port. It opens into the idle fuel passage. When the throttle valve starts to open, this port is uncovered and it will begin to supply fuel mixture to the engine. This is in addition to what is already supplied through the idle screw port.

This additional mixture will furnish enough extra fuel to allow the engine speed to increase to the point where the main discharge nozzle will function. Instead of the slot-shaped opening, some carburetors use a series of small round holes. As the throttle opening grows wider, it keeps uncovering extra holes. This type is illustrated in **Figure 10-25**. The individual holes perform the same function as the slot-shaped idle port. This is the *low speed circuit*, sometimes called the off-idle or idle transfer circuit. **Figure 10-25** illustrates the low speed circuit in action.

Problem—Not Enough Fuel for High Speed, Full Power

At normal cruising speeds, the main metering system can provide enough fuel. When the throttle reaches the wide open position, venturi vacuum peaks off (reaches its highest point). Since not enough fuel can pass the metering rod jet under this condition, engine performance will be weak.

Figure 10-25. Low speed circuit—part throttle. A—The throttle is closed. The idle screw port is feeding fuel and the idle port holes are inoperative. B—When the throttle is part way open, the idle port holes are uncovered and begin to feed additional fuel to the mixture. The idle screw port is also feeding the mixture.

Solution—Full Power Circuit

The solution is to allow extra fuel to bypass the main metering system. The power enrichment system is operated by engine manifold vacuum and spring tension. It enriches the fuel mixture by either bypassing, or increasing, the size of the main jet. Either system allows more gasoline to enter the main metering system when the engine is under load. The two main types of enrichment systems are the *power valve* and the *step-up rod*.

The power valve, **Figure 10-26**, is controlled by the manifold vacuum opposing the valve's spring pressure. High manifold vacuum holds the valve closed against spring pressure. When the engine is under a heavy load, the manifold vacuum drops. The lowered manifold vacuum cannot hold the valve closed against spring tension, and the spring pulls the valve open. When the valve opens, extra gasoline enters the engine through a passageway separate from the main jets.

The step-up rod, **Figure 10-27**, is a stepped, or tapered needle placed in the main jet. Manifold vacuum opposes spring pressure which tries to pull the needle out of the jet. Under light loads, manifold vacuum is high enough to push the needle far into the main jet, restricting fuel flow. When the engine is under a heavy load, vacuum drops off and spring tension can pull the needle out of the jet. The needle is tapered to match fuel flow to increases in air flow; the further it is pulled from the jet, the more fuel can flow through the jet. On some older carburetors, the needle is operated by linkage from the throttle plates.

Problem—Flat Spot on Acceleration

The carburetor, as discussed so far, would still allow a "flat spot" when sudden acceleration is attempted. This is

Figure 10-26. A—A cutaway view of a diaphragm power valve with routing passages for vacuum and fuel. Using the power valve on the secondary side allows a smaller main jet to improve fuel management during deceleration and braking. B—A cutaway view of a two-stage power valve. (Holley)

especially true at speeds below 30 mph (48 kmh). When the throttle valve is thrown open, the engine will hesitate, seem to die, and may even backfire through the intake manifold, then catch and accelerate. The momentary flat spot is the problem.

Solution—Accelerator Pump Circuit

An *accelerator pump*, using either a piston or a diaphragm is built into the carburetor. The accelerator pump is a small fuel pump which injects gasoline into the carburetor throat. In the diaphragm type, **Figure 10-28**, the diaphragm is operated by linkage connected to the throttle valve.

When the throttle is opened, the linkage causes the diaphragm to push fuel into the carburetor air horn. The pump

Figure 10-27. A—A metering rod is used to control the size of the jet opening. The large step of the metering rod is now in the jet. When the rod is raised, the small step will block the jet opening. B—When the metering rod is in the raised position, the small step will allow more fuel to pass.

Figure 10-28. A—An exploded view of one type of diaphragm accelerator pump. B—A cross-sectional view of the accelerator pump mounted on the carburetor. Note the pump discharge nozzle. (Pontiac)

can discharge fuel into the air horn through one or more *pump discharge nozzles*. Check valves ensure that the fuel flows in the proper direction and that air is not drawn into the system when the throttle is released. The system may use pump discharge jets to control the amount of fuel into the air horn.

Figure 10-29 shows a piston type accelerator pump. It is held in the top position by linkage connected to the throttle valve. The reservoir below the piston is filled with fuel. When the throttle valve opens, the linkage pushes the piston downward. This closes the inlet check ball and forces gasoline past the discharge check valve, through the pump nozzle, and into the air horn.

When the throttle is closed, the linkage raises the piston and the reservoir refills through the inlet check valve. A spring placed above the piston compresses when the throttle is opened quickly, allowing the piston to move down steadily and produce a steady stream of gasoline.

Problem—Engine Needs a Rich Mixture for Cold Starting

When an engine is cold, some of the gasoline condenses in the intake manifold. Since liquid gasoline will not burn, the carburetor must provide a rich mixture to allow

enough gasoline to stay in the vapor state. As it warms up, the mixture must lean out. When it is hot, the mixture must be even leaner.

Solution—Automatic Choke Circuit

To increase the amount of fuel entering the air horn, a *choke plate* is used. The choke plate is installed at the top of the air horn. When it is closed, vacuum builds up in the air horn. This draws extra fuel from the other carburetor systems, enriching the mixture.

On some older vehicles, a *manual choke* was used. This choke used a flexible control cable. One end of the cable was attached to the choke valve shaft lever and the other ended in a knob on the dash. Although some older cars used

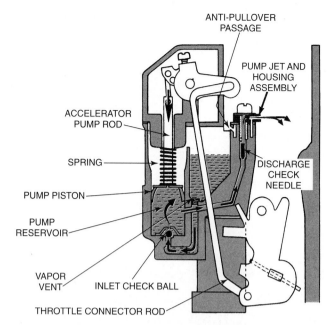

Figure 10-29. Mechanically operated accelerator pump piston. When the piston is forced down, it will compress gasoline in the pump reservoir, closing the inlet check valve and forcing gasoline by the discharge check needle. The pullover passage vents the discharge area to prevent vacuum from drawing gasoline from the accelerator discharge jet during normal operation. (Ford)

a manual choke, most modern carburetors are equipped with an **automatic choke**.

Choke Thermostatic Coil

The choke valve shaft extends through the carburetor into a round housing. Inside the housing, there is a **thermostatic coil spring** (a bimetallic spring formed of two dissimilar metals that cause the spring to wind or unwind, depending on temperature change). One end of the spring is attached to the housing cover and the other end is attached to a lever on the choke shaft.

The thermostatic coil is installed in a well in either the exhaust manifold or in the exhaust crossover (V-type engine) section of the intake manifold. When it is cold, the coil will hold the choke valve in the closed position. When the coil is hot, it will tend to lose its tension and allow the choke valve to open, **Figure 10-30**. Another type of choke, called the **divorced choke**, is installed on the manifold, and operates the choke plate through linkage.

Opening the Choke Plate

The choke plate must be fully closed to start the engine. However, as soon as the engine starts, it needs some air to continue running. Two methods are used to accomplish this.

Choke Vacuum Break

A small vacuum-operated piston or diaphragm is connected to the choke plate shaft by means of a link. As soon as the engine starts, the vacuum will pull on this piston or diaphragm and cause it to slightly open the choke plate

Figure 10-30. Thermostatic coil and cover. When cold, the spring pulls down in the direction of the arrow. The cover can be turned to increase or decrease spring tension.

against the pull of the thermostatic coil. This vacuum operated device is called a **vacuum break**. **Figure 10-31** shows a vacuum break diaphragm that is used to open the choke on most modern carburetors.

Figure 10-31. A cross-sectional view of a vacuum break diaphragm which is used to open the choke valve when needed. (Geo)

Offset Choke Valve

The choke shaft does not grasp the choke plate in the center, but is positioned so that it is slightly off center. When the engine starts, the velocity of air trying to enter the carburetor will push more on the long side and partially open the plate. See **Figure 10-32**. A small inlet valve is sometimes placed in the choke plate to admit extra air.

The cold thermostatic coil closes the offset choke plate. When the engine starts, air entering the carburetor will open the plate slightly. The vacuum piston or diaphragm will also pull to open the choke valve a little more. Between the two, they will offset the pull of the coil and open the valve enough

Figure 10-32. A cross-sectional view of a single barrel carburetor which places the choke valve plate in an "offset" position on the choke shaft. Also shown is a diaphragm accelerator pump circuit. (Carter)

to permit the engine to run. Note the choke action in **Figure 10-33**. Study the relationship of the parts. If the engine is accelerated, the vacuum pull on the piston will diminish and allow the choke valve to close more tightly and enrich the air-fuel mixture.

Choke Coil Heating

When the engine starts, the choke thermostatic coil must be heated so that it will gradually open the choke as the

Figure 10-33. Thermostatically controlled choke action. A—when the engine is stopped, the choke is closed. B—As the engine is started, the vacuum piston and offset choke valve force the choke open a small amount. C—When the engine is at operating temperature, the thermostatic spring allows the choke plate to fully open. (Toyota)

engine heats up. Older chokes used heated air drawn from the exhaust crossover passage by intake manifold vacuum. Passages and tubing allowed heated air to pass through the choke housing and heat the coil. This was called a **choke stove**. Divorced choke coils are directly warmed by heat from the engine.

Note that the choke circuit shown in **Figure 10-34** utilizes a vacuum break diaphragm unit to open the choke slightly as soon as the engine starts. Newer vehicles use an electrically heated coil to speed up the opening of the choke thermostatic spring, **Figure 10-35**. This is usually referred to as an **electric choke**. An older design passes engine coolant around the choke housing for heating.

Figure 10-34. Automatic choke, well type. The thermostatic coil may be placed in the exhaust crossover (hot) area of the intake manifold. This setup uses a diaphragm unit instead of a piston to partially open the choke when the engine starts. (Chevrolet)

Preventing Flooding

In case the carburetor **floods** the engine (puts too rich a mixture in the cylinders), a choke **unloader**, which is an additional lever attached to the choke shaft, is used to add more air to the mixture. In the event of flooding, the throttle valve is opened all the way, causing linkage from the throttle lever to strike the unloader trip lever and open the choke to allow air to enter the cylinders.

Fast Idle Cam

When the engine is warming up, it is necessary to increase the idle speed to prevent stalling. This is accomplished by connecting the choke shaft to a **fast idle cam**. When the choke is on, the fast idle cam swings out in front of the idle speed adjustment screw. This holds the throttle valve partially open to speed up the engine. As the choke opens, the fast idle cam swings down and the throttle returns to its

POSITIVE TEMPERATURE
COEFFICIENT (PTC)
CERAMIC HEATER

TEMPERATURE SENSITIVE
BIMETALLIC DISC

CHOKE
COVER

SILVER
CONTACTS

EXTERNAL
CONNECTOR

RIVET

GROUND STRAP

Figure 10-35. An electric assist choke. Note the rivets used to retain the choke cover. This prevents tampering with the choke setting. (Ford)

regular hot idle position. The fast idle cam is sometimes curved or notched, **Figure 10-36.**

Problem—Engine Needs More Power

Many engines are capable of producing more power than the carburetor will allow. To provide for smooth idle and low speed operation, the carburetor throats are relatively small. Small throats cause faster air speed, increasing the venturi vacuum and fuel mixing. However, these small throats will not let in enough fuel and air at high engine RPM. Making a large throat will make the engine faster at high speeds, but will increase roughness at low speeds.

Solution—Secondary Circuit

The **secondary circuit** consists of an additional carburetor throat or throats which allow extra air and gas into the engine when more power is needed. Not all carburetors have secondary systems. The secondary throats are equipped with throttle valves that are opened only when needed, as shown in **Figure 10-37.** The throat, or throats, used for normal driving are called the **primary circuit.**

When the accelerator is depressed to completely open the primary throttle valve, linkage also opens the secondary throttle valve. When the secondary throttle valve opens, extra air enters the engine through the secondary throat. A venturi system in the secondary throat delivers extra gasoline. Some secondary throttle valves are vacuum-actuated. These respond to changes in engine load. Using a carburetor with a secondary system allows the engine to run smoothly and get good mileage at small throttle openings while still performing well when extra power is needed.

Notice that only the primary barrels have a choke valve. No choke valve is needed in the secondary barrels since they are closed when starting. Although secondary systems were once found only on four-barrel carburetors, many two-barrel carburetors, with one of the barrels functioning as a secondary system, are used on four- and six-cylinder engines.

Other Carburetor Features

Many other devices are installed on the carburetor. They are used to improve carburetor performance, operate other engine systems, or help meet emission regulations. Other devices, installed elsewhere on the engine, improve carburetor operation. Some of the most common are covered below.

Hot Idle Compensator

To prevent stalling when idling in very hot weather, some carburetors utilize a thermostatically-controlled air valve called a **hot idle compensator, Figure 10-38.** When the carburetor becomes hot, the bimetallic strip will curl upward and open the hot idle air valve. This feeds extra air to the manifold below the throttle valve. The extra air compensates for an overly rich idle mixture due to heat-produced fuel vapor entering the carburetor. Hot idle compensators are used less on

COLD STARTING POSITION

WARM-UP POSITION

HOT POSITION

Figure 10-36. Action of fast idle cam during engine warm-up. As the choke opens, the fast idle rod will lower the fast idle cam. As the cam lowers, it will allow the idle throttle stop screw to close the throttle more and more. This will reduce engine speed. When the choke is fully open, the engine will idle at normal speed. (Bendix)

Figure 10-37. A schematic of a diaphragm-operated secondary throttle circuit. A vacuum signal from the primary venturi is aided by an increasing vacuum signal from the secondary venturi as the secondary throttle starts to open. Closing the primary throttle closes the secondary with mechanical override linkage.

Figure 10-38. Hot idle compensator. Heat will cause the bimetallic strip to open the air valve. (Pontiac)

Figure 10-39. Throttle return dashpot. When the throttle strikes the dashpot rod, the rod pushes the diaphragm back. Before it can move back, air must be forced out of the vent. This causes the diaphragm to move slowly. When the throttle lever is moved away, a spring will force the diaphragm out. Air will be drawn in the vent and the dashpot is ready to work again.

modern engines, since their presence makes exact fuel mixture control more difficult.

Throttle Return Dashpot

On cars equipped with automatic transmissions, the drag placed on the engine when the throttle is opened and then suddenly returned to idle will result in engine stalling. The **throttle return dashpot**, usually called the dashpot, is arranged so the throttle lever will strike the dashpot just before reaching idling range. The dashpot diaphragm rod will slowly collapse, allowing the throttle to slowly return to the idling position. This occurs when the car is stopped, **Figure 10-39**.

Some dashpots are built as an integral part of the carburetor. Some dashpots are combined with other idle control devices.

Electrical Idle Speedup Control Devices

Some engines have electrical solenoid controlled devices to vary the idle for certain special operating conditions. Such units used to control idle speed for various reasons are often termed throttle positioners, **Figure 10-40**.

To compensate for the increased load on the engine when the air conditioning compressor clutch is engaged, an **idle speed-up solenoid** is often used. The increased engine speed during idle also provides increased airflow for better

Figure 10-40. Various styles of vacuum and electric throttle positioners.

cooling. When the compressor clutch is energized, electricity is fed to a small solenoid on the side of the carburetor. The solenoid then opens an air valve, permitting increased airflow below the throttle plates.

On some engines, the idle speed-up solenoid is energized in third and fourth gears to hold the throttle plates slightly open when the engine is decelerating. This reduces engine emissions. **Figure 10-41** illustrates the idle speedup control.

Some engines are prone to **dieseling** (condition in which the engine continues to run when the ignition is turned off). Dieseling, sometimes called run on, is caused by the hotter combustion chamber temperatures in modern emission-controlled vehicles. To prevent dieseling, an **anti-dieseling solenoid** is used to set the hot idle. When the engine is turned off, the solenoid deenergizes, closing the throttle completely. The engine is deprived of air and cannot run.

Mixture Control Solenoid

A computer-controlled **mixture control solenoid** is used on most carburetors made recently. This solenoid is a type of electromagnet (coil of wire through which an electrical current is passed), used to move the rod. Electrical current to the solenoid is pulsed on and off to change rod position in response to engine fuel needs. The computer controls solenoid operation as needed. **Figure 10-42** shows one type of solenoid operated rod.

Figure 10-41. An idle speed-up solenoid assembly and its mounting location. (Ford)

Figure 10-42. A solenoid operated metering rod provides the control needed by the "closed loop" computer system employing an exhaust sensor. (Chevrolet)

Throttle Position Sensor

Throttle position is relayed to the control module by the **throttle position sensor**. As you learned in Chapter 9, throttle position sensors can be either resistance types or transducers. Throttle position sensors are usually installed on or in the carburetor bowl.

Devices for Preventing Carburetor Icing

It is possible for ice to form on the throttle valves. As the nozzles feed fuel into the air horn, it turns into a vapor. This vaporizing action chills the air-fuel mixture and the throttle bores in the throttle valve area. This condition, called **carburetor icing**, happens most often when the outside air temperature is just above freezing and humidity is high.

When the moisture-laden mixture contacts the chilled throttle valve, it condenses, then freezes. This pileup of ice can reach the point where, when the accelerator is released, the engine will stall because no air can pass around the throttle valve. Icing occurs during the warm-up period, and stops after the engine is fully warmed up.

Manifold Heat Control Valve

When the air-fuel mixture enters the manifold during the warm-up period, gases from the exhaust manifold are directed to the base of the intake manifold where the carburetor is attached. This warms the incoming mixture. When the engine is hot, the gases are directed away from the intake manifold. This action is controlled by the **manifold heat control valve**.

The manifold heat control valve can be operated by a thermostatic spring or by a vacuum diaphragm operated by a temperature switch. **Figure 10-43** shows the action of the heat control valve on an inline engine. On a V-type engine, the manifold heat control valve is located in the exhaust manifold on one bank. When cold, the heat control closes and directs some of the exhaust gases up through the intake manifold. After passing through, the gases flow out the exhaust manifold on the other side. When hot, the manifold heat control valve opens and both exhaust manifolds expel gas directly into the exhaust system.

Figure 10-43. Operation of a manifold heat control valve. Notice how hot gases are directed up and around the intake manifold passages.

On most modern carbureted engines, the intake air is heated by means of a thermostatically-controlled air cleaner, shown in **Figure 10-44**. See Chapter 14 for additional information about manifold heat control valves and thermostatic air cleaners.

Figure 10-44. A thermostatically controlled, heated air cleaner assembly being removed from a carburetor. There are many different styles and control systems.

Coolant Heated Manifold

Some engines are designed so that coolant is pumped through passages in the intake manifold. This **coolant heated manifold** provides a controlled temperature for the fuel mixture. **Figure 10-45** illustrates a coolant-heated intake manifold for a V-8 engine. The top view shows the complete manifold for a four-barrel carburetor. The shaded portion in the second sketch shows the intake passages. The bottom sketch shows the flow of coolant through the manifold.

Electrical Heating of Fuel Mixture

Some older engines utilize a thin **ceramic heater** built as part of the carburetor base-to-intake manifold spacer. The heating grids are located under the primary bores and provide rapid heating of the fuel mixture during cold startup and while

Figure 10-45. A coolant heated intake manifold. Coolant replaces hot gases in this installation.

Figure 10-46. An aneroid controlled, spring loaded valve compensates for changes in altitude. As altitude increases, the aneroid expands, opening the valve. When the engine is cold and the regular choke valve is closed, the auxiliary choke will also close to prevent excess air delivery. (Chrysler)

the engine is warming up. This improves fuel vaporization and reduces the length of time the choke must be closed. The heater is shut off by a thermostatic switch when the engine reaches a specified temperature.

Altitude Compensators

When operating at higher elevations, the fuel mixture tends to become overly rich as the air becomes thinner and contains less oxygen to sustain burning. On older carburetors, the mixture was simply adjusted or jets were changed to compensate for the thin air. Today, this problem is overcome by either adjusting the amount of fuel or the amount of air in the mixture using an *altitude compensator.*

On older engines, this adjustment was made by using an *aneroid*, which is a pressure sensitive sealed bellows. The aneroid can control either a fuel or airflow valve so as to maintain the proper air-fuel ratio at various altitudes. **Figure 10-46** illustrates the use of an aneroid to admit extra air as altitude increases. At lower elevations, atmospheric pressure collapses the aneroid which in turn holds the valve closed. As elevation increases, atmospheric pressure drops and the aneroid expands, pushing the valve open. This admits extra air into the stream of fuel, which leans the air-fuel ratio.

On computer-controlled vehicles, the oxygen sensor reads the decrease in oxygen content caused by higher altitude operation. Some computer control systems with carburetors are equipped with a barometric pressure sensor. The computer reads this and other inputs and makes adjustments accordingly. The operation of the computer control system is covered in detail in Chapter 15.

Other Carburetor Functions

In addition to its job of mixing air and gasoline in the proper proportions, the carburetor performs other functions. The carburetor may furnish an opening for the distributor vacuum advance line, or for various vacuum operated emission controls such as the EGR (exhaust gas recirculation) valve. The throttle linkage may be attached to kickdown switches for automatic transmissions, or air conditioner full throttle cutout switches. The carburetor may be connected to a throttle valve (TV) linkage or cable to operate the automatic transmission throttle valve.

Intake Manifold Design

The *intake manifold* is designed to carry fuel from the carburetor to the valve ports. They can be made of cast iron or aluminum. The V-8 engine mounts the manifold between the cylinder heads. Inline engines have the manifold bolted to the cylinder head. Intake manifolds usually have fittings for attaching vacuum lines and may have a mounting pad for the EGR valve or other emission controls.

It is not enough just to carry fuel from the carburetor to the cylinders. Each cylinder should get the same type and amount of fuel mixture. To design an intake manifold to deliver equal amounts of fuel to all cylinders is not easy. It is essential that the passages in the manifold be as nearly equal in length as possible. In addition, they should be smooth with gentle curves. **Figure 10-47** shows one specific V-8 intake manifold design for a dual carburetor.

Figure 10-47. An intake manifold for a V-8 engine which uses a two-barrel carburetor. (Chrysler)

Figure 10-49. A—A round, radial air flow, dry type, air cleaner element being removed from its housing. B—A flat, linear air flow, air cleaner element being removed from its housing. (AC-Delco)

Air Cleaners

It is essential that air entering the carburetor or throttle body is clean. A good **air cleaner**, properly cleaned or replaced at the proper intervals, will add greatly to the useful life of the engine.

Air Cleaner Element

An air cleaner draws air through a treated paper **air cleaner element** which will allow air to flow, but traps dirt particles, **Figure 10-48**. The paper is pleated accordion style for added filtering area. Air cleaner elements can be round (radial airflow) or flat (linear airflow), **Figure 10-49**.

Figure 10-48. A cutaway view of the linear flow air filter. These elements are generally used in remote housing locations. (Wix Corp.)

Carburetor Classifications

Since carburetors have been used for over 100 years, many different types have been made. However, all carburetors perform the same function and every carburetor can be placed into a specific classification. Carburetors are classified according to several criteria. While discussing carburetor classifications, it will be helpful to note the three sections of a carburetor that almost all carburetors have:

Air horn, the upper section of the carburetor containing the air inlet and air cleaner mounting bracket, and sometimes the fuel inlet, float assembly, and accelerator pump linkage and plunger.

Main body, the center section of the carburetor containing the float bowl (chamber) and some of the internal passages. The main body usually contains the venturi cluster and accelerator pump outlet nozzle.

Throttle plate or base, the lower section containing the throttle valve and associated linkage, and usually the idle mixture screw(s).

Some carburetors incorporate the main body and throttle body into one unit, but these three major sections are distinct on all carburetors.

Airflow Direction

Incoming air can enter the carburetors in three directions. The three carburetor designs based on these flows are *downdraft*, *updraft*, and *sidedraft*. Your basic carburetor was a downdraft type, **Figure 10-50.** While sidedraft and updraft carburetors are sometimes found on small engines and off-road equipment, they have not been used on cars and light trucks for many years.

Figure 10-50. A cutaway of a downdraft carburetor. (Deere)

Number of Throats

The number of throats, often called *barrels*, is a common way of identifying carburetors. Carburetors can be single barrel, two-barrel, or four-barrel designs. In the past, multiple carburetors (three two-barrel carburetors or two four-barrel carburetors) have been placed on engines.

Single-Barrel Carburetor

The basic carburetor illustrated earlier was a *single-barrel* model. A typical downdraft, single-barrel carburetor is shown in **Figure 10-51.** The single-barrel carburetor is used on three- and four-cylinder engines. Study the various parts.

Two-Barrel Carburetor

Many V-type engines and some inline engines use the *two-barrel* carburetor. This carburetor is basically two single barrel carburetors mounted side by side. Each barrel has its own discharge nozzle, idle port, accelerator discharge jet, and throttle valve. Some two-barrel carburetors make use of a secondary system, with one barrel as the primary and the other the secondary, **Figure 10-52.** On some V-type engines, each barrel feeds into a separate intake passage.

Four-Barrel Carburetor

A *four-barrel* carburetor can be thought of as a cluster of four, single-barrel carburetors. One group of two barrels is the primary side and the other two are the secondary side. Four-barrel carburetors are primarily used on V-8 engines, although some have been used on other engines with fewer cylinders. There is wide variation in four-barrel carburetor design. The carburetor illustrated in **Figure 10-53** is typical.

Some four-barrel carburetors have separate primary and secondary, or separate right and left float circuits, but most modern four-barrel carburetors have only one float. Most four-barrel carburetors have an airflow-operated auxiliary valve. The auxiliary valves are installed on top of the secondary throttle plates. They are mounted off-center and are pulled open by manifold vacuum only when engine load is sufficient to use the extra air and fuel. Therefore, even when the secondary throttle valves are opened at low speeds, the secondary system does not operate until the engine can use it.

Summary

The fuel tank holds the gasoline or diesel fuel until it is needed. A mechanical or electric fuel pump draws, fuel from the tank. The fuel is drawn out through a pickup tube with a screen on the end. The fuel flows through lines, then passes through a filter on its way to the fuel delivery system.

For efficient operation an engine used in a passenger car requires an air-fuel ratio that is constantly changing. For many years, this varied mixture was produced and delivered by the carburetor.

The carburetor contains a number of circuits designed to produce a proper air-fuel mixture for all engine needs. When the engine first starts, the choke valve is closed. The vacuum is strong in the area beneath the choke valve, resulting in a very rich mixture by reducing the air supply and increasing the withdrawal of fuel from the bowl. As soon as the engine starts, the choke partially opens. As the engine is idled to warmup, fuel is fed into the passing airstream by the idle screw port. The choke continues to open. When the engine is hot, it will be fully opened.

When the accelerator opens the throttle valve, the idle screw port fuel delivery is assisted by additional fuel from the idle port or part throttle holes just above the idle screw port. As the throttle continues to open, the air speed through the air horn and venturi increases until fuel begins to feed from the main discharge nozzle. At very high speeds where the throttle is wide open, or when the engine is loaded, additional fuel is administered a power valve or by a metering rod.

During the cruising and full power range, no fuel is fed by the idle port or idle screw port. To assist in smooth acceleration, an accelerator pump is provided to feed additional gasoline during acceleration only. Engine speed is controlled by the position of the throttle valve in the carburetor.

The air and fuel mixture is delivered to the combustion chambers by means of an intake manifold. The temperature of this mixture is raised during engine warmup by heat crossover passages, heated air intake, and in some cases, by running the coolant through passages in the intake manifold. Even distribution of fuel to all cylinders is very important.

Air entering the carburetor must be cleaned. Failure to clean the air will result in rapid deterioration of the engine. Air is generally cleaned by a dry-type air cleaner that utilizes special paper as the filtering element. Cleaners must be serviced regularly to maintain efficiency.

Carburetors can be classified as downdraft, updraft, and sidedraft types. Some carburetors are single-barrel, some two-barrel, and others have four barrels. All carburetors—despite shape, size and type—attempt to provide as nearly perfect an air-fuel mixture as possible for all engine needs.

Figure 10-51. An exploded view of a single barrel, downdraft carburetor. Types and construction vary widely. Study all the individual parts carefully. (Ford)

Figure 10-52. An exploded view of a two-barrel, downdraft carburetor. Note the main sections — air horn, main body, and the throttle. (Chrysler)

Figure 10-53. An exploded view of a four-barrel, downdraft carburetor. After studying carefully, how many parts are you able to correctly identify? (Pontiac)

Know These Terms

Fuel tank
Pickup tube
Tank gauge unit
Mechanical fuel pump
Diaphragm
Check valve
Pull rod
Return spring
Rocker arm
Pulsation damper
Electric fuel pump
Positive displacement
Non-positive displacement
Fuel filter
Fuel lines
Vapor lock
Air-fuel ratio
Carburetor
Air horn
Fuel bowl
Float
Needle valve
Needle seat
Rich
Lean
Bowl vent
Main discharge tube
Venturi
Venturi vacuum
Air bleed
Jets
Throttle valve
Main metering system
Float system
Carburetor circuits
Idle circuit
Idle mixture adjustment
    screw
Low speed circuit
Power valve
Step-up rod

Accelerator pump
Pump discharge nozzles
Choke plate
Manual choke
Automatic choke
Thermostatic coil spring
Divorced choke
Vacuum break
Choke stove
Electric choke
Flooding
Unloader
Fast idle cam
Secondary circuit
Primary circuit
Hot idle compensator
Throttle return dashpot
Idle speed-up solenoid
Dieseling
Anti-dieseling solenoid
Mixture control solenoid
Throttle position sensor
Carburetor icing
Manifold heat control valve
Coolant heated manifold
Ceramic heater
Altitude compensator
Aneroid
Intake manifold
Air cleaner
Air cleaner element
Main body
Throttle plate
Downdraft
Updraft
Sidedraft
Barrels
Single-barrel
Two-barrel
Four-barrel

Review Question—Chapter 10

Do not write in this text. Write your answers on a separate sheet of paper.

1. Fuel tanks are made from _____ .
   (A) thin sheet steel
   (B) aluminum
   (C) plastic
   (D) All of the above.

2. Internal baffles in the fuel tank prevent fuel _____ .

3. All of the following statements about mechanical fuel pumps are true, EXCEPT:
   (A) check valves are used to ensure that fuel flows through the pump in one direction.
   (B) the pump is operated by the camshaft.
   (C) a pull rod is fastened to the center of the diaphragm.
   (D) the return spring assists the rocker arm in moving the diaphragm.

4. An electric fuel pump that delivers a certain amount of fuel every time the pump makes one revolution is a _____ type.

5. How many check valves does an mechanical fuel pump use?
   (A) 2
   (B) 3
   (C) 4
   (D) One for every cylinder.

6. Name three materials commonly used to make fuel filters.

7. What is vapor lock?

8. The air bleed makes the gasoline particles _____ .

9. The fuel level in the carburetor is controlled by the _____ system.

10. A high fuel level will make the carburetor run _____ .

11. What does the use of carburetor jets prevent?
    (A) Too little gas going through a passageway.
    (B) Too much gas going through a passageway.
    (C) Lean carburetor operation.
    (D) Both A & B.

12. Engine speed is controlled by the _____ .

13. How is the idle mixture adjusted on late model engines?
    (A) Turning the mixture screw at the throttle body.
    (B) Turning the speed screw at the throttle body.
    (C) Adjusting the float level.
    (D) The mixture on late model engines cannot be adjusted.

14. What circuit is provided to assist the idle circuit when the throttle is opened just beyond an idle?

15. What circuit provides fuel for normal cruising speeds?

16. What operates the power valve or step up rod when full power is needed?

17. What circuit is installed in the carburetor to cure a "flat spot?"

18. What closes the automatic choke when the engine is cold?

19. During the warmup period, engines must idle fairly fast. What is the name of the device provided for this purpose?

20. When does the choke pull operate?

(A)   Before the engine is started.

(B)   As soon as the engine starts.

(C)   As the engine warms up.

(D)   When the engine is fully warmed up.

21.   If a cold engine becomes "flooded," what mechanism will force the choke valve open?

22.   What causes ice to form in a carburetor?

(A)   Gasoline vaporization.

(B)   Low temperatures.

(C)   High humidity.

(D)   All of the above.

23.   The manifold heat control valve directs _____ under the carburetor to raise the temperature and reduce icing.

24.   Which of the following types of carburetor could have a secondary circuit?

(A)   Single-barrel.

(B)   Two-barrel.

(C)   Four-barrel.

(D)   Both B & C.

25.   List two safety precautions to remember when dealing with the fuel system.

No matter what fuel or delivery system a vehicle uses, it must be in good operating condition for optimum engine performance. (Ford Motor Co.)

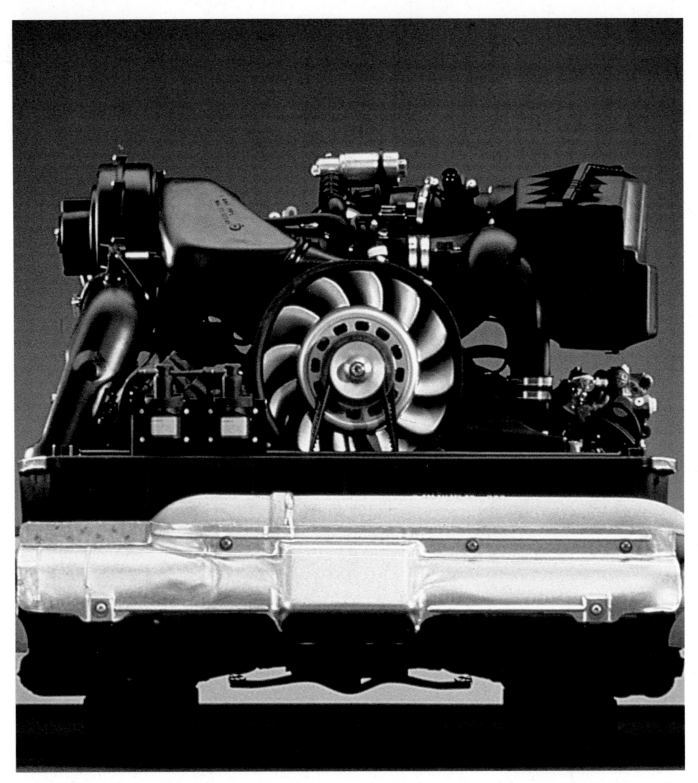

This opposed six-cylinder engine uses air for cooling. The fan is driven by the engine and air is channeled by the shroud surrounding the fan. (Porsche)

11

Cooling Systems

After studying this chapter, you will be able to:
- List the functions of an engine cooling system.
- Identify the two major kinds of cooling systems.
- Identify the major components of a liquid cooling system.
- Trace the flow of coolant through the liquid cooling system.
- Identify the basic parts of an air cooling system.

This chapter will cover the principles of cooling systems, why a cooling system is needed, and why the engine must operate within a certain temperature range. The different types of cooling systems and cooling system components will also be discussed.

The Need for a Cooling System

When fuel is burned in an engine, heat is produced. Modern engines can have combustion chamber temperatures in excess of 4000°F (2204°C). Of this heat, only about one-third is used to power the engine. The rest is unwanted heat. This unwanted heat must be removed. About one-third of the total heat leaves with the exhaust gases. This leaves one-third to be removed by the cooling system. The engine cooling system actually has three jobs:

- It must remove surplus or unwanted heat.
- It must maintain an efficient temperature under all operating conditions.
- It must bring a cold engine up to operating temperature as soon as possible.

As the temperature of the engine parts increases, a point may be reached where the oil will break down if the remaining heat is not dissipated. When this happens, lubrication is no longer possible and the engine will be ruined. On the other hand, a cold engine is very inefficient. A cold engine will run poorly, which can result in oil contamination, formation of engine deposits, increased wear, decreased horsepower, higher exhaust emissions, and poor fuel mileage. This is shown in **Figure 11-1**.

Two Methods of Cooling

When something is too hot, we either blow on it or pour water or some other liquid on it. These same two methods, highly refined, are utilized in cooling an internal combustion

Figure 11-1. The relationship between engine temperature and performance, engine wear, life, and fuel economy. Note that engine performance increases and wear decreases as the engine becomes hotter.

engine. Most car and light truck engines use a liquid cooling system. Some vehicle engines and many small one- and two-cylinder engines use air cooling.

Liquid-Cooled Engines

The *liquid-cooled engine* must have passages for the flow of liquid through the cylinder block and head. Indirectly, the liquid must contact the cylinder walls, combustion chamber, valve seats, valve guides, and all other engine parts. This is accomplished by taking the basic engine and building a container around it.

In actual practice, liquid circulation passages, called *cooling passages*, are cast into the engine block and cylinder head. When these passages are filled with a liquid, the engine is surrounded by a jacket of liquid. These cooling passages are often referred to as *water jackets*. See **Figure 11-2**. Although the liquid-cooled engine is sometimes referred to as a water-cooled engine, all modern engines must use a mixture of 50% water and 50% ethylene glycol antifreeze, usually called *coolant*. Antifreeze will be discussed in more detail later in this chapter.

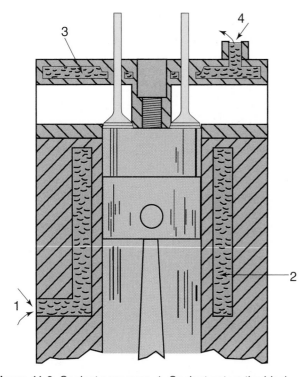

Figure 11-2. Coolant passages. 1–Coolant enters the block here, circulates around the cylinder to 2, and then flows up into the head 3, where it leaves at 4. Notice how coolant surrounds the cylinder, valve guides, head, spark plug seat, and top of the combustion chamber.

Holes are left in the block during the casting process. These holes are sealed by using stamped metal or brass plugs called *freeze plugs*. They are designed to allow for expansion should the coolant freeze. However, in spite of their name, block damage usually occurs if the coolant freezes.

Heat Transfer

Engine parts, such as the block and cylinder head, absorb the heat of the burning fuel. This heat is conducted through the part and into the coolant contained in the cooling passages. The coolant absorbs some of the heat from the part and transfers it to the outside of the engine, **Figure 11-3**.

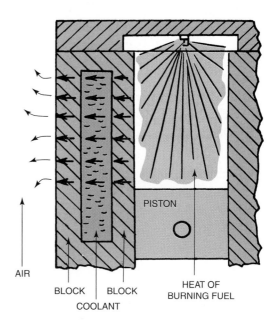

Figure 11-3. If coolant does not circulate, there is no transfer of heat. If this coolant is allowed to sit without circulating, the engine will literally burn up.

The engine coolant is the medium of heat transfer. It is able to absorb and release heat, and will not damage any other cooling system parts. However, the coolant will absorb just so much heat, then it will boil away. If the coolant stands still, it is of no value for cooling purposes. In order to function as a cooling agent, the coolant must move, or circulate through the engine. As the coolant is heated, it must be moved out of the engine and replaced with coolant that is not as hot. There must be no dead spots (areas in which there is little or no circulation), **Figure 11-4**.

A Pump Is Needed

To circulate coolant through the engine, a *coolant pump* is needed. Most pumps are *centrifugal pumps* utilizing an *impeller*, **Figure 11-5**. The impeller consists of a round plate fastened to a rotating shaft to which a series of flat or curved vanes are attached. When the impeller turns, the coolant is thrown outward by centrifugal force. By placing the impeller in a closed housing with an inlet to allow coolant to contact the front face of the vanes and an outlet to carry away coolant thrown outward, such a pump will move coolant efficiently, **Figure 11-6**.

The pump housing is made of cast iron or aluminum. The impeller shaft is supported on a double row of sealed ball bearings. A spring-loaded seal is used to prevent coolant leakage. For the pump to operate at engine speed, a way must be found to turn the impeller. To accomplish this task, a hub is cast on the front of the impeller shaft. A pulley is then bolted to this hub. Sometimes a fan is also bolted or attached to the

Figure 11-4. Circulation is vital. A—Notice that a torch has heated the coolant and the entire steel bar. The gauge reads hot. B—Coolant is circulating through the passages, carrying heat away from the bar. The gauge now reads cool.

Figure 11-6. If the impeller is placed inside of a housing, coolant directed to the center of the impeller is thrown outward into the housing, and an outlet directs the flow out of the housing.

Figure 11-5. Normal action of a coolant pump impeller. Note how coolant is thrown off in all directions. This impeller is inefficient in this state.

Figure 11-7. A—Water (coolant) pump mounted on the engine with the impeller inside the water jacket. B—Water pump removed. Note the six-blade, stamped steel impeller, and the O-ring pump body-to-block seal (Chrysler Corp.)

hub or pulley. One particular cooling pump is shown in **Figure 11-7**.

On some pumps, the impeller extends into the coolant passages of the engine, as in **Figure 11-7**. Some pumps are driven directly by the engine, **Figure 11-8**. Other pumps have the impeller enclosed in the pump housing, as in **Figure 11-9**. The coolant pump is usually secured to the front of the engine by bolts. Coolant pumps are usually referred to as **water pumps**.

Belt Drive

Figure 11-9 shows a **V-belt** being used to drive a coolant pump. The belt is driven by a pulley on the front of the crankshaft. This same belt may be used to drive other engine

Figure 11-8. Water pump which is gear-driven by the engine. Note that the thermostat is housed in the water pump body and that an air bleed is used to aid in removing all air from the system. Electric cooling fans are used with this arrangement. (Chevrolet)

Figure 11-10. This particular V-belt construction uses steel wires and is designed to drive the air conditioning compressor. (Gates)

accessories. Typical V-belt construction is shown in **Figure 11-10**. A modification of the V-belt is the *ribbed belt*, which is sometimes referred to as a *serpentine belt*, **Figure 11-11**. It is a wide belt with several ribs that act as several small V-belts.

All belts must be in good condition and properly adjusted. Excessive tightness will place a heavy load on the coolant pump's bearings, causing premature wear. Belt looseness will permit slippage, which will reduce pump and fan speed, possibly causing overheating. A loose belt will have a

Figure 11-9. Cutaway of a typical coolant pump. 1–Bolts-pump to block. 2–Bolts-fan and pulley. 3–Pump shaft. 4–Hub. 5–Coolant outlet. 6–Bypass. 7–Pump housing. 8–Seal. 9–Ball bearings. 10–Pulley. 11–V-belt. 12–Dust seal. 13–Seal spring. 14–Fan. 15–Coolant inlet. 16–Hose. 17–Block. 18–Bearing race. 19–Impeller.

Figure 11-11. This engine uses a ribbed belt to drive the coolant pump. Note the difference between this belt and the regular V-belt in Figure 11-10. (Ford)

tendency to whip or flap, which can cause intermittent heavy loading of the bearings and possible pump failure.

Controlled Circulation

The coolant must flow around the cylinders and pass up through the cylinder head on its way out. It must reach every part of the system. It is not enough to pump coolant into the bottom of an engine and let it flow out the top. If this were done, the coolant would rapidly circulate through some areas and would move slowly, or not at all through others, causing localized overheating.

The coolant may be channeled into parts of the engine by means of **distribution tubes**. **Figure 11-12** illustrates a typical distribution tube. The tube is placed in the coolant passages. The outlet holes are lined up to circulate coolant into the hard-to-cool areas in the engine.

Figure 11-13. Notice how the coolant nozzle pumps coolant. As the coolant leaves the small hole in top, it causes a strong circulation around the valve seat area.

Figure 11-12. This distribution tube may be located in the block, head, or both. It allows coolant to reach areas of the block which would not be readily accessible by the water jackets.

Some engines employ **coolant nozzles** to speed up circulation around the valve seats. A nozzle is shown in action in **Figure 11-13**. On most modern engines, the distribution tubes and nozzles are precision cast into the cylinder head, eliminating the need for separate tubes and nozzles. **Figure 11-14** illustrates the path the coolant takes on its way through the engine.

The Radiator

When the coolant leaves the engine, it is quite hot—often well over 200°F (93.3°C). If it were immediately pumped back into the engine, it would be too hot to absorb additional heat. Before the coolant can be reused, the heat must be removed. Cooling is accomplished by passing the coolant, as it leaves the engine, through a **heat exchanger**. This heat exchanger is usually referred to as a **radiator**.

Some radiators are made of brass and copper to facilitate cooling and to protect it from rust and corrosion. All joints are soldered. However, most modern radiators use aluminum and plastic in their construction to reduce the weight of the unit. The radiator is placed so that air can pass through it when the vehicle is in motion.

From the top- or side-mounted entry tank, coolant flows down or across through small copper or aluminum tubes. The tubes are flattened to provide the least resistance to airflow and have thin metal fins soldered over their entire length. The

Figure 11-14. Cooling system operation with one particular V-6 engine. Follow the coolant flow path arrows. (Chrysler Corp.)

tube and fin assembly is known as the **radiator core**. As the coolant makes its way through the core, it gives off heat to the tubes and fins. Since both copper and aluminum are excellent conductors, the tubes give off their heat, via the fins, to the air passing around them.

By the time the coolant reaches the outlet tank, it is cool enough to reuse. **Figure 11-15** shows a cross-section of a simple radiator with top and bottom tanks. Modern vehicles use cross-flow radiators, such as the one shown in **Figure 11-14**. The coolant enters one side tank and then passes through the horizontal tubes to the opposite tank, sometimes called the return tank.

The radiator usually contains a filler neck for adding coolant when necessary. Some filler necks are mounted on

Figure 11-15. In this downflow radiator, coolant enters the top hose connection 4, then passes into the top tank 3. From there it flows down through the core tubes 5. When it reaches the bottom tank 6, it has been cooled. 1–Filler neck. 2–Overflow tube. 7–Lower hose connections. 8–Drain petcock. Not shown are the thin fins normally soldered to the core tubes to help dissipate heat.

the vehicle's engine. The neck is sealed by a pressure cap, which is discussed later. The radiator may also contain another heat exchanger to provide cooling for the automatic transmission fluid. The ***transmission oil cooler*** can be a separate unit or placed in the return tank to give its heat up to the coolant after the coolant temperature has been reduced in the radiator core. Transmission oil coolers are shown in **Figure 11-16**.

Forced Air

To speed up the cooling action of a radiator, one or more power-operated ***fans*** are used to draw air through the radiator core. The fan can be driven by the engine, or by an electric motor, **Figure 11-17**. Engine-driven fans are an integral part of the water pump and are driven by the water pump's drive belt. Electric fans are mounted as independent units.

If an engine-driven fan is set too far back from the radiator core, it will recirculate the same air, **Figure 11-18A**. To avoid the loss of fan efficiency, engine-driven fans require a radiator shroud. This prevents recirculation of air, **Figure 11-18B**. Electric fans can be placed close to the radiator and do not require a shroud.

Fan Blades

Fans may have as few as two blades and as many as ten, depending on specific requirements. Blades are usually rounded and arranged in an uneven manner in an attempt to lessen noise. One type of fan employs flexible blades that reduce the pitch (angle at which the blade is mounted) at higher speeds, permitting the fan to turn more easily.

Figure 11-16. Two types of transmission fluid coolers. A—A cooler installed inside the radiator side tank. B—An auxiliary cooler mounted in front of the radiator assembly, with lines runing to the transmission.

> **STOP** **Warning: A fan can inflict serious injury. Keep hands and other objects away from the fan.** Electric fans can come on automatically, even when the vehicle is shut off. Do not stand in line with a revolving fan—a blade can fly out with lethal force.

Fan Clutches

As the vehicle gains speed on the road, air is forced through the radiator core. As a result, the fan becomes less and less useful as road speed increases. Since they require

Figure 11-17. This electric cooling fan assembly is used instead of the engine-driven fan. Many vehicles have more than one electric cooling fan. (Geo)

Figure 11-18 A—This fan is too far from the radiator which allows air recirculation. Some air is being pulled through the radiator, but a great deal is being recirculated through the fan. B—This fan shroud stops recirculation which improves airflow. Most vehicles have a thin sheet metal or plastic shroud attached to the radiator.

engine power to spin, some engine-driven fans have a device that causes the fan to slip, or freewheel above a certain engine RPM. See **Figure 11-19**. This device is called a *fan clutch*. Fan clutches are designed to save horsepower and to cut down on objectionable fan noise. Some fan clutches have a thermostatic control that will allow the fan to slip until the engine warms up and the fan is needed.

Electric Cooling Fans

Electric fans are driven by small electric motors. They are commonly used on front-wheel drive vehicles. The fan motor is usually controlled by a thermostatic switch installed in a coolant passage or in the radiator tank. Some vehicles have more than one cooling fan.

Figure 11-19. A thermostatically controlled, variable speed viscous fan drive unit. A—An exploded view of one particular setup. B—A cutaway of a viscous fan drive unit. (Dodge & Toyota)

When the engine is first stated, the electric fan does not run. As the coolant heats up, the fan comes on as needed to keep the engine from overheating. Some electric fans are operated by the engine control computer, which can also vary the fan's speed in some cases. The cooling fan will also stay on at all times while the vehicle's air conditioning system is operating.

Hoses

The radiator is connected to the engine and pump by means of rubber **hoses**. Hoses must be strong enough to withstand cooling system heat and pressure, while remaining flexible to withstand engine vibration. These hoses are of different diameters, depending upon the particular engine. There are three common types of hoses, as shown in **Figure 11-20**.

Figure 11-20. Radiator hose types. A—This common straight hose is made of rubber with one or two layers of fabric for strength. This hose will not stand much bending without collapsing. B—The molded or shaped hose shares the same construction as A. Since all the necessary bends are molded in, this hose will not collapse. C—The accordion hose will stand severe bending without collapse. It will also reduce the transfer of vibration from the engine to the radiator. D—The top hose has collapsed with bent. Middle hose has bent with no sign of collapse as it has a spiral spring-like wire inserted into it before bending. The wire is shown beneath the middle hose. All three types of hose may use the spiral wire in their construction. It can be molded in or placed in.

To bring hot coolant to the heater core, **heater hoses** are used. These hoses are smaller than the radiator hoses, and carry a smaller amount of coolant. A **heater shut-off valve** may be installed in the heater hoses. Heater construction and operation will be covered in more detail in Chapter 28. Some cooling systems make use of metal tubing as part of the coolant transfer system.

Hose Clamps

Hoses are secured to their fittings by **hose clamps**. There are two popular types. One is the adjustable, screw tightened type, and the other is the snap, or ring type. Both the screw and snap types have many adaptations. Four different styles of hose clamps are shown in **Figure 11-21**.

First Job Complete

As mentioned earlier, the cooling system has three jobs. The first job is to remove surplus heat from the engine. The second job is to maintain an even, efficient heat level. The third job is to bring a cold engine up to proper operating temperature as soon as possible after starting. The first job is completed by the coolant passages, pump, radiator, hoses, and fan, **Figure 11-22**. We will now discuss how the cooling system performs the last two functions.

The Thermostat

The system, as studied so far, would cool at a constant rate. If the capacity is sufficient to cool the engine in hot weather under heavy loads, it would obviously overcool in cold weather. At some engine speeds, the coolant may pass through the radiator too quickly to properly remove the excess heat, resulting in overheating. Some type of temperature control is necessary for good cooling system operation in hot and cold weather. To provide constant temperature control, a **thermostat** is installed in the cooling system. It is often placed directly beneath the top coolant outlet. The coolant outlet may have a bowl-shaped bottom to house the thermostat.

The Purpose of the Thermostat

The thermostat is designed to open at a predetermined temperature. When the engine is cold, the thermostat shuts off the flow of coolant from the engine to the radiator. As the coolant is confined to the engine, it heats quickly. When it reaches the thermostat's predetermined rated temperature, it opens and allows coolant to circulate. The thermostat will remain open until the temperature falls below its heat setting. The thermostat, therefore, has no effect on the maximum temperature of the engine.

If it is extremely cold, the thermostat may not open all the way. Coolant can circulate, but slowly, keeping the engine temperature at the proper level. The thermostat constantly changes the size of its opening in relation to coolant temperature. This action will bring a cold engine up to proper heat in a minimum amount of time. It will also maintain a minimum, efficient temperature level under all cold weather driving

Figure 11-21. A—A constant tension, spring-type hose clamp. B, C, and D—Three different screw-type hose clamps. D is the most commonly used. (Gates Rubber Co.)

Figure 11-22. Schematics illustrating the basic coolant flow through the various parts of a V-6 engine. Study both illustrations carefully. (Toyota)

conditions. See **Figures 11-23A** and **11-23B**. The thermostat will also allow the vehicle's heater to produce heat more quickly in cold weather.

Note in **Figure 11-24** how the coolant is heated in three stages. **Figure 11-24A** shows the thermostat closed, no flow

to the radiator, and with the top engine area (cylinder heads) heating. **Figure 11-24B** illustrates stage 2, with the entire engine heating up. **Figure 11-24C** shows the cooling system with the thermostat open and the coolant circulating throughout the system.

Figure 11-23. A—In a cold engine, a thermostat will remain closed to allow the coolant to heat quickly. B—As the engine begins to approach operating temperature, the thermostat will open and allow hot coolant to circulate.

Figure 11-24. The cooling system comes up to operating temperature in three stages. A—The coolant around the top of the engine is heated first. B—The coolant in the entire block has begun to heat and the thermostat will begin to open. C—This illustration shows that the coolant has begun to circulate through the radiator.

Thermostat Operation

The modern thermostat is operated by a wax pellet contained in a housing. Also in the housing is a valve that is operated by the wax pellet, **Figure 11-25A**. The thermostat is placed in the coolant outlet, so that the pellet case rests in the engine block coolant. When the engine is cold, there is no pellet action and the spring holds the thermostat valve closed.

As the engine coolant warms, the wax pellet is heated. This causes the wax to expand, forcing the rubber tightly

against the steel piston or pin, **Figure 11-25B**. When the coolant temperature reaches a predetermined level, the wax will have expanded to the point that the pressure on the rubber is so great that it will force the case downward against spring pressure. This pressure will pull the valve open and allow coolant to flow through the thermostat on into the radiator.

There are numerous pellet thermostat designs. Many have a pull-push valve similar to that shown while others operate a flap or a butterfly valve. The pellet thermostat is not pressure sensitive and works well in a fully pressurized cooling system. A small hole may be drilled in the thermostat valve. This acts as an aid when refilling the system as it permits air trapped in the block to escape as the coolant flows upward. In some vehicles where the radiator is lower than the engine, a *manual bleeder valve* is installed on top of the thermostat housing to help remove trapped air from the block. See **Figure 11-26**.

Figure 11-25. In a pellet type thermostat, the pellet end rests in block coolant. A—At this point, the engine coolant is cold and cannot pass by the closed thermostat valve. B—Coolant has now reached operating temperature. The wax pellet expands, squeezing the rubber against the piston hard enough to force the pellet case downward to open the valve. (Toyota)

Thermostat Heat Ranges

Thermostats are available in different heat ranges. Common heat ranges are the 180° and 195°F (82.2°-90.6°C) thermostats. The 180°F thermostat opens near this temperature and is fully opened around 200°F (93.3°C). The 195°F type starts opening near 195°F and is fully open around 218°F (103.3°C). Some thermostats range above 200°F.

These higher range thermostats raise the engine operating temperature and, in so doing, aids in emission (exhaust pollution) control. The exact thermostat temperature range used will depend on the type of engine, vehicle load, and the weather where the vehicle is operated.

MANUAL AIR
BLEEDER VALVE

BOLT

THERMOSTAT
HOUSING

GASKET

THERMOSTAT

ENGINE

BYPASS HOSE
CONNECTION

Figure 11-26. A manual bleeder valve assembly which is located in the upper half of the thermostat housing. When the valve is opened, it will allow trapped air in the cooling system to escape. (General Motors)

Internal Coolant Circulation

A thermostat will remain closed until the coolant in the engine reaches a specific temperature. If the coolant did not circulate until this temperature was reached, localized overheating (at the exhaust valves for instance) could occur. Therefore, the coolant in the engine must circulate within the engine cooling passages.

To allow the pump to circulate coolant through the engine when the thermostat is closed, a *bypass* is used. The bypass may be a fixed opening that allows coolant to recirculate within the block and heads during warmup. Coolant circulates from the cylinder head, back through the pump, and through the block and heads again. Most vehicles use a fixed bypass that allows continuous recirculation of a small portion of the coolant. When the thermostat opens, the pump can draw coolant from the radiator, and draws only a small amount of coolant through the bypass.

On some systems, the bypass is set up as shown in **Figures 11-27A** and **11-27B**. In **Figure 11-27A**, the thermostat is closed, the bypass cover finger is raised and coolant moves from the pump through the distribution tube to the open bypass pipe and into the pump. Coolant continues to recirculate until the thermostat is fully open. In **Figure 11-27B**, the pellet thermostat case has moved down, pulling the valve open and at the same time, forcing the finger to close the bypass pipe. Coolant now moves through the thermostat to the radiator.

Pressurized Cooling System

The modern engine produces tremendous heat. This heat could cause the coolant to exceed its boiling point and boil away. If the cooling system is pressurized (placed under pressure), the boiling point of the coolant is raised. A *pressurized cooling system* allows the coolant to circulate at a temperature that is closer to the engine's optimum operating temperature. Higher coolant temperatures allow the engine to run hotter which results in less exhaust pollutants.

Every one PSI (6.895 kPa) increase in cooling system pressure raises the boiling point by 3°F (1.66°C). By pressurizing the system to 15 PSI (103 kPa), the boiling point of the coolant will increase by 45°F (25°C). Since the boiling point of water is 212°F (100°C), pressurization makes it possible to operate an engine at temperatures exceeding 250°F (121°C) without boiling. Pressurization also increases coolant pump efficiency by reducing cavitation (coolant in the low-pressure area near the pump impeller blades turning to steam, allowing the pump impeller blades to spin in the air bubbles).

How System is Pressurized

Pressurizing a cooling system is done by placing a *pressure cap* on the radiator filler neck. The pressure cap presses firmly against a seat in the filler neck. As the coolant in the system heats, it also expands. As it continues heating and expanding, it squeezes the air on the top of the coolant.

Since the pressure cap has sealed the opening, the air cannot escape. When the pressure overcomes the spring holding the pressure cap seal valve closed, the seal valve will rise. As soon as the excess pressure (over what the cap is designed for) escapes, the spring closes the seal and keeps the predetermined system pressure constant. The escaping air passes out through the radiator overflow pipe.

When the engine is shut off and cools down, another small valve in the cap opens. As the coolant cools, it contracts and forms a vacuum in the radiator. This draws the vacuum valve open and allows air from the overflow pipe to enter the radiator. Without a vacuum valve, the radiator hoses could collapse.

Pressure Cap Operation

The radiator filler neck has a flange near the bottom. When the pressure cap is installed, it has a spring-loaded valve that seats against the flange. The spring-loaded valve has a valve in the center that opens when a vacuum is formed in the tank. This vacuum valve can also be spring-loaded. The large pressure release control spring is calibrated to open at a specific pressure (15-16 PSI or 103-110 kPa). **Figures 11-28A** and **11-28B** shows the operation of a pressure cap.

Coolant Recovery System

On older pressurized cooling systems, the cooling system could never be completely filled, since coolant expelled through the pressure cap was replaced by air when the engine cooled off. This meant that the cooling system could never be operated at full capacity. The *closed cooling system*, which had the addition of a *coolant recovery system*, provided vehicles with a cooling system that could be operated at full capacity. The major features are a *coolant reservoir* and a different pressure cap design. Some systems use the coolant reservoir as part of the actual cooling system. The pressure caps in these systems are mounted on the reservoir itself.

Figure 11-27. Thermostat and bypass housing action. A—The coolant is still cold and the thermostat is closed. The bypass pipe cover finger is up, exposing the bypass pipe opening. Coolant circulates from the pump, through the distribution tube, down through the bypass pipe to the pump. B—The coolant has heated, causing the pellet thermostat to open. This closes the bypass pipe and coolant flows through the thermostat valve to the radiator. (Volvo)

Figure 11-28. A—Coolant will expand until the pressure cap limit is reached. At that point, the cap will open and excess pressure will be released out of the overflow. B—When the coolant has cooled and contracted, this will form a vacuum in the radiator. The vacuum valve is drawn open and air passes into the tank through the overflow pipe. In a closed cooling system, coolant from the reservoir would flow back into the tank.

Coolant reservoirs are used to provide a storage place for coolant expelled from the radiator as the engine heats up. Coolant reservoirs are sometimes called *expansion tanks*, or *overflow tanks*. The pressure cap used with the coolant recovery system seals the radiator filler neck lower flange as well as the top flange of the neck, as illustrated in **Figure 11-28**. **Figure 11-29** shows the typical non-closed system cap. Note that the upper flange is sealed only by a thin

metal seal. This will prevent leakage if the system overheats, but does not form a positive airtight seal.

The coolant recovery system cap illustrated in **Figure 11-30** provides an additional seal ring for the filler neck upper flange. This cap provides a seal at both the upper and lower neck flanges. Note the nonloaded (no spring pressure) center vent valve. The overflow pipe is located between the two sealed areas and is connected to the coolant reservoir via a

Figure 11-29. This is a pressure cap used on many open cooling systems. Upper flange seal does not use a soft seal insert common on the lower flange seal and vacuum valve seal. (Chrysler)

NOTE:
WHEN INSTALLING RESERVOIR TANK CAP, ALIGN ARROW MARKS ON THE TANK AND CAP.

Figure 11-31. A closed cooling system reservoir tank. Excess coolant moves to the reservoir through a rubber hose. When system cools, coolant is drawn back into radiator from the reservoir.

Figure 11-30. Closed cooling system pressure cap. Note that this cap uses an additional soft seal to provide an airtight seal at the top flange. (Chrysler)

rubber hose. The hose (or a rigid pipe) passes through the cover of the coolant reservoir and extends to the bottom of the reservoir. On some vehicles, the hose is connected externally to the base of the reservoir. The reservoir usually has a cold and hot full mark, **Figure 11-31**. The radiator, unlike the older open system, is completely filled with coolant.

Coolant Recovery System Operation

When the coolant heats, it expands and flows up through the nonloaded center vent valve. This displaced coolant flows through the overflow pipe and on into the coolant reservoir. Any air that is in the system rises to the top of the coolant in the coolant reservoir and escapes out the coolant reservoir vent hose. At this point, the entire cooling system is completely filled with coolant and all air has been displaced.

As the coolant temperature nears the boiling point, the vent will be forced closed to create pressure on the system. At extremely high temperatures, the system may exceed the maximum cap pressure. When this happens, system pressure forces the bottom cap seal valve to raise off its seat and

dissipate the pressure in the form of coolant flow into the reservoir.

When the engine cools, the coolant contracts, forming a mild vacuum. This draws the cap center vent valve open and coolant, instead of air, is drawn into the system from the coolant reservoir. The recovery system allows the cooling system to operate more efficiently by eliminating air, which also reduces corrosion and overheating. The coolant level can be visually inspected without removing the pressure cap. To replace slight coolant losses, do not remove the pressure cap, merely bring the coolant in the reservoir up to the indicated level.

Temperature Indicators

The temperature of the coolant can be monitored by observing the *temperature gauge* or *warning light* on the dashboard. Temperature gauges use an electric sender and a gauge, as in **Figure 11-32**. Warning lights are operated by an on-off type of temperature switch, **Figure 11-33**. Many modern temperature gauge senders make use of electronic circuitry and also send an engine temperature signal to the on-board computer.

Using Antifreeze

To protect against engine and radiator freeze up in the winter and overheating in the summer, as well as to protect the system from rust and corrosion, manufacturers install *antifreeze*. Antifreeze is a chemical which contains *ethylene glycol*, with some *corrosion inhibitors* to reduce rust, and a small amount of *water soluble oils* to lubricate seals and moving parts.

Pure ethylene glycol freezes at about 9°F (-12°C), and water freezes at 32°F (0°C). However, when ethylene glycol and water are mixed, the freezing point of the mixture is lower than either liquid by itself. A two-third ethylene glycol and

Figure 11-32. An electric temperature gauge. Current from the battery flows through a wire coil that surrounds a bimetal (two different metals fastened together) hairpin. It then passes on to the terminal of the sender unit, traveling from the terminal through the spring to the temperature sensitive disc.

As coolant heats the disc, it will carry more electricity to ground. The resistance coil on the hairpin will start to heat up. This will transfer heat to the hairpin.

The expansion of two dissimilar metals in the hairpin causes it to bend as it heats. This bending actuates the gauge needle and causes it to move to hot.

As the coolant cools, the disc will slow down flow of electricity and the hairpin will cool, bending back to its original shape.

Figure 11-33. An engine coolant temperature sensor which is mounted in the thermostat cover. The sensor tip extends through the cover where it is submerged in the coolant stream. (Toyota)

one-third water mixture will not freeze until the temperature reaches approximately -67°F (-55°C). A 50-50 mixture will freeze at about -35°F (-37°C).

A mixture of antifreeze and water has a higher boiling point than plain water. Water boils at 212°F (100°C). A 50-50 mixture will not boil until its temperature is about 11°F (6°C) higher than the boiling point of water. Therefore an antifreeze/water solution will not boil until the temperature reaches about 223°F (106°C). If a pressure cap is used, the boiling point of the coolant mixture can be raised to almost 275°F (135°C).

Most manufacturers recommend a 50-50 mix of ethylene glycol antifreeze and water. A mixture of up to 70% ethylene glycol antifreeze and 30% water can be used in extreme hot or cold climates. Most manufacturers recommend a one or two year drain, flush, and refill cycle. Some manufacturers produce coolant that can last up to five years (100,000 miles [160,000 km]). This long-life coolant is orange or red for ease of identification. It is important to note that mixing long-life coolant with conventional antifreeze will reduce its effective service life.

Air-Cooled Engines

Many small engines are *air-cooled*. Air cooling was used on many automotive engines in the past. Vehicles with air-cooled engines were manufactured in great numbers well into the 1970s. A few modern vehicles continue to use air-cooled engines.

Air cooling is efficient and dependable. Generally an air-cooled engine warms up more quickly and operates at a somewhat higher temperature than the liquid-cooled engine. The disadvantage of air cooling is that there is no effective way to heat the passenger compartment during cold weather.

Basically, an air cooling system consists of *cooling fins* on the engine head and block, a fan to force air, a shroud to direct the air over the fins, and in some cases a thermostatically adjusted air control. Air cooling is most efficient when applied to engines that are constructed of aluminum. Aluminum is a better conductor of heat than cast iron. In fact, aluminum will conduct heat about three times better than cast iron. However, air cooling has been successfully used on cast iron engines.

It is essential that the engine block and head have a number of rather deep cooling fins. The fins are cast into the engine parts. The theory behind the use of fins is simple. Heat generated inside a metal container must pass through the walls of the container and be carried away by the airflow.

Assume that you have a square cylinder block of aluminum 6″ (15.24 cm) wide and 6″ (15.24 cm) high. Inside the block is your engine combustion chamber. As heat is generated by the burning fuel mixture, it will be conducted through the walls of the block and carried away by the air, **Figure 11-34**. If the engine produces enough heat in the combustion chamber, it is obvious that the block will not be able to dissipate the heat into the air fast enough and will eventually melt.

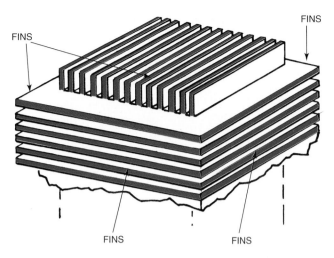

Figure 11-36. A block with finned surfaces on five sides would be able to give off a great deal of heat. This is the principle for the air-cooled engine.

Figure 11-34. Heat is conducted through the walls of the block and is carried away by surrounding air. All engines will give off some of their heat in this manner.

The rate at which the aluminum block will be able to cool itself will, to a considerable degree, be determined by the amount of block surface that is exposed to the air. Measuring and adding the lengths of the top and two sides of the block in **Figure 11-35**, you will find that three sides at 6″ (15.24 cm) per side equals 18 lineal inches. In other words, the air moving around the block can draw heat only from these 18 lineal inches of exposed surface. By adding fins to the sides and top, **Figure 11-35**, you can see how much more surface the air can strike. By adding 2″ (5.08 cm) fins to the top and sides, the air can now circulate over 162 lineal inches of block surface. The block now has nine times the cooling surface.

So far we have considered lineal (straight line) inches as viewed on three sides. If we consider our cylinder block to be square, this would give us five sides upon which to calculate the number of square inches of contact area. You will ignore the bottom side, as this would be fastened to the crankcase and would not be finned, **Figure 11-36**. By adding fins as

shown in **Figure 11-36**, you would now have a total of about 1800 in². (11 700 cm²) of contact area. This would be compared to five sides of the unfinned block at 180 in². (1170 cm²). This represents a sizable increase in cooling efficiency.

Moving The Air

In addition to adding fins, it is essential that you provide a fan or blower to produce a moving stream of air. The air, if not moved, will soon heat up and be unsuitable for further cooling of the finned surfaces. Air movement may be accomplished in several ways. One way is to have a separate fan or blower. Another method is to use the flywheel as a fan by casting fins on it. Engines designed to move rapidly through the air, such as motorcycles and aircraft, often use no fan, depending entirely upon forward momentum to provide a cooling stream of air.

Any vehicle with an air-cooled engine should not be operated for prolonged periods while standing still. Automotive engines use a separate fan, while most small engines use the flywheel fan, **Figures 11-37** and **11-38**. The separate fan in **Figure 11-37** does a better job, but it is not always possible to line up the fan with the fins. **Figure 11-38** demonstrates that even though the fan is throwing air, it is not directed onto the fins. From **Figure 11-38**, you can see that the flywheel fan throws air in a fashion similar to the way a coolant pump impeller throws coolant.

Both fans can lose efficiency by recirculating the air near the outer edges of the blades or by losing some of it. These problems are overcome by the use of an air shroud. The shroud prevents recirculation and also guides the air into the fins. **Figures 11-39** and **11-40** illustrate the use of shrouds. Some shrouds are designed to form a plenum chamber (an enclosed area in which the air pressure is higher than the surrounding atmospheric pressure).

A Thermostat is Sometimes Used

An air-cooled engine can run too cool. To prevent this, a thermostatically controlled shutter, or valve, is sometimes

Figure 11-35. If you add fins to the block, it will increase the amount of surface area exposed to the air.

Figure 11-37. An air-cooled engine uses a fan much like liquid-cooled engines to circulate air.

Figure 11-38. Like fans used on liquid-cooled engines, this flywheel fan is very inefficient without a shroud.

Figure 11-39. A separate fan with a sheet metal shroud. Notice that the shroud prevents recirculation and also guides air to the fins.

Figure 11-40. Flywheel fan with a sheet metal shroud. The shroud collects air thrown off by fan and guides it to fins. This fan acts as a centrifugal blower.

used to limit airflow. The air-cooled engine uses a bellows thermostat located in a spot that will allow it to accurately measure engine temperature.

The bellows is filled with liquid under a vacuum. If the bellows leaks, or in any other way becomes inoperative, the shutter will then return to the full open position. This eliminates the possibility of the shutter remaining in the closed position which could result in engine failure. **Figure 11-41** demonstrates the use of such a bellows.

Figure 11-41. A temperature control system for an air-cooled engine. When the engine is cold, the bellows thermostat contracts, closing the shutter. As the engine heats up, air passing over the engine will warm the thermostat, causing it to expand and open the shutter.

Summary

All internal combustion gasoline engines must be cooled, either with a liquid or air. The liquid-cooled engine commonly uses a 50-50 mix of water and ethylene glycol. In the liquid-cooled engine, the coolant must surround all the areas that are subjected to heat from the burning fuel charge.

The coolant is contained in an area referred to as the coolant passages or water jackets. When the engine is first started, the thermostat is closed and the coolant in the jacket cannot circulate. Pressure from the coolant pump then forces coolant through the bypass. This allows coolant to circulate from the pump into the block, then back into the pump.

As soon as the coolant in the engine reaches the predetermined operating temperature, the thermostat will open and allow the coolant to be pumped from the engine into the top or side radiator tank, depending on the type of radiator used. From this tank, the coolant flows through the radiator core to the other radiator tank. The coolant is then pumped back into the engine. The coolant repeats this circulation pattern over and over.

When the engine is started, the block heats quickly. The heat is transferred by conduction to the fins. Air, moved by a fan, passes through a shroud surrounding the fins. Moving air removes the heat from the cooling fins. The amount of air can be controlled by a thermostatic shutter.

Know These Terms

Liquid cooled engines	Heater hoses
Cooling passages	Heater shut-off valve
Water jackets	Hose clamps
Coolant	Thermostat
Freeze plugs	Manual bleeder valve
Coolant pump	Bypass
Centrifugal pump	Pressurized cooling system
Impeller	Pressure cap
Water pumps	Closed cooling system
V-belt	Coolant recovery system
Ribbed belt	Coolant reservoir
Serpentine belt	Expansion tank
Distribution tubes	Overflow tank
Coolant nozzles	Temperature gauge
Heat exchanger	Warning light
Radiator	Antifreeze
Radiator core	Ethylene glycol
Transmission oil cooler	Corrosion inhibitors
Fans	Water soluble oils
Fan clutch	Air-cooled
Hoses	Cooling fins

Review Questions—Chapter 11

Do not write in this book. Write your answers on a separate sheet of paper.

1. If an engine runs too cool, all of the following will happen, EXCEPT:
   (A) oil contamination.
   (B) deposit formation.
   (C) increased wear.
   (D) good fuel mileage.

2. What are the three jobs that the cooling system must perform?

3. There are two popular methods of cooling the engine. Name them.

4. To prevent dead spots and to produce a better than normal circulation in some vital areas, cooling systems use _____ .
   (A) distribution tubes
   (B) coolant nozzles
   (C) thermostats
   (D) Both A & B.

5. Modern radiators are constructed from _____ .
   (A) copper
   (B) aluminum
   (C) plastic
   (D) All of the above.

6. Fan clutches are designed to reduce _____ .
   (A) horsepower
   (B) noise
   (C) torque
   (D) All of the above.

7. The radiator heat exchanger removes heat from the _____ .

8. The thermostat should be completely closed when the engine is _____ .
   (A) cold
   (B) partially warm
   (C) fully warmed up
   (D) overheating

9. A 180° thermostat would just begin to open at _____.
   (A) 160°
   (B) 180°
   (C) 195°
   (D) 200°

10. The bypass valve prevents what problem?
    (A) Overcooling.
    (B) Overpressure.
    (C) Localized overheating.
    (D) Rust and corrosion.

11. Pressurizing the cooling system raises _____ .
    (A) engine load
    (B) coolant boiling point
    (C) thermostat opening temperature
    (D) pressure cap sealing

12. All of the following statements about coolant recovery systems are true, EXCEPT:
    (A) it allows the cooling system to be operated at full capacity.
    (B) the center vent valve of the pressure cap is non-loaded.
    (C) coolant is expelled into the coolant reservoir when the engine cools off.
    (D) the pressure cap has an extra seal at the top of the filler neck.

13. The freezing point a 50-50 mixture of water and ethylene glycol antifreeze is _____.

    (A)   9°F (-12°C)

    (B)   32°F (0°C)

    (C)   −67°F (-55°C)

    (D)   −35°F (-37°C)

14. A cooling system with a 50-50 mixture of antifreeze and water and a 12 pound pressure cap will begin to boil at _____ .

15. What is the major disadvantage of air-cooled engines for automobiles?

    (A)   They warm up too quickly.

    (B)   They are lighter.

    (C)   There is no effective way to heat the passenger compartment.

    (D)   They operate at higher temperatures than the liquid-cooled engine.

In order to operate at the high temperatures needed for good economy, modern engines need cooling and lubrication systems that are in good condition. Note the use of plastic and aluminum parts to further reduce heat. (Lexus)

12

Lubrication Systems

After studying this chapter, you will be able to:
- Explain the need for a lubrication system.
- Identify the major parts of a lubrication system.
- Explain engine oil classifications.
- Summarize the operation of an engine lubrication system.
- Identify the components of an engine lubrication system.
- List the different types of oil pumps.
- List the different types of oil filters.

This chapter will cover the causes of engine friction and reasons for a lubrication system. Also discussed will be the design and construction of the modern lubrication system and its major components. This chapter will also identify the jobs of engine oil, oil classifications, and how oil is cleaned and cooled.

The Need for a Lubrication System

If you were to start and run an engine without lubrication, it would last only a short time. The bearing surfaces in the engine would heat up and scuff. Eventually the engine would seize, or lock up. This occurs when lack of lubrication causes the moving parts in an engine to expand and overheat, tearing bits of metal from each other in the process, **Figure 12-1**. Eventually the parts will seize and refuse to move. The force that causes wear and heat and robs the engine of a portion of its potential power is called **friction**.

Friction

Friction is defined as the force that opposes movement between any two objects in contact with each other. The amount of friction depends on the type of material, surface finish, amount of pressure holding the two objects together, and relative amount of movement between the objects. You can see in **Figure 12-2**, that it takes a force to pull block A over block B.

Figure 12-2. It takes force to pull block A along the surface of block B. The force which counters the pulling force is called friction.

If you were to examine the contact surfaces of the two blocks under a microscope, you would find a series of sharp points, grooves, and other imperfections, regardless of how smooth they were polished. When the two objects are placed together, these jagged surfaces touch each other, **Figure 12-3**.

BEARING RUINED FROM LACK OF LUBRICATION

Figure 12-1. The size of this illustration is exaggerated to show the ruined journal and bearing. Oil would have prevented this.

SURFACE FINISH MAGNIFIED MANY TIMES (NOTE JAGGED EDGES)

Figure 12-3. Microscopic view (exaggerated) of block contact surfaces. All surfaces look like this, no matter how smooth they might feel or appear.

Friction Generates Wear and Heat

As soon as block A starts to move, the edges collide and impede the movement. If there is considerable pressure holding the two blocks together (bearing pressures in a normal engine can reach 1000 lbs. or 450 kg) and the movement is continued, two things happen. Each block will literally tear pieces from both itself and the other block. These tiny particles roll along under block A until they work out the back edge. Removal of these pieces is continuous and will result in wear.

Another byproduct of friction is heat. Put your hands together and rub them briskly back and forth. A fire can be started by rubbing two sticks together. These are examples of heat produced by friction. In an engine, the rubbing speeds and pressures are tremendous. Without lubrication, friction will build up enough heat to melt the bearings in a short time. It is impossible to completely eliminate friction between moving parts. If this were possible, perpetual motion machines could be easily constructed. The most that can be done is to reduce friction to an absolute minimum.

How Friction is Reduced

There are two kinds of friction, *dry friction* and *wet friction*. So far we have dealt with dry friction. Dry friction is when both rubbing parts are clean and free of other materials. Wet friction is when rubbing parts have other material or materials placed between them. Have you ever tried playing a fast game of basketball on a well-waxed gym floor? This is a good example of dry friction being changed into wet friction by placing something between your shoes and the floor—in this case, wax. It is obvious that the engine must operate under conditions of wet friction.

Bearing Construction and Friction

Bearing construction also plays a part in determining the amount of friction involved. There are two principal types of bearings used in engines. One is called a *friction bearing*. The friction bearing is literally two smooth surfaces sliding against each other. The only motion involved is a sliding effect. The babbitt insert and the crankshaft journal are examples of this type. The friction bearing is inexpensive and works well enough to be used in all automotive engines.

The other type is called an *antifriction bearing*. This bearing utilizes balls or rollers between the moving parts. One or more antifriction bearings is used in almost every part of a vehicle. Both types of bearings must be used wet. Ball and roller bearings are used in many small, high speed engines in motorcycles and outboard motors. **Figure 12-4** illustrates both bearing types.

Engine Oil

It has been found that high quality lubricating oil successfully reduces friction to an acceptable level. The oils used to lubricate engines are called *engine oil*, or sometimes *motor oil*. Since vehicle engines are not really motors, the term motor oil may seem incorrect. The term comes from the early days of the automobile, when the entire vehicle was called a motor.

Figure 12-4. Both friction and antifriction bearings need lubrication for long, trouble-free service.

Engine Oil Has Several Jobs

The most obvious job of oil is *lubricating* the engine's internal moving parts. But in addition to lubrication, the oil has other jobs in the engine. Engine oil must also assist in *cooling*. The steady flow of oil through the bearings carries away a great deal of the heat that is generated. Oil strikes the piston head and carries heat with it. As the oil is returned to the sump before being recirculated, it is much cooler by the time it reaches the bearings again.

Oil must also *seal*. Although the piston rings are closely fitted to the cylinder, they would not form much of a seal without oil as a final sealing agent. Engine oil also assists in sealing around valve stems. A good oil will also *clean*. The detergents in the oil assist in removing dirt and other impurities. They hold these impurities in suspension until they can be filtered out.

Refining Engine Oil

Engine oils are *distillated* from crude oil or petroleum that is removed from the earth through wells. The crude oil is heated and is then pumped into a tall *fractionating tower*, which contains trays at different heights. As each component of crude oil has a different *relative volatility*, they will evaporate at different temperatures. As the crude oil is heated, the lighter or more volatile (easily evaporated) components turn to a vapor or "flash" and begin to travel to the top of the tower.

As the crude oil vapor travels up the tower, the heavier or less volatile parts will condense and settle onto the trays. The lighter fractions are able to travel to the very top of the tower. A series of pipes are connected to the fractionating tower at the different tray heights. If the tower is operating properly and operating conditions are correct, a different fractionated liquid or gas will travel out of each pipe. The fractionated liquid or gas will enter a cooling tank and then will run down into storage tanks.

After the lubricating oil leaves the distillation tower, it still requires further refining and processing. Impurities are removed in a process that takes several steps. Various additives may also be added to produce oil for specific requirements. **Figure 12-5** shows the basic steps in engine oil refining.

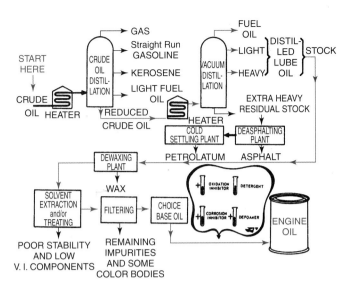

Figure 12-5. The refining of lubricating oil is a somewhat complicated task. Study the various steps involved. (John Deere)

Figure 12-6. The viscometer is used to measure the viscosity of engine oil. While appearing to be quite simple, it is a very important indicator of an oil's quality.

Oil Additives

Engine oils have many extra compounds called **additives** added to them during the refining process. Various additives such as oxidation inhibitors, detergents, defoamers, corrosion inhibitors, pour point depressants, and viscosity improvers (VI), may be added to produce oil for specific requirements. These additives are designed to improve the oil by keeping small foreign particles in suspension, fighting corrosion, reducing oxidization, minimizing carbon, water, lacquer, and gum formation, and reducing engine wear.

Modern oils have a high detergent quality that helps to keep the engine clean by preventing the formation of acids, carbon, lacquer, and gum deposits. These are all caused by the fact that some unburned gases and raw fuel can get past the piston rings and into the crankcase. Therefore, it is vital that the detergent additives in the oil hold these impurities in suspension until they can be trapped by the oil filter.

Oil Viscosity

Oil **viscosity** refers to the thickness or fluidity of the oil. In other words, it is a measure of an oil's ability to resist flowing. The Society of Automotive Engineers (SAE) has set low (0°F or -18°C) and high (210°F or 99°C) temperature requirements for oil. Oils that meet special SAE low temperature requirements have the letter W following the viscosity rating, such as 10W. Oils that meet the high temperature requirements have no letter, but are designated by a number such as 30.

Viscosity is determined by taking a sample of oil and heating it to a certain point. The heated oil is then allowed to flow out of a very precise hole. The length of time it takes to flow determines its viscosity rating. The faster it flows, the lower the rating. This testing device is referred to as a viscosimeter, **Figure 12-6**.

Viscosity Index

Oils thin out when heated and thicken when cooled. As a good engine oil must be reasonably thin for cold starts and thick at high temperatures, the **viscosity index** (VI) is important. The VI is a measure of an oil's ability to resist changes in viscosity with changing temperatures. When oils are heated, they tend to lose their body (resistance to oil film failure). If a given oil is thin at cold temperatures and does not thin out much more when heated, it is said to have a high VI. If the heating produces a great change in viscosity, the oil has a low VI.

Multi-Viscosity Oils

A **multi-viscosity oil** contains special hydrocarbon molecules commonly known as **polymers**. Polymers make the oil thinner when cold and thicker when hot. Polymers allow a multi-viscosity oil to meet the low temperature requirements of a light oil and the high temperature requirements of a heavy oil. Since they meet the viscosity and performance requirements of two or more SAE grades, they are marketed in such weights as 5W-30, 10W-30, 10W-40, and 20W-50. They are often referred to as multi-grade, multi-weight, all-season, and all-weather oil.

Choosing Oil Viscosity

Always follow the manufacturer's recommendation for viscosity rating. The most commonly used oils are 30, 10W-30, 10W-40, and 20W-50. 5W, 10W, or 5W-30 are recommended in areas where the temperature is frequently lower than 0°F (-18°C). These recommendations are based on engine design and the lowest anticipated temperatures.

Engine Oil Service Classification

Presently, there are nine oil **service grades** for automotive gasoline engines. The American Petroleum Institute (API) has classified these oils as SA, SB, SC, SD, SE, SF, SG, SH, and SJ for use in gasoline engines. The letter S indicates the oil is for use in **spark ignition** (gasoline) engines. **Figure 12-7** illustrates the typical API marking found on most oils intended for gasoline engines.

Figure 12-7. This symbol or "logo" is used on containers of engine oil to assist the buyer in selecting the proper oil. The oil's quality and service recommendation is given by API (American Petroleum Institute) numbers. In this example, Service SJ (oil for gasoline engines), the viscosity is indicated by the SAE (Society of Automotive Engineers) number 5W-30. The term "Energy Conserving II" indicates that this oil has additional friction reducers for improved fuel economy.

The API has classified oils for use in diesel engines as CA, CB, CC, CD, and CE. The C indicates that the oil is for use in **compression ignition** (diesel) engines. The second letter indicates the amount of anti-wear additives, oxidation stabilizers, and detergents. The eight current gasoline engine oil grades are discussed below.

SA and SB oils were the first engine oils to be classified by the API. They are recommended for light loads, moderate speeds, and clean conditions. They contain no additives and are known as **non-detergent oils.** These oils are still available for use in very old vehicle and stationary engines and are sometimes used in gearboxes and in two-stroke cycle engines. They should never be used in late model vehicle engines.

The first **detergent oil** was grade SC, followed over the years by SD, SE, SF, SG, SH, and SJ. The latest oil designation is SJ. This oil will also replace all former oil classifications. Most manufacturers do not bother to put the earlier grade designations on their oil, as they have been superseded by grade SJ. CF, CG, and CH are the latest oil grades for diesel engines and supersede CA, CB, CC, CD, and CE oils. Many oils have more than one classification.

Detergent oil is used to prevent the buildup of dirt, soot, and sludge in the engine. They hold impurities in suspension in the oil until they can be trapped by the oil filter. However, detergent oils may not be suitable replacements for non-detergent SA or SB, since the detergent qualities may loosen internal engine deposits, clogging the filter or engine oil passages.

Refer to the chart in **Figure 12-8.** Note the relationship between the previously used API classifications and the new ones in use today. Engine oils may also be classified according to manufacturer's specifications or to military specifications (standards developed by the US military for oils to be used by them).

Oil Change Intervals

The answer to this frequently asked question depends on so many variables that a general recommendation is very difficult to make. Many manufacturers state that oil does not have to be changed before 7500 miles (12 000 km) or every 6

	NEW API ENGINE SERVICE CLASSIFICATIONS	PREVIOUS API ENGINE SERVICE CLASSIFICATIONS	RELATED DESIGNATIONS MILITARY AND INDUSTRY
GASOLINE ENGINES	SA	ML	Straight Mineral Oil
	SB	MM	Inhibited Oil
	SC	MS (1964)	1964 MS Warranty Approved. M2C101-A
	SD	MS (1968)	1968 MS Warranty Approved, MC2C101-B, 6041 (Prior to July, 1970)
	SE	None	1972 Warranty Approved, M2C101-C, 6041-M (July 1970)
	SF	None	1980 Warranty Approved
	SG	None	1987 Warranty Approved
	SH	None	1994 Warranty Approved
	SJ	None	1998 Warranty Approved
DIESEL ENGINES	CA	DG	MIL-L-2104A
	CB	DM	Supp. 1
	CC	DM	MIL-L-2104B
	CD	DS	MIL-L-45199B, Series 3
	CE		
	CF		
	CG		
	CH		

Figure 12-8. Chart shows the relationship between the old and the new API Service classifications for gasoline and diesel engines.

months under normal conditions. However, the definition of normal conditions varies greatly. Any grade of engine oil will retain proper lubricating properties longer if:

- The engine is operated for reasonably long periods each time it is started.
- The engine is in good mechanical condition.
- The engine runs the majority of the time at its normal operating temperature (over 180°F (93.3°C) or higher).
- The engine has a good oil filter.
- The positive crankcase ventilation (PCV) system is functioning properly.
- The engine is operated at moderate to fairly high speeds.
- The engine is provided with an efficient air cleaner.
- The fuel system is properly adjusted.
- The engine is operated under clean conditions.

The conditions given are ideal. If an engine operates under them, the oil can be used for the maximum recommended time. Engines that are operated in dusty or dirty conditions, that are in poor mechanical condition, or that do not have a filtration system, should have the oil changed at least every 3000 miles (1800 km) or 3 months. Turbocharged and supercharged engines should have their oil changed every 3000 miles (1800 km) under all conditions.

Engine Lubrication Systems

Even the best oil is useless unless it can reach the engine's moving parts. The job of the lubrication system is to get the oil to the moving parts of the engine. How it does this is covered below.

How Oil Works

When oil is injected into a bearing, **Figure 12-9**, it is distributed between the bearing surface and the shaft, creating a film that separates the parts. The parts then revolve without actually touching each other. When the engine is shut off and oil is no longer supplied, the shaft will settle down on the bearing, squeezing the oil film apart. Some residual oil (oil that clings to the parts) will be retained.

OIL TENDS TO RESIST SLIPPING ON BEARING AND JOURNAL SURFACES

MOST OF SLIPPING OCCURS NEAR CENTER OF OIL FILM

Figure 12-10. The oil provides a thin film on which the shaft rides. This keeps the shaft separated from the bearing.

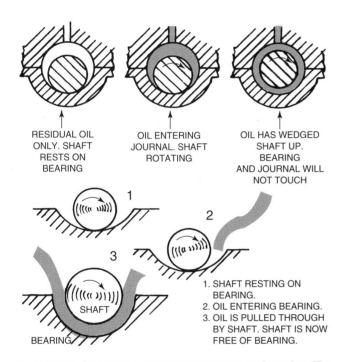

RESIDUAL OIL ONLY. SHAFT RESTS ON BEARING

OIL ENTERING JOURNAL. SHAFT ROTATING

OIL HAS WEDGED SHAFT UP. BEARING AND JOURNAL WILL NOT TOUCH

1. SHAFT RESTING ON BEARING.
2. OIL ENTERING BEARING.
3. OIL IS PULLED THROUGH BY SHAFT. SHAFT IS NOW FREE OF BEARING.

Figure 12-9. Oil enters a bearing by pressure and rotation. The pressurized oil enters the bearing and journal area as the shaft is rotating. The rotation of the shaft pulls the oil around. As more oil is pulled around, the shaft begins to ride on a thin film of oil, away from the bearing and journal.

The top of the film that contacts the shaft journal and the bottom of the film that contacts the bearing, resist movement to some extent. The sliding effect of the oil is achieved near the center of the film. See **Figure 12-10**. This slipping action allows the journal to spin easily and still not contact the bearing surface.

When the engine is started, the shaft will have only residual oil for the first few seconds of operation. This is why engines should be allowed to idle, in park or neutral, until the oil light goes out or the oil pressure gauge needle begins to rise. In cold conditions, additional time should be given to allow the oil to circulate. Other engine parts, such as the valve train and cylinders, are under the same load at all times and will not be unduly damaged if the engine is driven before they begin to receive oil.

Bearing Clearance

It is important that all bearings have the proper clearances. The ideal bearing clearance is loose enough for oil to enter, but tight enough to resist pounding. Oil clearances are very small, around .002″ (0.05 mm).

Three Types of Lubrication Systems

The engine bearings and all other moving parts are lubricated by one of three systems:

- Full pressure system.
- Splash system.
- Combination pressure-splash system.

The full pressure system will be discussed first.

Full Pressure System

The *full pressure system* draws oil from the *oil pan* by means of an *oil pump*. The pump then forces oil through drilled and cast passages, called *oil galleries*, to the crankshaft and camshaft journals. The crankshaft is drilled to permit oil to flow to the connecting rod journals. In some engines, the rods are drilled their full length to allow oil to pass up to the wrist pin bushings.

Bearing throw-off may be helped by spurt holes in the rod to lubricate the cylinder walls and camshaft lobes. Timing gears and chains, lifters, pushrods, and rocker arms are also oiled. In the pressure system, all bearings are oiled by either pumping oil into the bearings, or by squirting or dripping it on, **Figure 12-11**. The lubrication system also provides the pressure to fill the hydraulic lifters.

Splash System

The most basic *splash system* supplies oil to moving parts by attaching *dippers* to the bottom of the connecting rods. These dippers can either dip into shallow trays or into the sump itself. The spinning dippers splash oil over the inside of the engine. The dipper is usually drilled so that oil is forced into the connecting rod bearings. An oil pump may be used to keep the oil trays full at all times. The basic splash system is used primarily on small one-cylinder engines, **Figure 12-12**.

Figure 12-11. Notice how oil in the pressure system travels to all major bearings. When it passes through the bearings, it is thrown around, creating an oil spray and mist. The oil eventually returns to the oil pan sump.

Figure 12-12. This simple splash oiling system, while used mostly on small engines, is combined with the pressure system on some engines to provide additional oiling.

Combination Pressure-Splash System

This system uses an oil pump to supply oil to the camshaft and crankshaft bearings. The movement of the crankshaft splashes oil onto the cylinder walls and other nearby parts. Oil spurt holes in the connecting rods are used to spray oil onto the cylinder walls and piston pins.

Oil is also pumped to the cylinder head to oil the camshaft, rocker arms, and valves as applicable. Pressurized oil leaving the pushrods sprays oil around the valve cover, lubricating the rocker arms and valve stems. A nozzle is sometimes used to squirt oil onto the timing gears and chain. Some combination systems make use of a dipper to splash the oil, as in **Figure 12-13**.

Figure 12-13. Combination splash and pressure oiling system. Oil pump 6 draws oil up pipe 5 from the oil sump 9. It then pumps the oil to main bearings 1 through the discharge pipe 7. Oil is also pumped down discharge nozzle 8 where it sprays out and strikes dipper 3. This feeds oil into rod bearing 2. Tray 4 also holds oil for the dipper to strike.

Components of the Pressure-Splash System

The combination **pressure-splash system** best meets the needs of the modern engine and is therefore in almost universal use. Oil is constantly drawn from the bottom of the engine, pressurized, and distributed to the engine parts. The oil then drips to the bottom of the oil pan sump and begins the circuit again. The rest of this chapter will deal primarily with the components which develop pressure.

Oil Pan Sump

Oil is poured into the engine and flows down into the oil pan. One end of the pan is lowered to form a reservoir called a **sump**. Baffle plates and screens are sometimes used to prevent the oil from sloshing around and striking the crankshaft. The drain plug is placed in the side or bottom of the sump. See **Figure 12-14**

Figure 12-14. Oil pan with sump and baffle. There are many different designs for oil pans, sumps, and baffles.

Oil Pickup

Most engines have a rigid pipe leading down into the oil in the sump. The *oil pickup* does not touch the bottom to avoid picking up sludge. Some engines use a floating pickup. This pickup actually floats on top of the oil, drawing only from the top of the sump. As the oil level drops, the pickup will also drop to maintain a constant supply of oil.

All oil pickups use screens to exclude the larger particles that may be drawn into the system. In the event the screen becomes clogged, there may be a small valve that will be drawn open, allowing the pump to bypass the screen and obtain oil, **Figure 12-15**.

Figure 12-15. Oil pickup with filtering screen and a bypass valve. Note the gear type oil pump. (Chevrolet)

Oil Pumps

There are three principal types of oil pumps that have been used on engines. They are the gear, rotary, and vane pumps. The two most widely used are the gear and the rotary types.

Gear Pump

The *gear pump* uses driving and driven gears as the moving force to pump oil. These gears are placed in a compact housing. The driven gear revolves on a short shaft, while the driving gear is fastened to a long shaft. This shaft is turned by a spiral gear meshed with a similar gear on the camshaft. The teeth of the two gears must mesh with a minimum amount of clearance. The housing just clears the top, bottom, and sides of both gears.

An inlet pipe allows oil to be drawn in by the turning gear teeth. As the teeth move apart in the inlet side, they create a vacuum which draws in oil. The oil is carried around to the other side. As the teeth move together, they pressurize the oil, which is then discharged from the pump outlet. The pressurized oil then enters the rest of the lubrication system. The gear pump is efficient and produces high pressure and flow when needed. Gear pump operation is shown in **Figure 12-16**. An exploded view of a gear pump is shown in **Figure 12-17**.

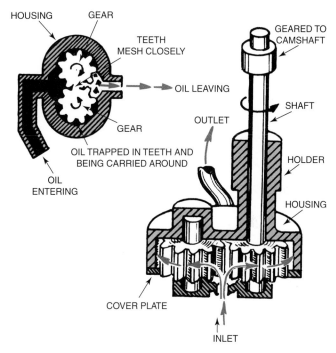

Figure 12-16. Gear oil pump. Notice how oil is caught in the gear teeth and carried around. As the pump spins rapidly, it will produce a steady stream of oil.

A different adaptation of the gear pump is shown in **Figure 12-18**. The driving gear (center) and driven gear (outer) teeth carry oil around to the outlet area. As the teeth mesh, the oil is compressed and forced through the outlet. An exploded view of a similar pump is shown in **Figure 12-19**.

Rotary Pump

A *rotary pump* uses a housing, an inner rotor, and an outer rotor. The outer rotor is cut away in the form of a star with rounded points. The inner rotor is shaped in the form of a cross with rounded points that fit in the outer rotor star. The inner rotor is much smaller. It is driven by a shaft turned by the camshaft.

The inner rotor is mounted off center so that when it turns, the rounded points walk around in the star-shaped outer rotor. This causes the outer rotor to revolve also. As the inner rotor walks the outer rotor around, the outer rotor openings pick up oil at the inlet pipe and pull it around until it lines up with the outlet. It is then forced out as the inner and outer rotor points close together. The oil cannot make a circuit around, as the inner rotor fits snugly against the outer rotor at

Figure 12-17. An exploded view of a gear type oil pump. Note the slot in the pump drive shaft which connects to a shaft from the distributor. (Jeep)

Figure 12-18. Gear oil pump using one gear with internal teeth and another with external teeth. As gears rotate, oil is carried past the filler block in the teeth of each gear. This oil is deposited in the outlet area. Since the gears mesh, the oil has no place to escape and pressure is built up, forcing oil through the outlet. (Deere & Co.)

Figure 12-19. One form of gear oil pump. The principle of operation is same as that in Figure 12-18. (Toyota)

one spot. **Figure 12-20** shows rotor pump operation. **Figure 12-21** is an exploded view of a rotor pump.

Vane Pump

The **vane pump** uses a round housing with a rotor placed off center. This rotor contains two or more vanes, or rotor blades, that fit into slots in the rotor. The vanes are held out against the round housing by springs between the vanes. Some designs feed oil under pressure to the inner vane ends. This pressure, along with centrifugal force, helps hold the vanes in firm contact with the housing wall.

As the shaft turns, the vanes are forced in and out to keep contact with the housing. As they move outward, they create a vacuum which draws oil in the inlet port. As the vane is forced in on the other side, it pressurizes the oil and pushes it out of the pump. As a steady charge is picked up, carried around, and squeezed out, the pump produces a good supply of oil. **Figure 12-22** shows the operation and an exploded view of a vane pump.

Pressure Relief Valve

An oil pump in good condition will produce pressures far beyond those necessary for lubrication. The pumps are designed to carry a large flow of oil, but when the usable pressure limits are reached, a **pressure relief valve** opens and allows oil to return to the sump. See **Figure 12-23**.

Figure 12-20. Rotor oil pump action. A—Pump inlet and outlet areas. B—Drive shaft turns the inner rotor, causing it to walk around in the outer rotor. The outer rotor will also turn in response. C—The rotor pulls around a charge of oil and forces it through the outlet. (1). While this is happening, another charge is moving around (2) and another is being picked up at the inlet (3). (Jaguar)

Figure 12-22. A vane type oil pump. A—Vane pump cross-sectional view. Follow the oil flow. B—Exploded view of a vane style oil pump. Note the blade (vane) springs which will keep the vane in contact with the pump chamber wall as they spin. (Deere & Co. and Allis Chalmers)

Figure 12-21. An exploded view of a dual rotor type engine oil pump, and related parts. (Honda Motor Co.)

Figure 12-23. Oil in the main oil gallery is under pressure from the oil pump. When pressure exceeds the setting for the oil pressure relief valve, it will push the plunger check valve back against the plunger spring pressure. When the valve is forced back far enough to expose the oil outlet channel, oil will pass from the main oil gallery, through the oil outlet, and back into the pan sump.

The relief valve will allow the pressure reaching the bearings to remain at a predetermined level. By varying spring tension, the pressure can be raised or lowered. The relief valve can be located right at the pump, **Figure 12-24**, or at any spot between the pump and the bearings.

Oil Galleries and Lines

Oil that is allowed to pass the pressure relief valve is carried to the bearing through the oil galleries. The main oil gallery runs lengthwise in the block and is connected to most of the other galleries. Most engines have two or three plugs in the back of the block at the end of the main gallery. During an

Figure 12-24. An exploded view of an oil pressure relief valve which is housed in the oil pump body. The relief valves can be located in many different areas, depending upon lubrication system design and construction. (Toyota)

engine overhaul, the plugs should be removed and the gallery cleaned.

Passages from the main gallery are drilled to the main bearings. The crankshaft is drilled to carry oil from the main journals to the rod journals. Some engines use separate lines to carry part of the oil flow. See **Figures 12-25** and **12-26**. Some rods are drilled through their full length to carry oil to the wrist pins. Others have tiny holes that line up with the crank journal once every revolution. When the two holes align, oil is squirted through the spit hole and onto the cylinder wall. Spit holes are also used to lubricate the camshaft lobes in some engines.

The timing chain is oiled either by spray, by oil discharged from the No. 1 camshaft bearing, or by oil discharged from an oil nozzle. The valve train is lubricated by oil spray and in the case of overhead valve engines, by oil pumped into the rocker arm shaft, through the rockers to the valves. Oil can also reach the rocker arms via hollow push rods. Some engines do not employ rocker arms, but operate the valves directly from the camshaft lobes, **Figure 12-26**. Camshafts receive oil under pressure to their journals. The lobes are lubricated by oil spray.

Oil Enters Bearing

The bearing receives oil from a hole drilled through the bearing support. The insert has a hole that aligns with the one

Figure 12-25. Oil flow through a V-6 engine. A—Cutaway showing the oil flow through the engine itself. B—An oil flow system schematic. Note that this engine uses an oil cooler. (Toyota)

in the bearing support. The oil passes through and engages the turning journal and is pulled around between the insert and journal. Some inserts have shallow grooves cut into them to assist in spreading the oil.

Oil is constantly forced through the bearings. Oil leaving a bearing is thrown violently outward. This helps to produce the fine oil mist inside the engine that is useful in lubricating hard-to-reach areas. All oil eventually flows back into the sump.

OIL PASSAGE IN CAMSHAFT

CAMSHAFTS

OIL SPRAY NOZZLE

OIL FILTER

OIL DRAIN

REAR OIL PUMP

OIL PASSAGE IN CRANKSHAFT

OIL PAN

OIL PICKUP

Figure 12-26. A full-pressure engine oiling system that uses a rotor oil pump. (Toyota)

Hydraulic Valve Lifters

Hydraulic valve lifters are used on many engines. One type of hydraulic lifter is shown in **Figure 12-27**. In this lifter, oil under pressure is forced into the tappet when the valve is closed. This extends the plunger in the tappet, so valve clearance is eliminated.

When the camshaft lobe moves around and starts to raise the tappet, oil is forced upward in the lower chamber of the tappet. This closes the ball check valve and oil cannot escape. Since oil does not compress, the valve is actually lifted on the column of oil and is supported by the oil while the valve is open.

When the cam lobe moves from under the tappet and the spring causes the valve to close, pressure in the lower chamber of the tappet is relieved. Oil loss from the lower chamber is replaced by oil pressure from the lubricating system.

Oil Filtration

After it has been in the engine a while, the oil becomes contaminated with dust, bits of carbon, metal dust, and sludge. Modern detergent oils keep these contaminants in suspension instead of allowing them to build up on the inside of the engine. If these impurities are allowed to remain in the oil, it will hasten engine wear. Engines are equipped with an oil filtering system to remove these harmful impurities.

Oil Filters

Many materials have been tried in an effort to find a satisfactory filtering medium. Cotton waste, plant fibers, metal, clay, and paper have all been used. Today, filters are grouped into two main classifications, *depth filters* and *surface filters*. Depth filters are made of various fibers, while surface filters are made of treated paper. A few filters used in heavy trucks and construction equipment are made of closely spaced metal plates. **Figure 12-28** illustrates the filtering principle used in cotton, paper, and metal filters.

Some oil filters use a permanent metal container that holds a replaceable filtering element, or cartridge. Most filters are one-piece disposable units in which the entire filter

Figure 12-27. A—The action of this hydraulic valve lash adjuster allows it to receive oil during normal camshaft rotation. B—Oil flow. C—Camshaft. D—Hydraulic valve adjuster body. E—Oil gallery. F—Valve stem. G—Cylinder head. H—"A" chamber. I—Plunger. J—Plunger spring. K—Body. L—Check ball cage. M—"B" chamber. N—Check ball spring. O—Check ball. B—Hydraulic valve lifter (non-roller type), showing the tappet action. Note that the hydraulic valve lash adjuster (1), is in direct contact with the overhead camshaft. (General Motors)

assembly is discarded. The filter assembly is usually installed on the bottom or side of the engine. One filter design is installed inside the oil pan.

Filter Operation

Oil is pumped into the container and surrounds the filter. The oil passes through the filtering element to the center outlet pipe. It is then returned to the sump or to the bearings, depending on the type of system. **Figures 12-29** and **12-30** illustrate full-flow and depth filters.

Figure 12-29. When a full-flow oil filter must be changed, the entire filter is replaced. 1–Relief valve. 2–Filter element (folded paper). 3–Body. 4–Connecting pipe. 5–Gasket. 6–Engine block. This pleated paper filter provides surface filtration in that all particles are trapped on the outer surface. (Volvo)

Figure 12-28. These materials are used to construct different types of oil filters. A—Cotton waste between thin perforated metal sheets. B—Paper treated with resins. C—Uno type uses thin layers of metal sheet held apart by bumps or bars.

Figure 12-30. Depth type filtration oil filter. 1–Housing. 2–Seal. 3–Oil inlet. 4–Oil outlet. 5–Check valve to prevent oil drain back when filter is mounted in either a horizontal or inverted (upside down) position. 6–Filter material. 7–Relief valve opens if filter clogs. (Volvo)

Full-Flow Filter System

On modern engines, the entire output of the pump goes through the filter. This is called the *full-flow filter system*. After passing through the filter, the oil goes to the oil galleries. In this way, all oil is filtered before reaching the bearings. In the event the filter becomes clogged, a small relief valve opens and allows the oil to flow directly to the bearings. This protects the bearings from damage due to lack of oil. See **Figure 12-31**.

Bypass Filter System

The *bypass* system is used on older vehicles. It differs from the full-flow system in that it does not filter the oil before it reaches the bearings. However, it is constantly filtering some of the oil in the system and then returning it to the sump. See **Figure 12-32**.

Figure 12-31. Note built-in relief valve in this full flow oil filter system. This valve allows oil to flow even if the filter becomes clogged. This system filters all oil before it reaches the bearings. (John Deere)

Filter Replacement Intervals

All oil filters, if not replaced, will eventually become clogged. The better the filter can remove contaminants from the oil, the sooner it can become clogged. Filter change intervals are subject to the same variables as were discussed in the section on engine oil changing. Replacement varies, but will average between 1000 and 6000 miles (1600 to 9600 km) per filter. Most manufacturers recommend changing the filter at each oil change or at every other oil change.

Crankcase Ventilation

Even in new engines, a certain amount of exhaust gas and unburned fuel gets by the piston rings and into the crankcase. This is called *blowby*, which causes pressure to build up in the crankcase. Unless it is vented, blowby will force oil to escape by the oil seals.

It is also important to remove the gases and raw fuel before they form moisture and acids in the oil. When the engine heats up, the unwanted blowby gases will evaporate and the ventilation system will remove them. If they are not removed, the oil will be quickly contaminated and the engine will be damaged.

On older engines, a vent pipe called a road draft tube was used to vent the crankcase. The road draft tube ran down below the engine. When the vehicle was in motion, a partial vacuum was formed at the end of the pipe, which drew air through a breather cap.

The cap was filled with an oil-soaked metal wool to prevent the entrance of dust and dirt. The road draft tube contained a baffle, which prevented oil vapor from being drawn through, **Figure 12-33**. Unfortunately, the road draft ventilation system allowed air pollutants to enter the atmosphere and did not do a thorough job of removing blowby. All modern engines use a *positive crankcase ventilation*, or *PCV* system.

Figure 12-32. This bypass filter system filters some of the oil all of the time, but does not filter oil before it reaches the bearings. (John Deere)

Figure 12-33. Airflow in a road draft crankcase ventilation system. Notice the filter material in both inlet and outlet.

Positive Crankcase Ventilation (PCV)

The PCV system uses intake manifold vacuum to draw fresh air through the engine. Clean air is taken from either the breather cap (open system) or the air cleaner (closed system). All engines now use the closed system to prevent fumes from leaving the engine during periods of high crankcase pressure or when the engine is stopped.

The air is pulled through the engine where it mixes with gases in the crankcase. The mixture of air and gases is then drawn into the intake manifold, where it is burned in the cylinders. A PCV valve controls air flow through the crankcase. **Figure 12-34** shows a cross-sectional view of a closed positive crankcase ventilation system. **Figure 12-35** illustrates the difference between the open and closed ventilation systems. The complete operation of the positive crankcase ventilation system will be covered in Chapter 14.

Oil Seals

Oil is retained in the engine by *gaskets*, *sealants*, and *oil seals*. Gaskets, such as the one in **Figure 12-36**, are used throughout the engine. Room temperature vulcanizing (RTV) and anaerobic sealants are used with or in place of some gaskets on modern engines. Seals are placed at the front and the rear of the crankshaft, **Figure 12-37**. Some crankshafts have an *oil slinger* cast into them, **Figure 12-38**. The slinger catches what oil may escape past the bearing and throws it outward into a catch trough that returns the oil to the sump.

Oil Pressure Indicators

Oil pressure can be determined by a dashboard mounted *oil pressure gauge* or *warning light*. An electric oil pressure gauge uses a different sender unit than that used by an electric water temperature gauge. **Figure 12-39** shows a

Figure 12-34. Vacuum created in the intake manifold draws air from the air cleaner and passes it through the engine. (Dodge)

Figure 12-36. A silicone rubber oil pan gasket is used to prevent oil leakage between the block and oil pan. (Chrysler)

Figure 12-35. Two types of positive crankcase ventilation systems. A—Closed type that draws air in through the air cleaner. B—Cutaway of the air flow control valve. C—Open type that draws air in through the breather cap. (Plymouth)

Figure 12-37. A cross-sectional view of a V-8 engine showing the front and rear crankshaft oil seals. (Ford)

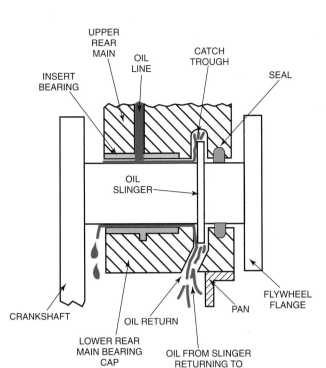

Figure 12-38. Oil that escapes past the bearing is stopped by the slinger and seal. Oil on the slinger is thrown out into the catch trough and returned to the sump. Some engines use a seal only. One type of seal is made of rope, oil impregnated and covered with graphite. Other crankshaft seals are made of synthetic rubber.

Figure 12-39. Study the schematic diagram of this electric oil gauge carefully. Electricity travels from the battery through the key switch to coil 2; then across wire 4 to coil 1 and on to ground. Both coils are connected by wire 4 to resistance unit 8, mounted on the engine.

Oil entering at 5 will raise diaphragm 6 causing sliding contact 7 to slide further out on the resistance unit, which will increase resistance.

When resistance is increased, coil 1 will strengthen its magnetic pull on armature 3. This will pull the armature and indicating needle over to read more pressure.

When oil pressure drops, the sliding contact will come back and decrease resistance. This strengthens coil 2 and weakens coil 1. Coil 2 will now pull the armature and needle down to read less pressure.

typical electric oil pressure gauge setup using the balancing magnetic coil principle. **Figure 12-40** shows a heating coil electric pressure gauge setup. Note the difference between this unit and the one in **Figure 12-39**. Some vehicles use a warning light to indicate when the pressure drops below a certain point. **Figure 12-41** illustrates a warning light system that warns of low crankcase oil level. The light warns of system failure, but does not indicate actual oil pressure.

Dipstick

A long metal rod, commonly referred to as a **dipstick**, is used to check the amount of oil in the crankcase sump. The

Figure 12-40. In a heated coil oil pressure gauge, current flows through both the gauge coil and the sender heating coil. Both coils heat up and cause the bimetal strips to bend. The gauge bimetal strips will move the indicator needle when it bends. How far the needle moves depends on how hot the bimetal strips get. The gauge bimetal temperature is controlled by the sender's bimetal strips. As the sender heats up, the bimetal strips bend away from ground, breaking the circuit. When the circuit is broken, the sender coil cools and the bimetal strips make contact again, reestablishing current flow. This process occurs over and over.

A—The sender diaphragm is not pushing the insulated contact up. The bimetal breaks current easily, so the coils heat for a short period. B—Oil pressure is high, which forces the diaphragm up, bending the grounded contact up. The sender coil will now have to stay on much longer to heat the bimetal enough to break contact. This keeps the gauge coil heated longer, imparting a greater bend to its bimetal strip. The indicator needle now moves further across the gauge indicating more oil pressure. (Deere & Co.)

Figure 12-41. A—Low oil level indicator light electrical circuit schematic. B—Cross-sectional view of the low oil level switch and its mounting location in the oil pan. As the floats travel down (from oil loss) on the reed guide, it will open a contact switch as it reaches a predetermined minimum oil level in the pan. This will turn on the indicator light on the instrument panel. (Mercedes-Benz)

Figure 12-42. Engine oil dipstick location as used by one vehicle manufacturer. Note the dipstick markings. (Ford)

dipstick is held in a tube, just long enough for the end of the dipstick to protrude into the sump. Some dipsticks are connected to the oil fill cap. It may be withdrawn and the oil level in the sump checked by examining the dipstick to see where the oil reaches. **Figure 12-42** shows a dipstick and its markings.

Cooling the Oil

Oil removes much heat from the pistons and cylinder walls and becomes quite hot. It is important that the oil have some way to rid itself of excess heat. In the average engine, this is accomplished by the airstream passing over the thin oil pan, thus drawing much heat from the oil. Some oil pans have fins cast into them to aid in the cooling. The cooling system keeps the cylinder block and head area within an acceptable temperature range thus limiting oil heat exposure. Oil moving through the filter gives off some heat to the airstream and the entire engine surface gives off heat. All these sources of heat removal will normally prevent excess heating of the oil.

Many high performance and heavy duty engines as well as some normal duty engines that may occasionally be exposed to heavy operating loads (trailer towing, steep roads, or extremely hot weather), are equipped with an *auxiliary oil cooler*. Numerous designs have been used. The oil can be cooled by air or coolant depending on the design.

One type of engine oil cooler is shown in **Figure 12-43**. This particular cooler fits between the oil filter and the engine block. Engine coolant circulates around the thin discs making up the oil compartment. As the oil passes through the cooler on its way to the filter, it is forced through the thin disc compartments where it gives off heat to the passing coolant.

Summary

Friction, the enemy of all engines, is controlled through the use of lubricating oil. Lubricating oil must cool, clean, seal, and lubricate. The viscosity, or weight, and the service rating, such as SH or CE, are important factors in choosing the proper oil for a specific engine.

Engine oil is drawn from the oil pan sump through a strainer by the oil pump. It is then pumped to all the major bearings through a network of oil galleries and tubes. Maximum oil pressure is controlled by a pressure relief valve.

ENGINE OIL COOLER ELEMENT

Figure 12-43. One type of engine oil cooler that utilizes circulating engine coolant to help reduce the oil operating temperature. In this unit, the oil travels through the cooler on its way to the oil filter. (Honda)

The most commonly used oil pumps are the gear and the rotor types that are either turned or actuated by the camshaft.

Upon entering the bearings, the engine oil separates the moving parts with a fine film. As it passes through the bearings, it is thrown outward in every direction. Oil drops down on some parts and is sprayed against others. The spinning parts create an oily mist that lubricates the other areas. It is then returned to the sump for recirculation. The system is ventilated to remove moisture, hot gases, and excessive pressure.

Modern engines filter the oil through the use a full-flow system. Even with filtering, oil must be changed periodically. The length of time between changes depends on driving conditions and the number of miles driven. Oil pressure is measured by means of a gauge or a warning light. The amount of oil in the sump can be checked by using the dipstick. Some engines are equipped with oil coolers.

Know These Terms

Friction	Oil galleries
Dry friction	Splash system
Wet friction	Dippers
Friction bearing	Pressure-splash system
Antifriction bearing	Sump
Engine oil	Oil pickup
Motor oil	Gear pump
Lubricating	Rotary pump
Cooling	Vane pump
Seal	Pressure relief valve
Clean	Hydraulic valve lifters
Distillated	Depth filter
Fractionating tower	Surface filter
Relative volatility	Full-flow filter system
Additives	Bypass
Viscosity	Blowby
Viscosity index	Positive crankcase
Multi-viscosity oil	ventilation (PCV)
Polymers	Gaskets
Service grades	Sealants
Spark ignition	Oil seals
Compression ignition	Oil slinger
Non-detergent oil	Oil pressure gauge
Detergent oil	Warning light
Full pressure system	Dipstick
Oil pan	Auxiliary oil cooler
Oil pump	

Review Questions—Chapter 12

Do not write in this book. Write your answers on a separate sheet of paper.

1. The amount of friction developed between moving parts depends on _____ .
   (A) the type of material
   (B) surface finish
   (C) pressure between moving parts
   (D) All of the above.

2. For purposes of illustration, friction was defined or divided into two kinds. Name them.

3. What is a frozen bearing?
   (A) A very cold bearing.
   (B) A very oily bearing.
   (C) A stuck bearing.
   (D) A loose bearing.

4. Name two kinds of bearings that can be used in an engine.

5. Name the two organizations which classify engine oil according to viscosity and grade.

6. A detergent oil prevents or reduces the formation of _____ .

7. A good engine oil has four tasks. What are they?

8. Polymers are used to make what kind of oil?

9. Technician A says that SAE 30 oil should be used for cold weather operation. Technician B says that SAE 5W-30 oil should be used for cold weather operation. Who is right?

   (A) A only.

   (B) B only.

   (C) Both A & B.

   (D) Neither A nor B.

10. The most common method of lubricating an automotive engine is _____ .

    (A) pressure

    (B) splash

    (C) combination pressure-splash

    (D) adding oil to the fuel

11. Name three types of oil pumps.

12. Which two of the above oil pumps are the most widely used?

13. The oil pressure in a system cannot exceed a predetermined pressure. How is this pressure controlled?

14. What is an oil gallery?

15. If only part of the oil leaving the oil pump is filtered, what kind of filter system is it?

16. Depth and surface are the two most popular types of _____ .

    (A) oil pumps

    (B) oil filters

    (C) bearings

    (D) hydraulic lifters

17. In the full-flow filtering system, what happens when the filter is clogged?

    (A) The engine is ruined.

    (B) The oil must be changed.

    (C) The bypass valve opens.

    (D) Both A & B.

18. What does the positive crankcase ventilation system (PCV) prevent?

    (A) Oil contamination.

    (B) Sludge buildup.

    (C) Crankcase pressure buildup.

    (D) All of the above.

19. In addition to gaskets, oil _____ are placed on the front and rear of the crankshaft.

20. What do you use to tell how much oil is in the sump?

    (A) An oil pressure gauge.

    (B) A warning light.

    (C) A dipstick.

    (D) The amount of time since last oil change.

13

Exhaust Systems

After studying this chapter, you will be able to:
- Explain the purpose of the exhaust system.
- Describe the operation of the exhaust system.
- Identify exhaust system components.

This chapter outlines the purpose of the exhaust system, describes various exhaust system designs, and identifies the major exhaust system components. While the exhaust system appears to be relatively simple, it is vitally important to the efficient operation of a vehicle's engine. Studying this chapter will prepare you for the material in Chapter 14, which discusses emission control systems.

Purpose of the Exhaust System

The purpose of the exhaust system is to route the exhaust gases from the engine, reduce exhaust noise, and keep the gases from entering the passenger compartment. The exhaust system must be free from leaks and vibration. It must be designed to prevent excessive **back pressure**. Back pressure occurs when the flow of exhaust gases is restricted, making it harder for cylinders to clear themselves during the exhaust stroke. Excessive back pressure can seriously reduce engine power and mileage. In extreme cases, back pressure can cause the exhaust valves to burn.

Exhaust System Designs

Every exhaust system functions in the same manner. Burned gases leave the engine through the exhaust ports and enter the exhaust manifold. From the manifold, gases travel through the exhaust pipe, catalytic converter, and muffler. The gases leave the vehicle via the resonator, if used, and the tailpipe.

There are two basic types of exhaust systems: single exhaust systems and dual exhaust systems. The following sections describe each type of exhaust system in detail.

Single Exhaust System

In the **single exhaust system,** only one exhaust pipe is used. See **Figure 13-1.** Note that this system has two oxygen sensors installed in the pipes. The purpose of the oxygen sensor is covered in Chapter 15. The pipe, converter, and muffler are sized in proportion to the engine displacement. Single

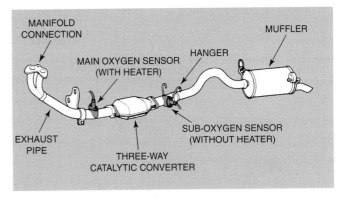

Figure 13-1. A single exhaust system. Note the main oxygen sensor and the sub-oxygen sensor. The sub-oxygen sensor rechecks the exhaust content and sends a signal to the electronic control unit to make any needed corrections to the air-fuel mixture. It also acts as a back up should the main oxygen sensor fail.(Toyota)

exhaust systems are the most common and are used on all types of engines.

Dual Exhaust System

The **dual exhaust system** is used primarily on V-type engines. It consists of two separate exhaust systems, each equipped with a catalytic converter and muffler. **Figure 13-2** shows a typical dual exhaust system. Because dual exhaust systems offer twice as much exhaust system capacity, they reduce back pressure. However, the components in a dual exhaust system do not get as hot as those in a single exhaust system. Therefore, dual exhaust components tend to corrode more easily.

A dual exhaust system also has a higher noise level since the noise reduction potential of self canceling action is lost. **Self canceling** occurs when the noise and pressure pulses of the engine cylinders cancel each other out when they are channeled through a single exhaust system.

There are many types of dual exhaust setups. Some systems have dual exhaust pipes from the engine to the catalytic converters and then join the pipes so that they use a single muffler and tailpipe. Many dual exhaust systems have an **equalizer pipe** that connects each exhaust pipe ahead of the mufflers or converters. See **Figure 13-3.**

Figure 13-2. One particular exhaust system with hangers, clamps, gaskets, etc., for a V-8 engine. Note the dual catalytic converters. (Chrysler)

Figure 13-3. Dual exhaust pipe assemblies with an equalizer pipe connecting the two pipes before the mufflers. The equalizer pipe helps to even out the pressure between the two sides. (Chrysler)

Exhaust System Components

The same basic components are found in all exhaust systems. The sections below explain the construction and operation of these components.

Exhaust Manifolds

Exhaust manifolds channel exhaust gases from the exhaust ports to the rest of the exhaust system. Exhaust manifolds are constructed of cast iron or stainless steel. Manifolds are manufactured with smooth, gentle bends to improve exhaust flow. **Figure 13-4** illustrates exhaust manifolds for a V-6 engine.

Some engines use steel tube exhaust manifolds, often called *headers*. They are carefully engineered to reduce restrictions. Each header tube is the same length between the exhaust port in the cylinder head and the collector box where the tubes connect to a single large exhaust tube, **Figure 13-5.** This allows the exhaust pulses to interact with each other to reduce back pressure. This interaction is called exhaust *scavenging*. Modern manifolds are accurately designed to take advantage of the exhaust scavenging effect. These manifolds are sometimes called *cast iron headers*.

The exhaust manifold is bolted to the cylinder head. Most manifolds use a gasket at the head attaching point, while some older manifolds rely on a metal-to-metal contact for sealing. The manifold may contain a heat control valve and passageways for air injection nozzles or an oxygen sensor. These are covered in detail in Chapter 14.

Exhaust Pipes

The *exhaust pipes* connect the exhaust manifold, muffler, converter, and resonator. Any pipe other than the tailpipe can be called an exhaust pipe. They are produced using coated and stainless steel. Exhaust pipes are often **double-walled** (made of two pipes, one pressed inside of the other) for added sound deadening. See **Figure 13-6.**

Figure 13-4. Right and left-hand side exhaust manifolds as used on a V-6 engine. Note that each manifold has its own heated oxygen sensor (HO$_2$S). (Honda Motor Company)

Figure 13-5. A stainless steel tube exhaust header. This header will increase the exhaust gas flow efficiency, reduce weight, and aid in catalytic converter warm-up. (Toyota)

Figure 13-6. A cutaway of a double-walled exhaust pipe.

Some exhaust systems make use of a **flexible tube** to allow for expansion and contraction as the system temperature changes. The tube is usually an accordion-shaped pipe covered with braided wire.

Catalytic Converters

All modern vehicles contain a catalytic converter. It is placed in the exhaust system before the muffler to clean exhaust gases. Most converters are clamped or bolted to the exhaust system. Catalytic converters are discussed in more detail in Chapter 14.

Mufflers

The muffler has the job of reducing engine noise without restricting exhaust flow enough to cause excessive back pressure. There are two basic muffler designs: the **reverse-flow muffler** and the **straight-through muffler**.

Reverse-Flow Muffler

The reverse-flow muffler uses a series of **muffler chambers** to cause the exhaust gases to reverse direction. This change in direction reduces the noise level, **Figure 13-7.** Small openings and slits between the various chambers allow the sound waves in each chamber to cancel each other. Internal **baffles** absorb and dampen more of the exhaust sounds. Many reverse-flow mufflers have a small hole at the bottom of the case to allow moisture and acids to drip out.

Figure 13-7. Cutaway of one type of reverse-flow muffler. (AP Parts)

Straight-Through Muffler

The straight-through muffler is sometimes called a "*glass pack*" or "*steel pack*" muffler, **Figure 13-8**. In this muffler, the exhaust passes straight through a perforated pipe (pipe with many holes or splits) that is surrounded by steel wool or fiberglass packing. The steel wool or fiberglass absorbs the noise.

The straight-through muffler is designed to minimize back pressure. Straight-through mufflers also require less space under the vehicle. A disadvantage of the straight-through muffler is the tendency of the packing to settle and break up, requiring early muffler replacement.

Figure 13-8. A straight-through muffler. Heavy fiberglass packing is used around the perforated pipe.

Another kind of straight-through muffler is shown in **Figure 13-9**. Instead of using fiberglass, the perforated sections of the pipe are surrounded with sound-deadening chambers. This design, termed a "*chambered pipe*," requires a minimum of space beneath the vehicle.

Figure 13-9. A chambered pipe exhaust system. A series of muffling chambers are incorporated into this system.

Resonators

Resonators are small extra mufflers designed to further reduce exhaust noise. They are usually found on more expensive vehicles, where the goal is to produce the quietest possible exhaust. Resonators may be reverse-flow or straight-through designs. They are generally installed near the end of the exhaust system to silence any resonance.

However, some newer vehicles have the resonator before the mufflers, **Figure 13-10**. *Resonance* is the vibration sound created or sustained within the exhaust system after the quieting action of the regular exhaust system.

Tailpipes

The *tailpipe* is the last pipe in the exhaust system. Most tailpipes are of single-wall construction. Many late-model tailpipes are welded to the muffler and may contain the resonator, if used.

Figure 13-10. This dual exhaust system contains a resonator. Note the spring hangers, which allow additional system flexibility. (General Motors)

Hangers

The exhaust system is suspended on *hangers* designed to provide support while allowing the system to flex. The hangers must not allow exhaust system noise and vibration to be transmitted to the vehicle body. They must provide shock protection and sound deadening and stand up to exhaust system heat and road debris. See **Figure 13-11**. On many modern vehicles, rubber retaining rings are used to attach the exhaust system to the hanger assemblies. They allow a greater degree of flexibility than a conventional hanger. **Figure 13-12** shows one type of retaining ring arrangement.

Some vehicle exhaust systems use rods that are welded onto the pipes. The ends of the rods fit into bushings or retaining rings, **Figure 13-13**. The use of these rods allows the exhaust system components to expand and contract as their temperature changes.

Heat Shields

The modern exhaust system, especially the catalytic converter, produces a great deal of heat. To provide sufficient ground clearance, these systems must be mounted close to the vehicle's floor pan. To prevent heat damage to various components under the vehicle and to prevent the transfer of heat to the passenger compartment, *heat shielding* is used on modern vehicles.

Heat shields generally consist of sheet metal housings placed around the hottest parts of the system, metal shields

Figure 13-11. Exploded view of an exhaust system's various support hangers and rubber insulator bushings. The style and location of the hangers vary by vehicle and manufacturer. (Toyota)

Figure 13-12. This exhaust system hanger allows flexing and reduces noise. Note the rubber retaining rings, or biscuits. (Volkswagen)

located between the floor pan and exhaust components, or heavy insulation placed under the carpet. Heat shields are also used under the catalytic converter to protect items under the vehicle from the heat produced by the converter. If this were not done, it would be possible for the converter to ignite dry grass or other flammable materials. **Figure 13-14** shows the heat shields used on one particular single exhaust system. Also note the flexible tube described earlier in this chapter.

Exhaust System Materials

Exhaust components are subjected to intense heat (as much as 1600°F or 871°C), corrosive gases on their inner surfaces, and water, dirt, salt, and debris on their outer surfaces. To provide proper service life, stainless steel is used for the

Figure 13-13. A metal hanger rod is welded to this muffler. It attaches to a frame hanger bracket with a rubber insulator. (Dodge)

converters and occasionally for some of the piping. Aluminized steel (coated with a layer of aluminum, inside and out) is widely used for exhaust pipes, tailpipes, and mufflers. These metals are highly resistant to corrosion. Because the catalytic converter produces tremendous heat, which also helps to drive out moisture, exhaust systems on late-model vehicles tend to last longer than systems on older vehicles

Sealing the Exhaust System

As mentioned earlier, it is vitally important that the exhaust system be sealed, both to reduce exhaust noise and to prevent exhaust gas entry into the passenger compartment. Important sealing principles are covered in the following sections.

Exhaust Pipe-to-Manifold Connections

An exhaust pipe-to-manifold connection may be one of several types. A flat-surface connection which utilizes a gasket is shown in **Figure 13-15.** The *semi-ball connector,* **Figure 13-16,** uses the ball seal on one side only and allows

Figure 13-15. Flat, gasketed exhaust manifold-to-pipe connection. (Volkswagen)

Figure 13-14. A complete exhaust system with heat shielding (in color) and a flexible tube. (Nissan)

Figure 13-16. Semi-ball manifold-to-pipe connection. This connection allows a degree of flexibility in response to engine and vehicle movement. (Cadillac)

some flexing without breaking either the seal or the manifold-pipe assembly. A gasket is not needed. Note the use of springs to maintain pressure under vibration and temperature changes.

A similar fitting makes use of a semi-ball gasket made of high-temperature fiber. The advantage of this type is that the gasket can compress to fit uneven surfaces. A **full-ball connector** having ball seals on both sides is shown in **Figure 13-17.** This design also provides some flexing without leaking.

Figure 13-17. Full-ball manifold-to-pipe connection. 1–Exhaust manifold. 2–Spherically flared exhaust pipe. 3–Flange. 4–Spherical conneciton adapter. 5–Self-locking hex head nut. 6–Hex head bolt. (Mercedes-Benz)

Pipe-to-Pipe Connections

Most connections between the exhaust pipes, tailpipes, mufflers, and resonators are pipe-to-pipe connections. Pipe-to-pipe connections are made by sliding one pipe into another and securing the connection with an **exhaust system clamp**, or **muffler clamp**, **Figure 13-18.**

Figure 13-18. A—U-bolt exhaust clamp. B—Band clamp. All clamps will provide a 360° leakproof seal when correctly installed. (Chevrolet, Goerlich Co.)

The pipes are carefully manufactured so that they can be assembled easily and will seal well when clamped. Typical clamp connections are shown in **Figure 13-19.** In many cases, an air tube from the air injection pump is attached to the catalytic converter using a small clamp, **Figure 13-20.**

Many catalytic converters are connected to the rest of the exhaust system with the semi-ball or full-ball connections discussed earlier. In many cases, pipe-to-pipe connections are welded together. When the connection is welded, the pipes must be cut off to replace the component. All connections must be tight and absolutely leak free.

Other Connections

Many other devices are attached to the exhaust system on modern vehicles. These include one or more oxygen sensors, air injector nozzles, and heat control devices. Oxygen sensors and air injector nozzles are usually threaded into the

Figure 13-19. Several typical exhaust system clamps and their positions in relationship to the pipes, muffler, etc. (Chrysler)

appropriate exhaust system component and require anti-seize compound on their threads. The manifold heat control device must move in its shaft. If the shaft opening begins to leak, the entire component should be replaced. Sometimes weights are clamped to the pipes to further reduce exhaust resonance.

Summary

Exhaust systems usually consist of an exhaust manifold, catalytic converter, muffler, resonator, exhaust pipes, tailpipe, and all the necessary connections, fittings, heat shields, and hangers.

Stainless steel is used for catalytic converters and some exhaust pipes. Aluminized steel is widely used for the remainder of the system. Exhaust systems on late-model vehicles last longer than systems on older vehicles because the catalytic converter produces more heat, which drives out additional moisture

Exhaust systems must not leak. They should quiet the exhaust and discharge it properly to the passing air stream. Exhaust pipe-to-manifold connections can be of many types. Gasketed flat-surface, semi-ball, and full-ball connections are often used. Pipe-to-pipe connections often slip together and are secured with clamps.

Know These Terms

Back pressure	Double-walled
Single exhaust system	Flexible tube
Dual exhaust system	Reverse-flow muffler
Self canceling	Straight-through muffler
Equalizer pipe	Muffler chambers
Exhaust manifold	Baffles
Headers	Resonators
Scavenging	Resonance
Cast iron headers	Tailpipe
Exhaust pipes	Hangers

Figure 13-20. This exhaust system has an air injection pump tube that is secured to the catalytic converter with a U-bolt clamp. (Dodge)

Heat shielding   Exhaust system clamp
Semi-ball connector   Muffler clamp
Full-ball connector

Review Questions—Chapter 13

Do not write in this book. Write your answers on a separate sheet of paper.

1. All of the following statements about exhaust system back pressure are true, EXCEPT:

    (A) excessive back pressure can reduce engine power and mileage.

    (B) back pressure occurs when the exhaust gas flow is restricted.

    (C) complete lack of back pressure can cause exhaust valves to burn.

    (D) excessive back pressure makes it harder for cylinders to clear themselves during the exhaust stroke.

2. List two types of muffler construction.

3. Where is double-wall construction used?

    (A) Exhaust pipes.

    (B) Mufflers.

    (C) Resonators.

    (D) Tailpipes.

4. A resonator is used to _____ .

    (A) reduce exhaust sounds

    (B) force air into the converter

    (C) prevent exhaust back pressure

    (D) cool the exhaust gases

5. Explain why exhaust systems on late-model vehicles last longer than those on older vehicles.

6. Technician A says that exhaust system hangers hold the exhaust system rigidly to provide support. Technician B says that the hangers cannot allow exhaust system noise and vibration to be transmitted to the vehicle body. Who is right?

    (A) A only.

    (B) B only.

    (C) Both A & B.

    (D) Neither A nor B.

7. The modern exhaust system produces a great deal of heat. When installing catalytic converters and exhaust pipes, all _____ must be in place to prevent damage to adjacent parts.

8. Modern manifolds are designed with tubes of equal length to make use of the exhaust _____ effect.

9. Many pipe-to-pipe connections are held together with _____ .

    (A) clamps

    (B) welds

    (C) gaskets

    (D) Both A & B.

10. Welded exhaust system components must be _____ if they need to be replaced.

Manufacturers are experimenting with zero emissions vehicles, such as this electric car. A three-phase alternating current motor delivers the driving force to the wheels. (General Motors)

14

Emission Controls

After studying this chapter, you will be able to:
- Define automotive emissions.
- List the three most harmful automotive emissions.
- List the three major classes of emission controls.
- Explain the operating principles of common emission control systems.
- Identify the major parts of common emission control systems.

This chapter covers the various types of emission controls used on modern vehicles. Many emission control devices have been developed over the last 30 years. Many early devices were developed as the need arose. Most modern emission controls are descendants of these devices. These modern systems are fully integrated into the overall engine system and are usually monitored and controlled by the engine control computer. After studying this chapter, you will understand how these systems work and how they are coordinated to keep emissions as low as possible. This chapter will also prepare you for the computer control information in Chapter 15.

The Need for Emission Controls

Many exhaust emissions, such as water, oxygen, nitrogen, and carbon dioxide, are of little concern. Others, such as **hydrocarbons** (HC), **oxides of nitrogen** (NO_x), and **carbon monoxide** (CO), can pose health and environmental problems if they are not controlled. For example, hydrocarbon emission into the atmosphere tends to produce photochemical (sunlight causing chemical reactions) smog.

Emission Control Systems

Progress has been made in the development of emission control devices. When properly maintained, these units do an excellent job of reducing harmful emissions. Emission controls may be divided into three general types:
- Engine modifications and controls.
- External cleaning systems.
- Fuel vapor controls.

Engine modifications and controls include the basic design of internal engine parts, such as combustion chamber shape, camshaft lift and duration, intake manifold design, and the controls used to alter ignition timing, fuel mixture, and combustion chamber temperature.

External cleaning systems are used to help the exhaust gases continue the burning process as they move through the exhaust system. These controls include the air injection system and the catalytic converter.

The **fuel vapor controls** are designed to prevent the escape of gasoline vapor, a common source of unburned hydrocarbons, from the tank filler cap, tank, carburetor, and other vehicle components. Also falling under vapor control is the control of engine crankcase fumes caused by unburned fuel leaking past the piston rings.

Engine Modifications and Controls

Engine modifications and controls are designed to more completely burn the fuel charge within the combustion chamber and to ensure that all gases leaving the chamber are as environmentally safe as possible.

Engine Modifications

In modern vehicles, internal engine parts are designed to balance the needs of performance, emissions, and driveability. The most common of these internal modifications are explained in the following sections.

Combustion Chamber Shape

The combustion chamber in modern cylinder heads is designed to reduce the amount of hydrocarbons in the exhaust. Older head designs had complex combustion chamber shapes, with areas that almost touched the piston head when the piston was at the top of the cylinder. This mixed the air and fuel more thoroughly, producing more power with less detonation. However, it caused unburned fuel to condense and cling to the sides of the combustion chamber without burning.

Combustion chambers in newer heads have simple shapes and small surface areas to reduce fuel condensation. They also have a larger volume, which lowers compression ratios. The combustion chamber area is reduced, minimizing the chance for fuel to become trapped.

Lower Compression Ratios

Modern engines have lower compression ratios than older engines. This allows modern engines to operate on low-octane unleaded gasoline without detonating or dieseling. Since lower compression also lowers the temperature of the combustion process, the oxygen and nitrogen are less likely to combine into NO_x. In addition, the lower compression allows the engine to operate on unleaded gas, which must be used if the vehicle has a catalytic converter.

Camshaft Designs

Modern camshafts have less **overlap** (the time when both the intake and exhaust valves are open) than older camshaft designs. Camshafts with large amounts of overlap give the engine good high speed performance. However, this overlap causes the incoming air-fuel mixture to be diluted by exhaust gases at idle and low speeds. On older engines, this dilution was overcome by rich idle mixtures. Since it is no longer desirable to have rich idle mixtures, overlap has been reduced to prevent exhaust dilution and roughness at low speeds. These "milder" camshafts reduce engine power to increase smoothness.

Hotter Thermostats

Cooling system thermostats used on modern engines do not begin to open until the coolant temperature has reached at least 190°F (88°C). Thermostats used on older vehicles opened between 160° and 180°F (71° and 82°C), depending on the vehicle.

The modern engine cooling system warms up quickly and operates at higher temperatures than older systems. This keeps the combustion chamber at higher temperatures for most of the time that the engine is operating. Higher temperatures reduce gasoline condensation on the combustion chamber surfaces and cylinder walls, reducing the levels of HC.

Fuel System Controls

Most fuel system controls involve producing a leaner air-fuel ratio—one in which there is a higher percentage of air.

Lean Carburetors

Carburetors and fuel injection systems on newer vehicles operate at an air-fuel ratio as close to 14.7:1 as possible. This is the ideal ratio for mileage and emissions, but not necessarily for power and driveability. Newer carburetors have smaller main jets, reduced accelerator pump output, and power valve springs that do not allow the power valve to open until the engine is under very heavy loads. The idle mixture screws are sealed to prevent readjustment. See **Figure 14-1.**

Modern carburetors are controlled by the engine computer through a mixture control solenoid, **Figure 14-2.** When the engine is warming up, or when wide open throttle operation is necessary, the air-fuel ratio may be enriched by the choke, accelerator pump, or power valve. Rich ratios are used as little as possible.

Other ways in which the carburetor has been modified to lower emissions are faster-opening chokes, more precise idle speed control, and the use of throttle positioners. These devices were covered in detail in Chapter 10.

Figure 14-1. Cross-sectional view of a carburetor with a sealed idle mixture adjustment screw and sealing plug. (Pontiac)

Lean Carburetor Dieseling

Due to lean carburetor mixtures, high operating temperatures, and fast idle speeds, some modern engines develop hot spots in the combustion chambers that ignite the fuel mixture and tend to keep the engine turning after the ignition key is turned off. This is commonly known as **dieseling** or **run-on.** Besides being extremely annoying, dieseling can produce a considerable amount of pollution.

To prevent dieseling, some engines employ an electric anti-dieseling solenoid. When the key is on, the solenoid keeps the throttle valve open far enough for normal idle. When the key is turned off, the solenoid allows the throttle to close completely. This shuts off all air, and the engine cannot diesel. Another setup automatically engages the air conditioning compressor drive clutch for several seconds whenever the key is turned off. This places the engine under a small load, causing it to slow down and stop without dieseling.

The ultimate solution to air-fuel ratio control is computer-controlled electronic fuel injection. Fuel injection, discussed in Chapter 9, has replaced the carburetor on all late model engines.

Quick Air-Fuel Mixture Heatup

To allow a cold engine to run properly with lean mixtures, the incoming air must be heated to prevent fuel condensation in the intake manifold. Heating the incoming air allows the choke to be opened sooner, reducing the amount of HC. It also helps prevent **carburetor icing.** Carburetor icing occurs when the lower air pressure in the carburetor venturi causes water vapor to freeze in the carburetor throat. This ice formation can cause the engine to run roughly or stall in cold, damp weather.

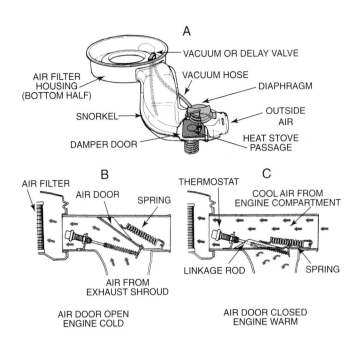

Figure 14-3. Two different types of thermostatic air cleaners (Thermac). A—This air cleaner uses a vacuum-operated diaphragm to control the heat stove. B & C—This illustrates the air door position on an air cleaner which uses a thermostat linkage assembly to open the air door. Study the air flow arrows. (AC-Delco & Sun Electric Corp.)

Figure 14-2. A—Electrically operated mixture control solenoid with O-ring seal, gasket, and electrical conneciton harness. B—Cross-section of a carburetor and mixture control solenoid mounted in place. This mixture solenoid is cycled up and down ten times a second to carefully control the air-fuel mixture. The solenoid is preset and sealed at the factory. (Pontiac)

Thermostatic Air Cleaner

The **thermostatic air cleaner** is one of the devices used to heat the incoming air. It employs a special valve in the air inlet section of the air cleaner housing. See **Figure 14-3.** When the valve is closed, ambient temperature air is drawn in. When the valve is fully opened, heated air (drawn from a shroud around the exhaust manifold) is admitted and the cooler air is excluded. At positions between fully open and fully closed, a blend of both heated air and ambient air is admitted. This permits smooth engine operation on relatively lean fuel mixtures.

The modern air control door is actuated by a vacuum valve or motor, **Figure 14-4.** When the engine is started cold, a vacuum motor is employed. The cold engine start position is shown in **Figure 14-4B.** The thermal sensor bleed valve is closed, and full vacuum is applied to the vacuum motor. This

pulls the diaphragm up against spring pressure and fully opens the air valve to allow the entrance of heated air.

When the thermal sensor warms, it opens the air bleed. This stops vacuum to the vacuum motor, allowing the spring to force the diaphragm down and close the valve, **Figure 14-4C.** A cutaway view of the complete thermostatically controlled air cleaner assembly is illustrated in **Figure 14-5.**

Early Fuel Evaporation System

The **early fuel evaporation system** (EFE) warms the incoming air by transmitting exhaust heat to the exhaust crossover under the intake manifold. A vacuum-operated valve provides this enriched flow of hot gases during cold engine operation. This improves engine performance and reduces emissions. On older vehicles, a thermal vacuum switch controls the EFE valve. Later EFE valves are controlled by a solenoid that is operated by the engine control computer.

When coolant temperature is below a certain point, the vacuum switch or solenoid applies vacuum to the EFE valve, which, in turn, diverts the gases up under the intake manifold before they exit through the exhaust system. See **Figure 14-6.** EFE systems were discussed in detail in Chapter 10.

Spark Timing Controls

A number of systems have been developed to alter ignition spark advance to meet most engine operating conditions. Most of these systems retard the operation of the vacuum advance unit, when used, or use the engine computer to modify the timing.

Figure 14-4. Operation of the thermostatically controlled air cleaner. Study each view and note the action of various controls in determining the position of the control damper.

Figure 14-5. Construction details of a thermostatically controlled air cleaner. The damper is blending both hot and cold air. (Buick)

Older vehicles may have a *vacuum advance restrictor,* which is attached between the vacuum advance unit and the intake manifold. On these systems, the advance unit is connected to manifold vacuum through a ported vacuum opening on the carburetor. The ported vacuum connection ensures that no vacuum reaches the advance unit at idle speeds.

A vacuum restrictor is inserted into the vacuum line. When the throttle is opened, ported vacuum is forced to pass through the restrictor. The restrictor prevents full vacuum from reaching the advance unit for up to 30 seconds after the throttle is opened. This lowers HC emissions while providing good highway mileage.

On other older vehicles, solenoid-operated vacuum valves are installed in the vacuum line from the manifold to the advance unit. These valves are energized by electrical switches on the transmission or speedometer. The vacuum advance cannot receive full vacuum until the vehicle is in high gear or has reached a certain speed. Some systems allow for overriding of the control system when engine or outside air temperature is below a certain point. When a temperature override switch opens, the solenoid is de-energized, providing full advance until the engine warms up. A vacuum advance control device is shown in **Figure 14-7.**

Since the introduction of computer engine controls, ignition timing has been precisely controlled by the engine computer. Modern systems use a spark control computer and a number of engine sensors to provide instantaneous timing control. This permits smooth engine operation on lean fuel mixtures.

Exhaust Gas Recirculation (EGR)

When peak combustion temperature exceeds 2500°F (1372°C), the nitrogen in the air mixes with the oxygen to produce oxides of nitrogen (NO_x). By introducing a metered portion of the hot exhaust gases into the intake manifold, the *exhaust gas recirculation system,* or EGR system, dilutes

Figure 14-6. A—Early fuel evaporation (EFE) coolant temperature operating switch schematic. B—Exhaust gases crossing under the intake manifold to warm the incoming air-fuel mixture. (OTC, Sun)

Figure 14-7. Various electrical solenoid-operated vacuum valves. A—Cutaway of an electrically operated vacuum valve. B—Overall system using a vacuum solenoid valve (VSV). This system uses the speedometer cable sensor to indicate vehicle speed. The amplifier boosts the weak speed sensor electrical signal so that it is strong enough to operate the vacuum solenoid valve. (Sun)

the incoming fuel charge and lowers combustion temperatures. This reduces the level of NO_x.

The amount of exhaust gas that is recirculated is controlled by an EGR valve. Such valves are widely used, as they can be designed to admit carefully controlled amounts of exhaust gases into the intake air stream. The exact amount required will vary according to engine speed and loading.

There are three basic types of EGR valves:
• Vacuum modulated (ported) valves.
• Back pressure modulated valves.
• Electronic-vacuum modulated valves.

Vacuum Modulated (Ported) EGR Valve

The **vacuum modulated EGR valve** uses a vacuum diaphragm to operate the gas flow control valve, or pintle. The vacuum tube is connected to a timed port in the carburetor or throttle body. The port is located just above the throttle valve in the idle position. When in the idle position, the throttle valve covers the port and no vacuum is applied to the EGR valve, **Figure 14-8A.** Note the diaphragm spring forces the valve closed and exhaust gas does not flow.

When the throttle valve is opened beyond the idle position, the port is uncovered and engine vacuum is applied to the EGR valve. The vacuum causes the diaphragm to raise

upward against spring tension. This draws the valve (pintle) upward, allowing exhaust gas to flow through the valve into the intake manifold. See **Figure 14-8B.**

The EGR valve remains closed during periods of idle or heavy deceleration (accelerator completely released). Flow is reduced or stopped during heavy acceleration because low engine vacuum is not strong enough to operate the diaphragm.

The EGR valve should remain closed when the engine is cold because a cold engine will run rough if the EGR valve is opened. On some engines, a temperature-sensitive control is placed between the EGR valve and the carburetor or throttle body. Below certain temperatures, the EGR vacuum line is closed, preventing the EGR valve from operating. A schematic showing how the timed port on an engine with a carburetor admits vacuum to the EGR valve diaphragm is shown in **Figure 14-9.**

Back Pressure Modulated EGR Valve

Some **back pressure modulated EGR valves** use two separate diaphragms, while others, such as the valve illustrated in **Figure 14-10,** utilize a single diaphragm that serves two separate functions.

Figure 14-8. Action of the vacuum diaphragm operated EGR valve. Note how the engine vacuum is used to open the valve in B.

Figure 14-9. When the throttle valve starts to open, the timed port is uncovered, admitting engine vacuum to the EGR vacuum diaphragm. This opens the pintle valve. (General Motors)

The power diaphragm portion, shown in **Figure 14-10A,** is secured between the outer edges of the diaphragm plate and the valve stem support housing. The center, or control diaphragm portion divides the chamber formed between the diaphragm plate and the valve stem support housing. The power diaphragm plate is spring-loaded. The spring closes the pintle valve when the engine is stopped or when intake vacuum cannot be applied to the power diaphragm.

In **Figure 14-10A,** the engine is operating. Timed vacuum is applied to the power diaphragm. The control valve is open as the control diaphragm is held down by the valve spring. As long as it remains open, air is allowed to enter and a vacuum cannot be formed above the power diaphragm. Until a sufficient vacuum is formed, the power diaphragm will remain down, keeping the pintle valve closed. Although exhaust gases cannot pass the pintle valve, they move up

through the hollow valve stem and enter the chamber beneath the control diaphragm. Pressure builds up in the chamber and attempts to force the control diaphragm upward.

In **Figure 14-10B,** the exhaust gas back pressure has risen to the point that it has forced the control diaphragm upward, causing it to seal off the control valve opening. Because air can no longer pass, vacuum is formed above the power diaphragm. Atmospheric pressure acting on the bottom of the power diaphragm housing assembly moved the entire unit up, opening the pintle valve. Exhaust gas now passes into the intake manifold.

Electronic EGR Valve

The operation of the *electronic EGR valve* is similar to that of a ported EGR with a vacuum regulator. The electronic EGR valve has a sealed cover. A solenoid valve opens and closes the vacuum signal, which in turn controls the amount of vacuum that is vented into the atmosphere. The solenoid is controlled by the engine control computer, which is discussed in more detail in Chapter 15. The EGR valve is cycled on and off many times per second. See **Figure 14-11.**

External Cleaning Systems

Unlike the systems discussed above, that reduce the amount of harmful gases produced by the engine, external cleaning systems clean up the exhaust gases after they leave the engine. The most common external cleaning systems are the air injection system and catalytic converter.

Air Injection System

Hydrocarbon and carbon monoxide emission through the exhaust system can be reduced by thoroughly burning the fuel remaining in the exhaust gases. This is performed by the *air injection system.* The air injection system is sometimes called an Air Injection Reactor, Thermactor, Air Guard, or simply, a smog pump.

The exhaust gases leaving the engine on the exhaust stroke contain unburned hydrocarbons (HC). The exhaust stream is still hot enough to continue burning these hydrocarbons, but there is not enough oxygen to do so. Injecting outside air into the burning gases as they pass the exhaust valve adds more oxygen, causing the burning process to continue. This consumes a great deal of the normally unburned hydrocarbons and changes a significant portion of the carbon monoxide gas into harmless carbon dioxide. **Figure 14-12** illustrates one setup for injecting air into the area near the exhaust valve.

Air Injection System Action

A typical air injection system is illustrated in **Figure 14-13.** Note that the air pump draws fresh air in through the air cleaner. Some other setups draw air through a separate filter. The air is compressed to a slightly higher value than that of the exhaust gases in the manifold. The compressed air is then directed, via a hose, to a check valve and into a distribution manifold. An air bypass valve, or diverter valve, and a switching valve may also be used.

Figure 14-10. An exhaust back pressure modulated EGR valve. A—When there is low back pressure, the valve remains closed. B—The exhaust back pressure closes the control valve. A vacuum forms above the power diaphragm plate, drawing the pintle valve up to the open position. (Buick)

Figure 14-11. An electronic EGR valve. An electrical signal is sent to the ECM by the pintle position sensor. The ECM then knows how much exhaust is flowing. This valve also uses vacuum to modulate EGR operation. (Buick)

Air Pump

The air pump, or compressor, is usually of the positive displacement vane type. A relief valve limits the amount of pressure the pump can develop. Spring-loaded carbon shoes

Figure 14-12. When air is injected into the exhaust stream, it provides the oxygen needed to keep exhaust gases burning. This helps reduce emissions of HC and CO. (Nissan)

permit sliding contact between the vanes and the rotor. The pump is belt driven from the engine. **Figure 14-14** shows a cutaway of a typical air pump.

As each rotating pump vane passes the intake chamber, **Figure 14-15,** air is drawn in. The next vane pushes the air around into the compression chamber. The compression chamber reduces the volume of the air, pressurizing it. Pressurized air is then discharged through the exhaust chamber. Note that the intake and exhaust chambers are separated by the section of the housing called the stripper.

Check Valve

The one-way check valve, **Figure 14-16,** is forced open by the air passing through to the distribution manifold. In the

Figure 14-13. Typical air injection exhaust emission control system. (Chevrolet)

Figure 14-14. Cutaway of an air injection pump. (Toyota)

Figure 14-15. End view of an air injection pump. Note how the outer edges of the vanes maintain constant contact with the housing wall.

event of pump failure, or any time that exhaust manifold pressure equals or exceeds pump pressure, the check valve will seat and prevent back feeding of hot exhaust into the hoses or pump.

Distribution Manifold and Air Injection Tubes

An air distribution manifold and air injection tube setup is shown in **Figure 14-16.** Some engines incorporate the distribution manifold and injection tubes as an integral part of the cylinder head.

Diverter Valve

When the throttle valve is closed quickly, gasoline continues to flow. This is most common with carbureted engines, where the manifold vacuum can draw fuel through the idle

system, but it can occur on some fuel injected engines. Since little or no air is entering the engine during this period, the flow of gasoline produces a rich mixture. The rich mixture will leave a considerable amount of unburned gas following the power stroke. When this unburned gas enters the exhaust manifold and meets the injected stream of oxygen, it will begin to burn again with explosive force, causing backfiring.

The *diverter valve* is designed to momentarily divert the air stream away from the injection nozzles. It does this by means of a vacuum diaphragm or an electrically controlled metering valve. See **Figures 14-16** and **14-17.**

Diverter valve action is shown in **Figures 14-18** and **14-19.** Airflow is passing through the diverter valve and on to the air injectors. When the throttle is suddenly released, heavy intake manifold vacuum is applied to the metering valve control diaphragm. The diaphragm is drawn downward, forcing the metering valve to block off the passage to the air injection manifold. This downward movement opens up the diverter passage and pump air is momentarily discharged into the atmosphere. See **Figure 14-19.**

Air Switching Valve

Some air injection emission control setups use *air switching valves*. In some systems, these valves can be made as an integral, combination unit. In other systems, separate valves are used to perform specific functions.

The switching valve can be used to perform the normal diverter valve functions. It can also be used to channel pump air to the intake manifold, exhaust manifold, or catalytic converter, as determined by system needs. **Figure 14-20** shows one switching valve that, during engine warm-up, channels pump air to the exhaust port area. When a specific engine temperature is reached, the valve diverts a large percentage of the air to the catalytic converter. Some air continues to be

Figure 14-16. Air injection system diverter valve functions. 1–Admitting air to the exhaust port. 2–Diverting air during deceleration. 3–Relieving excessive air pressure during high-speed operation. (General Motors)

Figure 14-17. The anti-backfire (diverter) valve admits air to intake manifold upon deceleration. The vacuum diaphragm forces the diverter valve open.

Figure 14-18. Deceleration diverter valve. This valve is shown in the open position. (General Motors)

sent to the exhaust manifold. The switching valve improves the operation of the air injector pump, converter, and EGR system to reduce emissions.

Pulse Air Injection

The *pulse air injection system* does not use an air pump. Instead, it employs the normal exhaust pressure pulsations to draw air into the exhaust manifold. This is similar to the exhaust scavenging effect discussed in Chapter 13. The momentary vacuum pulse draws fresh air in through an air injection tube. Continual alternating vacuum and pressure pulses produce a sufficient flow of fresh air to significantly increase exhaust burning (oxidization), thus reducing CO and HC emissions.

One setup employing the pulse air principle is shown in **Figure 14-21.** Note that a separate air pipe is used for each cylinder on this specific engine. Each pipe has a separate air check valve.

Pulse Air Injection Operation

The air injection tubes are connected to distribution (manifold) pipes that lead to an air filter, **Figure 14-22.** Some

Figure 14-19. Cutaway of a diverter valve. Note the construction. (Oldsmobile)

Figure 14-21. A pulse air injection system does not use an air pump. Exhaust pressure pulsations cause fresh air to be drawn in during the low pressure (vacuum) pulsations. (Buick)

Figure 14-20. An air injection system using an air-switching valve for dual-flow injection control. (Chrysler)

Figure 14-22. Pulse air injection system. Note how vacuum pulsation draws fresh air in through the injection tube. Airflow is from the air cleaner. (Saab)

installations use the air cleaner, while others use a separate filter. A one-way air check valve is used in the lines. Note that this arrangement also uses four injection tubes.

A different design pulse air system is shown in **Figure 14-23.** Instead of admitting fresh air to all the exhaust port areas, air is drawn into ports 3, 4, and 5 only. Air is fed continually (once per vacuum pulse) through pipe C. Air pipe D will allow air to be drawn into exhaust ports 4 and 5 only when the intake manifold vacuum is high enough to operate the diaphragm on check valve B. The system is shown with all pipes feeding air.

Pulse Air Check Valves Are Important

You will note that the various pulse air systems shown in **Figures 14-21** to **14-23** all use air check valves. The check valves open during the vacuum pulse phase but snap shut during the pressure phase. This prevents back-feeding of exhaust gases and ensures that fresh air is drawn in.

Catalytic Converter

A *catalytic converter* (reactor) is a device installed in the exhaust line to significantly lower levels of hydrocarbons (HC), carbon monoxide (CO), and in the case of some converters, oxides of nitrogen (NO_x).

Converters are of two basic catalyst types: the ***two-way converter*** (oxidation) and the ***three-way converter*** (oxidation and reduction). Both types employ either a pellet or monolith design.

Figure 14-23. Another pulse air injection setup. Air is fed into number 3 port constantly. Additional air is fed into number 4 port and into number 5 port during periods of high vacuum. (Toyota)

Two-Way Converter

The two-way converter is used to reduce CO and HC. All early converters and some later converters are two-way designs. They can be subdivided into the **pellet** and the **monolith**, or **honeycomb,** types. The pellet type is being replaced with the monolith type, which produces less back pressure in the exhaust system.

Pellet-Type Converter

In a pellet-type converter, thousands of tiny beads, or pellets, of porous aluminum oxide covered with a thin coating of platinum (Pt) and palladium (Pd) are placed inside a perforated container. The container, or "core," is then suspended inside the converter shell. Baffles are arranged in such a way that the exhaust gases enter from one side of the perforated core, flow through the pellet bed, and exit through the other end of the core.

Converters are made of stainless steel because of the very high operating temperatures, which can exceed 1600°F (872°C). The outer shell is lined with a layer of insulation to prevent heat transfer to other areas and to maintain high catalyst temperatures. A two-way, pellet-type converter is illustrated in **Figure 14-24.** Study the flow of exhaust through the converter.

Monolith Converter

In place of porous beads, the monolith, or honeycomb, converter uses a ceramic honeycomb-like block that is coated with alumina and treated with a very thin coating of platinum and palladium. All exhaust gases flow through this treated honeycomb mass. A monolith converter is shown in **Figure 14-25.**

Two-Way Catalytic Converter Operation

The two-way catalytic converter (in some cases two are employed) is placed in the exhaust system between the exhaust manifold and muffler. When the hot gases are forced

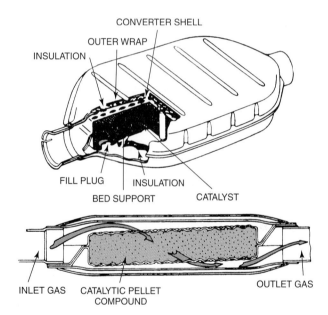

Figure 14-24. Two-way, pellet-type catalytic converter. Note how the exhaust gases are forced to travel through the catalyst bed (pellets). (Pontiac)

through the converter, they contact the catalyst-coated pellets or honeycomb, depending on the type. The catalyst causes a rapid increase in the exhaust temperature. This, in turn, causes the carbon monoxide and hydrocarbons to change (by means of an oxidizing process) into water (H_2O) vapor and carbon dioxide (CO_2). The two-way oxidizing converter does not reduce oxides of nitrogen (NO_x). The catalyst itself will not be altered or consumed by this process.

Three-Way Converter

The three-way converter, sometimes called the dual bed converter, uses an additional catalyst bed coated with

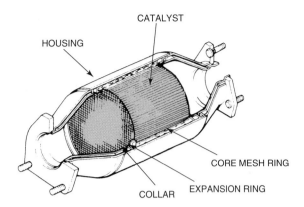

Figure 14-25. Two-way, monolith-type catalytic converter. The catalyst bed is of honeycomb construction to allow exhaust to flow through. (Honda)

platinum and rhodium (Rh). This bed not only helps reduce hydrocarbons and carbon monoxide, but it also lowers the levels of oxides of nitrogen.

One type of three-way, dual-bed monolith converter is shown in **Figure 14-26.** Note the use of two separate catalyst beds. They have a space between them into which air from the air injection pump may be forced.

Figure 14-26. Three-way, dual-bed monolith catalyst converter. Note the secondary air pipe (air from air injection pump). This converter lowers the levels of hydrocarbons, oxides of nitrogen, and carbon monoxide. (Ford)

The front bed (inlet end) is treated with platinum and rhodium and is termed a ***reducing catalyst*** (catalyzes reduction of NO_x). The rear bed is coated with palladium and platinum and is referred to as an ***oxidizing catalyst***. Study the construction of the three-way converter in **Figure 14-26.** Note the air inlet from the air injection pump and the exhaust flow pattern.

Operation of a Three-Way Converter

Exhaust gases pass first into the reducing catalyst. Levels of oxides of nitrogen are reduced. There is also some oxidizing of hydrocarbons and carbon monoxide. The air injection system forces air into the passage between the cat-

alyst beds. This adds oxygen to the exhaust gases, allowing a high oxidization heat level.

As the exhaust gases encounter the second oxidizing catalyst, tremendous heat is created and the resultant oxidizing process changes the carbon monoxide and hydrocarbons into water vapor and carbon dioxide. **Figure 14-27** illustrates the operation of the dual-bed, three-way converter system. Note how the air pump forces air into the center section of the converter.

Figure 14-27. Three-way, dual-bed, pellet-type catalytic converter. The air inlet pipe admits airflow from the air injection pump. Note the exhaust flow pattern. (Buick)

In order to prevent excessive heating of the three-way converter, the air injection system air switching valve will divert air from the converter under deceleration conditions, during wide open throttle, when engine temperature becomes excessive during a prolonged idle, and whenever the engine is cold and the choke or cold enrichment system causes a rich mixture. **Figure 14-28** shows the action of the air switching valve when engine temperature is relatively cool. Note how the air is diverted to the exhaust manifold to help in the reduction of carbon monoxide and hydrocarbons, which are produced in large amounts during warm-up.

Multiple Converters

Some vehicles have two catalytic converters. In these systems, one converter, which is often quite small, is located very close to the exhaust manifold. The other converter is larger and is located downstream in the exhaust system between the manifold and muffler. Vehicles with V-type engines may have two identical converters (one near each exhaust manifold) instead of a single converter located after the pipes join.

Figure 14-28. Dual-bed, air-injected, three-way catalytic converter system. When engine temperature exceeds 126°F (52°C), manifold vacuum is not applied to the air control valve, and the valve is passing pump air into the center section of the converter. Note the exhaust check valve, which prevents exhaust gases from feeding back into the air supply system. (Ford)

Diesel Catalytic Converters

This oxidizing catalytic converter is used to reduce exhaust smoke particulates. The oxidizing converter operates at normal exhaust system temperatures. The converter is not serviceable and sizes and shapes vary.

Fuel Vapor Controls

One of the major sources of automotive pollution in the past was the release of unburned hydrocarbons in the form of raw gas into the atmosphere. Major sources of these unburned gases were the gas tank vent and the crankcase breather tube. The following systems prevent the release of unburned hydrocarbons into the atmosphere from either of these sources.

Positive Crankcase Ventilation

The combustion process produces many gases. Some of these gases are very corrosive. A great deal of water (almost a gallon of water for each gallon of gasoline) is also formed. The high pressure in the cylinder during the firing stroke forces some of these gases and water vapor by the piston rings and into the crankcase area. To prevent acid and sludge formation in the crankcase and the dilution of the engine oil, these blowby gases must be removed.

For many years a simple road draft tube pulled the gases out of the crankcase and into the atmosphere. This created significant amounts of air pollutants. The *positive crankcase ventilation system*, or PCV system, removes the gases and allows them to be burned in the engine instead of being discharged into the atmosphere.

By connecting a hose between the engine interior and the intake manifold, engine vacuum will draw the crankcase fumes out of the crankcase and into the cylinders, where the gases will be burned along with the regular fuel charge. A schematic illustrating a typical PCV system is shown in **Figure 14-29.**

PCV Control Valve Is Needed

If allowed to flow into the intake manifold at all times and in any amount, the crankcase gases would upset the operation of the fuel system. To prevent this, it is essential that a PCV flow control valve, usually called a *PCV valve*, be incorporated into the system. The flow pattern for blowby gases through a PCV valve is shown in **Figure 14-30.**

PCV Control Valve Action

When the engine is stopped, no intake manifold vacuum exists and the PCV valve is held closed by spring action, **Figure 14-31A.**

During periods of idle or deceleration, vacuum is high. The tapered valve plunger is drawn into the metering opening. This reduces the size of the passageway, allowing only a small flow of crankcase gases to the intake manifold. See **Figure 14-31B.**

When the vehicle is operating at a normal load, the vacuum drops off somewhat, allowing the spring to push the plunger part way out of the opening. This increases the opening, and gas flow is reasonably heavy, **Figure 14-31C.**

During acceleration or heavy loading, manifold vacuum drops greatly. The spring instantly pushes the plunger further

Figure 14-31. PCV control valve action. As the tapered plunger moves out of the metering opening, the gas flow area is increased. (Toyota)

Figure 14-29. Schematic illustrating positive crankcase ventilation system. Note how crankcase blowby gases are drawn into the intake manifold, where they mix with the fuel charge for burning. (Suzuki)

Figure 14-30. Typical PCV valve. Note the flow of blowby gases through the valve. (Jeep)

out of the opening. Crankcase gas flow is now at its heaviest. Look at **Figure 14-31D.**

In the event of a backfire in the intake manifold, the reverse pressure allows the spring to fully close the valve, **Figure 14-31A,** preventing the flame from traveling into the crankcase. This prevents a possible explosion in the crankcase area.

Modern PCV systems are ***closed systems.*** In the closed system, fresh air enters the crankcase through the air cleaner. This keeps any vapors from escaping from the crankcase under heavy loads or when the engine is off. Older open systems drew air through a separate breather cap, which was usually mounted on the valve cover.

Evaporation Control System (ECS)

The ***evaporation control system*** (also called evaporative emission control system) is designed to prevent the release of either liquid gasoline or gasoline vapor into the atmosphere.

A typical evaporation control system is comprised of a nonvented (closed to the atmosphere) fuel tank with a sealed filler cap, a tank fill limiter, and a vapor separator. A vent line connects the tank to a charcoal canister. Other lines extend to the carburetor (when used) and intake manifold. The system may have a purge valve and an excess fuel and vapor return line to the tank. A rollover valve may also be used to prevent fuel leakage from the tank in the event the vehicle rolls over. A schematic of one specific evaporative control setup is illustrated in **Figure 14-32.** Study the various parts and their relationships to the overall system.

Evaporation Control System Operation

The fuel tank is sealed with a ***pressure-vacuum cap.*** This cap uses both a pressure relief valve and a vacuum relief valve to prevent excessive pressure or vacuum in the tank in the event of system failure. The valves remain closed under

Figure 14-32. An evaporation control system. Study and learn the names of all the parts. (Chrysler)

normal operating conditions. When pressure exceeds around 0.8 psi (5.52 kPa), or when a vacuum forms in excess of 0.1 Hg (0.69 kPa), the valves are activated to vent the tank. See **Figure 14-33.** The fuel tank breathes through the vent tube as fuel is consumed or when it expands or contracts from heating and cooling.

The tank shown in **Figure 14-34** is designed so that when it is filled to capacity, there is a sufficient air dome above the fuel to permit thermal expansion without forcing liquid gasoline into the vent lines. When filling the tank, the small orifice (hole) in the vent restrictor slows down the venting of the tank so that an air dome is present, thus limiting fill capacity.

Figure 14-33. Pressure-vacuum fuel tank cap. This cap will relieve either excessive pressure or vacuum, preventing tank or other system damage. (Chrysler)

Any vapors in the tank travel through the fuel tank vent tube to the ***charcoal canister***. On carbureted engines, the float bowl is also vented to the canister through a bowl vent valve. Vapors generated by "engine off heat soak" (heat from engine transferred to the carburetor after the engine is stopped) will be forced into the canister.

The canister is filled with activated charcoal granules (small particles). When the vapors touch the charcoal, the granules absorb and store the vapors. As long as the engine remains off, the vapors will be retained in the canister. When the engine is started, vacuum under the throttle valve will draw fresh air through the charcoal bed. As the air passes over the charcoal, it will pick up the stored vapors and draw them into the intake manifold, where they will be mixed with the fuel charge for burning. As the engine continues to run, the canister will be purged (cleaned) of vapors.

When the engine is stopped, tank and carburetor bowl (when used) vapor will again enter the canister. Study the system shown in **Figure 14-34.**

Canister Construction

All charcoal canisters contain a bed of activated charcoal (carbon), **Figure 14-35A.** Early designs have a replaceable fiberglass filter at the fresh air intake of the canister, **Figure 14-35B.** Canister vents vary with the type of system. Some canisters used with carbureted engines vent the canister directly to the carburetor, as in **Figure 14-34.** Some vents are contained in the canister and open when manifold vacuum builds up as the engine begins to run.

Another canister design has a canister purge valve, **Figure 14-36.** The purge airflow rate is controlled by the size of the orifice in the purge control valve. A thermal (heat controlled) vacuum switch controls vacuum to the purge valve. When engine operating temperature reaches a specified level, the thermal vacuum valve will apply vacuum to the purge valve and purge airflow will start. Note that this too is a closed system because clean purge air is drawn in from the air cleaner.

Liquid Fuel Control

In the closed fuel system, liquid fuel must never enter the canister. Evaporative control systems may use an air dome in the tank, a vapor separator, or a liquid check valve to prevent liquid fuel from leaving the tank.

Liquid-Vapor Separator

The liquid-vapor separator unit collects any liquid fuel and drains it back to the tank, preventing it from entering the charcoal canister. The separator is connected to as many as three vent lines. The rear vent standpipe in the separator has a hole near the bottom that permits any liquid fuel that may have been forced into the separator to drain back into the tank.

The liquid-vapor separator is mounted above the gas tank so that normal vehicle angles will always leave one vent above the fuel level and free to pass vapor to the canister. **Figure 14-37** illustrates an evaporation control system using a liquid-vapor separator.

Figure 14-34. Schematic of an evaporation control system. This setup uses a bowl vent valve. (Buick)

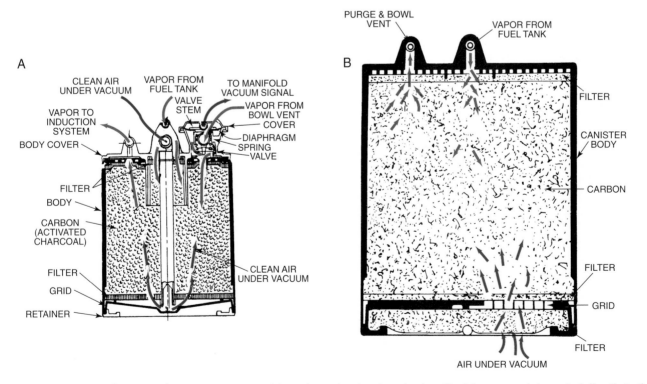

Figure 14-35. A—Cutaway of a vapor storage canister using only a bowl vent valve. Canister purge air is vented directly to the intake (induction) system. B—This vapor canister draws purge air up through an external filter at the bottom. The control valve is remotely located. This is an open-type canister. (Pontiac)

Figure 14-36. Cutaway of one type of charcoal canister purge valve. Study the construction. (OTC Tools)

Liquid Check Valve

The liquid check valve allows tank vapors to pass into the canister under normal conditions. If, however, liquid fuel starts filling up the check valve, the float will rise. This forces the needle into its seat, closing off the vent line until the liquid fuel drains back into the tank, **Figure 14-38.**

Rollover Check Valve

A rollover check valve can be used to seal off the tank vent line in the event a vehicle is turned upside down in an accident. Some rollover valves also incorporate a liquid separator valve as part of their construction. One form of rollover valve is show in **Figure 14-39.** When the valve is inverted, the steel ball forces the plunger to close the vent line.

Computer Monitoring of the Evaporation Control System

On most vehicles built after 1996, the computer operates the evaporation control system. The purge valve is operated by a computer-controlled solenoid. Other solenoids may be used to control the flow of vapor through the system.

The computer also monitors the evaporation control system. On many vehicles, the computer controls a small air pump. When energized by the computer, the pump pressurizes the fuel tank and related system components. After the desired pressure is achieved, the pump stops and the computer holds the purge valve closed while monitoring tank

Figure 14-38. Typical liquid check valve. Fuel entering the valve raises the float, forcing the needle to seal off the vent line. (Chrysler)

Figure 14-37. This evaporative control system employs a liquid-vapor separator to prevent liquid fuel from being forced into the charcoal (carbon) canister. (Toyota)

Figure 14-39. One type of rollover check valve. In the event of a rollover, the ball will depress the plunger, sealing the vapor line and preventing fuel leakage. (Chrysler)

pressure with a pressure sensor. If the pressure drops too quickly, the sensor reading alerts the computer to the fact that the fuel system is leaking to the atmosphere. The computer then sets a trouble code.

Some evaporation control systems do not pressurize the tank to check for leaks. Instead, the computer will cycle the purge valve under certain conditions. The computer then monitors the engine airflow and air-fuel ratio to determine whether the system is operating properly. If a problem is detected, the computer will set a diagnostic trouble code.

Computer-Controlled Emissions Systems

The computer-controlled emission system is covered extensively in Chapter 15. Using a computer provides optimum air-fuel ratios for a variety of operating conditions. In many cases, the computer controls the air-fuel ratio so precisely that some emission controls can be eliminated. Other emission controls are operated directly by the computer. Modern vehicles have low emissions with reasonable performance and good economy.

Emission Systems Caution

Proper emission reduction depends on a carefully balanced and integrated number of emission control devices and systems. When performing any emission-related adjustment or repair, keep in mind that an adjustment or alteration in one system will very often affect other systems.

Also, remember that it is against federal and state law to remove or disable any emission control device. Always follow the manufacturer's recommendations and specifications. Do not alter, disconnect, or override emission controls for any reason.

Summary

Automotive exhaust emissions of major concern include hydrocarbons, oxides of nitrogen, and carbon monoxide. Emission controls are of three basic types: engine modifications and controls, external cleaning systems, and fuel system vapor control.

Many engine modifications are used to reduce emissions, including reduced camshaft overlap, lowered compression, hotter thermostats, and modified combustion chamber shapes. Fuel systems are designed to produce an air-fuel ratio as close to 14.7:1 as possible. Proper choke control during engine warmup and driveaway is very important. Electric chokes may be used to speed up opening under certain conditions.

Heated air is drawn into the air cleaner during engine warmup. The thermostatically controlled air cleaner can admit all hot or all cold air, or it can blend the two together, depending on engine temperature.

Ignition timing must be kept within specified limits to reduce emissions. Many early devices used a restrictor or other controls to reduce the vacuum to the vacuum advance unit. Most modern vehicles have electronic advance mechanisms, which change timing based on inputs such as engine temperature, vacuum, and RPM.

To lower NO_x, a portion of the exhaust gas is allowed to enter the intake manifold. This lowers combustion temperatures. The exhaust gas recirculation (EGR) valve controls the flow of exhaust to the manifold. EGR valves can be the back pressure modulated, vacuum modulated, or electronic-vacuum modulated design.

Air injection systems force a stream of fresh air into the burning exhaust as it leaves the cylinder. This prolongs burning to reduce hydrocarbon and carbon monoxide emission. An engine-driven vane-type pump provides the air. Some setups use pulse air instead of a pump. A check valve prevents exhaust from entering the air system in the event of excessive exhaust pressure. A diverter valve is used to prevent engine backfiring during deceleration.

Catalytic converters reduce exhaust emissions. Converters can use either a pellet bed or a monolith catalyst. The oxidizing catalyst is treated with platinum and palladium and will change carbon monoxide and hydrocarbons into water and carbon dioxide. The reducing catalyst is treated with platinum and rhodium. It will reduce the amount of nitrates of oxygen. It will also oxidize hydrocarbons and carbon monoxide to some degree. Two-way converters use an oxidizing catalyst. Three-way converters contain both reducing and oxidizing catalysts.

Some converters utilize a controlled stream of injected air to improve their efficiency. The air injection system can be used as the air source. Systems can use more than one converter. The positive crankcase ventilation system removes fumes from the crankcase and burns them in the cylinders. The PCV valve controls the flow of gases.

The evaporative control system prevents the escape of liquid gasoline or gasoline vapor into the atmosphere. Vapors are stored in a charcoal canister until the engine is started.

1

They are then drawn off and burned in the engine. Canisters can be of open or closed design.

Computer-controlled emission systems offer the ultimate in emission control. The electronic system instantly makes adjustments needed to maintain the best air-fuel ratio. Care must be used when making adjustments on any engine system, as adjustments on one system may affect other systems. Follow manufacturer's specifications. Do not disconnect or alter emission controls.

Know These Terms

Hydrocarbons (HC)	Electronic EGR valve
Oxides of nitrogen (NO_x)	Air injection system
Carbon monoxide (CO)	Diverter valve
Engine modifications and controls	Air switching valve
External cleaning systems	Pulse air injection system
Fuel vapor controls	Catalytic converter
Overlap	Two-way converter
Dieseling	Three-way converter
Run-on	Pellet converter
Carburetor icing	Monolith converter
Thermostatic air cleaner	Honeycomb converter
Early fuel evaporation system (EFE)	Reducing catalyst
Vacuum advance restrictor	Oxidizing catalyst
Exhaust gas recirculation (EGR) system	Positive crankcase ventilation system (PCV)
Vacuum modulated EGR valve	PCV valve
Back pressure modulated EGR valve	Closed system
	Evaporation control system
	Pressure-vacuum cap
	Charcoal canister

Review Questions—Chapter 14

Do not write in this book. Write your answers on a separate sheet of paper.

1. The three major exhaust pollutants are _____, _____, and _____ .
2. List the three general types of emission controls.
3. The combustion chamber in modern cylinder heads is designed to reduce the amount of _____ in the exhaust.
   (A) CO
   (B) NO_x
   (C) HC
   (D) O_2
4. Camshaft overlap is _____ to improve idling with lean mixtures.

5. All of the following statements about lower engine compression ratios are true, EXCEPT:
   (A) lower compression ratios allow the use of low-octane gasoline.
   (B) NO_x formation is greater with low compression ratios.
   (C) lower compression allows the engine to operate on unleaded gas.
   (D) detonation is less likely with lower compression ratios.
6. Dieseling is caused by hot spots in the _____ .
   (A) block
   (B) intake manifold
   (C) combustion chamber
   (D) exhaust manifold
7. Technician A says that carburetor icing is reduced by the use of a thermostatic air cleaner. Technician B says that carburetor icing is reduced by the use of early fuel evaporation systems. Who is right?
   (A) A only.
   (B) B only.
   (C) Both A & B.
   (D) Neither A nor B.
8. Lowering the combustion flame temperature reduces the formation of _____ .
   (A) HC
   (B) NO_x
   (C) CO
   (D) O_2
9. Technician A says that the EGR valve admits exhaust gas to the intake manifold at all times. Technician B says that the PCV valve admits crankcase gases into the intake manifold at all times. Who is right?
   (A) A only.
   (B) B only.
   (C) Both A & B.
   (D) Neither A nor B.
10. The air injection system forces air into the _____ .
    (A) intake manifold near the intake valve
    (B) exhaust manifold near the exhaust valve
    (C) catalytic converter
    (D) All of the above, depending on the system.
11. The diverter valve is used on the air injection system to prevent _____ .
12. What unit provides air for the air injection system?
    (A) Fan.
    (B) Air pump.
    (C) Air cleaner snorkel ram pressure.
    (D) Intake system back pressure.

Figure 15-20. Cutaway view of a mixture control solenoid assembly which adjusts the fuel mixture on carbureted engines. The mixture control solenoid responds to electrical signals sent to it by the ECU.

engine. Some mixture control solenoids adjust air-fuel ratio by modifying the amount of air flowing through the main metering system. Mixture control solenoids were discussed in Chapter 10.

Ignition Devices

The ECU can control the operation of the ignition system by sending output commands to one of several ignition devices. The ECU can control the coil directly, or through a separate ignition module. The design of the computer control system dictates which device will be controlled.

Ignition Module

Many computer controlled ignitions have a separate *ignition module*, **Figure 15-21**. The module receives the triggering signal from the ECU based on inputs from the sensors. The module uses this triggering signal to create the spark. The module may also function as a sensor, passing the triggering signal from the distributor pickup or crankshaft position sensor on to the ECU.

Some ignition modules have a fail-safe provision as part of the ECU's limp-home mode. If the ECU fails, the ignition system will continue to operate with fixed timing settings until the vehicle can reach a service facility. Ignition modules were discussed in Chapter 8.

Ignition Coil

On some computer control systems, the *ignition coil* is directly operated by the ECU, **Figure 15-22**. The ECU interrupts the primary current flow to the ignition coil based on crankshaft sensor input. When the primary current to the coil

Figure 15-21. An ignition module and its mounting location as used by one vehicle manufacturer. (General Motors)

is interrupted, the ignition coil fires. This voltage is sent to the distributor and rotor for routing to the correct spark plug. The ECU can also control spark timing for maximum engine performance and efficiency.

Distributorless Ignition System

Distributorless ignition systems used on many modern vehicles do not use a conventional distributor, rotor, or coil. Distributorless ignition is comprised of one ignition coil for every two cylinders, an ignition module and a crankshaft and/or camshaft sensor. Distributorless ignition was discussed in Chapter 8. See **Figure 15-23**.

EGR System Solenoid

The *EGR system solenoid* controls vacuum between the intake manifold and EGR valve diaphragm, **Figure 15-24**. Another type has the solenoid inside and on top of the EGR valve, **Figure 15-25**. Also, note the valve position sensor, which is a variable resistor. This provides feedback on the position of the valve which tells the ECU the exact amount of exhaust gas flow recirculating.

If the exhaust flow is too much for operating conditions, the ECU then opens the solenoid valve. This vents atmospheric pressure to the EGR valve's diaphragm and the valve returns to its seat. When the engine is cold, the ECU determines that no vacuum is needed at the EGR valve diaphragm and vents the vacuum to the atmosphere.

Air Injection System

The *air injection system* may have a diverter valve and switching valve controlled by vacuum diaphragms, usually operated by the ECU through solenoid valves. These valves were discussed in Chapter 14. The solenoid valves are energized by the ECU. The ECU controls the diverter and switching valves to allow the incoming oxygen to combine most efficiently with the unburned gasoline.

Electric Fan Relay

Relays are used when an electrical component uses more current than can be handled by the ECU's internal

Figure 15-22. One particular electronic engine control system schematic. This system uses a computer-controlled ignition coil. Study the system carefully. (Toyota)

Figure 15-23. A 4.6-liter, electronic fuel injected (EFI) V-8 engine which uses a direct ignition system. There are two ignition coil pack modules, one on each side of the engine. Each module pack contains four ignition coils—one per spark plug. Note the position of the crankshaft and camshaft position sensors. (Ford Motor Company)

circuits. If the relay is the mechanical type, a small amount of current from the ECU energizes the relay solenoid, closing a set of contact points. In an electronic relay, the ECU current turns on a power transistor. A large amount of current can flow through the relay to the electrical component. Relays are discussed in detail in Chapter 17.

When an electric cooling fan is used, it remains off until the coolant temperature sensor signals the ECU that the engine has reached a predetermined temperature. Once the coolant temperature reaches around 227°F (108°C), the ECU energizes the *fan relay*, **Figure 15-26**, which turns the engine cooling fan on. Also, the fan relay is energized any time the air conditioner is turned on regardless of engine temperature.

Electric Fuel Pump Relay

On many vehicles, the fuel pump is controlled by the ECU through a relay. The ECU energizes the *fuel pump relay* when the key is turned to the on position, **Figure 15-27**. This causes the electric fuel pump to deliver fuel through the system. When the ECU detects that the engine is not running (loss of RPM signal pulses) after three seconds, the ECU

Figure 15-24. An exhaust gas recirculation (EGR) valve which is controlled through a solenoid vacuum valve by the electronic control module. Operation of the EGR valve is constantly monitored by the electronic control module which receives an electrical signal from the exhaust gas recirculation temperature sensor. If an abnormal temperature condition is detected, the ECM will turn the malfunction indicator lamp (MIL) on to alert the driver. 1—Ignition switch. 2—Main relay. 3—Electronic control module. 4—Sensed information. 5—EGR solenoid vacuum valve. 6—EGR modulator. 7—EGR valve. 8—Exhaust gas recirculation temperature sensor. 9—Intake manifold. 10—throttle body. 11—Exhaust gas. 12—Vacuum. 13—Air. 14—Battery (Geo)

de-energizes the relay. This reduces the chance of fire in the event of an accident.

Note that the oil pressure switch is wired parallel from relay to electric fuel pump. The oil pressure switch acts as a backup in the event the relay fails allowing the vehicle to start. However, it will take longer to start the engine as the oil must pressurize enough to close the contacts in the switch. Electrical current then passes through the switch and energizes the electric fuel pump.

Transmission Control Solenoids

On many automatic transmissions and transaxles, solenoids control some of the operations of the hydraulic system. The *transmission control solenoid* is attached to flow control valves in the hydraulic system. The solenoid moves the valve, which then modifies the flow of transmission fluid. Solenoids have been used to operate the torque converter lockup clutch on many older transmissions. In the transmissions and transaxles installed in newer vehicles, the solenoids operate the shift valves, selecting transmission shift points according to instructions from the ECU.

On-Board Diagnostic Systems

Although computer systems precisely control various operating conditions in modern vehicles, they are often very difficult to troubleshoot. To simplify the diagnosis and service of these systems, manufacturers have designed on-board diagnostic systems into their products.

Early on-board diagnostic systems were designed to monitor computer system parts, such as sensors and actuators. If a part failed, the ECU received an out-of-range electrical reading. The ECU would then set one or more trouble codes and turn on the MIL. These early systems are now called on-board diagnostics generation I, or *OBD I*, systems.

The latest on-board diagnostic systems not only detect failed parts, but they also monitor engine operating conditions that indicate the production of excessive emissions. These new systems are called on-board diagnostics generation II, or *OBD II*, systems. A typical OBD II system will monitor air-fuel ratio, engine misfires, engine temperature, catalyst efficiency, and other operating conditions. If the OBD II system determines that the vehicle is producing, or is about to produce, excess emissions, it will set a diagnostic trouble code and turn on the MIL.

Another important difference between OBD I and OBD II systems is the number of possible diagnostic trouble codes each system can produce. OBD I systems use a two-number trouble code format. Therefore, an OBD I system can have only 100 possible trouble codes. OBD II systems use a five-character alphanumeric code. The combination of letters and numbers allows for 8000 possible trouble codes.

Static Electricity

A technician can become charged with *static electricity* by friction or induction. Sliding across a seat, a technician can become charged by friction. A technician can become charged by induction by touching a ground while standing near a highly charged object. Many electronic components, including the ECU, can be destroyed by static electricity, **Figure 15-28.**

The static electricity charge while sliding across a seat can be as high as 25,000 V. The change remains static (at rest) in the body until the technician touches something made of metal or other conductive material. A high voltage spark jumps from the body to the object. If that object is an ECU, the transistors and IC's inside it will be destroyed. It only takes about 15 V, in some cases, to destroy the inner workings of an ECU and the static electrical discharge is far greater. Always ground yourself by touching the vehicleís body or a ground connection before handling the ECU.

Electromagnetic Interference

With the increasing amount of electronics and wiring in the modern automobile, it is difficult to keep signals from each circuit from crossing. For example, if sensor wires are routed too close to the ignition or other wires or are allowed to touch in some cases, *electromagnetic interference* or EMI, can result.

Figure 15-25. A—This computer-controlled EGR solenoid allows either vacuum to act on the valve's diaphragm or vents it to the atmosphere. Colored arrows indicate atmospheric pressure allowed to enter the lines when the solenoid valve is open, which prevents operation of the EGR valve. B—Sometimes solenoids are located on top of the EGR valve inside a sealed housing. Colored arrows indicate atmospheric pressure vented to the housing when the solenoid valve is open, preventing EGR valve operation. (Chevrolet & Oldsmobile)

Figure 15-26. A—Computer-controlled relays are used to energize the cooling fan, based on data from the coolant temperature sensor. B—Computer can energize the electric fuel pump relay when the ignition is turned to the run position, which sends current to the fuel pump motor. The relay will remain energized if the computer detects that the engine is running (engine rpm input). Note the oil pressure switch which is wired parallel to the relay. This acts as a bypass if the relay should fail, allowing the engine to be started. (Oldsmobile)

Figure 15-27. An electric fuel pump relay which is controlled by the electronic control module (ECM). A—Fuel pump mounting location as used by one manufacturer. B—Fuel pump relay and related wiring schematic. (Geo)

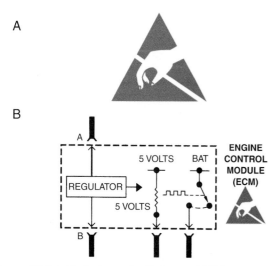

Figure 15-28. All electrostatic discharge (ESD) parts contain solid state circuits which are sensitive to static electricity. A—An electrostatic discharge symbol. This symbol is placed on the outside packing of any part that can be damaged by static electricity. B—Electrical part on an electrical schematic that is shown as electrostatic discharge sensitive. (General Motors)

In the past, electromagnetic interference was limited to ignition feedback that could be heard through the radio speakers. Today, electromagnetic interference from cellular telephones, police and CB radios, and other electronic accessories have been the cause of many problems in automotive systems. Wire harnesses on modern vehicles are carefully routed (and shielded in some cases) to reduce and prevent EMI.

Summary

An electronic control unit is used on modern vehicles to meet stringent fuel economy and emission control regulations. The ECU precisely controls the operation of the fuel, ignition, and other engine vehicle components to produce an air-fuel ratio as close to 14.7 to 1 as possible. Many modern vehicles combine the engine control unit and other system controllers into one large microprocessor which monitors and control most vehicle functions. The automotive computer control system is divided into three major areas, the ECU, the input sensors, and the output devices.

An ECU contains a central processing unit and four types of memory. The central processing unit controls the operation of the ECU. The memory is a set of instructions or programs that tells the CPU what to do. The program is stored in the read only memory (ROM), programmable read only memory (PROM), electronically erasable programmable read only memory (EEPROM), or erasable programmable read only memory (EPROM). The ROM or PROM have nonvolatile memories which means it will not lose any data when the battery is disconnected.

The random access memory (RAM) is a temporary storage place for data from the sensors including trouble codes. The RAM has a volatile memory which means its data is erased when the battery is disconnected. Keep alive memory (KAM) allows the ECU to compensate for engine component and sensor wear.

The input sensors measure the operating conditions of the engine or drive train, and convert them to an electrical signal that is then sent to the ECU. Some sensors produce their own voltage signal, while other sensors adjust the reference voltage sent to them. An output device is an electrical unit that is controlled by the ECU. The output device in turn controls some facet of engine or drive train operation. Output devices can be solenoids, relays, electric motors, or other electronic devices such as ignition modules.

Know These Terms

Computer

Electronic control unit (ECU)

Central processing unit (CPU)

Read only memory (ROM)

Programmable read only memory (PROM)

Erasable programmable read only memory (EPROM)

Electronically erasable programmable read only memory (EEPROM)

Random access memory (RAM)

Keep alive memory (KAM)

Open loop

Closed loop

Check engine light

Service engine soon light

Malfunction indicator light

Diagnostic trouble codes

Input sensors

Reference voltage

On-off switches

Pressure sensors

Crankshaft speed and position sensor

Camshaft position sensor

Magnetic pickup coil

Hall-effect switch

Optical sensor

Reed switch

Knock sensor

Thermistor

Coolant temperature sensor

Intake air temperature
    sensor

Manifold air temperature

Manifold vacuum sensor

Manifold absolute pressure

MAP sensor

Barometric pressure sensor

Airflow meter

Mass airflow sensor (MAF)

Oxygen sensor

Heated oxygen sensor

Throttle position sensor

Variable resistor

Transducer

EGR position sensor

Output device

Idle speed solenoid

Idle speed motor

Idle air control valve (IAC)

Fuel injector

Mixture control solenoid

Ignition module

Ignition coil

Distributorless ignition
    system

EGR system solenoid

Air injection system

Relay

Fan relay

Fuel pump relay

Transmission control
    solenoid

OBD I

OBD II

Static electricity

Electromagnetic interference
    (EMI)

Review Questions—Chapter 15

Do not write in this book. Write your answers on a separate sheet of paper.

1. Technician A says that the primary use of engine control computers on modern vehicles is to control exhaust emissions. Technician B says that the primary use of engine control computers on modern vehicles is to improve performance. Who is right?
    (A) A only.
    (B) B only.
    (C) Both A & B.
    (D) Neither A nor B.

2. The computer control system can be divided into three major subsystems. What are they?

3. What could be considered the fourth major subsystem?

4. Which of the following types of computer memory stores data temporarily?
    (A) Read only memory (ROM).
    (B) Programmable read only memory (PROM).
    (C) Random access memory (RAM).
    (D) All of the above.

5. When does the ECU go into open loop mode?
    (A) When the engine is cold.
    (B) When the engine is hot.
    (C) When the engine is at wide open throttle.
    (D) Both A & C.

6. Of read only memory (ROM), and programmable read only memory (PROM), which is contained on a chip? Which one can be removed from the main computer?

7. Computer system trouble codes are stored in _____ .
    (A) ROM
    (B) PROM
    (C) RAM
    (D) All of the above.

8. The simplest type of input sensor is the _____ .
    (A) on-off switch
    (B) pressure switch
    (C) magnetic pickup coil
    (D) reed switch

9. The ignition module can be an _____ .
    (A) output device
    (B) input sensor
    (C) knock sensor
    (D) Both A & B.

10. Reed switches are used to measure speed by measuring _____ .

11. In a piezoelectric element, electricity is produced by _____ .
    (A) heat
    (B) electricity
    (C) rotation
    (D) pressure

12. Temperature sensors measure the temperature of _____ and _____ .

13. Technician A says that manifold vacuum is the negative pressure in the intake manifold when the engine is running. Technician B says that manifold absolute pressure changes correspond to changes in manifold vacuum. Who is right?
    (A) A only.
    (B) B only.
    (C) Both A & B.
    (D) Neither A nor B.

14. The two types of throttle position sensors are _____ and _____ .

15. In a mass airflow sensor, the wire is heated by _____ .
    (A) the incoming air
    (B) electricity
    (C) engine heat
    (D) exhaust gases

16. The difference between the oxygen in the exhaust and the outside air causes _____ in the oxygen sensor.
    (A) heat
    (B) pressure
    (C) a chemical reaction
    (D) a short circuit

17. The mixture control solenoid is used only on engines with _____ .

(A) electronic ignition

(B) carburetors

(C) fuel injection

(D) air cooling

18. A relay is used when an electrical component uses more current than the _____ can handle.

(A) battery

(B) sensors

(C) ignition system

(D) internal computer circuits

19. The ECU energizes the electric fuel pump relay when _____ .

(A) the engine starts

(B) more fuel is needed for acceleration

(C) the key is turned to the on position

(D) the mechanical fuel pump stops operating

20. On a late model vehicle, the transmission control solenoids are used to control the automatic transmission _____ .

(A) fluid temperature

(B) shift points

(C) noise

(D) pump output

16

Charging and Starting Systems

After studying this chapter, you will be able to:

- Describe the construction and operation of an automotive battery.
- Explain the operating principles of a charging system.
- Identify the major parts of a charging system.
- Explain the operating principles of a starting system.
- Identify the major parts of a starting system.

This chapter will cover the fundamentals of vehicle charging and starting systems. The charging and starting systems are vital to the operation of almost every system on the vehicle. Without the electrical components discussed here, the ignition system, fuel injection, emission controls, electronic control unit, air conditioner, lights, and radio would not be functional. Studying this chapter will give you an understanding of the battery and charging and starting systems. These systems are the foundation for all other electrical equipment in the vehicle.

Battery

An electric current can be produced by means of a *lead-acid battery*. The battery stores this energy in chemical form until it is needed. The main purpose of the battery is to supply current for the ignition system and starter motor until the vehicle is running. The battery also acts as a source of extra power for the vehicle's electrical system. The various components of the battery are discussed below.

Battery Cells

A battery is constructed of separate elements, or *cells*, **Figure 16-1**. Each cell is made up of two groups of plates. Each battery cell has an open circuit voltage of 2 volts. Total battery voltage is determined by the number of cells. One group of plates forms the positive group, the other forms the negative group. The number of plates does not affect open circuit voltage.

Battery Cell Plates

The *positive plate* is a grid (wire-like, skeletal framework, made of lead and antimony or of lead and calcium), filled with lead peroxide (PbO_2) in sponge form. The *negative plate* is filled with porous lead (Pb) and expanders to prevent the lead from returning to an inactive solid state. Both are sandwiched together so that a negative group is next to a

Figure 16-1. Cutaway of a 12 volt battery. Note the arrangement of cells (each one supplies approximately 2 volts), cell connectors, and sediment chamber.

positive group. The plates are arranged negative, positive, negative, positive, and so on.

Insulating *separators* of nonconducting plastic, rubber, glass, cellulose fiber, or other types of material are placed between each set of plates. The separators keep the plates from touching each other and short circuiting. **Figure 16-2** illustrates a battery cell's positive and negative plates with separators. Note how the elements are kept away from the bottom of the container. This allows room for shedding plate material to deposit in the form of sediment. If this sediment touches the plates, it will cause a short circuit.

Electrolyte

The cell components are assembled in a hard rubber or plastic (such as polypropylene) battery box or case. The case has partitions to divide it into six compartments or cells. The

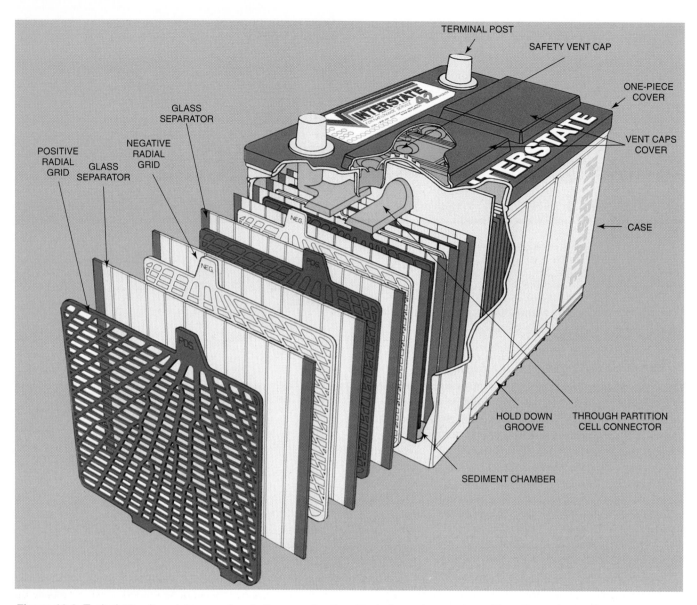

Figure 16-2. Typical 12-volt, maintenance free battery construction. Study the various parts and how they relate and connect to each other. (Interstate Battery)

cells are filled with an **electrolyte** solution made up of about 64% distilled water (H_2O) and 36% sulfuric acid (H_2SO_4), **Figure 16-3**. The electrolyte will slightly cover the top of the plates. The sponge form lead peroxide and porous lead allows the electrolyte to penetrate the positive and negative plates.

Battery Construction

Figure 16-4 shows how each cell is fitted into the individual compartments. As each element produces around 2 volts, 12 volts will be produced when they are connected in

H_2O		H_2SO_4		ELECTROLYTE
64% WATER	+	36% ACID	=	ELECTROLYTE
SP.GR. - 1.000		SP.GR.= 1.835		SP.GR. = 1.270

Figure 16-3. Chemical composition of battery electrolyte. Note the specific gravity of water compared to the sulfuric acid and the final electrolyte solution. (Deere & Co.)

Figure 16-4. Battery container showing placement of cell dividers. Note the use of a built-in charge indicator. (Chrysler)

series. **Figure 16-5** shows the elements in place in the battery box. After installation, each cell is connected to its neighbor by a lead cell connector or strap. The end cells are connected to the battery **terminals**.

Figure 16-6 illustrates all the various battery components and how they are joined together to produce the battery. Modern cars and light trucks have 12 volt batteries. Some older cars have 6 volt systems, while some agricultural vehicles have 8 volt systems. A few large trucks have 24 volt systems.

The electrolyte evaporated from older batteries, which required water to be added every few weeks. Modern batteries are sealed to reduce the amount of evaporation. Water cannot escape and condenses back into the electrolyte. These batteries are known as maintenance free batteries.

STOP Warning: The sulfuric acid in electrolyte can cause severe burns. Avoid contact and wear protective clothing. A battery will sometimes release explosive hydrogen gas as part of its chemical action. Do not smoke or create any sparks or flame near a battery, Figure 16-7.

Figure 16-5. Sectioned view of a complete 12 volt battery. Learn the names of all parts. (Prestolite)

Figure 16-7. Typical warning label placed on batteries. Use extreme care whenever you are handling or near batteries. Severe burns to skin and eyes, as well as battery explosions are possible.

Battery Chemical Action

The battery does not actually store electricity. When charging, it converts electricity into chemical energy. Chemical action of electrolyte, working on active material in the plates, causes a transfer of electrons from the positive plates to the negative plates.

The amount of chemical energy in a battery is not inexhaustible. If the battery is not recharged, it will eventually be unable to operate. **Figure 16-8** shows the typical current load for modern vehicles. The charging system must produce sufficient current output to cover all possible electrical needs.

Battery Discharging

When the battery is placed in a closed circuit, such as when the starter is being operated, a surplus of electrons at the negative post will flow to the positive post. An electric current is produced by converting chemical energy into electricity, **Figure 16-9**.

As the current flows, the battery starts discharging. The sulfate ion (SO_4) in the sulfuric acid (H_2SO_4) combines with the lead (Pb) in the plate materials to form lead sulfate ($PbSO_4$). The hydrogen ion (H_2) combines with the oxygen in the lead peroxide to form water (H_2O). As the current continues flowing, the rate of current flow and the electrolyte become weaker and weaker. Finally the battery is completely discharged.

Battery Charging

The battery can be recharged by passing an electric current back into the battery (with a battery charger or the

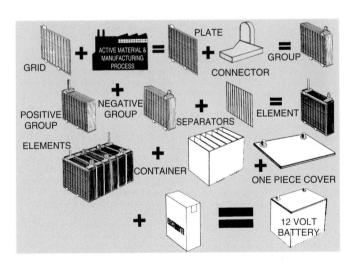

Figure 16-6. Study the manufacturing sequence that occurs in a battery's construction. Note in the final battery that the plates are joined by cell connector straps. (Firestone)

Some batteries may occasionally need water added to the electrolyte. Distilled water should be used whenever possible. Tap water can be used, however, in some areas tap water can contain chemicals that will reduce the life and efficiency of a battery. In the past, rainwater was collected and used to refill batteries. Freezer and refrigerator frost, when melted, is a good source of distilled water.

TYPICAL CURRENT LOAD OF MODERN CARS (IN AMPERES)		
SWITCH	ACCESSORY SWITCH LOAD	MAX. VEHICLE OPERATING LOAD
Parking	4 to 8	–
Low-Beam Headlamp	8 to 14	–
High-Beam (4) Headlamp	12 to 18	18
Heater	6 to 7	–
Windshield Wiper	2 to 3	3
Air Conditioner	10 to 15	15
Radio	0.4 to 1.8	1.8
Electronic Ignition	8 to 12	12
Alternator Field	3 to 5	5
Total		54.8
Summer Starting		100 - 400 Amperes*
Winter Starting		225 - 500 Amperes*

*Values vary with engine size, engine temperature, and oil viscosity.

Figure 16-8. Typical current load for various electrical units. The load will vary somewhat depending upon the type of system and vehicle. (Prestolite)

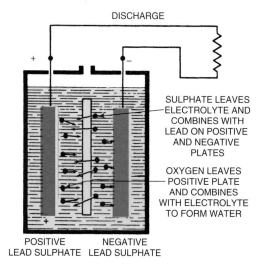

Figure 16-9. Normal chemical reaction during battery discharge. Note that the sulfate combines with the lead on the cell plates. This is why a battery is sometimes said to be sulfated. (Ford)

Figure 16-10. A—A battery charger can be used to charge a vehicle battery or to provide extra current for starting. B—Schematic of a battery cell and its chemical action during charging. Note that during charging the flow of electrons is from the positive electrode to the negative electrode. This is in reverse to battery current drain (discharge). (Bosch & Geo)

vehicle alternator) in a reverse direction. The sulfate (SO_4) ions leave the plates and combine with the hydrogen (H_2) from the water to form sulfuric acid (H_2SO_4). The lead (Pb) in the positive plates combine with the free oxygen (O_2) ions to form lead peroxide (PbO_2). If the battery plates and electrolyte are in good condition, the battery will eventually become fully charged, **Figure 16-10**.

Specific Gravity of the Electrolyte

When the battery is fully charged, the ***specific gravity*** (relative weight of a given volume of a certain material as compared with an equal volume of water) of the battery is

around 1.280. This is determined by drawing a sample of the electrolyte into a ***hydrometer***, **Figure 16-11**. The depth at which the marked float rests in the electrolyte determines its specific gravity. The mark at the top of the electrolyte is read; the higher the float, the higher the charge.

It is not possible to use a hydrometer on maintenance free batteries. Battery state of charge is often indicated by a temperature compensated hydrometer built into the battery. Such a unit is illustrated in **Figure 16-12**. It contains a small green or other color ball that floats when the electrolyte specific gravity is within a certain range. Below this range, the ball sinks.

Figure 16-11. To check the specific gravity of electrolyte, it is drawn up into a hydrometer. The specific gravity is related to battery state of charge. As the battery charge falls off, the float will sink lower and lower into the electrolyte. (Daihatsu)

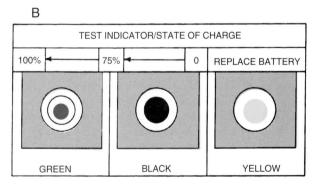

Figure 16-12. A—A cutaway of a built-in battery charge indicator. B—The sight glass or "eye" color indicates the battery's state of charge. (Dodge)

When the ball is floating, it shows as a bright green dot indicating the battery is 80% charged. When the ball sinks, the unit shows up dark, indicating the battery is discharged. If a light yellow color is visible, it indicates the electrolyte level is too low, **Figure 16-12.**

Temperature Correction

When reading a hydrometer, remember that the temperature of the electrolyte affects the specific gravity. Many hydrometers have built-in thermometers with temperature correction scales, **Figure 16-13.** The chart in **Figure 16-14** illustrates how temperature affects the efficiency of a battery. If a battery is discharged too much, the electrolyte can freeze and the battery will burst. The freezing point in relation to specific gravity is shown in **Figure 16-15.**

Figure 16-13. Temperature correction chart for hydrometer use. (Plymouth)

BATTERY EFFICIENCY AT VARIOUS TEMPERATURES	
TEMPERATURE	EFFICIENCY OF A FULLY CHARGED BATTERY
80°F – 26.7°C	100%
50°F – 10°C	82%
30°F – -1.1°C	64%
20°F – -6.7°C	58%
10°F – -12.2°C	50%
0°F – -17.8°C	40%
-10°F – -23.3°C	33%

Figure 16-14. The ambient air temperature can affect battery efficiency. It is obvious why a fully charged battery is a must for cold weather starting. (Ford)

SPECIFIC GRAVITY	FREEZING POINT DEGREES F	DEGREES C	SPECIFIC GRAVITY	FREEZING POINT DEGREES F	DEGREES C
1.100	+18	-8	1.220	-31	-35.0
1.120	+13	-11	1.240	-50	-46
1.140	+8	-13	1.260	-75	-59.4
1.160	+1	-17	1.280	-92	-69
1.180	-6	-21	1.300	-95	-71
1.200	-17	-27			

Figure 16-15. A battery's specific gravity can affect the electrolyte's freezing point. The electrolyte in a battery with a low charge can freeze and crack the case. (GMC)

Battery Ratings

Electrical size has almost no relationship to battery physical size. Often, a battery that is small in size can have a high cranking amp rating. This varies because of different battery materials and construction standards. Newer batteries are often smaller than the older batteries that they replace, but have higher electrical ratings. The list below shows the latest cold cranking and reserve capacity measurements:

- **Cold cranking amps** (CCA): The maximum amount of current that flows for 30 seconds at 7.2 volts, with the battery temperature at 0°F (-18°C). This measurement indicates how much current the battery can produce when cold, and is the standard measurement for modern batteries.
- **Reserve capacity** (RC): The number of minutes that the battery can produce 25 amps at 10.2 volts, with battery temperature at 80°F (26.7°C). Reserve capacity indicates how long the battery can operate the vehicle electrical system in the event of charging system failure.
- **Cranking amps** (CA): The maximum amount of current that flows for 30 seconds at 7.2 volts at a temperature of 32°F (0°C). This measurement is also called hot or marine cranking amps.

Parasitic Battery Loads

The electrical and electronic components found on modern vehicles can cause a small, continuous drain on the battery after the ignition is turned off. This is called **parasitic battery load**. Parasitic battery loads do not cause the battery to go dead, due to the small current draw (measured in milliamps), and should be considered normal. The chart in **Figure 16-16** shows some typical parasitic loads. An ammeter must be used to determine whether current flow is excessive.

Identifying Battery Terminals

The positive post of the battery, which is usually marked *POS*, or (+), is somewhat larger than the negative post and its

CURRENT DRAW IN MILLIAMPERES (mA)		
COMPONENT	TYPICAL PARASITIC DRAW	MAXIMUM PARASITIC DRAW
ABS-ECU	1.0	1.0
Alternator	1.5	1.5
Auto Door Locks	1.0	1.0
BCM	3.6	12.4
Chime	1.0	1.0
ECM	2.6	10.0
ELC	2.0	3.3
HVAC Power Module	1.0	1.0
Illuminated Entry	1.0	1.0
Keyless Entry	2.2	5.5
Radio	6.9	6.0
SRS	1.6	2.7
Theft Deterrent System	0.4	1.0

Figure 16-16. Parasitic loads (mA), of various electronic components. ABS-ECU-antilock brake system/electronic control unit. BCM-body computer module. ECM-electronic control module. ELC-electronic level control. SRS-supplemental restraint system.

top is sometimes marked in red. The negative post is the smaller of the two, and is sometimes marked in green or black. It is usually marked with a *NEG*, or (–), **Figure 16-17**.

On side terminal batteries, the positive connector is surrounded by a red plastic collar. On some side terminal batteries the cables cannot be interchanged as the positive connector is a different size than the negative.

The battery is usually located as close to the engine starter as possible to minimize voltage drop. The close location also reduces the length and cost of the wire necessary to connect the battery to the starter. An underhood location also makes the battery accessible for maintenance and replacement.

Figure 16-17. Typical features of a top post battery. Note the battery's specifications/warning label. (Geo)

The negative terminal is grounded on all vehicles, except for very old cars and trucks with 6 volt electrical systems and a few other older vehicles. The ground wire is fastened to the engine or to some other suitable metal location.

Dry-Charged Battery

Some batteries are shipped with the plates charged, but without electrolyte. This type of battery is considered to be **dry-charged**. If this battery is kept in a cool, dry area, it will remain charged for a long time. Unlike the wet battery, dry-charged batteries do not utilize trickle charging (charging constantly at a very low rate). When the battery is delivered to the customer, the electrolyte is added. Dry-charged batteries are used in motorcycles, lawn equipment, and some cars.

Charging System

The charging system uses the rotation of the engine to create electricity. The electricity recharges the battery and provides power to operate the various vehicle electrical systems. The modern charging system consists of the alternator and regulator. On many vehicles, the regulator is built into the alternator. Alternator and regulator construction and operation are explained in this section.

Alternator

The **alternator** is a belt-driven, electromagnetic device. After the engine is started, the alternator produces electricity to meet the needs of the vehicle and to keep the battery charged. The modern vehicle contains many circuits that place a heavy load on the electrical system. Since many vehicles are used in stop-and-go city driving, this makes it difficult to maintain the battery in a fully charged state. Therefore, the alternator must be extremely efficient at all speeds. A typical alternator used in one charging system is shown in **Figure 16-18**.

Using Magnetism to Produce Electricity

The alternator uses mechanical energy from the engine to create electricity. It can do this because of a basic fact of electricity and magnetism. You may want to review the section on magnetic fields and magnetism in Chapter 7.

When a magnetic field moves in relation to a wire, voltage is generated in the wire. The wire can be moved through a stationary magnetic field, or the magnetic field can be moved through a stationary wire. If the wire is part of a closed circuit, current will flow, **Figure 16-19**. If the wire is passed through the magnetic field in the opposite direction, the current flow in the wire will be reversed. The amount of current produced in the wire will depend on two factors:

- The strength of the magnetic field.
- The difference in speed between the wire and field.

As the wire moves relative to the field, the lines of force are distorted or bent around the leading side. You will notice in **Figure 16-20** that the arrow around the wire indicates the direction in which the magnetic field moves around the wire. This excites the electrons in the wire, causing them to flow.

Inside an actual alternator, a field coil, or **rotor**, with alternating (N) and (S) poles, spins inside a set of stationary

Figure 16-19. Inducing voltage in a wire. A—The wire is stationary and no current is flowing. B—The wire is being drawn swiftly through magnetic lines of force (in direction C). As the wire passes through the magnetic field, it will have voltage induced in it. As it makes a complete circuit, current flows (see needle on ammeter).

stator windings. Current produced in the stator windings is delivered to the rest of the vehicle's electrical system. The alternator field coil is excited (current passed through it) by connecting it to a battery. The current draw is relatively light, around 2 amps.

Alternator Construction

As mentioned earlier, the alternator spins a field coil with alternating (N) and (S) poles inside the stator windings. A round iron core is placed on a shaft, and the field winding is placed around the core. Two iron pole pieces are slid on the

Figure 16-18. Typical parts of an alternator. Study the parts and learn their names and their relation to each other. (Hyundai)

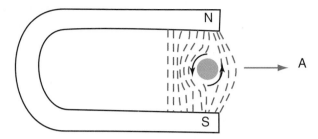

Figure 16-20. Wire passing through a magnetic field. The wire is passing through the magnetic field in direction A. Note how the lines of force are bent as the wire moves through the field. Two arrows around the wire indicate direction in which magnetic fields moves around wire.

shaft. They cover the field winding and are arranged so the fingers are interspersed. The fingers on one pole piece all form (N) poles. The fingers on the other form (S) poles. As the fingers are interspersed, they form alternate N-S-N-S- poles. **Figure 16-21** shows the complete rotor assembly in exploded form.

As the rotor magnetic fields cut through the conductor, voltage is generated and current flows in the complete circuit. As the alternating (N) and (S) pole fields pass around the conductor, the current will alternate, first one direction and then the other. See **Figure 16-22.**

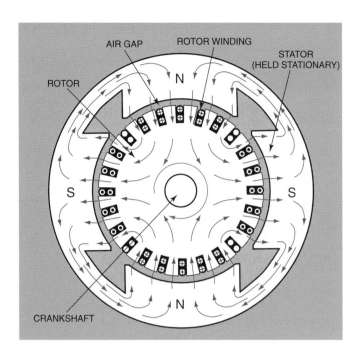

Figure 16-22. Rotor spinning inside the stationary stator assembly. Note the pattern of the magnetic lines of force. Note how they are similar to the magnetic fields you studied earlier. (Bosch)

Figure 16-21. The pole pieces and field winding in this rotor assembly are pressed on the shaft. (Bosch)

Rotor Drive

The rotor is attached to a pulley which is driven by a belt from a pulley on the engine crankshaft. The crankshaft pulley is the *drive pulley*, the rotor pulley is the *driven pulley*. The rotor pulley is much smaller than the crankshaft pulley, and therefore the rotor turns at a much faster speed than the engine crankshaft, **Figure 16-23.** Rotor speeds of over 10,000 RPM are common.

Brushes and Slip Rings

Direct current from the battery is fed to the field coil by using *brushes* rubbing against *slip rings*. One end of the

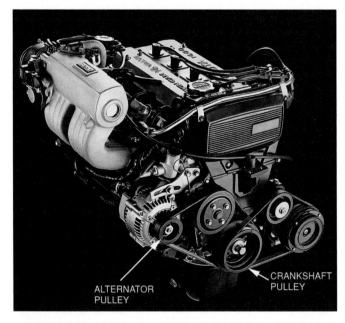

Figure 16-23. A four-cylinder engine showing the diameter difference between the alternator pulley and the crankshaft pulley. (Toyota Motor Corp.)

field coil is fastened to the insulated brush, while the other end is attached to the grounded brush. As the pole fields pass through the conductor, voltage is imparted in the conductor, and current flows in one direction. When the rotor turns 180°, and the (N) pole and (S) pole are at opposite positions, this causes current to flow in the opposite direction.

A phantom view of a typical alternator is shown in **Figure 16-24**. Study the location of the various components. The use of diodes will be explained later in this section. The rear view of an assembled alternator is illustrated in **Figure 16-25A**. Note battery, field, and sensing terminals. A sectional view of the same alternator is shown in **Figure 16-25B**.

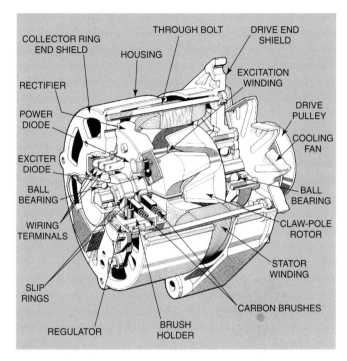

Figure 16-24. Cutaway view of an alternator showing the construction and layout of the various components. (Bosch)

Alternator Output

The stator windings are made up of three separate windings. The windings produces what is known as three-phase alternating current. When only one winding is used, single-phase current results. A curve illustrating single-phase alternating current flow is shown in **Figure 16-26A**. **Figure 16-26B** illustrates three-phase alternating current.

Notice that the distance between high points in the output is shorter. The important thing to remember is that the stator produces alternating current. The vehicle battery requires direct current. Before it can be used, alternating current must be *rectified* (changed) to direct current.

Diodes

Alternating current is rectified by *diodes*. Diodes have a peculiar ability to allow current to flow readily in one direction. When the current reverses and attempts to flow through in the other direction, current flow is stopped. Refer to Chapter 7 for more information about diodes.

The diodes are located in one end plate or shield. In the alternator illustrated in **Figure 16-27** four negative polarity diodes are pressed into the aluminum end plate. These are on the ground side. Four positive polarity diodes are pressed into a heat sink which is insulated from the end plate.

Figure 16-25. This alternator incorporates the voltage regulator into the alternator slip rings-end frame assembly. The regulator is a solid state electronic unit. (Chevrolet)

Remember that the stator has three windings. To rectify the current, each winding requires one negative and one positive diode. No matter which direction the current leaves any stator winding, the diodes are arranged to cause it to leave the alternator in the proper direction. The arrangement of the rectifiers will allow current to flow from the alternator to the battery, but will not allow current flow from the battery to the alternator.

The wiring arrangement of the stator and diodes is shown in **Figure 16-28**. A cross-sectional view of a diode is given in **Figure 16-29**. **Figure 16-30** shows a graphic representation of rectified current flow.

Figure 16-26. A—A single-phase alternating current wave. X represents positive half of wave and Y negative half. B—In three-phase alternating current, the phase outputs overlap, but do not coincide. (Delco-Remy)

Alternator Control

At idle, when the rotor is turning relatively slowly, the alternator can keep up with the demands of the vehicle electrical system. At normal vehicle speeds, the alternator can produce much more voltage and current than needed. To protect the alternator and the rest of the electrical system from damage, a means of reducing the output must be found.

As mentioned earlier in this chapter, there are two ways to control the amount of electricity produced in a wire: controlling the speed of rotor movement, or controlling the strength of the magnetic field. Since the rotor is driven directly by the engine crankshaft through belts and pulleys, controlling alternator speed would be difficult. The simplest way for controlling alternator output is to control the field strength.

To reduce alternator output, a *voltage regulator* is used. The voltage regulator controls the alternator output by adjusting the amount of current reaching the rotor. This controls the strength of the magnetic field passing through the stator windings. The regulator controls the field strength by reading voltage output from the alternator. If output voltage becomes too high, the regulator reduces field strength. If the output voltage drops, the regulator increases field strength.

Electromechanical Voltage Regulator

Older voltage regulators use contact points that are operated by electromagnetic coils. These were called *electromechanical voltage regulators*, since they used a combination of electrical and mechanical parts. You learned earlier that electricity can be used to produce magnetism. If current is

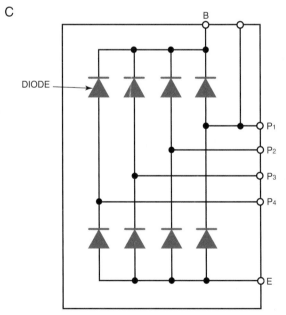

Figure 16-27. A—End view of an alternator. Note that the location of the diodes is next to an open vent in the alternator casing. B—This diode bridge contains eight diodes. Other diode bridges contain six. C—Electrical schematic for the diode bridge. (Acura)

applied to a coil placed around a bar of steel, the bar will become magnetized, **Figure 16-31**. The more turns of wire and the stronger the current, the more powerful the magnet. This principle is used in electromechanical voltage regulators.

Figure 16-28. Typical rectifier wiring arrangement. Note that the stator windings are connected to the diode rectifier bridge. (General Motors)

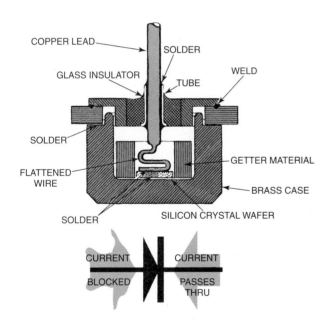

Figure 16-29. Cross-section of a diode (rectifier). Current is free to pass one way only. A diode, like a transistor, is a semiconductor (conducts electricity under certain conditions, acts as an insulator under others).

The field current passes through a contact point set. Some voltage regulators cause the field current to go through a resistor which reduces, but does not stop current flow. The points are held closed by a spring. A small amount of output current from the alternator is delivered to the coil under the point set. If the voltage becomes too high, the coil's magnetic

Figure 16-30. This rectified current flow wave pattern represents the three-phase alternating current depicted in Figure 16-26 after it has passed through the rectifier diodes. (Delco-Remy)

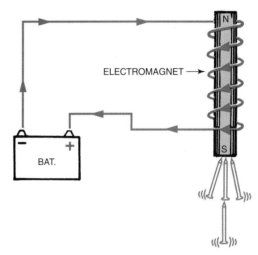

Figure 16-31. When current is passed through a coil surrounding an iron bar, the bar becomes an electromagnet. Notice how the bar attracts and holds nails while current is flowing.

field become powerful enough to overcome spring tension, opening the points. This breaks the field circuit to the alternator. Alternator output stops, causing the electromagnetic coil to lose its field. This allows the spring to close the points, restoring current flow to the field.

This process occurs over and over many times per second. Alternator voltage output is determined by the tension of the point closing spring. On some older electromechanical regulators, the spring is adjustable. **Figure 16-32** shows a wiring diagram of a typical alternator charging circuit using a two unit regulator. When an ammeter is used instead of an indicator lamp, a single unit regulator, **Figure 16-33**, can be used. The single unit regulator contains a voltage regulator only.

Electronic Voltage Regulator

All vehicles made within the last 15 years use an *electronic voltage regulator*. The electronic voltage regulator uses power transistors, integrated circuits, diodes, and other solid state parts to control alternator output. The electronic voltage regulator eliminates contact points and moving parts that can stick, oxidize, or wear. Some electronic regulators are remotely mounted. However, electronic voltage regulators are reliable, durable, and small enough to be incorporated into the alternator itself as shown in **Figure 16-34**.

Figure 16-32. This alternator wiring diagram shows the use of a two unit regulator. Note how the field relay operates the "no charge" indicator lamp. (Pontiac)

Figure 16-33. Schematic of a single unit voltage regulator. Note the use of an ammeter, eliminating the need for a field relay.

Figure 16-34. Exploded view of an alternator with a built-in-voltage regulator. (Toyota)

A charging circuit employing a transistor regulator is shown in **Figure 16-35**. The most important part in this regulator is the *Zener diode*, discussed in Chapter 7. The breakdown point of the Zener diode is set at the maximum charging system voltage. The Zener diode is nonconducting until this voltage is reached. At this point, the diode breaks down and transmits electricity.

Figure 16-35. Schematic of a charging circuit employing a transistor regulator.

This current flow, acting through other transistors, turns the power transistor off and stops the flow of field current to the alternator. This causes the voltage output to fall below Zener diode break down voltage, at which time the diode once again becomes nonconductive. This stops the current flow to the transistors and allows resumption of field current flow. The cycle is repeated thousands of times per second. The external wiring circuit for one remotely mounted transistor regulator is in **Figure 16-36**.

Figure 16-36. External wiring circuit as used on one charging system employing a remotely mounted transistor regulator. (Ford)

Built-In Electronic Regulator Operation

A common charging system circuit with a built-in regulator is illustrated in **Figure 16-37**. A small amount of current passes from the stator through the diode trio to the regulator. This equalizes the voltage on either side of the indicator light, putting it out, and tries to ground through resistor R3.

Figure 16-37. Charging system schematic showing a transistor voltage regulator. Note the diode trio. This unit rectifies current flow from ground through TR1 and the field windings to the stator windings. The rectifier diode bridge change stator ac voltage to dc output. (Chrysler)

When the stator voltage reaches a certain level, voltage going to ground through resistor R3 will increase to the point that it will cause Zener diode D1 to conduct. Forward-biased (voltage applied in direction causing current flow) transistor TR2 conducts and transistor TR3 is reverse-biased off. This turns transistor TR1 off. The field current and system voltage immediately decrease with TR1 off.

When system voltage decreases, voltage through R3 decreases and D1 stops conducting. This causes transistor TR2 to become reverse-biased off and transistors TR1 and

TR3 forward-biased on. Output voltage and field current will increase. This cycle is repeated thousands of times per second, holding alternator voltage output to a preset level.

Sudden voltage change across R3 is prevented by capacitor C1, and excessive back current through TR1 at high temperature is prevented by R4. TR1 is protected by D2 that prevents a high induced voltage in the field winding when TR1 is off. Voltage control temperature correction is provided by a thermistor (resistance decreases as temperature increases).

Computer-Controlled Voltage Regulation

Most vehicles today have several electronic control units (ECUs) that control the engine and other systems. ECU's can also be used to control voltage to the field winding, which eliminates the need for a separate regulator. The logic module tells the power module what to do in this charging system, **Figure 16-38**. The disadvantage of this system is if the portion of the ECU that controls voltage regulation becomes defective, the entire ECU must be replaced.

Alternator Operation

When the ignition key is turned on, the battery is connected to the field terminal through the voltage regulator. When the engine is started, it will drive the alternator rotor. As the turning rotor pole force fields cut through the stator windings, alternating current voltage is generated. The diodes rectify the alternating current into direct current. The alternator output leaves the positive terminal and travels to the battery. The return circuit is completed through the engine block and vehicle frame.

Brushless Alternator

Figure 16-39 illustrates a heavy duty, truck alternator with built-in voltage regulation. This particular unit, unlike light duty alternators, does not employ slip rings and brushes. All conductors carrying current are stationary (do not move). These are regulator circuit components, field winding, stator windings and rectifier diodes. Note the stationary (does not turn with rotor) field coil.

Starter System

To start an internal combustion engine, it must be cranked (rotated by an outside source). Small two-stroke engines are often cranked by pulling a rope which causes the internal engine parts to revolve. The first automobiles used a hand crank rod for starting. However, this method was dangerous and impractical. A method was soon developed to start the engine by using an electric starting motor, or **starter**.

The starter is mounted on the transmission housing and operates a small gear that can be meshed with a large ring gear attached to the flywheel. To energize the starter, the driver turns the ignition switch to start, which completes an electrical circuit to the starter. When the starter motor armature begins to turn, the starter gear moves out and engages the ring gear, which spins the crankshaft. When the engine starts, the driver breaks the starter electrical circuit by releasing the ignition key switch. This causes the starter gear to move out of mesh with the ring gear.

Figure 16-38. This power module controls voltage to the rotor windings, which is dependent on battery voltage. (Chrysler)

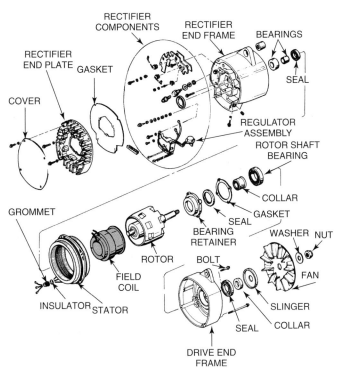

Figure 16-39. Heavy duty, truck type alternator with built-in electronic regulator. Note the stationary field coil and absence of slip rings and brushes. (Chevrolet)

Starter Motor Principles

All electric motors operate from the same fundamental principles. If a current carrying wire is placed in a magnetic field, the field set up around the wire by the moving current will oppose that of the magnetic field, **Figure 16-40**. If the wire is free to move, it will move out of the field.

Figure 16-40. Current carrying conductor in a magnetic field. The magnetic field around the wire (see small arrows) will oppose the magnetic field from the poles. This will cause the wire to be forced out in direction of arrow A.

Armature Loop

If the conductor is bent in the form of a loop, each side of the loop will set up a magnetic field. Since the current is traveling in opposite directions, the two sides will have opposing fields, **Figure 16-41**. This is called an *armature loop*. When the armature loop is placed in a magnetic field, both sides of the loop will oppose the magnetic field, but in opposite directions. This will cause the loop to rotate out of the field, **Figure 16-42**.

Figure 16-41. Note the direction of the magnetic field on each side of this armature loop.

Figure 16-42. Each side of the armature loop has a field moving in opposite directions. These fields will oppose the pole shoe field, causing the loop to rotate.

Commutator Segments

In order to pass an electrical current into the revolving loop, the loop ends must be fastened to *commutator segments*. Copper **brushes** rub against the turning segments, **Figure 16-43**. One loop would not give the starter motor sufficient power, so many loops are used. The ends of each loop are connected to a copper commutator segment, **Figure 16-44**.

The loops are insulated and formed over a laminated iron core. The ends of all loops are connected to the copper

Figure 16-43. In an actual starter motor, many loops and commutator segments are used. Each commutator segment is insulated from the shaft and other segments.

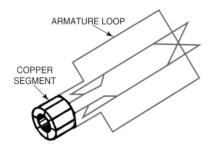

Figure 16-44. Many loops are required in a starter motor. Additional loops will increase the starter motor's torque.

commutator segments. The segments are insulated from the shaft and from each other. The core is supported on a steel shaft that, in turn, is supported in bronze bushings.

When current is fed into two of the four brushes, it flows through all the loops and out the other brushes. This creates a magnetic field around each loop. As the armature turns, the loop will move to a position where the current flow reverses. If this were not done, the magnetic field around the loops would push them out of one side of the field. As a result, they would be repelled when they entered the other side of the pole field. This constant reversal of current flow is accomplished by the commutator segments moving under the brushes. Two brushes are insulated and two are grounded.

Field Pole Shoes

Field pole shoes, usually called poles, are placed inside a steel cylinder (field frame). There may be four or more pole shoes. Two or more of the shoes are wound with heavy copper strips. Then, when current is passed through the coils, the pole shoes become powerful magnets. The field frame provides a low reluctance magnetic path, further strengthening the magnetic field.

Starter Electrical Circuits

The copper loops and field windings are heavy enough to carry a large amount of current with minimum resistance. Since they draw heavy amounts of current, they must not be operated on a continuous basis for longer than 15 seconds. After operating a starter for 15 seconds, wait a couple of minutes to let the starter motor dissipate some of its heat. A starter heats quickly, so prolonged use can cause serious damage.

Various wiring arrangements are used in starter construction. **Figure 16-45A** illustrates a four pole, two field winding. By wiring the field coil in parallel, resistance is lowered, and the field coils produce stronger magnetic fields. The other two poles have no windings, but serve to strengthen the field. **Figure 16-45B** shows a four pole, four winding armature wired series-parallel.

Figure 16-45C illustrates a four pole, three winding setup. Two of the windings are in series with themselves and the armature. One winding does not pass through the armature, but goes directly to ground. This *shunt winding* aids with additional starting torque. As starter speed increases, the shunt draws a heavy current and tends to keep starter speed within acceptable limits.

Figure 16-45D shows a four pole, four winding setup. Three windings are in series, one is a shunt winding. **Figure 16-45E** is a four pole, four winding setup with all windings in series. There are other setups, however, the circuits illustrated in **Figure 16-45** are the most commonly used.

Starter Motor Construction

Figure 16-46 shows an exploded view of the various parts of a typical starter motor. This particular starter has a four pole, three winding circuit. One of the windings is a shunt

Figure 16-45. Study these various starter wiring circuits. Continue at it until you have learned the different types and their wiring patterns. (Motorcraft)

winding. **Figure 16-47** shows a cutaway view of a typical starter using an overrunning clutch starter drive (discussed below). Note how the armature shaft is supported at both ends by a bronze bushing.

Starter Drive System

To provide a means for the starting motor to turn the engine, a drive system is used. It consists of a ***ring gear*** and a ***starter pinion gear***. These are explained in the following sections.

Ring Gear

The ring gear is attached to the flywheel of vehicles with manual transmissions. The ring gear is either welded or shrink fit, **Figure 16-48**, to the flywheel. In shrink fitting, the ring gear is expanded by heat and fitted on the flywheel while hot. As it cools, the metal contracts and the ring grasps the flywheel securely. Vehicles with automatic transmissions and

Figure 16-46. Exploded view of a typical starter motor. Learn the names and locations of all the parts. (Honda)

transaxles have a separate, lightweight ring gear assembly which bolts between the engine crankshaft and torque converter. The ring gear usually has 150 to 200 teeth.

Starter Pinion Gear

A small gear, called a starter pinion gear, is attached to the starter armature shaft. The pinion gear is much smaller than the ring gear (about 10 to 15 teeth) and must turn 15 to 30 revolutions in order to crank the flywheel one revolution.

Pinion Engagement Devices

It is necessary to mesh the pinion gear for cranking and demesh (disengage) the pinion when the engine has started. The two basic types of pinion engagement devices are the inertia type, and the overrunning clutch type. There are several designs of each basic type.

Inertia Starter Drive

With the ***inertia drive***, sometimes called the ***Bendix drive*** or ***self-engaging drive***, the armature shaft spins and the drive pinion stands still while the threaded sleeve spins inside the pinion. As the sleeve spins, the pinion slides out and meshes with the ring gear. As soon as the pinion reaches its stop, the turning sleeve causes the pinion to turn with it to crank the engine.

The pinion sleeve fits loosely on the armature shaft and is connected to a large spring that is fastened to the armature shaft. The spring absorbs the sudden shock of pinion engagement. When the engine starts, the pinion will spin faster than the armature turns the pinion sleeve. This will reverse its travel on the threaded pinion, and it will spin backward, free of the ring gear. A small coil spring will prevent it from working back into mesh.

Figure 16-49 illustrates the action of the inertia type pinion engaging device. In **Figure 16-49A**, the armature shaft and pinion sleeve begin to spin. The stationary pinion is sliding to the left. In **Figure 16-49B**, the sliding action is stopped, and the pinion begins to turn and crank the engine.

When the engine starts, **Figure 16-49C**, the pinion is spinning faster than the threaded pinion sleeve. This spins the pinion back out of mesh with the ring gear. An inertia drive, in place on a starter motor, is shown in **Figure 16-50**. Notice the threaded pinion sleeve and pinion. The pinion is weighted on one side, so it will tend to resist being turned until it has slid into mesh with the ring gear.

Overrunning Clutch

The one-way or ***overrunning clutch drive*** is engaged with the ring gear by an electric solenoid that actuates the shift linkage. In operation, the pinion is turned by the overrunning clutch. When the pinion is slid into mesh with the ring, the shifting mechanism completes the starter circuit and the overrunning clutch drives the pinion.

When the engine starts, the ring will spin the pinion faster than the starter armature is turning. The pinion is free to run faster because the overrunning clutch engages the pinion only when the armature is driving it.

Figure 16-51 illustrates a typical overrunning clutch starter drive. Note the pinion, drive shell and sleeve assembly, coil spring, and shift collar. The coil spring comes into use when the pinion teeth mesh against the ring teeth. The actuating lever, or shift lever, will continue to move the shift collar, compressing the spring. When the lever has moved far

HOLD-IN WINDING
PULL-IN WINDING
SOLENOID PLUNGER
RETURN SPRING
SHIFT LEVER
MESHING SPRING
DRIVER
OVERRUNNING CLUTCH STARTER DRIVE
PINION
ARMATURE SHAFT
BUSHING
STOP RING
HELICAL SPLINE
GUIDE RING
FIELD (EXCITATION) WINDING
ARMATURE
FIELD FRAME
POLE SHOE
COMMUTATOR
CARBON BRUSH
COMMUTATOR END SHIELD
BRUSH HOLDER
FIELD LEAD WIRE
SOLENOID SWITCH
CONTACT BREAK SPRING
CONTACT
MOVING CONTACT
TERMINAL

Figure 16-47. Cutaway of a starter motor using an overrunning clutch starter drive. Note the shift lever and solenoid. (Bosch)

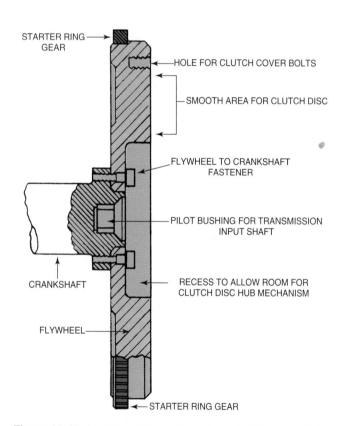

STARTER RING GEAR
HOLE FOR CLUTCH COVER BOLTS
SMOOTH AREA FOR CLUTCH DISC
FLYWHEEL TO CRANKSHAFT FASTENER
PILOT BUSHING FOR TRANSMISSION INPUT SHAFT
RECESS TO ALLOW ROOM FOR CLUTCH DISC HUB MECHANISM
CRANKSHAFT
FLYWHEEL
STARTER RING GEAR

Figure 16-48. A cross-sectional view of a typical flywheel. Note how the ring gear is placed on the flywheel. This particular ring gear is pressed on.

A — ARMATURE AND SHAFT BEGINNING TO ROTATE — FORCES STATIONARY PINION ENDWISE ON SHAFT

B — PINION MESHED IN FLYWHEEL — ALL PARTS NOW ROTATING TOGETHER, CRANKING ENGINE

C — ENGINE STARTS: EXCESSIVE FLYWHEEL SPEED DRIVES PINION OUT OF MESH

Figure 16-49. Bendix starter drive action. Note how the spring forces the starter gear back and forth. This allows the starter gear to mesh with the flywheel without gear clash. Another type of starter drive, called the overrunning clutch, are often mistakenly referred to as a Bendix drive. (Delco-Remy)

enough to close the starter switch, the pinion will turn and the compressed spring will force it into mesh with the ring gear.

Figure 16-51 illustrates an end view showing the spring-loaded clutch rollers. When the drive sleeve turns faster than the pinion and collar assembly, the rollers are wedged against the pinion, causing it to turn. When pinion speed exceeds that of the sleeve, the rollers retract and the pinion is free of the shell and sleeve assembly. **Figure 16-52** shows the overrunning clutch drive in place on a starter.

Figure 16-50. Cutaway of a starter motor with a Bendix drive.

Figure 16-51. In this overrunning clutch starter drive, the rollers lock the pinion and collar assembly to the drive member when the armature shaft is spinning the drive member faster than the pinion. (British-Leyland)

Starter Solenoid

If an iron core is placed inside a coil of wire, an electric current is passed through the coil, the iron core will be drawn into the coil. Such a unit is called a *solenoid*. A solenoid has many applications and can be used where a push or pull motion is desired. The primary job of the solenoid is to make the electrical contact between the battery and starter motor. A typical solenoid is shown in **Figure 16-53**. The solenoid is energized from the start position on the ignition switch.

Figure 16-54 shows how a solenoid can be used to pull on a starter shift lever. You will note that the solenoid in **Figure 16-55** not only pulled the starter shift lever until the pinion meshed, but it also closed the starter switch after the meshing was almost complete.

Figure 16-52. Cutaway of a starter motor using an overrunning clutch starter drive. This starter is engaged by an electric solenoid. It increases cranking torque by using reduction gears. (Chrysler)

Figure 16-53. A starting circuit solenoid schematic illustrating parts and related electrical wiring. When the starter solenoid is energized, the plunger is drawn (pulled) in, bringing the top of the pinion drive lever in. This forces the bottom to move out, moving the pinion gear into engagement with the flywheel gear and engine cranking begins. Note the starter safety switch. (Chevrolet)

Figure 16-54. Starter drive solenoid operation. A—The solenoid plunger has moved to the right, opening the starter switch and retracting the starter drive gear. The ignition switch is off. B—The ignition switch is on, energizing the solenoid, which draws the plunger into the coil. The plunger has engaged the drive gear and closed the starter switch. The starter will now crank the engine.

DISENGAGED

PINION PARTIALLY ENGAGED

PINION FULLY ENGAGED AND STARTING MOTOR CRANKING

Figure 16-55. Starter solenoid operation stages. Note the electric solenoid operation in each stage. (Chevrolet)

Starter Solenoid Operation

Figure 16-55 shows the starter solenoid in three stages of operation. In the disengaged position, the pinion is demeshed. The solenoid plunger is released and no current is flowing. The partially engaged stage shows current from the starter switch flowing through both the pull-in and the hold-in coils. Both coils are drawing the plunger inward, causing it to pull the shift lever. The pinion is just starting to engage.

The cranking stage shows the plunger pulled into the coil. The pinion is fully engaged. The hold-in coil is operating, but the pull-in winding has cut out. The plunger has operated the starting switch and current is flowing from the battery through the switch and to the starter. When the engine has started, the hold-in coil will cut out and the plunger will move out, retracting the pinion and opening the starter switch, **Figure 16-55**. Starters with self-engaging inertia drives generally use a solenoid to open and close the starter switch.

A starter motor employing a solenoid and overrunning clutch with permanent magnets is shown in **Figure 16-56**. A somewhat different method of actuating the starter drive is illustrated in **Figure 16-57**. In this setup, a movable pole shoe is connected to the starter drive shift lever. When the starter is in the off position, one of the field coils is grounded through a set of contacts.

When the starter is first actuated, a very heavy flow of current through this field coil pulls on the movable pole shoe. The shoe, in turn, engages the starter drive. When fully engaged, the field coil contacts open and normal starter operation takes place. A holding coil keeps the sliding pole shoe in the engaged position. When current to the starter is interrupted, the pole shoe moves back and disengages the starter drive.

Reduction Gear Starters

To increase starter torque, some starter drives are driven through a *reduction gear*. The reduction gear is used in high

Figure 16-57. Starter design using one movable pole shoe as a means of actuating the starter drive. (Jeep)

speed starter motors. The reduction gear reduces speed to increase starter torque. A common reduction gear starter is shown in **Figure 16-58**.

Planetary Gear Reduction Starter

Planetary gears have been used in automatic transmissions to obtain desired gear reduction for many years. Planetary gearsets are also used for reduction in some starter motors, **Figure 16-59**. This design decreases the overall size and weight of the starter by approximately 35% while maintaining the needed starter torque.

The planetary gears, located on the shaft, mesh with the teeth of the internal or ring gear. Most reduction gear starters use permanent magnets which eliminates the field coil windings. There are six permanent magnets mounted inside the armature housing which reduce current draw while starting,

Figure 16-56. A cutaway view of a permanent magnet starter motor. Six small magnets are located inside the field frame. They take the place of the current carrying field coils. This type of starter is lighter than those using field coils. (Chevrolet)

Figure 16-58. Exploded view of a typical reduction gear starter motor assembly. Note the heat shield used to help protect the starter from excessive engine and/or exhaust heat. (Geo)

Figure 16-59. The magnets are aligned according to polarity and cannot be removed from the housing. The magnets are permanently affixed to the housing.

Starter Actuating Switches

In addition to the solenoid-operated switch that directs battery current to the starter, it is necessary to furnish current to the solenoid. On most vehicles, turning the key to the fullest travel closes a switch to the solenoid. However, current must first pass through a *neutral safety switch*, **Figure 16-60**, before energizing the solenoid.

On some vehicles equipped with manual transmissions, the clutch must be depressed to close the neutral safety switch. On vehicles equipped with automatic transmissions, the gear selector must be placed in park or neutral for current to flow through the neutral safety switch to the solenoid. This prevents the vehicle from being started when the transmission is in gear.

Figure 16-59. Exploded view of a planetary gear reduction starter motor assembly. Note the use of an overrunning clutch. (Honda)

Figure 16-60. Starting circuit including neutral safety or clutch start switch. If the switch remains open, the vehicle will not start. (Geo/General Motors)

Summary

A battery is an electrochemical device used to supply current for starting the vehicle. It contains positive and negative plates that are connected in such a way as to produce six groups of cells. The plates are covered with electrolyte. A charged battery will gather a surplus of electrons at the negative post. When the battery is placed in a completed circuit, the electrons will flow from the negative post, through the circuit, and on to the positive post.

The battery is charged by passing electricity through it in the reverse direction of battery current flow. The battery's state of charge is checked by using a hydrometer to determine the specific gravity of the electrolyte. Upon starting, the alternator will recharge the battery. Vehicle batteries are usually 12 volt, though other battery sizes are used by trucks and commercial vehicles. Be careful of battery electrolyte—it is dangerous. Batteries can explode and should never be exposed to sparks or open flame.

The primary job of the alternator is to supply the necessary current for the electrical needs of the vehicle and to keep the battery charged. The alternator operates by using magnetism to change mechanical energy (rotation) into electricity. It is necessary to control the maximum voltage and current output developed by the alternator. This is done by using the regulator.

On older regulators, an electromagnet breaks a set of contact points and interrupts current flow to the field circuit when system voltage exceeds the alternator's designed output. As the points vibrate, they produce a smooth, controlled alternator output. The battery, alternator, and regulator work together and the function of any one unit is dependent upon the action of the other two.

Battery condition and electrical load determine the current and voltage requirements. The alternator produces the required voltage and current and the regulator controls the alternator output on a level consistent with system needs.

The starter is used to crank the engine for starting purposes. The starter motor utilizes a current carrying series of armature loops placed in a strong magnetic field produced by field coils. As the armature loops are repelled by the magnetic field, the armature is forced to spin. By arranging a sufficient number of loops and connecting them to commutator bars or segments, current in the loops keeps reversing so the repelling force will remain constant. This allows the armature to continue spinning.

The starter uses large copper conductors in both the field and armature circuits. The field and armature are connected in series via four brushes. Since the field strength is very strong, the starter motor will produce enough torque to crank the engine. Starters draw heavy current loads and therefore heat quite rapidly. They must not be operated continuously for longer than 15 seconds without a brief rest in which to dissipate the heat.

The starter pinion that engages the flywheel ring gear uses one of two different designs. One uses the Bendix drive. This type spins a pinion sleeve that causes the pinion to slide out on the sleeve until it engages the ring. The overrunning clutch type moves the starter pinion into mesh by means of a shift lever actuated by a solenoid. When this starter drive is used, the overrunning clutch is used to allow the drive pinion to freewheel when the engine starts, until it is drawn out of mesh. The starter is energized by the solenoid. The solenoid is energized by operating the ignition switch, through a neutral safety switch.

Know These Terms

Lead-acid battery	Diode
Cells	Voltage regulator
Positive plate	Electromechanical voltage regulator
Negative plate	
Separator	Electronic voltage regulator
Electrolyte	Zener diode
Terminals	Starter
Specific gravity	Armature loop
Hydrometer	Commutator segments
Cold cranking amps	Brushes
Cranking amps	Field pole shoes
Reserve capacity	Shunt winding
Parasitic battery load	Ring gear
Dry-charge	Starter pinion gear
Alternator	Inertia starter drive
Rotor	Bendix drive
Stator	Self-engaging drive
Drive pulley	Overrunning clutch drive
Driven pulley	Solenoid
Brushes	Reduction gear
Slip rings	Planetary gears
Rectified	Neutral safety switch

Review Questions—Chapter 16

Do not write in this book. Write your answers on a separate sheet of paper.

1. Technician A says that each battery cell of a 12 volt battery produces 12 volts. Technician B says that most of the battery electrolyte is sulfuric acid. Who is right?

    (A) A only.
    (B) B only.
    (C) Both A & B.
    (D) Neither A nor B.

2. All of the following statements about batteries are true, EXCEPT:

    (A) an automotive battery contains positive and negative plates.
    (B) a 12 volt battery will contain three cells.
    (C) the battery electrolyte contains water.
    (D) a battery stores chemical energy.

3. What two devices are able to charge a battery?

4. How do you check the specific gravity of a battery?

5. How are the battery posts identified?

6. A battery that is low on electrolyte should be filled with _____ .

    (A) rainwater
    (B) distilled water
    (C) sulfuric acid
    (D) hydrochloric acid

7. A dry-charged battery is shipped without _____ .

    (A) plates
    (B) terminals
    (C) individual cells
    (D) electrolyte

8. Which of the following alternator parts rotates?

    (A) Rotor.
    (B) Stator.
    (C) Diodes.
    (D) Brushes.

9. Which of the following alternator parts change alternating current into direct current?

    (A) Rotor.
    (B) Stator.
    (C) Diodes.
    (D) Pulley.

10. The alternator slip rings are used with _____ to transfer current.

11. What are the two methods of controlling field strength in the alternator rotor?

12. Of the answers to question 11, which is controlled to control the output of the alternator?

13. Modern voltage regulators use _____ to control the alternator.

    (A) contact points
    (B) electromagnetic coils
    (C) brushes
    (D) electronic components

14. A Zener diode allows electricity to flow when the _____ passes a certain point.

    (A) temperature
    (B) amperage
    (C) voltage
    (D) phase shift

15. When the voltage on either side of the indicator light is equal, the light _____ .

    (A) goes out
    (B) comes on
    (C) flashes
    (D) flickers

16. An internal combustion engine must be _____ by an external source before it will start.

17. If a magnetic field surrounds a wire, in what direction will the wire try to move?

    (A) Away from the field.
    (B) Toward the field.
    (C) At right angles to the field.
    (D) It does not move.

18. What are the two purposes of the shunt circuit in the starter motor?

19. Which of the following starter parts do not rotate during starter operation?

    (A) Armature windings.
    (B) Commutator bars.
    (C) Drive pinion.
    (D) Pole shoes.

20. Technician A says that starter motors can be used continuously for up to ten minutes before stopping. Technician B says that the starter motors used with reduction gears are capable of higher speeds than conventional starter motors. Who is right?

    (A) A only.
    (B) B only.
    (C) Both A & B.
    (D) Neither A nor B.

21. Name the two general classes of starter drive mechanisms.

22. Some starters have a movable pole shoe to _____ .

    (A) increase starter torque
    (B) reduce starter speed
    (C) engage the starter drive
    (D) prevent starter overheating

23. The overrunning clutch engages the pinion only when the _____ is driving it.
    (A) starter motor armature
    (B) engine ring gear
    (C) starter solenoid
    (D) Both A & B.

24. The primary job of the starter solenoid is to provide an electrical connection between the battery and the _____.
    (A) ignition switch
    (B) starter motor
    (C) alternator
    (D) drive mechanism

25. Many starter solenoids are attached to linkage which engages the _____ with the flywheel during cranking.

Modern vehicles are thoroughly tested to ensure that their electronic systems will not be affected by electromagnetic interference. The antenna array is capable of generating radio waves across a wide spectrum. The blue material on the chamber walls is for electromagnetic absorption. (Chrysler)

17

Chassis Electrical

Upon completion of this chapter, you will be able to:
- Identify and define chassis wiring and related electronic components.
- Identify and define circuit protection devices.
- Identify and define common vehicle chassis lights.
- Identify common chassis electrical equipment.

This chapter will cover the basic principles of chassis electrical systems, such as chassis wiring, vehicle lights, safety devices such as horns and windshield wipers, and comfort items such as power windows and door locks. Devices such as radios and CD players are not within the scope of this text. Other chassis electrical systems, such as blower motors and anti-lock brakes, are covered in the chapters dealing with these systems. Studying this chapter will allow you to become familiar with the electrical components and associated wiring that are used on the vehicle body and chassis.

Chassis Wiring

Chassis wiring consists of all of the vehicle wiring that is not directly connected with the engine and drive train. This wiring extends throughout the vehicle body. Wiring to devices that will not be operated except when the vehicle is being driven, such as the windshield wipers and radio, is routed through the ignition switch. Wiring to vehicle systems which can be operated at any time, such as lights and horns, is powered directly from the vehicle battery, **Figure 17-1**.

Wire Sizes

The size of a particular vehicle wire will vary with the amount of current that is expected to flow through it. Wire size is measured by its gage. The higher the gage number, the smaller the wire diameter. Wire to a single bulb might have a gage of 16 or 18 while battery cable is 4 or 6. The gage standard used to measure most automotive wire is called the *American Wire Gage* or AWG.

Figure 17-1. Chassis wiring is located throughout the vehicle. Each assembly contains many wires that connect to a variety of electrical components. This illustration shows a wiring assembly for a theft prevention system only. (Honda)

Wiring Harness

Almost all vehicle wiring is installed as part of a **wiring harness**. Wiring harnesses are groups of vehicle wires wrapped together for ease of installation. The actual wires are encased in **looms**. The looms help reduce chafing and other damage and keep the wire in a neat package. Wiring harnesses have molded electrical connectors that attach to electrical components or other harnesses.

Some vehicles use a **printed circuit** for at least part of their wiring needs. The printed circuit shown in **Figure 17-2** is a vinyl plastic sheet with the circuits etched or printed on it. Since the printed material is electrically conductive, power flows through the paths of the printed circuit in the same way that it flows through standard wiring.

Many electrical circuits operate on very low voltages. These low-voltage circuits must be protected from stray electrical impulses and magnetic fields. To accomplish this, many wires and electrical devices are **shielded** (surrounded with grounded metal covers). In some cases, the wire or device that produces a magnetic field is shielded. More commonly, the low-voltage wiring that could be affected is shielded.

Figure 17-2. An instrument cluster printed circuit board. (Dodge)

Many Circuits

The modern automobile has a large number of electrical circuits. A typical wiring diagram, **Figure 17-3**, shows a cruise control circuit. The electrical circuits, with the addition of many accessory items, are becoming so complex that wiring diagrams are often broken down by sections. Some common wiring circuit symbols are shown in **Figure 17-4**.

Figure 17-3. A typical electrical system diagram showing a cruise control circuit as used by one manufacturer. (Toyota)

Legends of Symbols Used on Wiring Diagrams

Symbol	Name	Symbol	Name
+	Positive	→»—	Connector
−	Negative	—→	Male Connector
⏚	Ground	>—|	Female Connector
Fuse symbol	Fuse		Denotes Wire Continues Elsewhere
Gang Fuses with Bus Bar symbol	Gang Fuses with Bus Bar		Denotes Wires Goes to One of Two Circuits
Circuit Breaker symbol	Circuit Breaker		Splice
Capacitor symbol	Capacitor	J2 2	Splice Identification
Ω	Ohms		Thermal Element
Resistor symbol	Resistor	TIMER	Timer
Variable Resistor symbol	Variable Resistor	Multiple Connector symbol	Multiple Connector
Series Resistor symbol	Series Resistor	Optional symbol	Optional — Wiring with / Wiring without
Coil symbol	Coil	"Y" Windings symbol	"Y" Windings
Step Up Coil symbol	Step Up Coil	88:88	Digital Readout
Open Contact symbol	Open Contact	Single Filament Lamp symbol	Single Filament Lamp
Closed Contact symbol	Closed Contact	Dual Filament Lamp symbol	Dual Filament Lamp
Closed Switch symbol	Closed Switch	L.E.D. symbol	L.E.D.—Light Emitting Diode
Open Switch symbol	Open Switch	Thermistor symbol	Thermistor
Closed Ganged Switch symbol	Closed Ganged Switch	Gauge symbol	Gauge
Open Ganged Switch symbol	Open Ganged Switch	Sensor symbol	Sensor
Two Pole Single Throw Switch symbol	Two Pole Single Throw Switch	Fuel Injector symbol	Fuel Injector
Pressure Switch symbol	Pressure Switch	#36	Denotes Wire Goes Through Bulkhead Disconnect
Solenoid Switch symbol	Solenoid Switch	#19 STRG COLUMN	Denotes Wire Goes Through Steering Column Connector
Mercury Switch symbol	Mercury Switch	INST PANEL #14	Denotes Wire Goes Through Instrument Panel Connector
Diode or Rectifier symbol	Diode or Rectifier	ENG #7	Denotes Wire Goes Through Grommet to Engine Compartment
Bi-Directional Zener Diode symbol	Bi-Directional Zener Diode	Grommet symbol	Denotes Wire Goes Through Grommet
Motor symbol	Motor	Heated Grid Elements symbol	Heated Grid Elements
Armature and Brushes symbol	Armature and Brushes		

Figure 17-4. An assortment of electrical symbols for one vehicle manufacturer's wiring diagrams. Learning these symbols will greatly improve your ability to use and understand electrical diagrams. (Chrysler)

Color Coding

All chassis wires are **color coded** to make identification of individual wires easy. This is true of wires installed in wiring harnesses. Color codes can be single wire colors, or colors with contrasting stripes or bands. The use of stripes and bands makes hundreds of color combinations possible, **Figure 17-5**.

WIRE COLORS ARE INDICATED BY AN ALPHABETICAL CODE.

B = BLACK   L = BLUE   R = RED
BR = BROWN   LG = LIGHT GREEN V = VIOLET
G = GREEN   O = ORANGE   W = WHITE
GR = GRAY   P = PINK   Y = YELLOW

THE FIRST LETTER INDICATES THE BASIC WIRE COLOR AND THE SECOND LETTER INDICATES THE COLOR OF THE STRIPE.

EXAMPLE: L - Y

L   -   Y
(BLUE)   (YELLOW)

Figure 17-5. One example of a wiring color code as used in a wiring diagram. These will vary between manufacturers. (Toyota)

Terminal Blocks and Junction Blocks

To connect separate wires and harnesses, terminal blocks and junction blocks are used. They consist of plastic blocks with metal screw terminals to attach each wire. The wire ends have eye terminals to connect to the terminal screws.

The **terminal block** is used to supply current to several circuits from one feeder source. The hot wire (wire connected to source of electricity) is attached to one terminal. This terminal is connected to all others by a bus bar (metal plate).

The **junction block** serves as a common connection point for a number of wires. It may be of the terminal screw or the plug-in type. Unlike the terminal block, the junction block connects one wire to a corresponding wire on the other side with no common bus bar. Junction blocks are also known as power distribution centers.

Circuit Protection Devices

It is necessary to protect electrical circuits against **shorting** (an exposed part of the circuit accidentally touching ground) that could burn up the wiring. The electrical units must be protected against overloads also. **Circuit protection devices** are installed in series with the electrical device or wiring to be protected. They are used to break the circuit to prevent damage to the other equipment in the circuit. The most common types of circuit protection devices are the fuse, fusible link, and the circuit breaker, discussed below.

Fuses

When the current in a circuit becomes excessive (exceeds the amount of current that it can safely handle), a **fuse** will blow and break the circuit. To restore circuit opera-

tion, the fuse must be replaced. Older fuses consists of a glass tube with metal end caps. A built-in conductor carries the current from one cap to the other. This conductor is designed to carry a specific maximum load.

Most fuses in current use look like the fuses shown in **Figure 17-6**. Both use a soft conductor that melts when fuse capacity is exceeded, **Figure 17-7**. Most are color coded to identify amperage. All of the vehicle fuses are usually contained in a single holder known as a **fuse block**. A fuse block is shown in **Figure 17-8**. Some add-on electrical devices may have a fuse in the wiring to it. This is called an **inline fuse**.

Circuit Breaker

A **circuit breaker** feeds current through a bimetallic strip and a set of points to the remainder of the circuit. When circuit amperage exceeds the breaker's rating (the amount of current it is designed to handle), the bimetallic strip heats and bends to separate the points. Once it cools, it will close and reestablish the circuit. If the overload condition still exists, it will heat and reopen.

The circuit breaker can open and close quite rapidly. This gives it an advantage over a fuse. An overload will burn out a fuse and the circuit will not function until the fuse is replaced. This could cause an accident if a fuse were used in a headlight circuit. However, a circuit breaker will cause the lights to flicker on and off rapidly, but will still produce enough light to allow the driver to pull safely off the road, **Figure 17-9**.

SOFT CONDUCTOR

FUSE ELEMENT   MAXIFUSE

AUTOFUSE   MINIFUSE

Figure 17-6. An assortment of fuses. All of these fuses give specific amperage rating and use. They are all color coded to indicate their current (amperage) rating. The color tan is used for a 5 amp rating, blue for 15 amps, green for 30 amps, etc. (Chevrolet)

BLOWN FUSE DUE TO OVERLOAD

MELTED CONDUCTOR

A

BLOWN FUSE DUE TO THERMAL FATIGUE - CYCLING ON AND OFF

CRACKED CONDUCTOR

B

C

10A   15A

Figure 17-7. A and B—These illustrations show two common failures common in fuses. C—*Never* replace a blown fuse with a fuse of a higher amperage rating. Extensive electrical system and/or part damage can result. (Hyundai)

WIRING ASSEMBLY
TURN SIGNALS AND BACK-UP LAMPS
INSTRUMENT PANEL LAMPS
ACCESSORIES
RUBBER GROMMET
HEATER BLOWER MOTOR FUSE
RADIO FUSE
TURN SIGNAL FLASHER
EMISSION CONTROL
COURTESY LAMPS
AUXILIARY FUEL TANK
EMERGENCY WARNING AND STOP LAMPS
WIRE TIE
TO FOG LAMPS
TO INDICATOR LAMPS

Figure 17-8. A fuse block that utilizes miniature fuses. Some vehicles have more than one fuse block. (Ford)

TWO STRIPS OF DISSIMILAR METAL
COLD OR NORMAL
POINTS CLOSED
A

HOT
POINTS OPEN
B

Figure 17-9. Normal operation of a circuit breaker. A—When the breaker is carrying a normal load, the contact points remain closed. B—If the breaker is overloaded, the bimetallic strip heats up. This causes the strip to curve upward, separating the contact points and breaking the circuit.

Fusible Link

A circuit may be protected by the use of a special wire that acts as a fuse. This wire is called a ***fusible link***. A fusible link uses a soft conductor and is one or two sizes smaller than the rest of the circuit wiring. When the fusible link is subjected to an overload condition, it begins to heat, causing the insulation to blister and smoke. If the overload is continued, the insulation ruptures and the fusible link eventually burns out, breaking the circuit, **Figure 17-10**. The fusible link must be replaced once the cause of the overload condition is repaired.

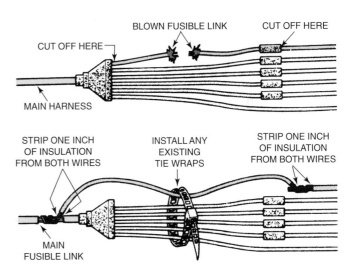

BLOWN FUSIBLE LINK   CUT OFF HERE
CUT OFF HERE
MAIN HARNESS

STRIP ONE INCH OF INSULATION FROM BOTH WIRES
INSTALL ANY EXISTING TIE WRAPS
STRIP ONE INCH OF INSULATION FROM BOTH WIRES
MAIN FUSIBLE LINK

Figure 17-10. The fusible link prevents system damage due to shorts and overloads. Note, at top, how the outer insulation has melted off the link. Fusible link repair requires cutting off the burnt link at the solder joint and installing new fusible link. (Chrysler)

Vehicle Lights and Light Switches

The modern vehicle contains many lights in addition to the normal headlights, brake lights, turn signal lights, and taillights. Lights installed in a modern vehicle include several different types of interior lights, trunk light, glove compartment light, underhood light, and dashboard indicator lights. All of these lights will be discussed in the following sections.

A wide variety of bulb shapes are used on modern cars and trucks. All lamps contain one or more *filaments*. The filament is a resistance element that glows when current passes through it. Lamps that have two filaments can be used for two separate lighting jobs. The filament is contained inside a vacuum-filled bulb to increase its service life. Lamps must be of the proper candlepower or lumen rating (measurement of light intensity) and voltage. Lamps are also rated by wattage and amperage.

Headlights

The headlights are one of the most important safety features on any vehicle. Obviously, the headlight must be constructed to provide a high intensity light beam, much brighter than that provided by normal service bulbs. The modern headlight can be either the sealed beam or the halogen light. Each type is discussed in the following sections.

Some late-model vehicles have *daytime running lamps.* These lamps, which are generally part of the headlight assembly, make the vehicle more visible during daylight hours. Daytime running lamps are connected to the ignition switch and illuminate whenever the ignition is on.

Sealed Beam Headlight

The *sealed beam* headlight is an airtight unit containing the lens and mirrored interior surfaces to reflect the light produced by the filament. See **Figure 17-11.** The sealed beams used on vehicles with two headlights and the outer lights on four headlight systems contain two filaments, one each for low and high beams. The inner lights on four headlight systems contain only one high beam filament.

Halogen Headlight

The *halogen* headlight is common on modern vehicles. The halogen gas allows the filament to be much brighter than older sealed beam designs, with about the same service life. Some halogen headlights are manufactured as direct replacements for the old sealed beam headlights, **Figure 17-12.**

Figure 17-12. One type of halogen headlamp. Some designs use removable bulbs. (Chrysler)

On some newer vehicles, instead of replacing a complete sealed beam headlight, only the lamp is replaced. The filament is contained in a halogen gas-filled bulb that installs in the rear of a *composite headlight assembly*. An exploded view of the halogen bulb and composite assembly is shown in **Figure 17-13.**

Headlight Switch

Headlights are operated by the driver through the *headlight switch*. **Figure 17-14** shows a knob style headlight switch, while **Figure 17-15** shows a rocker style headlight switch. On some newer vehicles, the headlight switch is included as part of the turn signal lever, **Figure 17-16.**

The headlight switch also operates the taillights and marker lights. The headlight switch also contains a *rheostat*,

Figure 17-11. Exploded view of a sealed beam headlamp assembly. Note the adjusting screws for headlamp aiming. (Jeep)

Figure 17-13. An exploded view of one type of halogen bulb headlight assembly. This bulb may be replaced by unscrewing the lock ring. The lock ring and bulb may then be removed from the composite assembly. (Geo)

Figure 17-14. One type of headlamp switch and mounting arrangement. (Ford)

Figure 17-15. A "rocker" style headlight switch is mounted on the instrument cluster. (Geo)

Figure 17-16. A "twist" style headlight switch. This unit is mounted on a stalk (usually the turn signal lever) attached to the steering column. Note the auto setting. In the auto position, an automatic light control sensor will determine the lighting conditions of the vehicle's surroundings and will turn on the headlights and taillights automatically if the sensor reads a low light condition. (Toyota)

which is used to adjust the brightness of the dashboard lights. The headlight switch may also be used to operate the interior lights when the doors are closed. Most headlight switches contain an overload breaker, instead of a fuse.

Dimmer Switch

A **dimmer switch** is located in series with the headlight circuit. It is a simple switch that directs current to one of the two terminals, but never to both. One terminal leads to the high beam filament, the other to the low beam. The high beam terminal also feeds current to the high beam indicator lamp on the dash.

The dimmer switch on older vehicles was located on the floorboard close to where the driver's left foot would rest, but on late-model vehicles, the dimmer switch is installed on the turn signal lever. On some vehicles, the dimmer switch wiring passes through the headlight switch. This additional safety feature allows the driver to flash the headlights at other vehicles before passing, **Figure 17-17**.

Figure 17-17. A steering column mounted multifunction switch with a built-in turn signal, headlight dimmer, and "flash to pass" function. (Chrysler)

Stoplights and Switches

A brake pedal operated **stoplight switch** is provided to operate the brake lights, that are either single or dual filament lamps. The switch is a simple on-off type. When the brake pedal is depressed, the lights come on. When the pedal is released, the lights go off.

Older stoplight switches were operated by hydraulic pressure in the brake system. Newer stoplight switches are mechanical and are energized when the brake pedal is pressed. On some older vehicles, the brake light wiring passes through the turn signal assembly so that the brake lights are bypassed when the turn signals are being used. Modern vehicles usually have separate lamps for the brake and turn signals, **Figure 17-18**.

Turn Signals and Switches

The **turn signal selector** lever mounted on the steering column contains contacts which send current to the **turn signal lights** on the left or right side of the vehicle, as well as

Figure 17-18. One particular type of brake pedal stoplamp switch. Some stoplamp switches are part of the cruise control and anti-lock brake systems. (Geo)

Figure 17-20. A turn signal flasher and wiring schematic. Study carefully. (Lexus)

left-right dashboard indicators. The lever is operated by the vehicle driver. A *canceling cam* in the steering column returns the lever to the centered position when the steering wheel is returned to the straight-ahead position, **Figure 17-19**.

The turn signal wiring contains a *flasher unit*, **Figure 17-20**, which causes the turn signal lights to flash on and off rapidly. The turn signal flasher unit is usually installed on the fuse block or in a special holder under the vehicle dashboard. At one time, the turn signals and brake lights used the same filament, usually in the same bulb as the taillight filament. Modern practice, however, is to use separate filaments in separate bulbs for each function.

The *hazard warning flasher* switch will send current to the turn signal lights on both sides of the vehicle when turned on. The flasher switch is usually installed on the steering column and is part of the turn signal switch assembly. The

hazard flasher unit is separate from the turn signal flasher, and is usually installed on the fuse block, or under the vehicle dashboard. Some flashers are called combo-flashers and contain the turn signal and hazard warning flasher in one unit. See **Figure 17-21**.

Backup Lights and Switches

Backup lights are single filament lamps with no connection to the other vehicle lights. *Backup light switches* are located on the transmission, in the neutral safety switch assembly (covered later), or the transmission linkage. The backup lights operate only when the vehicle is placed in reverse gear.

Figure 17-19. An exploded view of the top of a steering column showing the turn signal cancel cam. (General Motors)

Figure 17-21. A—Turn signal flasher unit and a simple wiring circuit. B—Turn signal/hazard warning flasher assembly with wiring connector and harness. (Toyota & Chrysler)

Dashboard Lights

There are two major groups of vehicle dashboard lights. The first, *illuminating lights*, light up the speedometer and other gauges if used, and the wiper, headlight, and heater-air conditioner controls. The second group, *indicator lights*, warn of engine problems, such as charging system problems, overheating, low oil pressure, and computer system problems, **Figure 17-22.**

The illuminating lights are controlled through the headlight switch. A rheostat is used to vary their brightness. There are usually several lights, although a few modern vehicles use only a few bulbs and distribute their light through a *fiber optic* (light carrying) harness.

Indicator lights are installed on the dashboard and are either computer-controlled or operated by *senders*. Typical indicator lights monitor engine temperature, oil pressure, and charging system condition. These lights are either red- or amber-colored. Indicator light senders are simple on-off switches, operated by temperature changes (engine temperature lights), or pressure changes (oil pressure lights). The charging system light is usually operated by the alternator voltage regulator. Typical computer-controlled indicator lights include the ECU check engine and the anti-lock brake malfunction indicator.

Convenience Lights

This group of lights includes all of the lights that are not required for vehicle safety, but are installed to illuminate the passenger sections of the vehicle. The vast majority of these lights are single filament lights operated by on-off switches installed in the chassis, doors, glove compartment, or trunk.

Some courtesy lights are operated by a mercury switch, **Figure 17-23.** Examples are the trunk and underhood lights. The mercury in the switch will not make contact when the

Figure 17-22. This instrument panel shows a variety of warning type indicator lights. The anti-lock brake (ABS) and malfunction indicator lamp (MIL) are computer-controlled. (Toyota)

Figure 17-23. A wiring schematic showing an underhood lamp that is turned on and off with a mercury switch. Here, the switch is shown in the off position. When you open the hood, the mercury will flow over the switch contacts, completing the circuit and the light will come on. Closing the hood causes the mercury to flow back to the off position. (Chrysler)

trunk or hood is down. However, when the hood or trunk lid is raised, the mercury flows into contact with the electrical connectors, closing the circuit and allowing the light to come on.

Chassis Mounted Solenoids and Relays

The **solenoids** used in the vehicle chassis are similar to those used to energize the vehicle starter. They are used to operate door locks and trunk releases. Relays are a type of solenoid that closes electrical contacts instead of operating a mechanical device. They are used to direct large current flows that might overheat and damage a switch. Switches used to control most solenoids are spring-loaded to return to the off position, preventing accidental operation.

Motor Control Relays

Control relays are similar to starter solenoids. A small current flow energizes a magnetic winding, closing a set of contact points to control high current to another unit, such as a motor or heating coil. Use of relays eliminates having to pass heavy current through the dashboard controls or the ECU, **Figure 17-24**.

Many relays used on late-model vehicles are power transistors with no moving parts. Relays prevent circuit overheating them and voltage drop from the resistance of extra wiring. This reduces electricity consumption and increases reliability. Relays on the modern vehicle are used to operate many high current electrical devices.

Trunk Release Solenoids

Trunk release solenoids are single position solenoids operated by a switch installed in the vehicle glove compartment or instrument cluster, **Figure 17-25**. Power to the trunk release switch passes through the ignition switch and keyless remote module, if equipped. This keeps unauthorized persons from opening the trunk.

Power Door Lock Solenoids and Switches

Power door lock solenoids are two position solenoids, **Figure 17-26**. The solenoids have two windings, allowing them to move a control rod in two directions. When the control switch is moved in one direction, the solenoid moves the door lock to the unlocked position. When the switch is moved in the other direction, the solenoid moves the door lock to the

Figure 17-24. An electric cooling fan schematic circuit showing several motor control fan relays. Note how the coolant temperature switches turn the fan on and off at specific coolant temperatures. (Toyota)

Figure 17-25. An electric trunk release solenoid and its dash-mounted operating switch. Some trunk release switches are located in the glove box or in other locations in the passenger compartment. (Hyundai)

Figure 17-26. Several door lock solenoids and their control rods. The solenoids can be controlled by the master switch, which is usually mounted in the driver's door panel, or by separate switches at each door. (Hyundai)

locked position. Power door locks use simple wiring with separate circuits for the lock and unlock positions. See **Figure 17-27**.

Some power door lock systems have an electronic module added to the circuit as part of a keyless entry system. This system can be used to lock or unlock the vehicle or open the trunk by the driver using a key fob, **Figure 17-28**.

Horns and Horn Relays

The *horn* makes use of an electromagnet, vibrator points, and a diaphragm. Referring to **Figure 17-29**, you will see that the electromagnet field coil will attract the metal armature whenever the contact points are closed. Current flows through the horn relay contact points, energizing the electromagnet. The electromagnet draws the armature up, the diaphragm (thin metal disc) will be bent upward.

When the armature moves upward, it causes the points to open and break the circuit. The electromagnet releases the armature and it moves downward, flexing the diaphragm in the other direction. As it moves down, the points close and the armature is again drawn upward. This cycle is repeated very fast. These small up-and-down pulsations of the diaphragm cause the sound. Sound is magnified by passing it through a long or a spiral trumpet, **Figure 17-29**.

Horn Relay

By using a relay between the battery and the horn, it is possible to run a wire from the battery to the relay and from the relay to the horn. When the driver actuates the relay with the horn button, it will complete the circuit and the horn will blow. As this is the shortest possible route, resistance and voltage drop will be low. **Figure 17-30** shows a typical horn circuit using a relay. This particular circuit is operational at all times.

When the driver depresses the horn button, the circuit is completed and current will flow. Current will flow through a heavy wire to the relay, across the closed points, on to the horn and to ground. As soon as the horn button is released, the armature pops up, breaking the points, and the horn stops blowing.

By using the relay, it is possible to use a short run of heavy wire to avoid voltage drop. It is also possible to actuate the relay from a distance. Headlight relays are constructed in a similar fashion.

Rear Window and Mirror Defrosters

The heater *grid* consists of a series of fine wires applied to the surface of a rear window or mirror, **Figure 17-31**. The grid material has a calibrated resistance that opposes current flow, creating heat. Current flows through the grid, producing heat to defrost the window or to melt ice or snow. The temperature flow through the grid is kept constant by a load sensing device. Most glass defrosters are controlled by a dashboard switch working through a relay.

Chassis Mounted Motors

Chassis mounted motors include the windshield wiper motor, power door and vent windows, tailgate windows, sliding door motors, and sunroof motors, as well as motors that operate convertible tops and power antennas. The modern vehicle may have as many as ten small dc motors to operate various systems.

Switches used to control these motors, except for the windshield wiper motor, are spring loaded so they return to the off position when the operator's hand is removed. This prevents accidental operation of the motor, with resulting motor overheating and damage.

Windshield Wiper Motors and Controls

Windshield wiper motors, **Figure 17-32**, are high torque motors capable of overcoming the binding effects of ice on the wiper blades and mechanisms. For this reason, wiper motors are very durable, requiring relatively little maintenance.

Figure 17-27. An electrical wiring schematic for a four-door vehicle equipped with power door and trunk locks. Study the schematic thoroughly. (Lexus)

Figure 17-29. A cross-sectional view of an electric horn. The horn air chamber has a snail shell construction. This design will produce maximum sound volume from the rapidly vibrating diaphragm. (Deere & Co.)

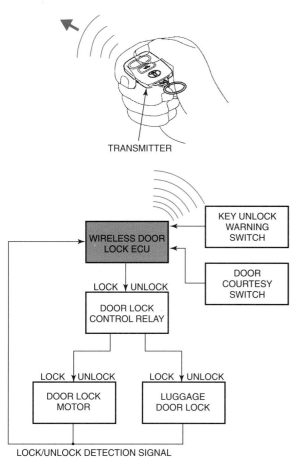

Figure 17-28. A—A wireless, battery operated, keyless remote transmitter. B—The transmitter sends a radio wave (signal) to the wireless door lock electronic control unit (ECU) receiver. The ECU will send the proper signal to the door lock control relay, which will trigger the door or trunk lock motors. (Toyota & Chrysler)

Windshield wiper motors have special park mechanisms which cause the wiper blades to return to the fully down position when they are turned off. Some older wiper motors were equipped to operate the windshield washer pump, but most modern designs use a separate pump located on or in the washer reservoir.

Figure 17-30. A dual horn electrical circuit schematic. The relay used here is similar to relays used in other systems. (Dodge)

Power Window, Tailgate, Sliding Door, and Sunroof Motors

These are generally high torque motors, able to overcome the drag of dry or tight operating mechanisms and glass channels. Most of these motors have built-in overload switches or circuit breakers to prevent overheating damage. The majority of these motors are operated by on-off switches located on the vehicle dashboard, door, or console. See **Figure 17-33**.

Convertible Top Motors and Switches

The convertible top motor on modern vehicles is used to drive a hydraulic pump to power hydraulic cylinders rather than working directly to raise and lower the top. These motors also have built-in overload protection and are operated by a spring-loaded on-off switch.

Power Antenna Motors and Switches

Power antenna motors are simple in construction and are usually operated through an automatic relay. Some power

Figure 17-31. A—An electrical schematic for a rear window defogger. B—A vehicle with a rear window defogger. Note that this car also uses outside heated mirror defoggers, similar to the rear glass, even through no wires are exposed. Study the electrical circuit carefully (Hyundai & Lexus)

Figure 17-32. An electric windshield wiper motor, gear drive mechanism, and wiper linkage assembly. (Chrysler)

antennas are controlled by a manual 3-position switch. The relay is energized when the radio is turned on, or by the ignition switch when the radio is already on, **Figure 17-34**.

Electric Gauges

Electric gauges, including oil pressure, temperature, fuel, and ammeter, were discussed in the chapters covering systems using these gauges. Gauge illumination is provided by the vehicle dashboard lighting system.

Cruise Control

Most older *cruise control* systems were operated by various electromechanical devices. However, the latest cruise control systems are operated by ECU's. Cruise control systems consist of several common components which include:

- Vehicle speed sensor.
- Operator controls.
- Control module.
- Throttle actuator.

Vehicle Speed Sensor

The vehicle speed sensor uses a rotating magnet to generate a small electrical signal. It is usually mounted on the drive shaft or is driven by the transmission or transaxle governor assembly. It sends a speed signal to the control module. The speed sensor may also send a signal to the engine control computer.

Operator Controls and Control Module

The operator controls are used to set the desired speed. Control location varies between manufacturers, but is usually mounted on the turn signal lever. The operator can set the speed, and can also make minor adjustments to speed as necessary.

Another operator control is the brake pedal release switch, usually mounted on the brake pedal bracket. When the driver presses on the brake pedal, the switch sends a signal to the cruise control module to disengage the cruise control. The control module processes the inputs from the controls and speed sensor and produces an output signal to the throttle actuator.

Throttle Actuator

The throttle actuator opens and closes the vehicle throttle to maintain the operator set speed. Throttle actuators can be electric motors directly operated by the control module. In most cases, however, the throttle actuator is a vacuum diaphragm servo connected to a vacuum controller. The module operates the vacuum controller, which in turn operates the vacuum diaphragm.

Air Bag Systems

Air bag systems are becoming standard equipment on most new vehicles. These systems are designed to inflate or *deploy* when a vehicle is involved in a frontal collision of sufficient force. Most air bag systems consist of several common components, including a diagnostic control module, frontal impact sensors, coil assembly, and inflator module. These components work together to fully deploy the air bag within 50 milliseconds of impact. After deployment, the air bag will deflate in approximately 100 milliseconds.

Figure 17-33. A—An electrical schematic for a power window motor and switch system. Note the theft deterrent and door lock ECU. B—A vehicle illustrating the various window motors, operating switches, and their locations. (Lexus)

Figure 17-34. An electrical schematic illustrating one particular power radio antenna system. This antenna will go up and down by turning the radio on or off. (Honda)

Air bag systems are often called **supplemental restraint systems**. It is important to remember that air bags are a supplement to seat belts, they *do not replace them*. Anyone driving or riding in any vehicle should always wear their seat belt.

Diagnostic Control Module

The **diagnostic control module** performs several functions. The module serves as a monitoring system for the air bag components. It can warn the driver of system malfunctions by activating the air bag indicator light, and stores trouble codes, used for system diagnosis.

Most diagnostic control modules provide the air bag system with an alternative source of power in case battery voltage is lost in an accident. This reserve power can last up to 30 minutes after the battery has been disconnected. The diagnostic control module also contains a **safing sensor,** designed to prevent accidental deployment. This sensor must close simultaneously with one of the impact sensors to trigger the inflator module. The safing sensor prevents a faulty impact sensor from activating the air bag system.

Impact Sensors

One or more **impact sensors** are located on the front sector of a vehicle's chassis or on each side of the radiator housing. An impact sensor is an open switch, designed to close on impact. It will close only when the impact is severe enough to warrant air bag deployment. A ball type impact sensor is shown in **Figure 17-35**.

Coil Assembly and Inflator Module

The **coil assembly** consist of two current-carrying coils attached to the steering column. As the steering wheel is rotated, the coils maintain a continuous electrical connection between the inflator module and diagnostic control module. The coil assembly is often referred to as a *clock spring*.

The **inflator module** is located in the center of the steering wheel and above the glove box on passenger side air bag systems. The module contains the inflatable fabric air bag, an initiator squib, and an inflator (gas generating material). The inflator module is covered with a trim piece. A cutaway of an inflator module is shown in **Figure 17-36**.

Air Bag Operation

When a vehicle is involved in a collision that is severe enough to warrant air bag deployment, the impact sensors close. If at least one impact sensor and the safing sensor in the diagnostic module close, the module sends a signal to the initiator squib. The squib then generates a thermal reaction which, in turn, ignites the gas generating material (sodium azide based propellant) in the inflator. The material releases a large amount of harmless gas, which quickly fills the air bag. The air bag deployment process is shown in **Figure 17-37**.

Side Air Bags

Some late-model vehicles have **side air bags**, which are installed in the door panels or the seats, **Figure 17-38**. Side air bags operate in the same manner as conventional air bags. However, they are designed to deploy during a side impact.

Figure 17-35. Cutaway view of an electromagnetic impact sensor. During vehicle impact, the gold plated sensing ball will move forward inside its stainless steel tube. The ball movement is controlled by a viscous air damping force and a bias magnet. The sensor can be produced to respond to various crash speeds by the ball and tube clearance, ball travel distance, and the bias magnet strength. (Breed Automotive Corporation)

Figure 17-36. A cutaway view of an inflator module. Study all of the parts. (Breed Automotive Corporation)

Summary

Chassis wiring extends throughout the vehicle body. It consists of all vehicle wiring that is not directly connected with the engine and drive train. Wiring to electrical systems can pass through the ignition switch, or is powered directly from the vehicle battery.

Almost all vehicle wiring is part of wiring harnesses. All chassis wires are color coded. Circuit protection devices are used to break the circuit to prevent damage to the other equipment in the circuit. The most common types of circuit protection devices are the fuse, fusible link, and the circuit breaker.

The modern vehicle uses headlights, taillights, brake and turn signal lights, interior lights, trunk light, glove compartment light, underhood light, and dashboard indicator lights. A wide variety of lightbulb shapes are used on modern cars and trucks. Bulbs are composed of a filament inside of a glass bulb which glows when current passes through it. All of the air has been removed from the bulb to increase filament life. The modern headlight uses either sealed beams or halogen bulbs in a composite assembly.

Figure 17-37. A schematic illustrating the air bag deployment process when a vehicle is involved in a frontal collision. Note the dual air bag arrangement. (Toyota Motor Corporation)

Figure 17-38. Side air bags help protect the vehicle's occupants in the event of a side impact. (Cadillac)

Solenoids are used to operate door locks and trunk releases. A relay is an electromagnetic unit designed to make and break a circuit. The relay can be a distance from the operator and will still function with only a ground wire and switch. Electric horns use an electromagnet, vibrator points, and a diaphragm to produce sounds. The horn is operated through a relay.

Rear window and mirror defrosters consist of a grid of fine resistance wires applied to the glass surface of the rear window or mirror. Current passing through the grid produces heat to melt any ice.

Chassis motors are used to operate the windshield wipers, power windows and vent windows, tailgate windows, sunroofs, convertible tops, and power antennas.

Disconnect the battery when working on the electrical system. Make sure that all electrical components are properly fused. Wires must be insulated, away from hot areas, and secured to prevent chafing. Wire terminals should be clean and tight.

Know These Terms

Chassis wiring
American Wire Gage (AWG)
Wiring harness
Looms
Printed circuit
Shielded
Color coded
Terminal block
Junction block
Shorting
Circuit protection device
Fuse
Fuse block
Inline fuse
Circuit breaker
Fusible link
Filament
Daytime running lamps
Sealed beam
Halogen
Composite headlight
    assembly
Headlight switch
Rheostat
Dimmer switch
Stoplight switch

Turn signal selector
Turn signal lights
Canceling cam
Flasher unit
Hazard warning flasher
Backup lights
Backup light switch
Illuminating lights
Indicator lights
Fiber optic
Senders
Solenoid
Horn
Grid
Cruise control
Air bag system
Deploy
Supplemental restraint
    system
Diagnostic control module
Safing sensor
Impact sensor
Coil assembly
Inflator module
Side air bags

Review Questions—Chapter 17

Do not write in this book. Write your answers on a separate sheet of paper.

1. Is a wire with a gage of 17 smaller or larger than a wire with a gage of 8?

2. What is the gage of a wire decided by?
   - (A) Wire diameter.
   - (B) Wire length.
   - (C) The wire material.
   - (D) Both A & B.

3. Technician A says that electrical devices that can not be operated except when the vehicle is being driven are wired through the ignition switch. Technician B says that units that can be operated at any time are powered directly from the vehicle battery. Who is right?
   - (A) A only.
   - (B) B only.
   - (C) Both A & B.
   - (D) Neither A nor B.

4. Chassis wiring consists of all vehicle wiring that is not directly connected with the vehicle _____ .
   - (A) engine
   - (B) lighting
   - (C) drive train
   - (D) Both A & C.

5. What are the three most common types of circuit protection devices?

6. Any new electrical component installed on a vehicle must have a _____ .

7. All of the following statements about chassis mounted solenoids and relays are true, EXCEPT:
   - (A) chassis solenoids are similar to starter solenoids.
   - (B) solenoids are used to operate convertible top hydraulic pumps.
   - (C) relays are a type of solenoid that close electrical contacts.
   - (D) using relays prevents damage to switches.

8. Technician A says that small up-and-down pulsations of an internal diaphragm produce the sound in an electric horn. Technician B says that the electric horn operates by flexing a strong spring. Who is right?
   - (A) A only.
   - (B) B only.
   - (C) Both A & B.
   - (D) Neither A nor B.

9. Which of the following motors are not controlled by a spring loaded switch?
   - (A) Windshield wiper motor.
   - (B) Power window motor.
   - (C) Convertible top motor.
   - (D) Power antenna motor.

10. What is a bulb filament?

11. Technician A says that the dimmer switch is connected in series with the headlights. Technician B says that the rheostat in the headlight switch is connected in series with the headlights. Who is right?
    - (A) A only.
    - (B) B only.
    - (C) Both A & B.
    - (D) Neither A nor B.

12. A blown fusible link is _____ .
    - (A) repaired
    - (B) replaced with a length of copper wire
    - (C) replaced with the same gage of wire
    - (D) Either A or C.

13. Technician A says that the convertible top motor on modern vehicles drives a hydraulic pump. Technician B says that power antenna motors are usually operated by a 3-position switch. Who is right?
    - (A) A only.
    - (B) B only.
    - (C) Both A & B.
    - (D) Neither A nor B.

14. What does the air bag system safing sensor prevent?

15. Briefly explain how the air bag is inflated once the diagnostic control module sends the signal.

Cutaway of a manual transmission clutch assembly. Although it looks complicated, it is quite simple in design and operation. (Federal-Mogul)

18

Engine Clutches

After studying this chapter, you will be able to:
- Explain clutch operation.
- Name the different types of clutches.
- List the various clutch release mechanisms.
- Define the basic parts of a clutch.
- Identify the parts of a clutch.

The function of the clutch assembly in cars and trucks with manual transmissions or transaxles is to connect or disconnect the flow of power from the engine to the drive line. Although there are many variations in the design of clutches, all work on the same basic principle. This chapter concerns the clutch assemblies used on modern vehicles with manual transmissions and transaxles.

Clutch Purpose

A *clutch* is a mechanism designed to connect or disconnect power from one working part to another. In a vehicle, the clutch is used to transmit engine power and to disengage the engine and transmission when shifting gears. It also allows the engine to operate when the vehicle is stopped without placing the transmission in neutral (out of gear).

Clutch Construction

The modern clutch is a single plate, dry disc. It consists of five major parts: flywheel, clutch disc, pressure plate assembly, throw-out bearing, and clutch linkage. Other parts which make up the clutch assembly are the transmission input shaft and clutch housing. To best illustrate clutch construction and operation, each part will be discussed in order.

Flywheel

In addition to providing a base for the starter ring gear, the *flywheel* forms the foundation on which the other clutch parts are attached. The flywheel used with manual transmissions is thick to enable it to absorb a large amount of heat generated by clutch operation.

The clutch side is machined smooth to provide a friction surface. Holes are drilled into the flywheel to provide a means of mounting the clutch assembly. A hole is usually drilled directly into the rear of the crankshaft. This hole allows a bearing to be installed in the center of the flywheel.

The bearing in the center of the flywheel will act as a support for the outboard end of the transmission input shaft. It is referred to as a *pilot bearing*. The pilot bearing may be either a ball bearing or a bronze bushing. Both must be provided with lubrication, **Figure 18-1**.

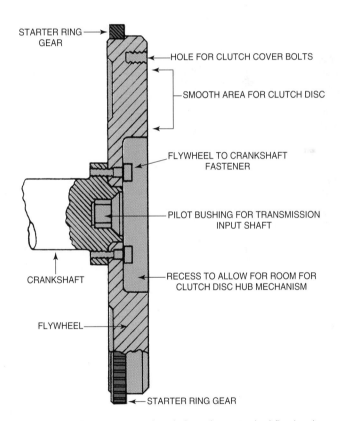

STARTER RING GEAR

HOLE FOR CLUTCH COVER BOLTS

SMOOTH AREA FOR CLUTCH DISC

FLYWHEEL TO CRANKSHAFT FASTENER

PILOT BUSHING FOR TRANSMISSION INPUT SHAFT

CRANKSHAFT

RECESS TO ALLOW FOR ROOM FOR CLUTCH DISC HUB MECHANISM

FLYWHEEL

STARTER RING GEAR

Figure 18-1. This cross-sectional view shows typical flywheel design. The flywheel provides the foundation on which the clutch is built.

Dual Mass Flywheel

A dual mass flywheel is sometimes used with diesel engines. To help absorb engine power stroke pulsations, springs mounted inside the flywheel act as a shock absorbing unit when the flywheel sections partially compress, smoothing out the power flow. They also help to reduce stress on the clutch and transmission parts, **Figure 18-2**.

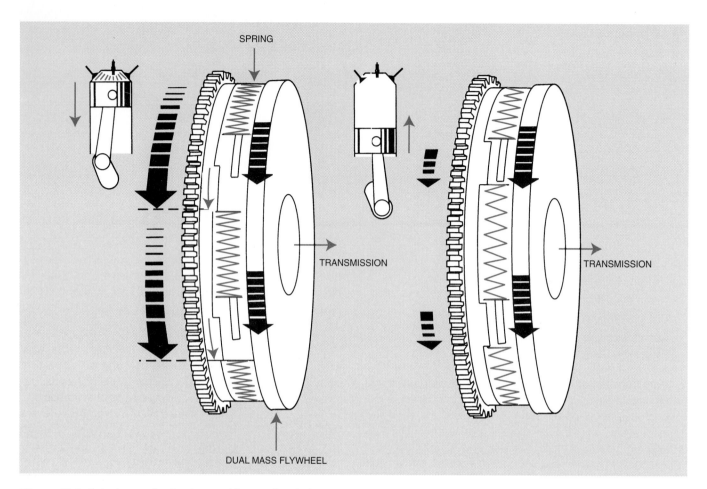

SPRING

TRANSMISSION

TRANSMISSION

DUAL MASS FLYWHEEL

Figure 18-2. A dual mass flywheel assembly can absorb the power stroke pulsations of a diesel engine by using heavy coil springs mounted between the two-piece flywheel. (Luk Incorporated)

Clutch Disc

The **clutch disc** is round and constructed of thin, high quality steel with a splined (grooved) hub placed in the center. The hub **splines** engage splines on the transmission input shaft. The clutch disc can move back and forth on the shaft, but when the disc is turned, the shaft must turn also.

Both sides of its outer edge are covered with friction material. It is often made of asbestos or other high temperature material and copper wires either woven or molded together. It is riveted to the disc.

 Warning: Clutch friction materials can contain asbestos—a known carcinogen (a substance that can cause cancer). Disassembling the clutch can produce small airborne particles of asbestos. Breathing these particles may cause cancer.

To assist in smooth engagement, the disc outer edges are often split and each piece cupped. The friction material is riveted to these segments. When the disc is compressed, these cupped segments act as a spring-like cushion.

The inner hub and thin outer disc are fastened together in such a manner as to allow a certain amount of radial (circle around the center) movement between them. This movement

is controlled by stop pins. Coil springs act as a drive unit between the hub flange and outer disc. These springs act as a dampening device, softening the torque thrust when the outer disc is pressed against the flywheel. It also helps to transmit this thrust to the hub. Vibration is controlled by a molded friction washer between the clutch hub flange and outer disc. **Figure 18-3** illustrates the edges of the cupped segments. Notice how the friction material is riveted to the segments. A typical clutch disc is shown in **Figure 18-4**.

Pressure Plate Assembly

There are two basic types of **pressure plates**, the **coil spring pressure plate** and the **diaphragm spring pressure plate**. The basic operating principles of each are the same. The difference lies in the type of apply spring used.

Pressure Plate Disc

The clutch pressure plate disc is the same in each type of pressure plate assembly. It is made of a thick piece of cast iron for maximum heat absorption. It is round and about the same diameter as the clutch disc. One side of the pressure plate is machined smooth. This side will press the clutch disc facing area against the flywheel. The outer side has various shapes to facilitate attachment of springs and release mechanisms, **Figure 18-5**.

Figure 18-3. Side view of a clutch disc. Notice how the segments are cupped to produce a cushion effect that assists in smooth clutch engagement. A—Cupped segment. B—Rivet. C—Lining.

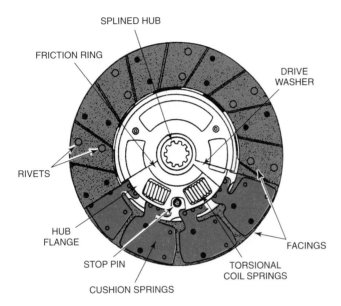

Figure 18-4. One type of clutch disc. Note the splined hub and arrangement of torsional coil springs that cushions the shock of engagement.

Figure 18-5. Pressure plate. The pressure plate is spring-loaded and presses the clutch disc against the flywheel.

Coil Spring Pressure Plate Assembly

In addition to the pressure plate itself, the coil spring pressure plate assembly contains a number of coil springs, a **pressure plate cover**, and **release levers**. The springs are used to provide pressure against the pressure plate. Various numbers of springs are used, depending on the type of service for which the pressure plate is designed. The springs push against the clutch cover and pressure plate, **Figure 18-6**.

Figure 18-6. Clutch springs—coil type. Size and number of springs will vary with clutch design.

The release levers are designed to draw the pressure plate away from the clutch disc. One end of the release lever engages the pressure plate. The other end is free and is designed to be pressed inward. Between the two ends, the lever is hinged to the clutch cover by means of an eyebolt.

There are generally three release levers. Some levers are of the semi-centrifugal type. This type has a weight added to its outer end. As the clutch assembly spins, centrifugal force will act upon these weights and cause them to exert additional pressure against the pressure plate. This assists the springs. Release lever location and action is shown in **Figure 18-7**.

The clutch cover bolts to the flywheel and acts as a base for the springs. The pressure plate release lugs pass through slots in the cover, allowing the cover to drive the pressure plate.

Coil Spring Pressure Plate Operation

When the throw-out bearing (discussed later) pushes against the clutch release levers, and sufficient pressure is applied to the fork, the release levers will draw the pressure plate back, releasing the clutch disc. As the throw-out bearing contacts the whirling release fingers, the bearing will rotate. The sleeve is held by the clutch throw-out fork. The action of the entire throw-out assembly is shown in **Figure 18-8**.

Diaphragm Spring Pressure Plate Assembly

Instead of coil springs, the diaphragm spring pressure plate uses a single diaphragm spring. General clutch construction is the same. The difference is in the pressure plate spring. The diaphragm spring is round and thin. It is made of high quality, heat-treated steel and is constructed with a dished profile to produce the necessary spring effect. A number of fingers radiate from the edges where they terminate in an open center.

One application cuts six of the fingers somewhat shorter to assist in cooling. The remaining twelve are left full length, **Figure 18-9**. Another version bends the six fingers upward. Weights are attached to produce a centrifugal effect to assist spring pressure at high rpm.

Figure 18-7. Release lever action. A—Here, the release lever is free and the pressure plate is engaged. B—When the release lever is pushed inward, it draws the pressure plate away from the flywheel. C—A weight is added to the centrifugal-type release lever. When the clutch revolves, the weight is thrown outward, adding to spring pressure.

Figure 18-8. A cross-sectional view of a coil spring clutch assembly. As the clutch pedal is depressed, the throw-out bearing travels forward against the release levers. As the levers pivot, the pressure plate will pull backwards to collapse the clutch coil springs and release the pressure on the disc. The disc is now separated from the pressure plate and flywheel. This interrupts the power flow traveling from the engine to the transmission input shaft. As the clutch pedal is released, the collapsed coil springs force the pressure plate forward to apply pressure on the clutch disc, pinning it to the flywheel. Power flow to the transmission input shaft begins.

The outer edge of the diaphragm engages the pressure plate. The fingers point inward and dish out slightly. Two pivot rings are placed a short distance from the outer edge. The pivot rings are secured by means of a stud to the clutch cover. One pivot ring is on the outside of the diaphragm, the other is on the inside.

The pressure plate is driven by three double spring steel straps. The straps are riveted to the cover and bolted to the pressure plate. The throw-out bearing contacts the ends of the fingers. The fingers then act in place of release levers, **Figure 18-10.** An exploded view of a diaphragm clutch arrangement is illustrated in **Figure 18-11.**

Diaphragm Pressure Plate Operation

When the throw-out bearing applies pressure to the diaphragm fingers, the entire diaphragm is bent inward. The action can best be described as the same sort of effect as squeezing the bottom of an oil can. The inner pivot ring prevents the outer edge of the diaphragm from moving inward, so when the center of the diaphragm is pressed inward, the outer edges pivot outward. When the fingers are released, the diaphragm resumes its original position.

Figure 18-12 shows the position of the diaphragm when the clutch is engaged. Notice how the fingers point outward, causing the diaphragm to pivot on the outer pivot ring. This action presses the diaphragm outer edge tightly against the pressure plate. The clutch disc is held firmly.

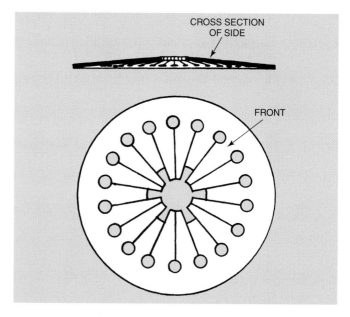

Figure 18-9. Diaphragm spring. Note the evenly spaced short fingers for cooling.

Now study **Figure 18-13.** The throw-out bearing has pressed the fingers in. The diaphragm now pivots on the inner pivot ring and the outer edges lift the pressure plate away from

Figure 18-10. Diaphragm spring action. Dotted line shows the diaphragm in the disengaged position. Notice how the outer edge moves back and forth, depending on the position of the fingers. (Chevrolet)

Figure 18-11. Exploded view of a diaphragm clutch assembly. Learn all the part names. (Honda)

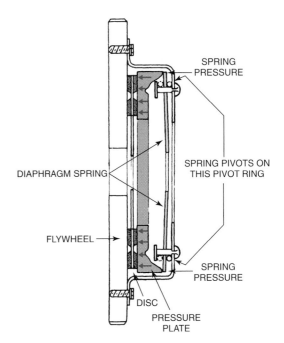

Figure 18-12. Diaphragm spring clutch in engaged position. The disc is pinched between the pressure plate and the flywheel. Notice the spring pressure produced by the diaphragm at the outer edges. (Chevrolet)

Figure 18-13. Diaphragm spring clutch in disengaged position. The throw-out bearing has moved the clutch diaphragm fingers inward. This pulls the outer edge back, retracting the pressure plate and leaving the clutch disc free. (Chevrolet)

the clutch disc. The disc is free and the clutch is disengaged. A complete diaphragm clutch assembly is shown in **Figure 18-14**.

Balance Marks

Most flywheel and pressure plate assemblies have *balance marks*. At the factory, the flywheel and clutch pressure plate assembly are bolted together and balanced. After balancing, they are marked so that if the transmission or clutch assembly must be serviced, flywheel balance may be retained. The flywheel, clutch disc, pressure plate, release levers, springs, and cover are shown in their respective positions in **Figure 18-15**.

Clutch Release Lever Operating Mechanism

Another essential part of the clutch is the *release lever operating mechanism*. This consists of a ball bearing normally referred to as a *throw-out bearing*. This bearing is

mounted on a sleeve or collar that slides back and forth on a hub that is an integral part of the transmission front bearing retainer.

The throw-out bearing is filled with grease at the factory and does not need service during its useful life. Another type of throw-out bearing that is used on many foreign vehicles is the graphite type. This throw-out bearing employs a ring of

1—Pilot bearing.
2—Facing.
3—Disc.
4—Facing.
5—Dampener spring plate rivet.
6—Dampener spring outer plate.
7—Driven member stop pin.
8—Dampener spring.
9—Dampener spring plate.
10—Pressure plate.
11—Retracting spring bolt.
12—Pressure plate retracting spring.
13—Spring pivot ring.
14—Clutch spring.
15—Spring retainer bolt.
16—Spring retainer bolt nut.
17—Spring pivot ring.
18—Throw-out fork.
19—Release bearing and support assembly
20—Fork ball head stud.
21—Ball retainer
22—Cover

Figure 18-14. Exploded view—diaphragm spring clutch. This type of clutch uses the diaphragm fingers as release levers. (Luk, Inc.)

Figure 18-16. Clutch throw-out bearings. A—Ball bearing type. B—Graphite type.

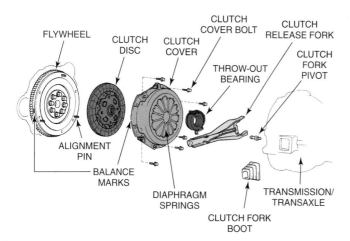

Figure 18-15. Various clutch parts in sequence. Note the balance marks and alignment pins which are used for reassembly. (Geo)

Figure 18-17. Clutch throw-out fork. The fork engages the throw-out bearing and pivots on a ball stud.

graphite to press against a smooth plate fastened to the clutch levers, **Figure 18-16.** The throw-out bearing sleeve is moved in and out by a ***throw-out fork*** or ***clutch fork.*** This fork is usually pivoted on a ***ball head stud.*** A ***return spring*** pulls the fork away from the pressure plate, **Figure 18-17.**

Clutch Housing and Input Shaft (Clutch Shaft)

The clutch housing bolts onto the engine and surrounds the flywheel and clutch mechanism. The housing is made of cast iron or aluminum. The bottom section of some housings are open, while other housings form a complete enclosure. Housings usually have openings to allow air circulation to cool the clutch and vent excess dust. The transmission can either bolt to the housing, or be an integral part of it.

The transmission input shaft passes through the clutch mechanism and its outboard (outer) end is supported by the clutch pilot bearing. The shaft is splined near the end, and the clutch disc rides on it at this point, **Figure 18-18.**

Complete Assembly

Figure 18-19 shows an exploded view of the entire clutch mechanism. Notice the use of the graphite throw-out bearing and the full enclosure clutch housing. The transmission input shaft is not shown. **Figure 18-20** shows a cross-section of a clutch fully assembled. The transmission input shaft is shown in place. Both pilot and throw-out bearings use an antifriction ball bearing.

Other Types of Clutches

There have been a great number of clutch types used over the years. The two shown in this chapter completely

Figure 18-18. Clutch housing and input shaft, showing the flywheel, clutch disc, and hub. The remainder of the clutch mechanism is now shown. This housing forms the full enclosure. Notice how the outboard end of the input shaft is supported by the pilot bearing pressed into the flywheel.

1—Flywheel.
2—Locating pin.
3—Clutch plate with lining.
4—Pressure plate.
5—Release lever pin.
6—Release lever retainer.
7—Release lever.
8—Release lever plate.
9—Pressure plate spring.
10—Clutch cover.
11—Cover bolt.
12—Fork and lever seal.
13—Retaining plate screw.
14—Release bearing.
15—Release bearing retainer spring.
16—Seal retaining plate.
17—Fork and lever thrust washer.
18—Fork and lever shaft bushing.
19—Clutch fork and lever.
20—Fork and lever shaft bushing.
21—Fork and lever thrust washer.
22—Clutch to gearbox bolt.
23—Starter cover screw.
24—Cover.
25—Clutch to gearbox bolt.
26—Split pin for drain hole.
27—Clutch housing.
28—Fork and lever shaft.
29—Taper pin.
30—Eyebolt nut.
31—Release lever strut.
32—Eyebolt.
33—Anti-rattle spring.
34—Flywheel to crankshaft bolt.
35—Lockwashers.

Figure 18-19. Exploded view—clutch assembly. Only one release lever is shown—there are actually three. The number of springs used will vary from five to seven in an average clutch.

dominate the automotive field today. Some heavy-duty clutches utilize extra springs and two clutch discs with a second pressure plate that is smooth on both sides sandwiched between them.

1—Engine flywheel.
2—Drive disc.
3—Pressure plate.
4—Eye bolt.
5—Strut.
6—Anti-rattle spring.
7—Release lever pin.
8—Adjusting nut.
9—Release lever.
10—Release bearing and support assembly.
11—Trans. drive gear bearing retainer.
12—Release fork ball stud.
13—Retainer.
14—Clutch release fork.
15—Pressure spring.
16—Cover.
17—Input shaft.
18—Engine crankshaft.
19—Pilot bearing.

Figure 18-20. Cross-section of an assembled clutch. Study and learn the names of the clutch parts. (GMC)

Clutch Operation

Remember that the flywheel, clutch cover, release levers, and pressure plate all revolve as a single unit. The transmission input shaft and the clutch disc are splined together, forming another unit.

The only time the clutch disc will turn (vehicle standing still) is when it is pinched between the flywheel and pressure plate. When the release levers draw the pressure plate away from the flywheel, the clutch disc will stand still while everything else continues to revolve. When the pressure plate travels back toward the flywheel, the disc is seized and forced to turn the transmission input shaft, **Figure 18-21**.

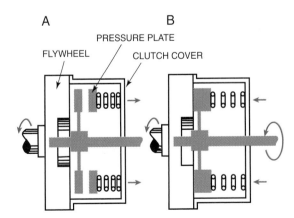

Figure 18-21. Clutch operation simplified. A—The flywheel, pressure plate, springs, and clutch cover are revolving. The clutch disc and clutch shaft are stopped as the pressure plate is disengaged. B—When the pressure plate is engaged, it seizes the clutch disc and the entire unit revolves.

Clutch Pedal Linkage

A way must be provided to connect the clutch fork to the clutch pedal. This is accomplished by the **clutch linkage**. There are two principal kinds of clutch linkage used to actuate the clutch throw-out fork, the **mechanical linkage** and the **hydraulic linkage**.

Mechanical Linkage

The mechanical linkage system incorporates the use of levers and rods or cables connected between the clutch pedal and throw-out fork. When the pedal is depressed, the force is transmitted to the fork by the mechanical linkage. **Figure 18-22** illustrates a simple rod and lever hookup. **Figure 18-23** shows a mechanical linkage using a cable.

Figure 18-22. One mechanical clutch linkage arrangement. When the clutch pedal is depressed, the clutch throw-out fork is actuated. (Plymouth)

Hydraulic Linkage

The other system uses hydraulic power to control the fork. On many vehicles, the mechanical linkage required to operate the fork would be extremely complicated. The hydraulic control simplifies the job. It also reduces the amount of clutch pedal effort by the driver.

When the clutch is depressed, it actuates a small **clutch master cylinder**, **Figure 18-24**. The pressure created in the master cylinder is transmitted to a **slave cylinder** bolted near the fork. The slave cylinder is connected to the fork with a short adjustable rod. When pressure is applied to the slave cylinder, it operates the fork. An exploded view of one type of hydraulically-operated clutch setup is shown in **Figure 18-25**. Both master and slave cylinders are of simple design. Regardless of position or obstructions, they are connected with hydraulic tubing. The principles of hydraulics will be discussed in more detail in Chapter 23.

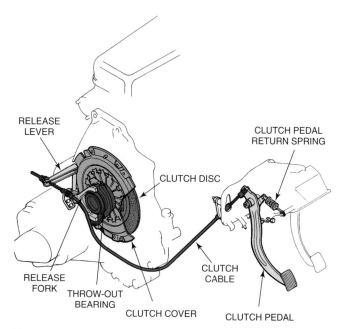

Figure 18-23. One type of mechanically operated clutch release system using a clutch cable to actuate the clutch release lever and fork. (Mazda)

Figure 18-24. Hydraulic clutch control. Clutch pedal movement builds pressure in the master cylinder that in turn actuates the slave cylinder. (Mazda)

Another type of hydraulic clutch is shown in **Figure 18-26**. In this type, the throw-out bearing and slave cylinder are combined into a single unit. When the slave cylinder is actuated, it pushes the throw-out bearing into contact with the

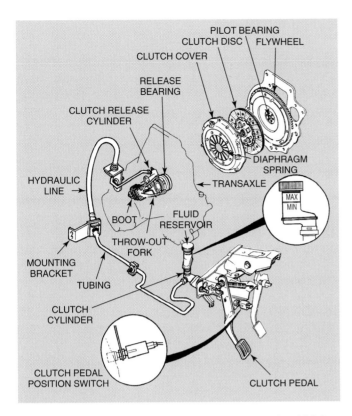

Figure 18-25. An exploded view of a clutch assembly which is used with a manual transaxle. Note the use of a hydraulic system to actuate the throw-out lever. (Kia Motors)

Figure 18-26. Exploded view of one style of hydraulic throw-out bearing and slave cylinder unit. Note the older style two-piece bearing assembly. (Luk Inc.)

release fingers of the pressure plate. This design eliminates the need for a clutch fork and related linkage.

Self-Adjusting Clutch

Most modern clutch assemblies have no adjustments and, with the exception of checking the hydraulic fluid level in

the master cylinder, are maintenance free. Some older vehicles use a *self-adjusting clutch linkage*. The self-adjusting mechanism is a mechanical arrangement that is attached to the clutch pedal and mounting bracket, **Figure 18-27**. The cable that is used with this clutch cannot be made shorter or longer by cutting.

Figure 18-27. Self-adjusting clutch mechanism. Note the teeth on the quadrant and pawl. (Oldsmobile)

The position of the clutch cable may be altered by adjusting the position of the quadrant (toothed-type ratchet) in relation to the clutch pedal. This unit keeps proper cable tension and makes adjustments as the clutch lining wears down. The pawl is shown in engagement with the quadrant teeth in **Figure 18-28**.

When the clutch pedal is in the normal driving position (not depressed), the pawl is held away from the quadrant with a metal stop located on the bracket. In this position, the quadrant hub spring works against the spring force being applied

Figure 18-28. Exploded view of a self-adjusting clutch setup. Note the clutch cable and how it is attached to the quadrant. (Oldsmobile)

at the throw-out (release) bearing. The cable is now in a "balanced" state, with correct tension being applied.

As the clutch pedal is depressed, the pawl will travel away from the metal stop. At this point, the pawl spring will push the pawl down and into engagement with the quadrant teeth. Continued depression of the pedal pulls on the cable, which in turn, forces the throw-out bearing against the fingers or levers in the pressure plate, releasing the clutch.

As the pedal is released, the quadrant returns to its resting position and the pawl is disengaged from the quadrant by the metal stop. The cable is once again in a balanced state of even tension. As the lining wears off the clutch disc, the pawl will engage a different tooth on the quadrant, providing proper compensation for the extra travel.

Clutch Pedal Free Travel

The *free travel*, or *free play* of the clutch pedal is most important. When the clutch pedal is released, the throw-out bearing must not touch the release levers. It must clear for two reasons. As long as it touches, it will continue to rotate. This will shorten its useful life. Also, if the throw-out bearing is not fully released, it may bear against the release levers hard enough to partially disengage the clutch. Any removal of pressure plate force will cause the clutch to slip. When slippage occurs, the clutch facing will overheat and burn up.

All manufacturers specify the amount of free travel that must be allowed. Free travel, or pedal travel, means how far the clutch pedal can be depressed before the throw-out bearing strikes the release levers. The distance the pedal moves from the full out position until it becomes hard to push is the free travel, **Figure 18-29**.

RELEASE BEARING
STRIKES RELEASE LEVERS

PEDAL FULL OUT

FREE TRAVEL

Figure 18-29. Clutch pedal free travel. Always refer to the manufacturer's recommendations for the proper pedal height.

Clutch Cooling

By their very nature, clutches generate considerable heat. You will notice that all clutch covers have openings and that the clutch housings are also provided with openings to facilitate air circulation.

Riding the Clutch

Some drivers develop the habit of riding the clutch (resting their foot on the clutch pedal). The natural weight of the leg will cause the throw-out bearing to contact the release levers. Any additional pressure may even cause the clutch to slip. This can cause premature clutch failure. The clutch pedal should only be touched when the transmission needs to be shifted or disengaged from the engine.

Will a Clutch Explode?

Clutches used in racing and other competition engines can, and sometimes do, explode. The high RPM and horsepower sets up tremendous forces. If the clutch fails, parts are thrown violently outward, which can shatter the clutch housing. The flying clutch parts and metal can endanger the driver and anyone standing nearby.

In any vehicle used for competition, it is imperative that a **scatter shield** be used to protect the driver and others in the event of clutch failure. A scatter shield is a heavy steel plate or fabric blanket that covers the clutch housing. It should extend down the sides to prevent parts from striking anyone standing nearby. It must be bolted or welded securely into place.

Summary

A clutch is necessary to assist in smooth starting, shifting gears, and allowing the vehicle to be stopped without putting the transmission in neutral. The clutch is designed to connect or disconnect the transmission of power from one working part to another—in this case, from the engine to the transmission.

Automotive clutches in use today are of the single plate, dry disc type. The flywheel, clutch disc, pressure plate, springs, clutch cover, and operating mechanism linkage make up the primary parts of the typical clutch. One type uses coil springs as a means of loading the pressure plate. Another type uses a diaphragm spring.

In the operating position (engaged), the clutch disc is held firmly between the flywheel and pressure plate. When the flywheel turns, the disc turns the transmission input shaft to which it is splined.

To disengage the clutch, the clutch pedal is depressed. Either through mechanical or hydraulic linkage, the throw-out fork pushes the throw-out bearing into contact with the pressure plate release levers. The levers draw the pressure plate away from the clutch disc to release it. When the disc is freed, the flywheel and pressure plate assembly continue to rotate, even though the disc and input shaft are not moving.

There are two principal types of throw-out bearings, the ball bearing type and the graphite type. Most vehicles use the ball bearing type. The clutch disc is designed to assist in smooth engagement by torsion springs in the hub assembly as well as cupped segments to which the friction facing is riveted.

Clutch free pedal should be adjusted according to the manufacturer's specifications. Some older clutches are self-adjusting. Others must be manually (by hand) adjusted as the lining wears down. Never ride the clutch.

Know These Terms

Clutch	Throw-out bearing
Flywheel	Throw-out fork
Pilot bearing	Clutch fork
Clutch disc	Ball head stud
Splines	Return spring
Pressure plate	Clutch linkage
Coil spring pressure plate	Mechanical linkage
Diaphragm spring pressure plate	Hydraulic linkage
	Clutch master cylinder
Pressure plate cover	Slave cylinder
Balance marks	Self-adjusting clutch linkage
Release lever	Free travel
Release lever operating mechanism	Free play
	Scatter shield

Review Questions—Chapter 18

Do not write in this book. Write your answers on a separate sheet of paper.

1. The clutch is used to disengage the engine and transmission when _____ .
   - (A) the driver is shifting gears
   - (B) the vehicle is stopped and the engine is running
   - (C) the vehicle is being reversed
   - (D) Both A & B.

2. Why is the flywheel thick?

3. Technician A says that the pilot bearing may be either a ball bearing or a bronze bushing. Technician B says that the pilot bearing does not require lubrication. Who is right?
   - (A) A only.
   - (B) B only.
   - (C) Both A & B.
   - (D) Neither A nor B.

4. The clutch disc hub splines engage splines on the _____.
   - (A) pressure plate assembly
   - (B) transmission input shaft
   - (C) flywheel
   - (D) rear of the crankshaft

5. What clutch part actually locks the clutch disc to the flywheel and pressure plate assembly?
   - (A) Flywheel.
   - (B) Clutch disc.
   - (C) Pressure plate assembly.
   - (D) Throw-out bearing.

6. What clutch part releases the clutch?
   - (A) Flywheel.
   - (B) Clutch disc.
   - (C) Pressure plate assembly.
   - (D) Throw-out bearing.

7. What are the two main classes of pressure plate springs?

8. The pressure plate cover is bolted to the _____ .

9. The _____ operates the throw-out bearing.

10. If the clutch pedal has no free travel, which of the following is least likely to occur?
    - (A) The throw-out bearing will last longer.
    - (B) The clutch will be partially disengaged.
    - (C) The throw-out bearing will touch the release levers.
    - (D) The clutch will slip and overheat.

11. Even though most competition engines use heavy-duty "beefed up" clutches, what additional unit must be installed to safeguard the driver and spectators?

12. Technician A says that clutches have aligning punch marks so that the pressure plate can be reinstalled in the same position as it was originally. Technician B says that aligning punch marks are used to preserve clutch assembly balance. Who is right?
    - (A) A only.
    - (B) B only.
    - (C) Both A & B.
    - (D) Neither A nor B.

13. The outboard end of the transmission input shaft is supported by the _____ .
    - (A) clutch disc
    - (B) clutch housing
    - (C) pilot bearing
    - (D) Both B & C.

14. Why does the clutch housing have openings?
    - (A) To allow air circulation.
    - (B) To allow oil to drip out.
    - (C) To allow dust to fly out.
    - (D) Both A & C.

15. Define the term "riding the clutch."

Cutaway view of a six-speed manual transmission. A unique feature of this transmission is that it has two overdrive gears. (General Motors)

19

Manual Transmissions and Transaxles

After studying this chapter, you will be able to:

- Explain how a manual transmission operates.
- Identify the basic parts of a manual transmission.
- Trace power flow through transmission gears.
- Identify the differences between a manual transmission and manual transaxle.
- Identify the similarities between a manual transmission and manual transaxle.
- Identify the basic parts of a manual transaxle.
- Trace power flow through transaxle gears.

This chapter covers the purpose, construction, and operating principles of manual transmissions and transaxles. Manual transmissions and transaxles are operated by the driver in conjunction with the manual clutch, discussed in Chapter 18. The basic operating principles and designs of all manual transmissions and transaxles have some similarities. Studying this chapter will familiarize you with the basic operating principles and component parts of manual transmissions and transaxles.

Manual Transmissions and Transaxles

Before beginning to discuss the principles of *manual transmissions* and *manual transaxles*, it would be helpful to state the differences between the two. Transmissions are always used on vehicles with front engines and rear-wheel drive. Transaxles are used on vehicles with front engines and front-wheel drive. Some transaxles are used on vehicles with rear engines and rear-wheel drive. Although they look very different, the purposes and layout of all manual transmissions and transaxles is similar.

The Engine Needs Help

An internal combustion engine would have enough power to operate a vehicle without a transmission if the vehicle was operated on level roads and maintained sufficient speed. When the vehicle must be started from a standstill, or when attempting to negotiate steep grades, the engine would not provide sufficient power and the vehicle would stall.

Much less torque is required to drive a vehicle rolling on level ground than up a steep hill, **Figure 19-1**. To enable the engine to increase torque to the drive train, it is obvious that

ONCE A CAR IS ROLLING ON LEVEL GROUND ENGINE IS ENOUGH TO KEEP CAR MOVING

THIS IS TORQUE

Figure 19-1. A minimal amount of torque is required to move a vehicle on level ground. Torque is the twisting force on an axle. (Chevrolet and Honda)

something must be used to multiply torque, **Figure 19-2**. The simplest torque multiplier is a manual transmission. By using a transmission as a torque multiplier, it is possible to adapt the available power of the engine to meet changing road and load conditions.

How Is Torque Multiplied?

If you (an engine) exerted all your strength (power) and still failed to lift a certain object (drive a vehicle), you could multiply your strength by using a *lever and fulcrum*, **Figure 19-3**.

If you weigh 200 lbs. (90.72 kg) and get on the lever 5 ft. (1.52 m) from the fulcrum, a force of 1000 ft.-lbs. (1350 N•m) will be exerted. Then if a weight of 500 lbs. (226.8 kg) is placed on the other end of the lever 1 ft. (30.48 cm) from the fulcrum, it would exert a force of 500 ft.-lbs. (675 N•m). By using a simple torque converter or multiplier, you can now raise 500 lbs. (226.8 kg) with ease. How much weight could you raise by standing on the lever at point A in **Figure 19-4**?

To give another example, if you weigh 200 lbs. (90.72 kg) and want to lift 4000 lbs. (1800 kg) you would have to stand 20 ft. (6.09 m) from the fulcrum. In order to raise the weight a short distance, you must depress the end of the lever a distance 20 times as much as the distance the weight has been raised. See **Figure 19-5**.

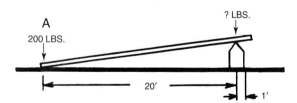

Figure 19-2. Additional torque is required when a vehicle is on a steep grade. The original torque from the engine is not sufficient, so it is necessary to increase torque by means of a torque converter or multiplier. Torque is multiplied through the use of transmission gears. (Chevrolet and Honda)

Figure 19-3. Lever and fulcrum. A weight of 200 lbs. at A will raise weight of 500 lbs. at B because the original weight is multiplied by using a lever and fulcrum.

Figure 19-4. Problem: If you are standing on the lever at A, how much weight will you be able to lift?

You will note that as your (engine's) strength (torque) is increased, the speed with which the weight (vehicle) is moved becomes slower. This is true, as you would find it necessary to depress the lever a greater distance as you moved farther from the fulcrum. From a study of this simple lever and fulcrum, it is possible to make these deductions:

- If the speed of an engine remains constant and its torque is multiplied, the engine will lift more weight, but will take longer to do it.
- If the speed of an engine remains constant and its torque is reduced, it will lift less weight, but will lift it faster.

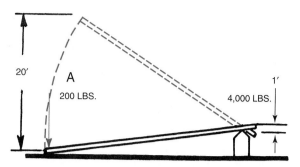

Figure 19-5. If the speed with which you depress the lever remains constant, the more you multiply your strength and the slower the weight will rise. To raise 4000 pounds, it is necessary to depress the level 20' to raise the weight 1'.

Therefore, as engine torque multiplication increases, the vehicle road speed will decrease and as torque multiplication decreases, the vehicle road speed will increase, with the engine RPM remaining constant.

Torque Multiplication through Gears

The same principles used in the lever and fulcrum example can be applied to automotive transmission gears. Consider the fulcrum as the vehicle drive shaft, the amount of weight to be lifted as the torque required to turn the shaft, the engine torque as the person's weight, and the body of the gear as the lever. Then it is easy to see how the gear multiples the torque. **Figure 19-6** shows this principle.

Figure 19-6. Principle of gear torque multiplication. The larger the driven gear is in relation to the driving gear, the greater the torque multiplication. As torque is increased, the driving gear must turn more times to turn the driven gear once.

You can see that as the size of the gear is increased, the same amount of pressure on a tooth will produce an increase in torque. In **Figure 19-6A**, the driving gear tooth is 1 ft. (30.48 cm) from the center of the shaft. If it were pushing down with a 200 lb. (90.72 kg) force, the driving tooth would be exerting a 200 ft.-lb. (270 N•m) push on the tooth of the driven gear.

As the driven tooth is 4 ft. (1.22 m) from the center of the drive shaft, it would exert an 800 ft.-lb. (1080 N•m) force on the drive shaft. In **Figure 19-6B**, the force of the driving gear would be the same, but as the driven tooth is now 2 ft. (60.96 cm) from the center, it would exert a force of only 400 ft.-lbs. (540 N•m) on the drive shaft.

Transmission Gear Ratios

The modern manual transmission can provide the driver with up to six forward **gear ratios** (difference in the number of teeth on each gear). The **reduction gears** provide gear ratios of approximately 3.5:1 (stated as 3.5 to 1) for the lowest gear, to about 1.5:1 for the highest. The **direct drive gear** has a 1:1 gear ratio. The **overdrive gears** have a gear ratio of about .7:1.

By selecting one of the ratios, it is possible to operate the vehicle under all normal conditions. In addition, torque is multiplied more through the differential gears. This will be discussed in Chapter 22. Ratios vary from vehicle to vehicle, depending on engine horsepower and vehicle weight. A **reverse gear** is also used. The reverse ratio is usually about 3:1.

Typical gear ratios for manual transmissions and transaxles are shown in **Figure 19-7**. Note that the five-speed transmission has an overdrive ratio. The overdrive ratio is incorporated into newer transmissions to increase fuel mileage and lower emissions.

Transmission Gear Construction

Transmission gears are made of high quality steel, carefully heat-treated to produce smooth, hard surface gear teeth with a softer, but very tough interior. They are drop-forged (machine hammered into shape) while red hot. The teeth and other critical areas are cut on precision machinery.

TYPICAL MANUAL TRANSMISSION/TRANSAXLE GEAR RATIOS		
THREE-SPEED	FOUR-SPEED	FIVE-SPEED
1ST GEAR, 3:1	1ST GEAR, 3.5:1	1ST GEAR, 3.2:1
2ND GEAR, 2:1	2RD GEAR, 2:1	2ND GEAR, 2:1
3RD GEAR, 1:1	3RD GEAR, 1.5:1	3RD GEAR, 1.4:1
REVERSE, 2.5:1	4TH GEAR, 1.00:1	4TH GEAR, 1:1 (DIRECT DRIVE)
	REVERSE, 3:1	5TH GEAR, 0.853:1 (OVERDRIVE)
		REVERSE, 3:1

Figure 19-7. Average transmission gear ratios for three-, four-, and five-speed transmissions. Actual transmission gear ratios will be different from these.

The teeth on transmission gears are cut into **spur** and **helical** patterns. The helical gear is superior in that it runs more quietly and is stronger because more tooth area is in contact. Helical gears must be mounted firmly, since there is a tendency for them to slide apart due to the spiral shape, **Figure 19-8**. **Gear end play** in the cluster gear and some other gears and shafts is controlled by the use of bronze and steel **thrust washers**. These washers are installed on the end of the gear shafts between the moving gears and the stationary transmission case, **Figure 19-9**.

There must be some clearance between the gear teeth to allow for lubrication, expansion and possible size irregularity. This clearance is very small (a few thousandths of an inch). **Figure 19-10** illustrates backlash (clearance between face and flank areas) and also gives gear tooth nomenclature.

Figure 19-8. Gear tooth shapes. A—The helical tooth is cut at an angle to the centerline of the gear. B—The spur gear is cut straight across (parallel to gear centerline). C—The left side gear is helical gear, the right side is a spur gear. (Land-Rover)

COUNTER FIFTH GEAR ASSY. (5-SPEED)

COUNTER REAR BEARING (5-SPEED)

COUNTER CENTER BEARING

COUNTER FRONT BEARING

GEAR SPLINE NO. 5 AND SYNCHRONIZER RING (5-SPEED)

THRUST WASHER (5-SPEED)

COUNTER SHAFT

Figure 19-9. A thrust washer location on one Five-speed manual transmission. The locations and numbers used will vary. (Toyota Motor Corp.)

Transmission Cases

The **transmission case** holds the transmission gears, shafts, bearings, and washers. It bolts to the rear of the engine, or to the clutch housing. Many transmission cases and clutch housings are one-piece units. Most transmission cases are made of cast iron or aluminum and have a separate

Figure 19-10. Elementary gear tooth nomenclature. Pitch line or pitch diameter is the true diameter used in calculating exact gear ratios. The outside circle is the full diameter of the gear. The root circle is the minimum diameter of the gear.

extension housing, which supports the output shaft. This housing may also contain the speedometer gear. The rear engine mount is usually attached to the extension housing.

Transmission Construction

The gears in all manual transmissions and transaxles are *sliding gear* types, which are moved in and out of engagement by the driver through *shift linkage*. The four main classes of transmission/transaxle gears are reduction, direct drive, overdrive, and reverse, **Figure 19-11.** The

following sections explain the workings of various manual transmissions and transaxles.

A typical transmission consists of a housing, four shafts, bearings, gears, synchronizers, and a shifting mechanism. **Figure 19-12** shows the four shafts and bearings in their relative positions in the housing. The shafts are held in place by pins pressed through the case and shaft or by the presence of external housings over the shaft openings.

Figure 19-12. Housing shafts and bearings. The input and output shafts turn while the countershaft and reverse idler shaft remain fixed. 1—Clutch pilot bearing. 2—Input shaft bearing. 3—Input shaft. 4—Countershaft supported in housing. 5—Countershaft. 6—Reverse idler shaft supported in housing. 7—Housing. 8—Output shaft roller bearing. 9—Output shaft. 10—shaft ball bearing. 11—Input shaft gear teeth.

Figure 19-11. Reduction, direct drive, overdrive, and reverse gears as mounted on the shaft. (Ford Motor Co.)

Synchronizing Mechanism

Once the vehicle is in motion, the drive line will turn the output shaft continuously. As a result, the sliding gears will also be turning. When an attempt is made to mesh them with any of the cluster gears (which tend to stop when the clutch is depressed), the gear teeth will be subjected to damaging impact forces. The sound of *gear clash* when shifting results from the sliding gear teeth literally smashing against the cluster gear.

It is obvious that for one gear to mesh with another quietly and without damage, both gears must be rotating at nearly the same speed. Modern manual transmissions and transaxles have *synchronized* gears, with special internal clutches to prevent gear clash when shifting. The purpose of the synchronizer is to move ahead of the unit that is to be meshed, seize the other unit, and bring the rotational speed of both units together. Once both units are rotating at the same speed, they may be meshed.

Synchronizer Operation

Figure 19-13 is a simplified version, illustrating the operating principle of the synchronizing device. A is the input shaft and it is stopped with the clutch disengaged. In order to mesh the spinning splined hub B on the output shaft with the splined recess D on the input shaft, it will be necessary to start turning the input shaft. Notice that cone ring E is an extension of hub B. The ring is supported on pins that fit into holes in the hub. The ring is held out by springs G.

As sliding hub B is moved toward splined recess D, ring E will touch cone-shaped bottom H of recess. As the hub is moved closer to the recess, the springs G will force cone ring E tightly against the bottom of the cone recess. As the cone ring is turning, it will impart torque to the input shaft and start it turning. As the hub moves closer, spring pressure increases and cone ring will be jammed into cone recess with enough force to spin the input shaft at nearly the same speed of hub B. The hub may then be meshed into the recess with no grinding or shock.

The simplified synchronizer as shown in **Figure 19-13** would be for direct drive. By putting a cone ring (called a blocking ring or synchronizing cone) on both sides of the hub, **Figure 19-14**, it could be shifted the other way and engage the splined recess in the output shaft second gear. For this arrangement, the second gear would no longer be a sliding gear and would not be splined to the output shaft. The second gear would become a constant mesh gear and would be turned whenever the cluster gear is revolving. It would rotate on the output shaft either on a bushing or roller bearings.

When direct drive or overdrive is desired, the sliding clutch hub would be shifted into the input shaft recess. For second gear, the clutch hub would be shifted back until meshed with the second gear. When the hub engages the second gear, the output shaft would be locked to the second gear through the clutch hub. The output shaft would be driven by the cluster second speed gear driving the locked output shaft second gear. Both shifts would be quiet, as the synchronizer would equalize or synchronize their speeds before meshing as in **Figure 19-14**.

Figure 19-13. Simplified synchronizer. As clutch hub B is shifted toward splined recess D, cone ring E will strike cone recess H and spin the input shaft. Hub B is then meshed into splined recess D without grinding. Cone ring pins and springs are forced into the clutch hub.

Figure 19-14. Constant mesh second gear with synchromesh in second gear and direct drive. Output shaft second gear 7, is free to rotate on output shaft 10. A roller bearing or bushing is provided at 9. A snap ring 8 keeps the second gear from moving back and forth. When synchromesh hub 5 is moved into the second gear splines 6, second gear is locked to output. Other parts include: 1—Input shaft. 2—Supported inner end of output shaft. 3—Input splines. 4—Cone synchronizer ring. 11—Cluster second gear. 12—Countershaft. 13—Cluster assembly. 14—Cluster drive.

Study the *synchronizer assemblies* (unit containing the synchronizers) illustrated in **Figure 19-15**. This popular type splines the hub to the shaft, but does not permit end movement of the hub. The synchronizer assembly is shifted forward or backward on the hub. This action forces (by means of inserts) the blocking rings to equalize gear speeds before the synchronizer assembly engages the other gear to lock the gear to the hub. Current practice is toward full synchronization for all forward gears and reverse. This permits first or reverse gear to be engaged while the vehicle is still in motion.

THIRD AND OVERDRIVE SYNCHRONIZER

Figure 19-15. Two synchronizer units used for first, second, third, and overdrive gears. The hub is splined to the shaft. The synchronizer assembly is moved back and forth on hub to connect it with the selected gear. (Ford)

Various Types of Synchronizer Shapes

Although shapes vary, all synchronizer units in use today use a cone (blocking ring) that precedes the movement of either the clutch hub, or in many cases, the synchronizer assembly. The cone engages a tapered surface on the part to be engaged to synchronize the speed before meshing. As you study the transmissions and transaxles in this chapter, determine the location and operation of the synchronizers.

Transmission Operation

To show how the transmission works, the four shafts with gears are shown in **Figure 19-16**. By studying the illustration, you will see that the transmission is in neutral. Notice that the *input shaft* is turning, but the *output shaft* is standing still. Also note that the input shaft gear is always driving a

Figure 19-16. Transmission in neutral. Input shaft 13 is revolving. Input gear 1 is driving the entire cluster gear assembly. All cluster gears are connected to this cluster body. The reverse idler cluster gear 8 is driving reverse idler gear 7. Output shaft 6 is not moving as both sliding low and reverse gear 5 and sliding high and second gear 4 are in neutral positions. 2—Splined stub. 3—Splined recess on sliding gear 4. 6—Output shaft is splined to allow the gears to be shifted back and forth. 8—Cluster reverse idler gear. 9—Cluster low gear. 10—Cluster second gear. 11—Cluster body. 12—Large constant mesh cluster gear. 14—Countershaft. 15—Cluster bearing.

shaft referred to as the *counter gear* or *cluster gear*. The cluster gear revolves on roller bearings. The cluster gear is constantly in mesh with the *reverse idler gear shaft*.

The cluster gear assembly has gears which are all cut on the same steel blank. The large gear at the front is the drive gear and the following gears are used in reduction gear ratios. On transmissions with overdrive, one or two of the cluster gears will be used to provide overdrive ratios. The last gear on the cluster is usually the reverse gear. When the input shaft is turning, the cluster gear also turns, but in an opposite or counter direction.

The reverse idler gear turns when the cluster gear is turning. The reverse idler gear has a pressed-in internal bushing and rotates on the stationary reverse idler shaft. There are two gears that are always in contact: the input shaft gear and cluster drive gear, and the cluster reverse gear and reverse idler gear. These are called *constant mesh gears*.

The output shaft is splined and two gears are placed on it. Both gears are free to move back and forth on the splines. The smaller of the two is the second speed gear. Notice that it has a splined recess in its face. This splined recess is designed to slip over a splined stub protruding from the input shaft. The larger sliding gear is the low and reverse gear. It can be shifted into mesh with either the reverse idler gear or the low cluster gear. Study **Figure 19-16** and trace the flow of power (indicated by arrows).

The following sections explain the operation of a typical manual transmission with synchronizers. Note the presence of the counter gear and reverse idler gear under the input and output shafts. Although three-speed manual transmissions are increasingly rare, a three-speed transmission is used in this section to simplify the explanation of gear and synchronizer operation.

Neutral

Figure 19-17 shows the transmission in neutral. Notice that the input shaft drives the cluster gear, which in turn drives the constant mesh second speed gear. As the second gear

Figure 19-17. Manual transmission in neutral. Power flow is from the input gear to the cluster drive gear to the output constant mesh second gear. Since the synchromesh synchronizer assembly is in neutral, constant mesh second gear will revolve on the output shaft and no power will be transmitted beyond this point. (Pontiac)

turns on the output shaft, no power is transmitted. This transmission uses a strut-type synchronizer. The synchronizer assemblies are in a neutral position. The sliding low and reverse gear is also in a neutral position.

First Gear

When the transmission is shifted into first gear, the clutch is depressed, releasing the clutch disc. The input shaft and cluster gear will stop turning. The output sliding low gear is shifted forward and meshed with the cluster low gear. The output second gear is left out of mesh. When the clutch is engaged, the input shaft will turn the cluster gear. The cluster gear will revolve at a slower speed. The cluster low gear, being smaller than the output shaft low sliding gear, will turn the output shaft at a slower speed, **Figure 19-18.**

Figure 19-19 illustrates the transmission in first gear. The synchronizer assembly is still in the neutral position, but the sliding low and reverse gear has been shifted into mesh with the cluster low gear. The output shaft speed will be

Figure 19-18. Transmission in first gear. The sliding low and reverse gear has been shifted forward and is meshed with the cluster low gear. Output shaft is now turning. All gears that are in mesh with another gear are shown with simulated teeth.

Figure 19-19. Manual transmission in first gear. Power flow is from the input gear to the cluster drive gear, from cluster low gear to output sliding low and reverse gear. As the sliding low and reverse gear is meshed, power is transmitted to output shaft. (Pontiac)

roughly one-third that of the input shaft, giving a gear reduction of 3:1. This reduction multiplies the engine torque, but gives less forward speed.

Second Gear

When ready for second gear, the clutch is depressed to break the flow of power from the engine. The low sliding gear is moved to a neutral position and the second sliding gear is meshed with the cluster second gear. The clutch is then released and the flow of power is resumed with less torque multiplication. See **Figure 19-20.**

Figure 19-20. Transmission in second gear. The sliding low gear has returned to the neutral position. The sliding second gear is moved into mesh with the cluster second gear. Output shaft now turns faster with less torque multiplication.

Notice that the cluster second gear is larger in proportion to the sliding second gear. **Figure 19-21** shows the transmission in second gear. The synchronizer assembly has been shifted back until it engages the splines or small teeth on the second gear. The gear reduction is now around 2:1 and torque falls off, but speed picks up.

Most transmissions have four or five forward gear ratios and one reverse. A few have six forward speeds. Transmissions are generally equipped with helical gears to assure longer life and quieter operation. One gear (usually low or reverse) may be of the sliding type, or all forward gears may be of constant mesh design.

A synchromesh unit is designed to provide smooth gear shifting without clashing or grinding. The transmission consists of the input and output shaft assemblies, the cluster gear, and the reverse idler assembly. All are housed in a strong steel or aluminum housing.

The shafts revolve on roller and ball bearings. The second speed gear and reverse idler gear are sometimes mounted on bronze bushings. The input and output shafts are secured by means of snap rings and bearing retainers. End play in the cluster gear is controlled by the use of bronze and steel thrust washers.

The transmission housing can be bolted to the clutch housing or cast as an integral part. The transmission housing often acts as a base for the rear engine mount. On front-wheel drive vehicles, the transmission and differential assemblies are installed in a single housing, referred to as a transaxle. Transaxles are also used on vehicles with rear engines and rear wheel drive.

Transaxles operate in the same way as rear drive transmissions and rear axle differentials, but place all parts together. The manual transaxle has the same kinds of gears, synchronizers, and shifting mechanisms as a manual transmission. The major differences between the transmission and transaxle are the shape of the case, and the placement of the parts within the case. The transaxle may use a drive chain or two gears to transfer power inside of the transaxle. The transaxle has two axles connecting the transaxle to the front wheels.

The gears are selected either by a console or floor mounted shift stick or steering wheel column shift control. The transmission is lubricated by filling the housing partially full of gear oil or automatic transmission fluid. As the gears turn, they throw the oil to lubricate all parts. Leakage is controlled by oil seals at both front and rear ends.

Know These Terms

Manual transmission	Sliding gears
Manual transaxle	Shift linkage
Lever and fulcrum	Gear clash
Gear ratio	Synchronized gears
Reduction gears	Synchronizer assemblies
Direct drive gear	Input shaft
Overdrive gears	Output gear
Reverse	Counter
Spur	Cluster gear
Helical	Reverse idler gear shaft
Gear end play	Constant mesh gears
Thrust washer	Transaxle case
Backlash	Shifter forks
Transmission case	Shift linkage
Extension housing	Speed shifting

Review Questions—Chapter 19

Do not write in this book. Write your answers on a separate sheet of paper.

1. When would an internal combustion engine have enough power to operate a vehicle without a transmission?
   (A) When the vehicle is started on a level road.
   (B) When the vehicle is operated on level roads at sufficient speed.
   (C) When the vehicle is operated on steep hills at sufficient speed.
   (D) When the vehicle is operated in reverse.

2. If the speed of an engine is constant and its torque is multiplied, the engine will be able to move _____ weight.

3. What is the relationship between torque multiplication and speed?
   (A) When torque goes up, speed goes up.
   (B) When torque goes up, speed goes down.
   (C) When torque goes down, speed goes down.
   (D) Changes in torque do not affect speed.

4. A gear ratio of 2.5:1 is a(n) _____ gear.
   (A) overdrive
   (B) direct drive
   (C) reduction
   (D) neutral

5. A gear ratio of .8:1 is a(n) _____ gear.
   (A) overdrive
   (B) direct drive
   (C) reduction
   (D) neutral

6. Name the four shafts used in the transmission.

7. Technician A says that synchronizing the gears prevents gear clash. Technician B says that synchronizing the gears reduces gear damage. Who is right?
   (A) A only.
   (B) B only.
   (C) Both A & B.
   (D) Neither A nor B.

8. The manual transmission is lubricated by _____ .
   (A) an oil pump
   (B) oil pressure from the engine
   (C) splash lubrication
   (D) Both A & C.

9. Two gears that are always engaged with each other are called _____ gears.

10. What problem do thrust washers prevent?

11. The parts that are located inside of the transmission or transaxle are called shift _____ .

12. All of the following statements about four- and five-speed transmissions are true, EXCEPT:
    (A) they increase fuel mileage.
    (B) they reduce acceleration.
    (C) they are more efficient than a three-speed unit.
    (D) they are more efficient than an automatic transmission.

13. Technician A says that the inner bearing on the input shaft is a bronze bushing. Technician B says that the reverse idler gear is always supported on roller bearings. Who is right?
    (A) A only.
    (B) B only.
    (C) Both A & B.
    (D) Neither A nor B.

14. Transmission housings are made of _____ or _____ .

15. Why is speed shifting considered a foolish practice by expert drivers?

A transmission is but one component in a vehicle's drive train. However, the entire drive train can be affected if the transmission is in poor operating condition. (Ford)

Cutaway of a four-wheel drive sport utility vehicle. Can you find any four-wheel drive components in this illustration? (General Motors)

20

Four-Wheel Drive

After studying this chapter, you will be able to:

- Explain the purpose of four-wheel drive.
- Explain the operation of four-wheel drive transfer cases.
- Identify the components of four-wheel drive transfer cases.

Four-wheel drive is becoming more popular as the number of off-road and sport utility vehicles increases. Four-wheel drive is also useful for driving on wet or ice covered roads. This chapter covers the design and operation of four-wheel drive units and the differences between full-time and part-time four-wheel drive systems. Front wheel locking hubs are also discussed.

Purposes of the Four-Wheel Drive

Four-wheel drive is useful for driving off-road, when traction to all four wheels is desirable. Until recently, most four-wheel drive vehicles were either trucks or off-road vehicles. Since powering all of the wheels adds to vehicle stability when driving on roads that are covered with ice, many passenger cars and vans are now equipped with four-wheel drive. Four-wheel drive systems are used with both manual and automatic transmissions.

Four-Wheel Drive Components

The main four-wheel drive components are the transfer case, drive shafts, front and rear differentials, and a drive selection system. Some also use locking devices at the front hubs to engage the front-wheel drive. The drive shafts and differentials are identical to those used on two-wheel drive vehicles. For more information on differentials and drive shafts, refer to Chapter 22.

Four-Wheel Drive Designs

There are two types of four-wheel drive, based on engine placement. In a vehicle with conventional engine placement, the rear-wheel drive components are the same as they would be with a two-wheel drive setup. A *transfer case* is installed between the transmission output shaft and the drive shafts.

The transfer case directs power to the front wheels when needed. Both drive shafts are attached to the transfer case. The rear drive shaft sends power to the rear differential assembly as in a two-wheel drive system. The front drive shaft sends power to the front differential assembly. This design is by far the most common type of front-wheel drive design.

In the front-wheel drive vehicle, the front wheels are driven in the same manner as they would be on a two-wheel drive vehicle. The transfer case is installed on the transaxle, or may be a part of it. On some designs, both axles have separate differentials. Other designs have the front differential as part of the transaxle assembly. The front wheels are driven at all times. In four-wheel drive, power travels through the rear drive shaft to the rear differential assembly. The two designs are shown in **Figure 20-1.**

Transfer Case

The purpose of the transfer case is to divide the power flow so that both the front and rear wheels are driven by engine power when necessary. Engine power enters the transfer case from the transmission output shaft. Power is transmitted to each drive shaft either through a set of *gears* or a *chain and sprocket* set. **Figure 20-2** shows the power flow in four-wheel drive for the two transfer case types.

Transfer cases can be either full- or part-time units. The full-time unit with a chain drive is the most common today. Full-time systems have a *differential assembly* or a viscous coupling to compensate for changes in front and rear axle speeds. Both systems are explained below.

Full-Time Transfer Case

Most automobiles, vans, and some light trucks use a *full-time transfer case*. The full-time unit delivers power to the front and rear axle assemblies all of the time. The case is constructed from either aluminum or cast iron. Most cases include a high and low range. High range is about 1:1 and low range is 2:1. **Figure 20-3** shows an exploded view of a full-time transfer case. Note the viscous coupling. Study and learn the part names and locations.

Full-Time Transfer Case Operation

The full-time transfer case drives all four wheels whenever the vehicle is moving. These transfer cases use either a differential assembly or viscous coupling to compensate for differences in front and rear axle speeds during turning and driving over irregular surfaced terrain. By compensating for different driving conditions, the full-time transfer case will permit the vehicle to be continuously operated in four-wheel drive on hard and dry surfaced highways.

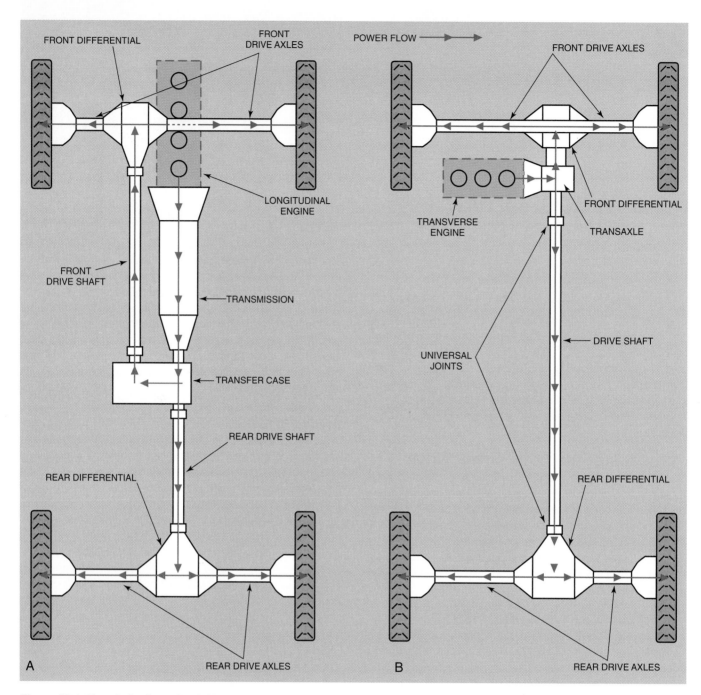

Figure 20-1. Two similar four-wheel drive systems and the power flow through each. A—A longitudinal engine and transmission with primary rear-wheel drive. B—Transverse engine position. No separate transfer case is used with this particular transaxle arrangement.

Figure 20-2. A—Power flow through a part-time gear set transfer case. Shown is the pattern for four-wheel drive high range. The front shift fork slides the sleeve of the front clutch onto the toothed clutch ring. This couples the rear output shaft to the front output shaft. The front and rear shafts now turn together—power flows to all wheels. B—Four-wheel drive, high-range power flow through a part-time, chain drive transfer case. (Suzuki and General Motors)

Figure 20-3. An exploded view of a viscous coupling full-time case. Note this unit uses a drive chain in place of a gear set. When the speed difference between the front and rear wheels becomes higher because of vehicle driving conditions, the speed difference is absorbed by the operation of the viscous coupling. (Toyota Motor Corporation)

Full-Time Transfer Case with Differential Unit

Note in **Figure 20-4** that the drive chain transmits power from the drive sprocket to the differential case sprocket. A differential unit inside the case applies driving torque to both front and rear transfer case output shafts. The differential allows the front and back shafts to rotate at different speeds while still applying power. This permits constant use of four-wheel drive.

This unit is equipped with a limited-slip differential that will provide some drive to either the front or rear axle if one wheel is spinning. For very severe traction situations, the unit has a mechanism to lock out (stop) the differential action. This provides direct drive to both front and rear drive shafts. An exploded view of another full-time transfer case is illustrated in **Figure 20-5**. Note the use of a viscous coupling. This transfer case is available with or without a low range reduction unit. **Figure 20-5** does not show the reduction unit.

Another type of full-time transfer case is shown in **Figure 20-6**. It uses a chain drive and a standard differential unit. Low and high range is accomplished through gearing. This unit may be locked out whenever excessive wheel spin is experienced. The lockout must be disengaged whenever the vehicle is driven on dry paved roads.

Full- and Part-Time Transfer Cases with Viscous Couplings

These transfer cases operate somewhat like the differential equipped unit above. The basic difference is the **viscous coupling** used in place of the mechanical limited-slip differential.

The viscous coupling consists of a series of plates with ridges or grooves. The plates do not touch. The coupling is filled with a thick silicone fluid that fills the spaces between the plates. The coupling is placed so that power to the rear wheels must pass through it. See **Figure 20-7**.

During normal operation (no wheel spin), the viscous coupling does not operate. When excessive wheel spin is present (causing pronounced speed variations between front and rear axles), the coupling transfers torque to the axle having the best traction.

The silicone fluid in the coupling is very thick, or viscous, and will not thin due to heat. As one axle overspeeds because of wheel slippage, the coupling rotational speed also increases. As the coupling speed becomes higher, the fixed clutch plates are forced to rotate in the silicone fluid as they increase in speed. As fluid is forced between the clutch plates and displaced (moved), it expands, creating friction and more resistance to higher input speed.

Figure 20-4. Schematic showing power flow through a full-time transfer case. Note that the power is supplied to the front and rear axles in both low and high range. (Jeep)

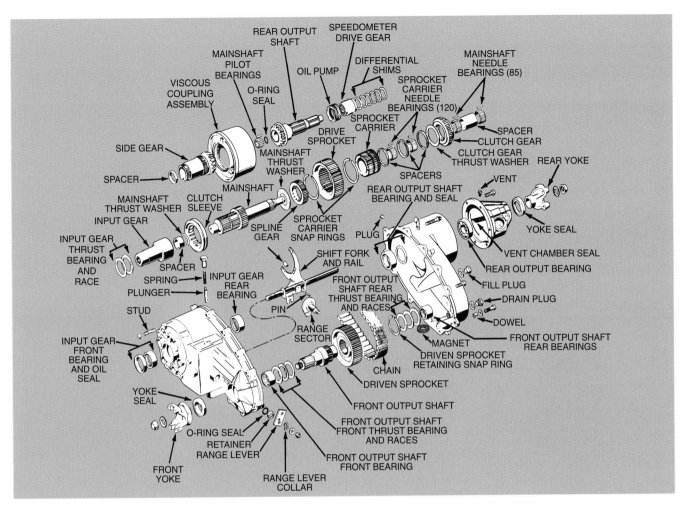

Figure 20-5. An exploded view of a full-time, select-drive transfer case. Note the magnet which is used to catch and hold any ferrous (iron) particles in the fluid. This helps to prevent premature wear on the bearings, chain, etc. (Chrysler)

Figure 20-6. Cross-sectional view of a full-time transfer case. A—High-range input gear. B—Input shaft. C—Low-range input gear. D—Sliding clutch. E—Counter (or cluster) gears. F—Front axle drive sprocket. G—Interaxle differential front gear. H—Driven sprocket. I—Drive chain. (General Motors.)

Figure 20-7. A cross-sectional view of the power flow through a full-time transfer case. Note the viscous coupling action. (Toyota Motor Corporation)

The coupling does not lock the axles together, but controls the amount of axle slippage by sending maximum torque to the slower moving axle. Note that some viscous coupling transfer cases also have an internal differential assembly. An exploded view of a viscous coupling transfer case is shown in **Figure 20-8**.

19. Input Shaft
20. Viscous Clutch
21. Sun Gear Shaft Thrust Washer
22. Planet Carrier Assembly
23. Planet Carrier Assembly Thrust Washer
24. Output Shaft Assembly
25. Extension Housing Bolts
26. Breather Assembly
27. Output Shaft Bearing Snap Ring
28. Output Shaft Bearing
29. Ring Gear Snap Ring
30. Ring Gear
31. Front Output Shaft Oil Seal
32. Input Shaft Oil Seal
33. Sun Gear Shaft Bearing
34. Output Shaft Bearing Snap Ring
35. Output Shaft Bearing
36. Output Shaft Oil Seal
37. Speedometer Tone Wheel
38. Input Shaft Pilot Bearing
39. Output Shaft Rear Bearing
40. Identification Tag
41. Drain/Fill Plug

1. Front Output Flange Nut
2. Steel Flat Washer
3. Rubber Sealing Washer
4. Output Shaft
5. Front Output Flange
6. Speed Sensor Bolt
7. Speed Sensor
8. Extension Housing
9. Front Cover Bolts
10. Rear Case Half
11. Front Cover
12. Front Output Shaft Spacer
13. Drive Chain
14. Driven Sprocket
15. Magnet
16. Drive Sprocket Spacer
17. Drive Sprocket
18. Sun Gear Shaft

Figure 20-8. Exploded view of a chain drive transfer case which uses a viscous clutch assembly. (Chevrolet)

Part-Time Transfer Case

Many older four-wheel drive systems used a **part-time transfer case**. The part-time transfer case is also used on some late model vehicles. The part-time unit will deliver power to the rear wheels only, or to the front and rear wheels, as determined by the driver. Part-time four-wheel drive transfer cases should not be operated on dry, hard surfaced roads.

The part-time transfer case housing is made of cast iron or aluminum. Power is transmitted through a series of gears

and/or chains. Most incorporate a high and low range, which provides a gearing arrangement around 1:1 (high range) or 2.6:1 (low range). **Figure 20-9** shows an exploded view of one type of part-time transfer case. Study the parts and learn their names and locations.

Part-Time Transfer Case Selection Control

On all part-time four-wheel drive vehicles, a drive range selection control is included. The part-time transfer case is

Figure 20-9. Exploded view of a transfer case which uses a two-piece input-output shaft. Note the drive chain and planetary gear assembly. (Ford Motor Company)

normally in two-wheel drive and is placed in four-wheel drive only when needed. The driver can select one of three different drive modes:

- Two-wheel drive high range.
- Four-wheel drive high range.
- Four-wheel drive low range.

A neutral range is also available for towing. These ranges are operated by either moving a lever on the vehicle center console, floor, by pressing a button, or turning a switch on the dash. Although it would be possible to operate in two-wheel drive low range, transfer case shift linkage does not allow selecting this range. A lever control for a part-time transfer case is shown in **Figure 20-10**.

Transfer Case Action—Low Range, High Range

Follow the power flow in **Figure 20-11**. Start with the transmission output shaft, which is splined to the transfer case main drive gear. The main drive gear is in constant mesh with the idler cluster gear. The idler turns freely in needle bearings on the idler shaft. Note that the idler cluster is made up of two gears, one large (high range) and one small (low range). These gears are in constant mesh with the output gears. Both output gears turn freely in bushings on the transfer case output shaft.

The **sliding clutch** is splined to the output shaft. In the neutral position, it is centered between, but not engaging the output gears. Low range (high engine RPM, low wheel RPM) is engaged when the sliding clutch is shifted into engagement with the low range output gear. High range (low engine speed RPM, high drive wheel RPM) is engaged when the sliding clutch is moved into engagement with the high range output

Figure 20-10. This four-wheel drive truck uses a lever control to shift the part-time transfer case into its different ranges. While some vehicles use this type of lever control, electronic controlled push button or switch control is also used. (GMC)

gear. The output gear that is engaged with the clutch turns the sliding clutch. Since the clutch is splined to the output shaft, the shaft also turns.

Part-Time Four-Wheel Operation

The transfer case output shaft is made of two parts. The long section is driven by the sliding splined clutch. This long section of the output shaft, in turn, will drive the rear drive shaft. The shorter front section is connected to the long section only when the four-wheel drive sliding splined clutch (splined to and constantly turned by long section) is moved into engagement with the splined end of the short shaft.

Figure 20-11. Power flow through a part-time transfer case in four-wheel, high range (1) and four-wheel low range (2). A—Sliding clutch. B—High range input gear. C—Input shaft. D—Pinion gears. E and F—Side gears. G—Drive sprocket. H—Driven sprocket. I—Counter gear. J—Low range input gear. K—Transmission output shaft. (Chevrolet)

When two-wheel drive is desired, the short output shaft is disconnected by moving the four-wheel sliding clutch out of engagement. The long shaft will then drive the rear drive shaft, but will not apply torque to the front. Four-wheel drive is engaged by moving the four-wheel clutch into engagement with the short shaft. Torque will then be applied to both front and rear drive shafts.

Vehicles equipped with this type of transfer case must never be operated in four-wheel drive on dry, hard-surfaced roads. The vehicle's front wheels will rotate slightly faster (follow a more curved path) than the rear. As a result, windup increases in the entire drive train until something breaks.

Windup is the development of internal stresses between the front and rear axle parts, caused by differences in speeds between the front and rear axles. Either the tires will break loose (slip) on the pavement, or a vehicle drive train part will be damaged. Since it is very difficult for the tires to break loose on hard, dry road surfaces, the vehicle will probably be damaged.

On another type of transfer case, **Figure 20-12**, the front drive shaft and ring gear assembly is driven at all times. A *vacuum motor*, **Figure 20-13**, is used to disconnect the front wheels from the front axle. The vacuum motor operates a shift collar, similar to the collar used with a manual transmission synchronizer, installed in the front drive axle. Some transfer cases use a cable system to disconnect the front axle.

In **Figure 20-14**, an electrical actuator moves the shift fork and differential sleeve to engage the front axle. The actuator is filled with a gas charge which expands when heated. As the gas expands, it moves the shift fork to engage the front axle. When the electrical current to the actuator is turned off, the gas cools. The shift fork return spring moves the fork back to its resting position, disengaging the axle, **Figure 20-13**.

Transfer Case Lubrication

The transfer case is lubricated by filling the housing partially full of lubricant. The movement of the chain and gears throws lubricant throughout the case to lubricate all parts. Most have their own internal pumps. Transfer cases are lubricated by gear oil, usually 75W-90 weight or automatic transmission fluid. Transfer case leakage is controlled by oil seals at the front and rear output shafts, and by other seals, sealants, and gaskets where necessary. Viscous couplings, where used, are filled with silicone in a sealed assembly and are not serviceable.

Locking Hubs

Some four-wheel drive vehicles use front *locking hubs* to engage and disengage the front wheels and front drive axle. This type of arrangement is considered a part-time four-wheel drive, but is not controlled by internal parts in the transfer case. The locking hub is a device which locks the front wheels to the front axle at the wheel hub.

Some locking hubs are engaged and disengaged automatically by the use of one-way or overrunning clutches in the front drive axles. These one-way clutches will transfer power in one direction, but will freewheel (overrun) if power is applied

Figure 20-12. Cross-sectional view of a planetary gear-type transfer case. Gear ratios are: Two-wheel and four-wheel high range —1.00:1. Four-wheel low range—2.566:1. The case holds 1.1 quarts (1.0 liters) of SAE 75W-90 gear lubricant. Note the drive chain and the oil pump. (Toyota Motor Corporation)

Figure 20-13. A cutaway view of the front axle and vacuum motor assembly. The vacuum motor operates the shift collar to engage or disengage the front axle. (Toyota Motor Corporation)

in the other direction. These clutches lock up whenever the engine is driving the front wheels through the transfer case and unlock when the transfer case is returned to two-wheel drive operation. Other locking hubs can be automatically released by moving the transfer case to the two-wheel position and backing up the vehicle a short distance. A typical locking hub is shown in **Figure 20-15**.

Figure 20-14. Exploded view of a four-wheel drive front axle assembly. The electric/gas differential actuator moves the shift fork, which slides the differential sleeve on and off the output shaft to engage and disengage the front axle. (General Motors)

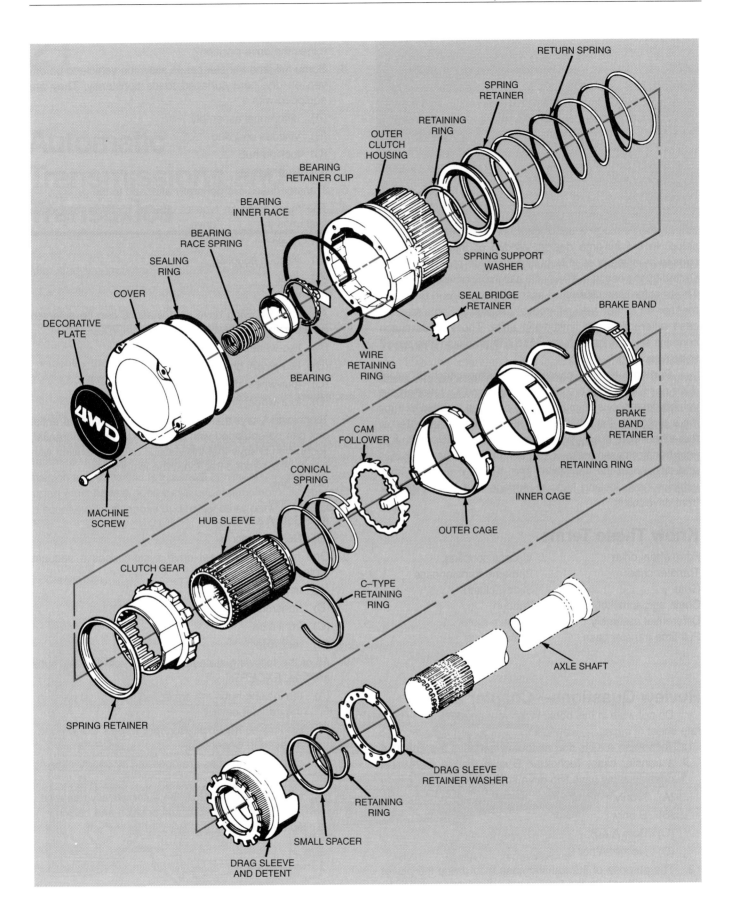

Figure 20-15. Exploded view of an automatic locking hub assembly. Study the various parts, their locations, and names. Manual locking hubs are also used. (General Motors)

When the vehicle reaches cruising speed, the turbine will be rotating at almost the same speed as the impeller and the stator will begin to impede the flow of fluid. However, at cruising speeds, fluid will strike the stator in the same direction as impeller rotation. This will cause it to unlock and the converter will function as a simple hydraulic coupling.

Stator locking and unlocking action is produced by using a one-way or overrunning clutch. Overrunning clutches can be of the sprag or roller type. These will be discussed in more detail under holding members in this chapter. Note the location of the stator one-way clutch in **Figure 21-14**.

Figure 21-14. This stator unit uses a one-way roller clutch. Notice that the stator can turn in only one direction similar to an overrunning clutch.

Torque Converter Operation

The preceding sections covered the individual components of the torque converter. The following sections discuss the operation of the converter assembly. The following section describes the action of the converter when it is accelerating from rest and when it reaches cruising speed.

Accelerating from a Stop

With the transmission in drive range and engine idling (rest), there is very little transfer of torque from the impeller to the turbine when the vehicle is standing still. As the engine is accelerated from a stop, impeller speed increases rapidly. As impeller speed increases, fluid is thrown into the turbine with increasing force. Leaving the turbine, the fluid strikes the stator, **Figure 21-15**.

As the stator is forced backward by the fluid, the one-way clutch will lock it up. The fluid flow is then diverted before it reaches the impeller. As this vortex flow increases in speed, more and more torque is applied to the turbine. The maximum torque multiplication is delivered when the impeller has reached its highest velocity, and the turbine is standing still or at **stall**. This condition is shown in **Figure 21-15**.

Figure 21-15. The turbine is at stall and the stator is not turning at this time. The roller clutch prevents the stator from turning in a counterclockwise direction. (General Motors)

Cruising Speed

As the turbine begins to turn, torque multiplication tapers off. When turbine speed increases to about 90% of impeller speed, the fluid leaving the trailing edges of the turbine will change its angle so that it begins to strike the rear face of the stator.

This change of angle is caused by the fact that even though the fluid is being thrown toward the stator, the turbine is moving by the stator faster than the fluid is moving toward the stator. As the turbine speed surpasses the fluid speed, the fluid strikes the back of the stator blades, causing the stator overrunning clutch to unlock and freewheel with the turbine. Since there is no torque multiplication, the converter performs much like a fluid coupling. This condition is known as the **coupling point**, **Figure 21-16**.

Figure 21-16. Torque converter "coupling" point. At this time, the converter is acting as a fluid coupling. The turbine and pump are turning at approximately the same speed. The stator has become neutral (inactive). (General Motors)

Torque Multiplication Curve

The ratio between **torque multiplication** with the turbine at stall and the coupling point is illustrated in **Figure 21-17**. Notice how torque multiplication drops off as turbine speed increases. The torque converter provides a variable drive ratio as opposed to the manual transmission's three or four fixed ratios. This provides a smooth flow of power that automatically adjusts to varying load conditions within the limit of the unit.

Figure 21-17. A torque curve chart. (Ford)

Lockup Torque Converters

The normal converter allows some slippage, even at cruising speeds. This is due to the fact that the only connection between the pump and turbine is the transmission fluid. To prevent this slippage and improve fuel economy, most modern converters are equipped with a **lockup clutch** or **torque converter clutch**. The entire assembly is called a **lockup torque converter**.

Lockup Torque Converter Operation

Before lockup, the turbine and impeller are mechanically free of each other and drive is through the transmission fluid. There is no contact between the turbine and clutch friction surface. The lockup converter operates like a conventional torque converter. See **Figure 21-18A**.

When lockup conditions are present, fluid will move through a passage in the transmission input shaft. It will flow into the space between the turbine and clutch apply piston. The clutch apply piston will engage the clutch friction surface to lock the converter housing and turbine together. This action is shown in **Figure 21-18B**.

When the lockup clutch is activated, the engine and transmission input shaft are mechanically locked together. Slippage is reduced to zero and the vehicle gets better mileage. The elimination of slippage between the converter blades and the fluid also eliminates the major source of transmission fluid heating, extending fluid life.

Lockup Converter Control System

The lockup clutch is never applied until the vehicle is at a certain speed, or the transmission is in at least second gear. If the converter was locked at idle, it would stall the engine. To allow converter lockup, most computer control systems are designed so that the transmission must be in third or fourth gear, with vehicle speed above 35 to 40 mph (56-64 kmh) and

Figure 21-18 A—Lock-up clutch in the released position. Note the clearance between the clutch friction surface and converter housing. B—Clutch is in the applied position. A mechanical connection between the pump housing and turbine now exists. (LUK Automotive Systems)

without an excessive engine load (such as from steep hills or heavy acceleration). There are several lockup control systems, depending on the vehicle manufacturer. This will be discussed in more detail under hydraulic control systems.

Planetary Gearsets

Additional torque multiplication must be obtained for acceptable vehicle operation. Gears are needed to accomplish this. To accomplish this, the automatic transmission makes use of planetary gears.

A **planetary gearset** can be used to obtain reduction, overdrive, and direct drive gear ratios. The planetary gearset can also be used to reverse direction. The planetary gearset is compact and is in constant mesh. **Figure 21-19** illustrates a typical planetary gearset.

The planetary gearset is so named because of its resemblance to the solar system. The central gear is the **sun gear**. Circling around the sun gear on their own shafts are the **planet gears** or pinions. The planet gears are held in a **planet**

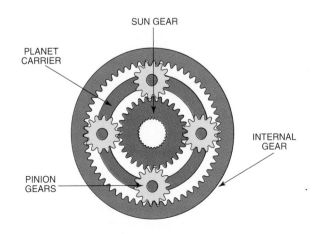

Figure 21-19. A typical planetary gearset. (General Motors)

carrier, but can rotate on their shafts. The outer gear is called the internal gear or *ring gear*. All planetary gearsets use this basic arrangement.

Torque Increase

If the ring gear is held and power is applied to the sun gear, the planet gears are forced to turn and walk around the internal gear. This action causes the pinion carrier to revolve at a lower speed than the sun gear. Speed reduction and torque increase are large, **Figure 21-20**.

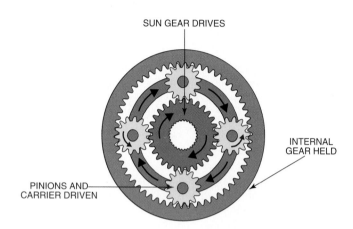

Figure 21-20. A planetary gearset in a large torque increase. (General Motors)

If the sun gear is held and the ring gear is driven, the planet gears will walk around the sun gear. This causes the pinion carrier to move slower than the internal gear. Torque will increase, however, the speed decrease is small. See **Figure 21-21**.

Figure 21-21. A planetary gearset in a small torque increase. (General Motors)

Direct Drive

When any two members of the planetary gearset are locked together, planetary action is stopped. Under these conditions, the gearset will revolve as a solid unit, providing direct (1:1) drive with no change in torque or speed, **Figure 21-22**.

Figure 21-22. A planetary gearset in direct drive. (General Motors)

Overdrive

If the ring gear is held, and the planet carrier is driven, the planet gears must walk around inside the ring gear. This causes the sun gear to move faster than the planet carrier. Speed will increase and torque will decrease. See **Figure 21-23**.

Reverse

By holding the planet carrier and driving the sun gear, the planet gears are forced to rotate about their pins. This causes them to drive the internal gear in a reverse direction at a reduced speed, **Figure 21-24**.

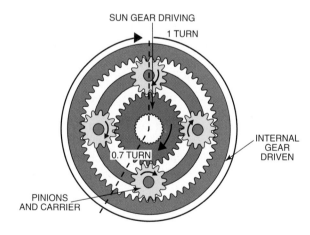

Figure 21-23. Relationship between rpm of the pinion carrier and internal gear. Every time transmission output shaft turns the pinion carrier .7 of a turn, the internal gear is forced to rotate a full turn. This causes the overdrive output shaft to revolve faster than the transmission output shaft. (General Motors)

Planetary Gearsets in Automatic Transmissions

The action of the three- and four-speed transmission gearsets in **Figures 21-25** and **21-26** illustrate general gearset operation.

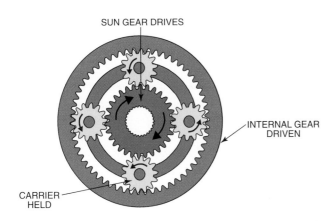

Figure 21-24. A planetary gearset in reverse. (General Motors)

Simpson Geartrain

The **Simpson geartrain** was used on three-speed transmission for many years. The Simpson geartrain is composed of two planetary gearsets. The sun gear of each set is connected together to form what is called a common sun gear. The action of the Simpson geartrain is shown in **Figure 21-25**. Note that the input shaft is turning, but none of the internal clutches have been applied (clutches and bands will be explained in the next section) when the transmission is in neutral. Power cannot flow through the planetary gears.

In first gear, the rear clutch is applied, which sends power through the front ring gear. The rotation of the ring gear rotates the front planet gears, driving the sun gear, but in the reverse direction. The sun gear drives the rear planetary gearset and the rear ring gear. The rear planet carrier is held by an overrunning clutch, similar in operation to the one used in the torque converter stator. The action of the rear planet gears reverses the rotation of the power flow. This reversal of power flow rotates the output shaft in the same direction as engine rotation. The combined action of the two planetary gearsets gives a reduction of about 2.5:1.

In second gear, a band is applied to stop the sun gear by stopping the rotation of the sun gear shell. With the sun gear stopped, power from the front ring gear turns the planetary gears and carrier around the stopped sun gear. Since the front planet carrier is splined to the output shaft, it is carried around in the same direction as engine rotation with a gear reduction of about 1.5:1. Note that the rear planet and ring gears are turning, but have no effect on power transfer.

CLUTCHES AND THE BAND ARE RELEASED
NEUTRAL

THE INTERMEDIATE BAND IS APPLIED. THE REVERSE AND HIGH CLUTCH DRUM, THE INPUT SHELL, AND THE SUN GEAR ARE HELD STATIONARY.

THE FORWARD CLUTCH IS APPLIED. THE FRONT PLANETARY UNIT RING GEAR IS LOCKED TO THE INPUT SHAFT.
SECOND GEAR

BOTH THE FORWARD AND THE REVERSE AND HIGH CLUTCH ARE APPLIED. ALL PLANETARY GEAR MEMBERS ARE LOCKED TO EACH OTHER AND ARE LOCKED TO THE OUTPUT SHAFT.
HIGH GEAR

THE FORWARD CLUTCH IS APPLIED. THE FRONT PLANETARY UNIT RING GEAR IS LOCKED TO THE INPUT SHAFT.

THE LOW AND REVERSE CLUTCH (LOW RANGE) OR THE ONE-WAY CLUTCH (D1 RANGE) IS HOLDING THE REVERSE UNIT PLANET CARRIER STATIONARY.
FIRST GEAR

GEAR RATIOS		
FIRST 2.46:1		
	SECOND 1.46:1	
		HIGH 1.00:1
		REVERSE 2.17:1

THE REVERSE AND HIGH CLUTCH IS APPLIED. THE INPUT SHAFT IS LOCKED TO THE REVERSE AND HIGH CLUTCH DRUM, THE INPUT SHELL, AND THE SUN GEAR.

THE LOW AND REVERSE CLUTCH IS APPLIED. THE REVERSE UNIT PLANET CARRIER IS HELD STATIONARY.
REVERSE

Figure 21-25. Transmission action during the various speed ranges in a three-speed automatic transmission. (Ford)

In high gear, the band is released and the front clutch is applied. This causes the sun gear and front ring gear to be locked together, becoming a solid unit driving at a ratio of 1:1. Again, the rear planet gears and ring gears are turning, but have no effect on power transfer.

In reverse, the front clutch is applied, and the sun gear is turned by engine power. The rear planet carrier is held stationary by a band or clutch. The planet gears reverse the rotation of the ring gear as well as producing a reduction of about 2:1. In reverse, the front ring gear and planet gears turn, but have no effect on power transfer.

Compound Planetary Gearset

Figure 21-26 shows the start of a planetary gearset as used in a four-speed transmission. Notice that the primary sun gear and shaft are one piece and are splined to the converter turbine. The short planet gears are engaged with the sun gear. The long planet gears will engage with the reverse sun gear. The single ring gear engages the long planet gears. This type of planetary gear arrangement is known as a **compound planetary gearset**, sometimes called a *Ravigneaux gearset*. The compound planetary gearset was used for many years in two- and three-speed transmissions.

Figure 21-26. A compound planetary gearset from a four-speed automatic transmission. Power from the engine is transmitted to the input shaft by the torque converter clutch. All forward gears and reverse can be attained by this one gearset. (Subaru)

Holding Members

To operate the planetary gearsets, **holding members** are needed. The holding members are used to either direct engine power through one of the members of the planetary gearset, or to lock the member to the transmission case. Modern three- and four-speed automatics need at least two holding members applied in every gear. The different types of holding members are discussed in the following sections.

Bands

A **band** is a flexible steel device that encircles a rotating part, usually a clutch drum. One end of the band is secured to the case and may have an adjuster. The other end is fastened

to a hydraulic piston or servo. The band face is covered with a friction lining. When the band is tightened, it will stop the part. A band always stops the rotation of a part by locking it to the transmission case. Bands can be either single wrap, **Figure 21-27**, or double wrap, **Figure 21-28**. The double wrap holds tighter, but the single wrap can be applied and released more smoothly and quickly.

Figure 21-27. A "single-wrap" band with linkage parts. (Dodge)

Figure 21-28. A "double-wrap" band and linkage parts. (Dodge)

Band Servos

A hydraulic piston called a **servo** is used to apply the band. It consists of a cylinder in which a piston is placed. An opening is provided at one end to admit fluid. The piston is held in the released position by spring pressure. Servos may be installed in the case or inside the transmission or transaxle itself.

When pressurized fluid enters the cylinder, the piston is forced forward, either actuating the band through direct contact or by actuating linkage. When the fluid pressure is reduced, the spring will return the piston and the band will release.

Some servos have openings on both sides of the piston. In this case, fluid can be used to assist in servo release. These servos are said to have an **apply side** and a **release side**. Other servos have two or more internal pistons. **Figure 21-29** shows a cross-section of a servo. This unit acts directly on the band through a piston rod or stem.

Figure 21-29. Cutaway of a direct acting servo. Oil pressure may be applied to either side of the piston, causing it to move in the desired direction. (Ford)

The servo in **Figure 21-29** is of the direct acting type. Note the band adjusting screw and how the piston may be applied and released by fluid pressure. **Figure 21-30** shows a servo operated through an actuating lever. This type is used to save space and provide more leverage on the band.

Figure 21-30. Cutaway of a lever-type band servo. Note that the servo movement is transmitted through a lever. The pivot point is positioned to cause the lever to increase the force of the apply piston.

Multiple Disc Clutch

Figure 21-31 shows a **multiple disc clutch** or **clutch pack**. The **clutch hub** is splined to the primary sun gear shaft. A stack of **clutch discs** (the number varies) is arranged in a **drum**. One set of discs is splined to the clutch hub; the other set is splined to the clutch drum. The internal splined and external splined discs alternate in the drum. The clutch pack is usually used to drive moving parts. However, a clutch pack is used in some transmissions to lock parts to the case in a manner similar to a band. See **Figure 21-32**.

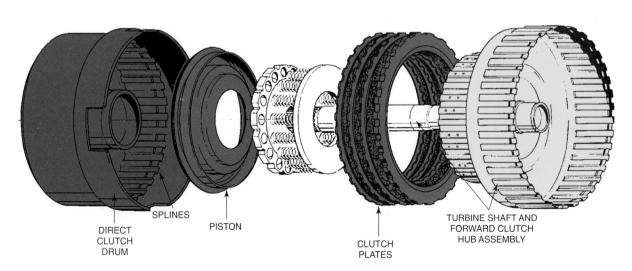

Figure 21-31. A multiple disc clutch (direct type) which is splined (connected with grooves or slots) to the clutch drum. (General Motors)

REACTION
CARRIER ASSEMBLY

OIL DEFLECTOR

LOW AND REVERSE
CLUTCH PLATES
ASSEMBLY

LOW AND REVERSE CLUTCH
SELECTIVE PLATE

LOW AND REVERSE
WAVED PLATE

THRUST BEARING

TRANSMISSION
CASE

INTERNAL REACTION
GEAR SUPPORT

INTERNAL
REACTION GEAR

REACTION
GEAR BEARING

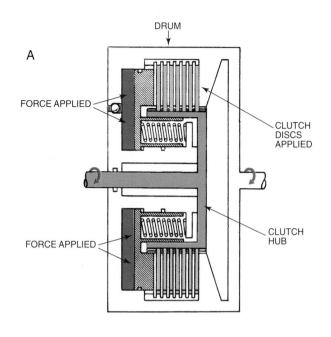

A

DRUM

FORCE APPLIED

FORCE APPLIED

CLUTCH
DISCS
APPLIED

CLUTCH
HUB

PLATE TAB

SPLINE

LOW AND REVERSE
CLUTCH PLATE

TRANSMISSION
CASE

Figure 21-32. A clutch pack can lock certain parts to the transmission case when applied much like a band does. Note how the clutch plate tabs fit into the splines cast into the case. (Chevrolet)

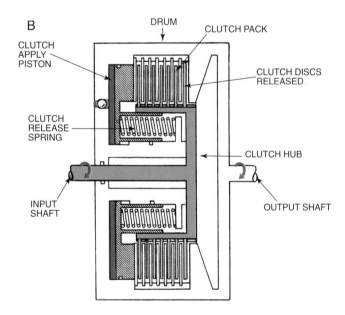

B

DRUM   CLUTCH PACK

CLUTCH
APPLY
PISTON

CLUTCH DISCS
RELEASED

CLUTCH
RELEASE
SPRING

CLUTCH HUB

INPUT
SHAFT

OUTPUT SHAFT

Figure 21-33. A—Multiple disc clutch schematic. Oil pressure is now acting against the clutch apply piston. The piston overcomes spring pressure and squeezes the clutch discs and plates together. As some discs are attached to the drum output shaft assembly and others to the hub (in an alternating arrangement), this squeezing action locks the hub and drum together. The hub now turns the output shaft. B—In this illustration, the hydraulic pressure is not acting on the clutch apply piston. With no oil pressure, the clutch release springs separate the clutch discs. The clutch hub turns but cannot drive the output shaft-drum assembly. (General Motors)

A *clutch apply piston* in the clutch drum squeezes the plates together when fluid pressure is applied to the piston. When the clutch piston is applied, the discs are pressed together to lock the clutch hub and drum together, **Figure 21-33A.** The clutch hub splined to the input shaft drum is part of the output shaft. With the clutch applied, both shafts are locked together and revolve as a solid unit. A heavy spring releases the discs when fluid pressure drops. See **Figure 21-33B.** Study the four-speed transmission in **Figure 21-34.** Note the number and layout of clutch packs.

Figure 21-34. A cross-sectional view of a lock-up torque converter and clutch pack members mounted on a four-speed automatic transaxle. (Honda)

Overrunning Clutches

Overrunning clutches, sometimes called *one-way clutches*, have the ability to lock when they are rotated in one direction and unlock when rotated in the other direction. The two types of overrunning clutches are the roller clutch and the sprag clutch. They are explained in the following sections.

Roller Clutch

The *roller clutch*, **Figure 21-35**, consists of three parts: an inner hub with tapered cams on the outside surface, a series of hardened steel rollers (one per cam surface), and an outer ring or race. The rollers are held in position by a steel cage. Each roller has a return spring to keep it from jamming in the released position.

Note in **Figure 21-35A** that the outer race is attempting to turn counterclockwise. This forces the rollers up the cam surfaces until they are wedged tightly against the outer race. The outer race will then be held stationary. When the race attempts to turn in the clockwise direction, **Figure 21-35B**, the rollers disengage and return to their low positions on the cams. The outer race is now free to turn. Therefore, the roller clutch becomes a holding member if it is turned in the counterclockwise direction, but freewheels if turned in the clockwise direction.

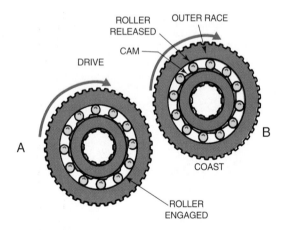

Figure 21-35. Roller clutch action. A—As the hub is being driven by the transmission output shaft, the rollers have traveled up the cams and seized the outer race thus driving it. B—The accelerator has been released and the inner hub has slowed down. This causes the clutch rollers to travel back down the cams and release the outer race, allowing it to freewheel or overrun. (Chevrolet)

Sprag Clutch

Sprag clutches are occasionally used, but they have mostly been replaced by the more durable roller clutch. Instead of using round rollers that walk up a tapered step to lock up the clutch, the sprag clutch uses a flat unit with curved edges. When the outer race is turned one way, the sprags tip and present their narrow diameter. This allows the outer race to turn.

When the race attempts to rotate in the opposite direction, the sprags tip the other way and present the long diameter. This causes them to jam between the two races, locking them together and preventing rotation. See **Figure 21-36**.

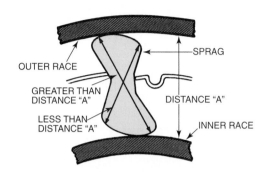

Figure 21-36. Cross-section view showing sprag clutch construction. (Cadillac)

Hydraulic Control System

The hydraulic control system dictates the operation of the other parts of the transmission. While an entire book could be dedicated to the study of the principles of fluid power or hydraulics, we will confine ourselves to saying that:

- Unlike air, liquids cannot be compressed.
- Since liquids cannot be compressed, they are an excellent way to transfer power.
- This hydraulic power can be used to operate holding members.
- All transmission operations are controlled with, or through, hydraulic power.

The following sections will explain how hydraulic pressure is developed and used in the automatic transmission and transaxle. The section begins with an outline of the major hydraulic system components common to all transmissions and transaxles.

Fluid Pump

Pressure is developed by a transmission *fluid pump*, sometimes called an oil pump. The pump draws fluid from the transmission *fluid pan* and creates *hydraulic pressure*, which is then directed to other parts of the transmission to fill the converter, operate the holding members, and control shifting. The pump is driven by the engine, usually through driving lugs on the rear of the converter. Therefore, whenever the engine is running, the pump is producing power to operate the rest of the hydraulic system.

Several types of fluid pumps have been used in automatic transmissions. One is the variable output, or *vane pump*. Output is altered by moving the outer vane cylinder, **Figure 21-37**. Another is the *rotor pump*, **Figure 21-38**. Another widely used pump is the *internal-external gear pump*. Look at **Figure 21-39**.

ILL.
NO.   DESCRIPTION

ILL. NO.	DESCRIPTION
8	Screw, Auxiliary Valve Body Cover/Auxiliary Valve Body
41	Screw, Auxiliary Valve Body to Case Cover
46	Screw, Aux. Valve Body Cover/Valve Body
21	Control Valve & Fluid Pump Assembly
302	Plug, Bore Line Boost Valve
303	Valve, Line Boost
304	Pin, Valve & Spring Retaining
305	Pin, Coiled Spring Line Boost Plug
306	Pin, Throttle Valve Bushing
307	Sleeve, Spring Retaining
308	Valve, Shift T.V.
309	Spring, Shift T.V.
310	Plug, Valve Bore
311	Ball, Pressure Relief
312	Spring, Pressure Relief
313	Spring, 1-2 Accumulator
314	Bushing, 1-2 Accumulator
315	Valve, 1-2 Accumulator
316	Valve, 2-3 Shift
317	Valve, 2-3 Throttle
318	Spring, 2-3 Throttle Valve
319	Bushing, 2-3 Throttle Valve
320	Valve, 1-2 Shift
321	Valve, 1-2 Throttle
322	Spring, 1-2 Throttle Valve
323	Bushing, 1-2 Throttle Valve
324	Ball, Lo Blow Off
325	Spring & Plug Assembly, Lo Blow Off
326	Plug, Lo Blow Off Valve
328	Retainer, Valve Body Pipe
330	Cover, Auxiliary Valve Body
331	Gasket, Auxiliary Valve Body Cover
332	Valve, Conv. Cl. Control
333	Solenoid Assembly
334	Screw, Solenoid
335	Switch, Pressure — 3rd Cl.

ILL. NO.	DESCRIPTION
337	Seal, O-Ring (Solenoid)
338	Switch, Gov. Pressure — 2nd Cl.
339	Harness, Solenoid Wire
343	Body, Auxiliary Valve
344	Sleeve, Auxiliary Valve Body
345	Pin, Slide Pivot
346	Ring, Fluid Seal (Slide to Cover)
347	Seal, O-Ring (Pump Slide)
348	Slide, Pump
349	Support, Pump Slide Seal
350	Seal, Pump Slide
351	Ring, Pump Vane
352	Vane Pump
353	Rotor, Fluid Pump
354	Bearing Assembly, Pump Shaft & Seal
355	Spring, 3-2
356	Valve, 3-2 Regulating Control
357	Filter, Auxiliary Valve Body
358	Plug, Pump Spring Retaining
359	Spring, Pump Priming
360	Spring, T.V. & Reverse Boost Valve
361	Valve, T.V. Boost
362	Bushing, T.V. & Reverse Boost Valve
363	Valve, Reverse Boost
364	Spring, Pressure Regulator
365	Valve, Pressure Regulator
366	Bushing, T.V. Plunger
367	Plunger, Throttle Valve
368	Spring, Throttle Valve
369	Valve, Throttle
370	Pipe, Valve Body
371	Pin, T.V. & Reverse Boost Bushing
372	Plug, Bore (Pressure Regulator)
373	Retainer, Bore Plug Pressure Regulator
375	Plug, Valve Bore Isolator
376	Ring, Valve Retaining
377	Retainer, Throttle Valve
380	Valve, Orifice Control
381	Spring, Orifice Control Valve
382	Plug, Valve Bore

Figure 21-37. Exploded view of a vane-type oil pump and the many related parts as used by one manufacturer. (Chevrolet)

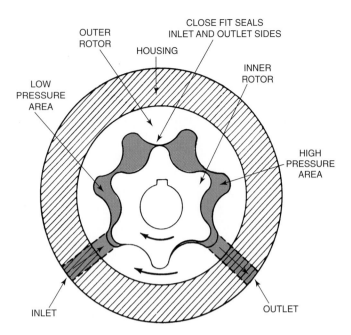

Figure 21-38. A rotor style oil pump. Note that the arrangement of gears resembles a gear oil pump.

Figure 21-39. A—Note the action in a transmission internal-external gear oil pump. B—Exploded view of the gear-type oil pump. (Toyota)

Control Valves

The flow of hydraulic pressure is controlled by *spool valves*. Spool valves are used to perform different functions, such as filling the torque converter and operating the transmission as needed. The major spool valves used in all automatic transmissions are discussed in the following sections.

Many of the spool valves and other components are installed in a *valve body* attached to the bottom of the transmission case. Some transmissions and transaxles have two or more valve bodies. Many transaxles have the valve body mounted on the side of the case to save space.

Main Pressure Regulator

The *main pressure regulator* monitors the pump output to control the system hydraulic pressure. When pressure exceeds the amount required, the valve opens and bypasses fluid back to the sump. This produces an overall system pressure, usually called *line pressure*.

The main pressure regulator valve setting is controlled by spring tension on the valve. See **Figure 21-40**. To increase line pressure during heavy acceleration or in reverse, pressure from other parts of the hydraulic system is used to assist the pressure regulator spring. Some transmissions have a separate regulator valve to control torque converter pressure.

Figure 21-40. A gear oil pump, pressure regulator, and hydraulic circuit. These vary by manufacturer. (General Motors)

Manual Gear Selection

The transmission may be placed in any desired gear by moving a gearshift lever, located on the steering column or console. This moves the linkage connected to the manual valve in the transmission. The shift indicator shows the operator which gear has been selected. See **Figure 21-41**. A console floor shift mechanism is shown in **Figure 21-42**. Manual gear selection is often use to test automatic transmissions for proper operation.

Figure 21-41. A steering column mounted gear shift cable arrangement and its path to the transmission. (Dodge)

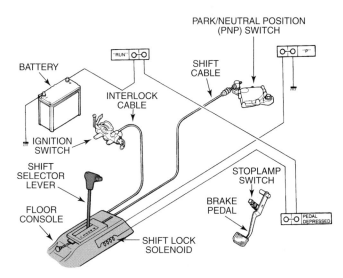

Figure 21-42. A console (floor) gearshift linkage arrangement. This system uses a brake transaxle shift interlock (BTSI) to prevent the transmission from being placed into gear without depressing the brake pedal. (Geo)

Simple Hydraulic System

The simple hydraulic circuit shown in **Figure 21-43** is but one part of the overall hydraulic system. Modern hydraulic systems are much more complex, but operate from the same basic principles shown here. Other valves are used to cushion shifts, provide passing gear, and control the lockup torque converter. The principles shown here apply to all automatic transmissions.

Manual Valve

The *manual valve* is operated by the driver to engage the transmission/transaxle in park, reverse, neutral, drive, second, or low, and other available gears, **Figure 21-43**. The manual valve linkage can be a series of rods and links or a cable.

The manual valve will move to the selected drive position. From the manual valve, the line pressure will go to the low band servo. The fluid pressure will apply the servo and tighten the band. When the vehicle is accelerated, torque will be imparted and the vehicle will move forward in the low gear. Note that the servo applies the band by overcoming a return spring on the band side of the servo.

Shift Valve

To enable the transmission to change gears, another line must be added that will run from the main line to a *shift valve*. The shift valves redirect hydraulic pressure to the transmission or transaxle holding members to obtain different gears in drive range. The movement of one shift valve will cause one up or down shift between two different gears. The fluid will leave the shift valve and branch out. One line will go to the high range clutch unit, another to the low range servo. The shift valves are moved by the throttle and governor valves.

Throttle Valve

The *throttle valve* tries to move the shift valve to the downshift position. The throttle valve is controlled by linkage from the engine throttle plates or by a vacuum modulator operated by engine manifold vacuum. The throttle valve is connected to the foot throttle through linkage or a cable. The throttle valve linkage is often referred to as the throttle valve rod or cable, or just *TV linkage*.

When the throttle is depressed, the throttle valve is moved, transmitting fluid pressure to the shift valve. The amount of pressure depends on the distance the throttle is moved. With either system, the more the throttle is depressed, the higher the throttle pressure.

Governor Valve

The *governor valve* tries to move the shift valve to the upshifted (higher gear) position. Some governor valves are mounted directly on the output shaft. Other governors are installed in the case and driven by the output shaft through gears. The higher the shaft speed, the higher the governor pressure.

As the vehicle accelerates, the governor unit will spin faster and faster. At a predetermined speed, the governor valve will open and fluid pressure will travel to the shift valve. See **Figure 21-44A**. When governor pressure reaches a

Figure 21-43. A manual control valve. This is one valve of the many which are used in the valve body of the modern automatic transmission. (Chrysler)

Figure 21-44. A—Schematic of governor valve in closed position. Note that the main line oil pressure cannot pass the governor valve. B—A schematic of a governor valve in the open position. Note that the main line oil pressure is now passing through the valve. (GMC)

certain level, the tension of the shift valve spring will be overcome and the shift valve will move to the left. **Figure 21-44B** shows the governor pressure building up against the shift valve. Note the different types of governors in **Figure 21-45**.

Detent Valve

The *detent valve* is used to achieve a forced downshift, sometimes called the detent or passing gear. The detent valve may be operated by mechanical linkage or by an electric solenoid. The detent linkage will be the same as the TV linkage, while the solenoid will be operated by a switch on the accelerator linkage.

The detent valve is used to force the transmission to downshift to the next lower gear. It supplies extra pressure to the shift valves to overcome governor pressure and move the shift valve to the downshifted position. The transmission detent will feel the same as a downshift when the vehicle is coasting to a stop.

Lockup Torque Converter Control Valve

The *lockup torque converter control valve* is used to ensure that the lockup converter clutch applies at cruising speeds and releases when the vehicle comes to a stop. The hydraulic control system may have a valve and an electric solenoid. The solenoid is computer-controlled, while the valve is operated by the throttle and governor pressures. On late model vehicles, the converter lockup clutch will apply without fluid pressure or control from the hydraulic system.

Transmission and Transaxle Shifting

Now let's put these circuits together. When the manual valve is opened, fluid pressure actuates the low band servo. The vehicle then moves forward in the low range. Fluid pressure also travels to the shift valve and the governor, **Figure 21-46**. When the vehicle reaches a predetermined road speed, the governor will have opened enough to allow fluid pressure to flow to the shift valve and force it open. When the shift valve opens, fluid pressure flows to the clutch piston and band servo.

Figure 21-45. Various transmission governors used by different manufacturers. A—Governor assembly mounted on the transmission output shaft. B—Explolded view of an output shaft driven governor. This is the same unit shown in A. C—Cross-sectional view of a gear driven governor. D—Exploded view of a gear driven governor assembly with a speed sensor. (General Motors & Dodge)

Figure 21-46. Schematic of transmission fluid flow in low range. The manual valve is open and pressure is applied to the low band servo, governor, and shifter valve. When the governor is closed, no pressure is applied to the open shifter valve. When the shifter valve closes, no pressure is applied to the low band servo or clutch.

Figure 21-47. Schematic of transmission fluid flow in high range. Vehicle speed has opened the governor. Governor pressure opens the shifter valve, sending line pressure to both servo pistons and to the clutch. Servo releases and clutch applies. The transmission is now in high range.

As the pressure builds up in the clutch, a corresponding pressure builds up in the servo. The pressure from the shift valve is equal to the pressure on the other side of the servo. With the pressure equal on both sides of the servo piston, the return spring can release the band.

As the servo piston moves to the left, the pressure in the clutch unit will build up rapidly, eventually locking the clutch unit. The transmission is now in high range and will remain there until vehicle speed falls below the shift point. When this happens, governor pressure is lost, the clutch disengages and manual valve pressure reapplies the low band servo. All this is done automatically. **Figure 21-47** shows the circuit in high gear.

Governor Operation

As the vehicle moves forward in low gear, the output shaft spins a governor unit. Centrifugal force throws the governor weight outward, opening the governor valve. Fluid pressure channeled to the governor unit flows to the shift valve, **Figure 21-48**. When the vehicle is not moving, the governor weight is in and fluid pressure is stopped at the governor.

Varying the Shift Point

In the simple systems shown in **Figures 21-46** and **21-47**, the point at which the transmission shifts into high and downshifts into low are controlled by the governor. These points are always constant. In a real transmission, however, the shift points must vary according to load requirements. For rapid acceleration, the transmission should stay in the low range for a longer period. When attempting to pass at low speeds just above the downshift point, it is desirable to have the downshift occur when needed.

Figure 21-48 Governor pressure acting on shifter valve. Governor weight has been thrown out by centrifugal force. The governor valve is open and main line pressure is passing through the governor to the shifter valve.

Using Throttle Pressure to Vary the Shift Point

To delay the upshift, throttle pressure opposes governor pressure on the other side of the shift valve. Throttle pressure varies with throttle opening. The more the accelerator pedal is depressed, the more throttle pressure is sent to the shift valve.

A typical shift valve is shown in **Figure 21-49**. Note that governor pressure is available on one side of the shift valve. Governor pressure is attempting to move the valve to the upshifted position. On the other side of the valve, throttle pressure tries to keep the shift valve in the downshifted position. The interaction of governor pressure and throttle pressure causes the shift valve to change gears at a speed that is best suited to the load on the engine.

Throttle Valve

Pressure enters the valve at (A), **Figure 21-50**. It travels around the small spool section and exits through (B). It is bypassed to chamber (C) at the spool end (D). The pressure pushes on the shifter valve regulator plug and on the spool at (D). Spring pressure (E) is controlled by the TV cable. When the throttle opening is small, spring pressure (E) is light. Fluid pressure at (D) forces the spool valve to the right against the light spring pressure. As the spool valve moves to the right, it starts to block opening (A). As the size of opening (A) is reduced, the fluid pressure entering the valve is also reduced.

Figure 21-50. Throttle valve operation. Oil pressure balances spring pressure by moving the spool valve until opening "A" admits the proper pressure. A throttle valve (TV) rod or cable adjusts the spring pressure.

Figure 21-49. Typical shift valve arrangement. Throttle pressure opposes governor pressure, causing the valve to change gears at a speed best suited to engine load.

If the spring is pushing to the left with a force of 15 lbs (66.75 N), the spool will be forced to the right until entrance (A) is small enough to admit enough fluid to overcome spring pressure. The valve will then be balanced. If spring pressure is increased, it will force the spool to the left, increasing opening (A) and fluid pressure will build up in (C). This will force the

spool to the right until opening (A) is again closed far enough to balance fluid pressure with spring pressure.

Vacuum Modulator

Many older vehicles use a **_vacuum modulator_** in place of the TV rod or cable. Some newer transmissions use a vacuum modulator as well as a TV cable. The modulator utilizes engine vacuum, a very reliable indicator of engine loading. The modulator provides an accurate means of controlling the throttle valve. The throttle valve is also called the modulator valve.

The vacuum modulator consists of a container separated into two areas by a flexible diaphragm. A spring forces the diaphragm rod to apply pressure to the throttle valve to increase TV pressure. The modulator is constantly altering throttle valve pressure in accordance with engine vacuum, **Figure 21-51A**. In operation, engine vacuum causes the diaphragm to move away (against spring pressure) from the throttle valve, lowering the pressure. As engine loading varies, vacuum fluctuates.

An altitude sensitive modulator is illustrated in **Figure 21-51B**. It incorporates an evacuated (air removed) bellows. The collapsing bellows tends to force the diaphragm toward the throttle valve. At sea level, atmospheric pressure is high,

Figure 21-51. A—A vacuum modulator can control the throttle valve by varying pressure on the push rod. B—Altitude sensitive modulator. Note the evacuated bellows. (Ford)

adding to diaphragm pressure and raising TV pressure. As altitude increases, atmospheric pressure decreases, resulting in a decrease in TV pressure. The altitude compensating bellows is capable of providing a more uniform shift feel regardless of elevation.

Detent Valve

When the driver depresses the accelerator to the floor, the kickdown or detent valve is moved by either the linkage or solenoid and opens an additional passage to the shift valves. If governor pressure is low enough, the shift valve will be moved to the downshifted position. If the vehicle is moving too fast, the governor pressure will be too high to overcome and the transmission will stay in high. See **Figure 21-52**. To prevent band and clutch slippage, another passage from the detent valve opens to assist the main pressure regulator in raising line pressure.

Additional Shift Valves

Three- and four-speed automatic transmissions and transaxles require more shift valves. A two-speed unit requires one shift valve, a three-speed automatic needs two shift

Figure 21-52. A manual detent downshift valve and related parts. (Geo & Dodge)

valves, and a four-speed unit needs three shift valves. All shift valves operate in the same manner. The higher gear shift valves have stronger springs and different sized valve areas. Therefore, the governor must be turning faster (higher road speed) to cause the valve to move to the upshifted position.

Lockup Converter Control Valves

The converter control valve can be thought of as another shift valve. Governor and throttle valve pressures operate on the valve to move it to the applied and released positions as

needed. The major difference is that this valve usually receives its apply side pressure from one of the shift valves when it moves to the upshifted position. This ensures that the converter clutch will not be applied until the transmission/transaxle is out of first or second gear, depending on the design. See **Figure 21-53**.

On other designs, the converter clutch is operated by a solenoid, **Figure 21-54**. The solenoid may be controlled by an electric speed or gear relay or by an ECU. Some early systems use a vacuum switch that disengages the clutch when the engine vacuum drops. The transmission hydraulic system must still act on the lockup valve to make sure that the clutch is not applied at low speeds.

Figure 21-53. Exploded view of a lock-up torque converter control valve. Note the hydraulic fluid feed tube. (Chrysler Corp.)

Figure 21-54. A torque converter clutch (TCC) electric solenoid valve. This solenoid is operated by the electronic control unit (ECU). By locking the converter clutch, slippage is reduced between the two, increasing fuel economy. (Chevrolet)

Computer-Controlled Shifting

On many vehicles produced during the last few years, an electronic control unit is used to shift the transmission or transaxle and apply the converter clutch. The transmission still has shift valves, however, they are operated by solenoids controlled by the ECU. There is no TV linkage or governor valve.

The transmission hydraulic system, including the shift pattern, converter lockup, and sometimes the line pressure is controlled by the ECU. A computer-controlled transmission schematic is shown in **Figure 21-55**. The ECU used to control transmission operation is often incorporated with the engine ECU and is sometimes referred to as a powertrain control module.

Accumulators

Almost every transmission or transaxle has at least one *accumulator* to cushion the servo or piston apply. **Figure 21-56** illustrates one type. The accumulator reduces the initial apply pressure by bleeding off some of the fluid to the servo or clutch. Fluid entering the servo or clutch piston is also sent

Figure 21-56. Exploded view of an accumulator housing and internal parts from a four-speed automatic transmission. The accumulators help reduce the shock (harshness) when the transmission shifts. 1—Piston spring for 4th clutch accumulator. 2—3rd clutch accumulator piston spring. 3—Square cut seal. 4—4th clutch accumulator piston. 5—Snap ring. 6—Torque signal compensator valve. 7—3rd clutch accumulator piston. 8—4th clutch accumulator piston pin. 9—Torque signal compensator spring. 10—Square cut seal. 11—Direct oil gallery plug. 12—Accumulator housing. 13—Accumulator housing valve body bolt. 14—Accumulator housing valve body bolt. (Chevrolet)

Figure 21-55. One particular computer-controlled, automatic transaxle operation schematic. (Honda Motor Co.)

to the accumulator piston. The accumulator spring contains a spring that is gradually compressed by the entering fluid. The accumulator allows a soft initial band or clutch application that is immediately followed by additional heavy pressure for firm engagement.

Complete Control Circuit

Figure 21-57 shows the complete hydraulic system as used in a four-speed automatic transmission. Note the extra shift valves. The various hydraulic system circuits must be compact and every possible means used to avoid external tubes or other awkward fluid transfer arrangements. Many of the shafts and other units are drilled to carry fluid.

Trace each valve and circuit and compare its operation to the simple system we looked at earlier. Most of the control valves are housed in the valve body. An exploded view of just some of the many components of a control valve body is shown in **Figure 21-58**.

Figure 21-57. A complete hydraulic control circuit for a four-speed automatic transmission. This schematic shows transmission operation with the engine running and the transmission in park. Study all the circuits very carefully. (General Motors)

Figure 21-58. Exploded view of the accumulator end of an electronic control valve body for a four-speed automatic transmission. 1—Control body valve assembly. 2—Forward accumulator oil seal. 3—Forward accumulator piston. 4—Forward accumulator pin. 5—Forward spring. 6—Forward abuse valve. 7—Forward abuse valve spring. 8—Bore plug. 9—Coil spring pin. 10—Low overrun valve. 11—Low overrun valve spring. 12—Forward accumulator cover. 13—Bolt. 14—1–2 Shift valve spring. 15—1–2 Shift valve. 16—1–2 Shift solenoid. 17—2–3 Shift solenoid. 18—2–3 Shift valve. 19—2–3 Shuttle valve. 20—1–2 Accumulator valve spring. 21—1–2 Accumulator valve. 22—1–2 Accumulator valve sleeve. 23—Bore plug. 24—Actuator feed limit valve. 25—Actuator feed limit valve spring. 26—Bore plug. 27—Pressure control solenoid. 28—Pressure control solenoid retainer. 29—Retainer.

Transmission Case

The transmission case contains the internal shafts, gears, and holding members. It is also the mounting surface for the valve body, servos, pump, and linkage. Modern transmission cases are made of aluminum. Cases are vented to relieve internal pressure.

Transmission Lubrication

The transmission is lubricated by special fluid which circulates through the unit. *Automatic transmission fluid* or *ATF*, is composed of mineral oil combined with additional additives that assist in lubrication and keep the oil from breaking down. Most modern automatic transmissions and transaxles use *Dexron III/Mercon*. Dexron III replaces Dexron II, which had been in use for many years and is still available in some areas.

Some manufacturers, such as Honda, specify a different type of fluid. Type F fluid was used in Ford transmissions manufactured until the late 1970s. Do not use fluids marked with the letters AQ-ATF or Type A, Suffix A. These fluids are obsolete and are not suitable for modern vehicles. Dexron II should never be used in a transmission designed to use Dexron III/Mercon.

Fluid Filter

Another important part of the transmission is the *filter*, which keeps dirt and metal out of the other parts. The transmission filter contains a paper filtering element inside of a metal housing. Filter shapes can vary and a few filters contain bypass valves. The filter is always placed in the pump intake, or suction, so that it can filter the transmission fluid before it enters the hydraulic system. It is always installed in the bottom of the transmission, where it can pick up fluid from the pan.

Fluid Cooling

Transmission fluid is cooled by circulating it, via tubes, to a external transmission cooler installed in the outlet side tank of the radiator. These coolers were discussed in more detail in Chapter 11. The fluid gives up its heat to the radiator coolant. The fluid always comes directly from the torque converter, which is the hottest part of the transmission. On downflow radiators, the cooler is located in the bottom tank. Extra coolers are sometimes installed in front of the vehicle radiator. These coolers remove heat by direct contact with the air. See **Figure 21-59**.

Figure 21-59. One type of automatic transmission fluid cooler which is mounted in front of the radiator. This particular cooler setup is for a transmission that is used with a diesel engine. (Dodge)

Summary

The automatic transmission eliminates the clutch pedal and manual gearshifting. After the driver has selected the range, the transmission shifts itself up or down depending on road speed, throttle position, and engine load. The operation of the automatic transmission and automatic transaxle is similar. The difference is in the placement of component parts and power flow.

The automatic transmission/transaxle assembly consists of a torque converter, planetary gearsets, holding members, oil pumps, and a hydraulic control system. The fluid must be cooled, and some actions of the transmission are controlled by the operator to select certain speed ranges. The torque converter can multiply the engine torque, thereby giving a wide range of power. The amount of multiplication is dependent on converter design and position between stall and coupling point.

The transmission or transaxle has one or more planetary gearsets to produce reduction, direct drive, overdrive, and reverse. Holding members, called bands, multiple disc clutches, or overrunning clutches, are used to control the planetary gearsets. The clutches and bands are actuated by hydraulic pressure produced by an engine-driven fluid pump. The fluid pressure is directed and controlled by a series of valves. Hydraulic pressure is distributed by fluid passageways in the valve body, case, and shafts.

The automatic transmission shifts in response to speed and load conditions. Speed ranges such as drive, low, and reverse can be selected by the driver through mechanical linkage connected to a control valve in transmission. Fluid is

cooled by piping it to a cooler unit in one of the radiator tanks. Lubrication is provided by transmission fluid as it circulates through the unit.

Know These Terms

Automatic transmission
Automatic transaxle
Torque converter
Fluid coupling
Impeller
Turbine
Hydraulic coupling
Rotary flow
Vortex flow
Slippage
Stator
Stall
Coupling point
Torque multiplication
Lockup clutch
Torque converter clutch
Lockup torque converter
Planetary gearsets
Sun gear
Planet gears
Planet carrier
Ring gear
Simpson geartrain
Compound planetary
    gearset
Holding members
Band
Servo
Apply side
Release side
Multiple disc clutch
Clutch pack

Clutch hub
Clutch discs
Drum
Clutch apply piston
Overrunning clutch
One-way clutch
Roller clutch
Sprag clutch
Fluid pump
Fluid pan
Hydraulic pressure
Vane pump
Rotor pump
Internal-external gear pump
Spool valves
Valve body
Main pressure regulator
Line pressure
Manual valve
Shift valve
Throttle valve
TV linkage
Governor valve
Detent valve
Lockup torque converter
    control valve
Vacuum modulator
Accumulator
Automatic transmission fluid
    (ATF)
Dexron III/Mercon
Filter

Review Questions—Chapter 21

Do not write in this book. Write your answers on a separate sheet of paper.

1. Technician A says that the torque converter takes place of the conventional clutch used on standard transmissions. Technician B says that the torque converter is less efficient than the hydraulic coupling at high speeds. Who is right?
   (A) A only.
   (B) B only.
   (C) Both A & B.
   (D) Neither A nor B.

2. Which of the following torque converter parts is turned directly by the engine crankshaft?

   (A) Turbine.

   (B) Stator.

   (C) Impeller.

   (D) All of the above.

3. Which of the following parts is installed to turn a hydraulic coupling into a torque converter?

   (A) Turbine.

   (B) Stator.

   (C) Impeller.

   (D) All of the above.

4. When the torque converter lockup clutch is applied which of the following parts does not transmit power?

   (A) Transmission input shaft.

   (B) Turbine.

   (C) Impeller.

   (D) Converter housing.

5. The stator is unlocked when the turbine speed is _____.

   (A) zero

   (B) one-half of impeller speed

   (C) almost the same as impeller speed

   (D) Both A & B.

6. What mechanical device allows the stator to lock and unlock?

7. Stall speed is greatest when the turbine speed is _____.

   (A) zero

   (B) one-half of impeller speed

   (C) almost the same as impeller speed

   (D) Both A & B.

8. Converter coupling point is reached when the turbine speed is _____ .

   (A) zero

   (B) one-half of impeller speed

   (C) almost the same as impeller speed

   (D) Both A & B.

9. All of the following statements about planetary gearsets are true, EXCEPT:

   (A) the sun gear is always in the center of the gearset.

   (B) the planetary gears are always in mesh.

   (C) planetary gears take up more room than sliding gears.

   (D) a single planetary gearset can provide reduction and overdrive.

10. A planetary gearset can be used to _____ or _____ torque.

11. A planetary gearset can be used to _____ the direction of rotation.

12. If the sun gear and ring gear are locked together, what gear ratio is produced?

   (A) 1:1.

   (B) 1.5:1.

   (C) 2:1.

   (D) 3.5:1.

13. If the planet carrier is held stationary, and the sun gear drives, which part of the gearset is driven?

14. Technician A says that, when the planet carrier is held stationary, and the sun gear drives, the driven member will rotate in direct drive. Technician B says that a planetary gear member may be locked to the case by a band or a clutch. Who is right?

   (A) A only.

   (B) B only.

   (C) Both A & B.

   (D) Neither A nor B.

15. Bands are applied by _____ .

   (A) servos

   (B) accumulators

   (C) clutch apply pistons

   (D) overrunning clutches

16. A servo may have an _____ side and a _____ side.

17. The two commonly used types of one-way or overrunning clutches are the _____ and the _____ .

18. Technician A says that a multiple disc clutch may be applied by a servo. Technician B says that the multiple disc clutch plates have alternating inner and outer splines. Who is right?

   (A) A only.

   (B) B only.

   (C) Both A & B.

   (D) Neither A nor B.

19. The three types of pumps in common use in modern automatic transmissions and transaxles are the:

20. What does the shift valve control?

   (A) Band and clutch operation.

   (B) Gear changes.

   (C) Upshifts and downshifts.

   (D) All of the above.

21. Which valve controls overall system (line) pressure?

   (A) Manual valve.

   (B) Throttle valve.

   (C) Main pressure regulator.

   (D) Detent valve.

22. Which valve tries to move the shift valve to the upshifted position?

   (A) Throttle valve.

   (B) Governor valve.

   (C) Detent valve.

   (D) Manual valve.

23. What is the purpose of the accumulator?
    (A) Cushion shifts.
    (B) Cushion band and clutch apply.
    (C) Increase line pressure.
    (D) Both A & B.

24. Which valve tries to keep the shift valve in the down-shifted position?
    (A) Throttle valve.
    (B) Main pressure regulator.
    (C) Governor valve.
    (D) Manual valve.

25. Technician A says that the turning output shaft operates the throttle valve. Technician B says that the governor valve can be operated by TV linkage or a modulator. Who is right?
    (A) A only.
    (B) B only.
    (C) Both A & B.
    (D) Neither A nor B.

26. State three things that make the automatic transaxle different from the automatic transmission.

27. Transmission fluid goes to the fluid cooler directly from the _____ .
    (A) torque converter
    (B) sump
    (C) servos
    (D) valve body

28. The add-on transmission cooler transfers fluid heat directly to the _____ .
    (A) coolant in the radiator
    (B) coolant in the engine
    (C) outside air
    (D) cooler fluid in the pan

29. None of the following transmission fluids should be used in the latest model automatic transmissions and transaxles, EXCEPT:
    (A) AQ-ATF.
    (B) DEXRON III/MERCON.
    (C) Type A Suffix A.
    (D) Type F.

30. The CVT transmission uses a metal drive belt with _____ to provide the different gear ratios.
    (A) a Simpson gear train
    (B) compound planetary gearsets
    (C) variable diameter pulleys
    (D) sliding gears

22

Axles and Drives

After studying this chapter, you will be able to:
- List the basic parts of a rear-wheel driveline.
- Explain the function of each rear-wheel drive shaft part.
- List the basic parts of a front-wheel driveline.
- Explain the function of each front-wheel drive axle part.
- Describe various types of front- and rear-wheel drivelines.
- Explain the construction of the solid rear-wheel drive axle assemblies.
- Explain the construction of the independent rear-wheel drive axle assemblies.
- Describe the front drive axles used on four-wheel drives.
- Explain the operation of the ring and pinion.
- Explain the operation of the differential unit.
- Explain the operation of limited-slip differentials.
- Compare rear-wheel and front-wheel drive differential assemblies.

This chapter will cover the differential assemblies and drive axles used on rear-wheel, front-wheel, and four-wheel drive vehicles. After studying this chapter, you will be familiar with the principles and component parts of rear-wheel drive shafts, CV axles, and the operation of the rear-wheel drive ring and pinion and differential assembly. Some of the information in this chapter is useful in understanding the operation of the four-wheel drive systems discussed in Chapter 20.

Rear-Wheel Drive Shafts

For the transmission output shaft to drive the differential pinion gear shaft, it is necessary to connect these two units by means of a *drive shaft*, **Figure 22-1.** All rear-wheel drive vehicles have a drive shaft.

Figure 22-1. Top view showing drive shaft connecting the transmission to the differential.

Drive Shafts

The rear-wheel drive shaft is hollow to reduce weight, but has a diameter large enough to give the shaft great strength, **Figure 22-2.** Steel, aluminum, and graphite are used in drive shaft construction. Some have a rubber-mounted torsional damper.

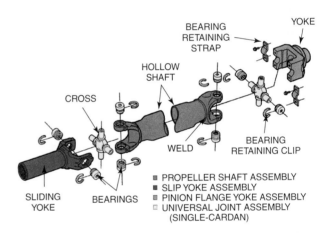

Figure 22-2. Typical drive shaft. Yokes are welded to a hollow shaft. Note the sliding yoke on one end. This allows the driveline to adapt to changes in length as the suspension moves up and down. (General Motors)

A yoke and splined stub (where used) are welded to the ends of a hollow shaft. The shaft must run true and be carefully balanced to avoid vibrations. The drive shaft is often turning at high speeds and can cause great damage if bent, imbalanced, or if there is wear in the flexible joints.

Drive Shaft Must be Flexible

When the rear wheels strike a bump or a hole, the rear axle housing moves up or down in relation to the frame. Since the transmission is mounted to the frame, it becomes obvious that to allow the rear axle to move up and down, the driveline or drive shaft must be able to flex, **Figure 22-3.**

The driveline angle changes as the vehicle travels over different grades, bumps in the road, and as the engine mounts wear over time. A solid driveline would begin to vibrate as the driveline angle changes, eventually resulting in a bent drive

Figure 22-3. All drive shafts must flex. A—Normal operating angle of drive shaft. B—This shows how a bump forces the differential up. Notice how the drive shaft angle changes. Since the transmission is fixed to the frame and the differential has limited movement, the drive shaft must flex.

shaft or broken driveline component. To allow the drive shaft to move without breaking, a flexible joint is used. This is called a *universal joint*, **Figure 22-4.** By using a universal joint, torque can be transmitted constantly while the rear axle is moving up and down, **Figure 22-5.**

Figure 22-4. Simple universal joint. Shaft A is transmitting torque in a horizontal plane. Shaft B is transmitting the same torque, but at a different angle. The yokes swivel around the ends of the cross, imparting a degree of flexibility to the universal joint.

Figure 22-5. Universal joints in action. As the rear axle moves up and down, the universal joints allow the driveline angles to change without binding.

Universal Joint

The ***cross and roller*** universal joint, sometimes called a ***cardan universal joint***, consists of a ***center cross*** and two ***yokes***. The yokes are attached to the cross through needle bearing assemblies, usually called ***bearing caps***. The bearing caps are retained in the yoke by snap rings, injected plastic, U-bolts, or bolted plates. The bearing cap rollers surround the cross ends. These cross ends are called ***trunnions***. This allows the yokes to swivel on the cross with a minimum amount of friction.

Figure 22-6 shows an exploded view of a typical cross and roller universal joint. Notice that the trunnions are smoothly finished. A hollow in each trunnion leads to the center of the cross. A grease fitting is placed in the center. When lubricated, grease will flow out to each needle roller

Figure 22-6. Universal joint cross with bushing and roller assemblies. (General Motors)

A cutaway view of a cross and roller universal joint is shown in **Figure 22-7.** Note that this particular setup employs injection molded plastic rings to secure the bearing cups or bushings in the yoke. Many original equipment universal joints do not have a grease fitting. If the joint needs lubrication, it must be disassembled and packed with grease.

Figure 22-7. Cross and roller universal joint employing injection molded plastic "rings" to secure the bearing cup or bushing to the slip yoke. Plastic is forced into an injection hole and flows into a ring groove cut in the bushing and yoke. The plastic hardens and secures the bushing. (General Motors)

Slip Yoke

As the rear axle moves up and down, it swings on an arc that is different from that of the driveline. As a result, the distance between the transmission and rear axle will change to some extent, **Figures 22-7** and **22-8.**

Figure 22-8. A slip yoke in position on the transmission output shaft, extending inside the transmission housing. The plug in the yoke helps to retain grease and prevents the entry of dirt into the splines. (General Motors)

To allow the driveline to adjust to these variations in length, a splined sleeve or **slip yoke** is needed. The end of the transmission stub shaft has a series of splines cut into it. The universal slip yoke sleeve has corresponding splines cut into it. The slip yoke sleeve is slipped over the splined transmission drive shaft stub and the universal joint is bolted to the rear axle output shaft. The shaft can move by the slip yoke sliding in the sleeve splines. Some two-piece shafts have a slip yoke on both shafts, **Figure 22-9.**

Figure 22-9. A two-piece drive shaft assembly which incorporates two slip yokes, one on each shaft. Note the center supporting bearing. (General Motors)

How the Wheels Drive the Vehicle

When the drive shaft turns the differential, the axles and wheels are driven forward. The driving force developed between the tires and the road is first transferred to the rear axle housing. From the axle housing, it is transmitted to the vehicle in one of two ways:

- Through leaf springs that are bolted to the housing and shackled to the frame.
- Through control or torque arms shackled (bolted, but free to swivel) to both frame and axle housing. This system is common on vehicles with rear coil springs.

These drive systems are referred to as a **Hotchkiss drive**. See **Figure 22-10** for a side view of these drive systems. Some older vehicles used a drive system called a torque tube drive. This system transferred power through a torque tube that surrounded the drive shaft and which was bolted to the axle housing and pivoted to the transmission by means of a large ball socket.

Figure 22-10. Methods used to transfer driving force from the rear axle housing to the vehicle frame. A—Force transmitted through leaf springs. B—Force transmitted through control rods.

Hotchkiss Drive

The Hotchkiss drive is in almost universal use today. It consists of an open drive shaft secured to the transmission output shaft and differential pinion gear shaft. Front and rear universal joints are used. If both joints are of the cross and roller type, a slip yoke must be provided.

The slip yoke allows the driveshaft length to change as the vehicle goes over road irregularities. The internal splines of the slip yoke engage the external splines of the transmission output shaft. As the length changes, the splines slide in relation to each other. The rear axle drive thrust is transmitted to the frame through springs or control arms.

The main task performed by the Hotchkiss drive is that of transmitting transmission output shaft torque to the differential. Wheel drive thrust is not transmitted through the driveline. A typical Hotchkiss drive is shown in **Figure 22-11.**

Two-Piece Hotchkiss

On some vans, trucks, and large cars, the drive shaft would be so long that vibration problems would almost always occur. To reduce excessive drive shaft length, a **two-piece Hotchkiss drive** is often used. This design uses three universal joints. With a two-piece drive shaft, it is necessary to use a **center support bearing**. This support consists of a ball bearing held in a dustproof housing that is supported by the frame. Rubber is generally incorporated in the mount to reduce noise and vibration transfer to the frame. The rubber will also allow some additional movement of the shaft without binding.

Figure 22-11. A typical Hotchkiss drive setup as used by one vehicle manufacturer. (Chrysler)

Figure 22-12 illustrates a typical center support bearing. Note that the front drive shaft rests in the rubber cushioned bearing. Many two-piece drive shafts install the slip yoke at the center support, as shown in **Figure 22-13.** This center support is also on rubber mounts. Both front and rear shafts in a two-piece Hotchkiss drive are illustrated in **Figure 22-13.**

Figure 22-12. One type of two-piece drive shaft center support bearing. A sealed ball bearing, mounted in rubber, is used to support the two shafts where they meet. (GMC)

Figure 22-13. Two-piece Hotchkiss driveline—assembled. This setup uses three universal joints; two on one shaft, one on the other. A rubber cushioned center support bearing is used where the two shafts connect. (Chrysler)

Universal Joint Can Cause Fluctuating Shaft Speed

If a conventional universal joint is driving at an angle and the speed of the driving shaft is constant, the speed of the driven shaft will fluctuate. The driven shaft speed will rise and fall two times for every revolution. This is due to the fact that the angle of drive is not equally divided between the two shafts, **Figure 22-14.**

Figure 22-14. Schematic showing principle of constant velocity universal joint. A—The necessary location for the ball socket that will keep the drive angle evenly divided between shafts 1 and 2. B—Coupling yoke and ball socket. Note how both shafts form the same angle—3 and 4. (Chevrolet)

When using a universal joint on each end of a drive shaft, the shaft speed fluctuation can be greatly reduced if both universal joint yokes are lined up in the same plane. The chart in **Figure 22-15** illustrates drive shaft speed fluctuations.

With the joint yokes in the same plane, **Figure 22-16**, the torque of the drive shaft will be smoothly transmitted to the pinion shaft. The drive shaft speed will rise and fall from the front joint action, but the fluctuation will be canceled out by the action of the rear joint.

Rear-Wheel Drive Constant Velocity Universal Joint

A *constant velocity universal joint* uses two conventional universal joints in a single housing to produce an even transfer of torque without speed fluctuations. Constant velocity universal joints provide a smooth transfer of power.

The joint design makes constant speed transfer possible by automatically dividing the drive angle equally between two shafts. **Figure 22-17** shows a cutaway view of an assembled joint. **Figure 22-18** shows a one-piece drive shaft utilizing two constant speed universal joints.

ONE REVOLUTION OF PROPELLER SHAFT

SPEEDS OF DRIVEN SHAFT FOR DRIVING SHAFT SPEED OF 1000 RPM

30°

1200
1100
1000
900
800

0 ◄— ACCELERATION —► 90 ◄—DECELERATION —►180 ◄— ACCELERATION —► 270 ◄—DECELERATION —► 360
DEGREES OF ROTATION

CONVENTIONAL UNIVERSAL JOINT SHOWING FLUCTUATIONS

CONSTANT VELOCITY UNIVERSAL JOINT, NO FLUCTUATIONS

Figure 22-15. Drive shaft speed fluctuation chart. As the universal joint turns, the angle formed by the cross changes. It never divides the angle equally between two shafts, (except for one brief moment as cross angle shifts from one extreme to the other). This causes acceleration-deceleration fluctuation that transmits torque in a jerky fashion. Dotted line illustrates even speed when a constant velocity universal joint is used. Undulating line (waving) represents speed fluctuation with conventional universal joint.

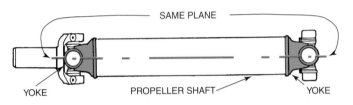

SAME PLANE

YOKE   PROPELLER SHAFT   YOKE

Figure 22-16. To prevent driveline fluctuations, universal joint yokes must be in the same plane. (General Motors)

FRONT SLIP YOKE   DRIVE LINE TUBE

CONSTANT VELOCITY UNIVERSAL JOINTS

Figure 22-18. A one-piece drive shaft incorporating a constant velocity universal joint at each end. This produces a very smooth transfer of torque. (Cadillac)

GREASE CAVITY
CENTERING BALL
WASHER   BALL SEAT
SEAL   WASHER
TUBE

BALL SUPPORT TUBE YOKE
CENTER COUPLING YOKE   SPRING   FLANGE YOKE

Figure 22-17. Cutaway of an assembled constant velocity joint. Note the centering ball and seat arrangement. This joint uses injected plastic retaining rings. (General Motors)

Constant Velocity (CV) Axles

One of the most obvious differences between vehicles with front-wheel drive and those with rear-wheel drive is the presence of two drive axles with flexible joints. These are called *constant velocity axles*, or *CV axles*.

CV axles allow the front wheels and front suspension to move up and down over bumps and to be turned while still delivering power. The CV axles can also change length to accommodate suspension movement without breaking. The CV axles must do all of this without transmitting excessive vibration into the passenger compartment.

CV Axle Shafts

The typical CV shaft is solid, although some CV shafts are hollow tubes similar to the rear-wheel drive shaft. CV axle shafts are always smaller in diameter than the rear drive shaft. Most CV axle shafts are one-piece units, as in **Figure 22-19.**

On high performance, luxury, and some four-wheel drive vehicles, the longest axle shaft may be a two-piece unit, as in **Figure 22-20.** This shaft has a center support bearing similar to the bearing used in a two-piece Hotchkiss drive shaft. The axles are held in place by nuts at the wheels, which tighten the axle to the front wheel bearing assembly, **Figure 22-21.**

Types of CV Joints

CV joints perform the same functions as the universal joint on rear-wheel drive vehicles. CV joints can drive the vehicle and compensate for steering actions while producing less vibration than a universal joint. **Figure 22-22** illustrates one particular front-wheel drive CV joint and shaft assembly.

Figure 22-19. One type of front-wheel drive axle setup. This one uses two one-piece drive shafts of unequal length. (Chrysler)

Figure 22-20. A two-piece axle shaft assembly which uses constant velocity (CV) joints. This CV axle also uses a center support bearing. (Sterling)

Front-wheel drive axles are equipped with inboard (inside) and outboard (outside) CV joints. **Figure 22-23** shows one such arrangement. CV joints are used on the front axles of some four-wheel drive vehicles and rear-wheel drive vehicles with independent rear suspensions.

There are two basic CV joint types: *tripod* and *Rzeppa* (also called ball and channel) type. Both of these are constant velocity designs. The Rzeppa joint is by far the most common. Some two-piece shafts may use a cross and roller joint in applications where driveline flexing is not a factor.

Tripod Joint

Figure 22-24 shows the tripod joint. It is composed of three trunnions inside of a three channel housing. Unlike the cross and roller universal joint, the tripod joint trunnions can slide back and forth in the channels as the joint rotates.

Figure 22-21. A cutaway view of a front hub assembly and drive axle. The axle is secured to the hub with a nut. The hub is pressed into a double-row angular ball bearing which requires no service or adjustment. (Lexus)

Figure 22-22. An exploded view of a four-wheel drive front axle and constant velocity joint. (Toyota)

Figure 22-23. Cutaway view of inboard and outboard CV joints. The short CV axle can transmit engine power flow with minimal vibration. (Honda)

This maintains the same drive angle through the joint, allowing power to be transmitted without speed fluctuations. Inboard CV joints are usually tripod joints.

Rzeppa Joint

Figure 22-25 illustrates the Rzeppa CV joint, which was invented in 1926 by Alfred H. Rzeppa. It consists of a series of balls in a slotted cross and housing assembly. During operation, the balls slide back and forth in the slots as the joint rotates. Since the drive angle through the joint is not subject to fluctuations, power flows smoothly through the joint at any angle. Outboard CV joints are usually Rzeppa joints.

CV Joint Boots

High stress is constantly placed on both types of CV joints, so they must be continuously lubricated. Although the grease used in CV joints is heavy, it would be flung from the turning joint if a means of retaining it was not used. This is

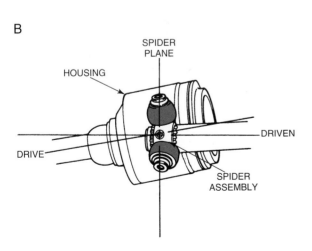

Figure 22-24. A—Exploded view of a tripot constant velocity joint. B—Tripot joint operation. The tripot joint uses three balls on needle bearings to transmit torque between the spider (splined to the axle shaft), and the housing. As the joint revolves, the three balls will change their positions to stay in the same plane with the spider. The balls can move in and out to allow for length changes as the suspension travels up and down. (AC Delco)

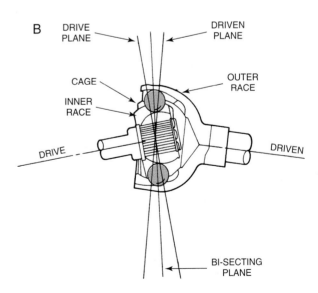

Figure 22-25. A—Exploded view of a Rzeppa (ball style) constant velocity joint. B—The Rzeppa joint as the balls operate in a bisecting plane between the angles of the axle shaft. As the joint revolves, the position of the balls will change so they can remain in this bi-secting plane. The position of the balls is controlled by the cage's elongated openings. (AC Delco)

accomplished by *CV joint boots*, **Figure 22-26.** CV boots are bellows-shaped covers made of rubber or plastic. These boots completely seal the interior parts of the CV joint. Grease flung outward is caught by the boot and flows back into the joint when the vehicle speed decreases.

CV joints will usually last the life of the vehicle if the boots are not damaged. If the boot becomes damaged, the CV joint lubricant will be thrown out and dirt and water will enter, eventually resulting in joint failure. The boots should be inspected frequently and replaced if they are damaged.

Figure 22-26. An exploded view of a front-wheel drive axle that incorporates a CV joint at each end. The boots protect the joint from dirt and water while providing a leak-proof grease retaining cover. (Cadillac)

Rear-Wheel Drive Axle Assemblies

Rear-wheel drive axle assemblies have several important functions. They must hold the wheels on, keep them upright, and propel the vehicle forward or backward. They must drive the wheels in such a manner that one can turn faster than the other, while allowing both to receive torque, **Figure 22-27.**

Drive axle assemblies must distribute the driving force of the drive shaft to the wheels, and transmit it to the frame through the rear suspension. The axle assembly provides an anchor for springs, supports the weight of the vehicle, and

Figure 22-27. A—Differential and axle operation as a rear-wheel drive vehicle is traveling straight ahead. The differential case turns as the ring gear is driven by the pinion. The differential pinion shaft and gears rotate along with the differential case. The wheels and axles rotate at the same speed, so the side gears receive torque (force) from the differential pinions equally. B—As the vehicle turns left, the differential case turns as the ring gear is driven by the pinion. The differential pinion shaft and gears rotate along with the differential case. The "outer" wheel turns at a speed which is faster than the "inner" wheel, causing the side gears to rotate at different speeds. The side gears cause the differential pinion gears to rotate on the differential pinion shaft. C—Differential action when one wheel has very little, or no traction. The power flow is the same as when turning, but with only a single axle and side gear revolving. This is an "open" (not traction) type differential. (General Motors)

forms the foundation for the rear brakes. Obviously, the axle assemblies must be well constructed.

Rear-Wheel Drive Axle Components

The rear axle assembly is used on all vehicle with rear-wheel drive. The basic axle assembly may be broken into several major sections: axle housing, axles, ring and pinion, and differential. These components form the basic rear-wheel drive axle unit.

Axle Housing

The **axle housing** is usually made of cast steel, aluminum, or stamped steel parts welded together. Two basic types of axle housings are used: the **solid axle** and the **independent axle**. An independent rear axle is shown in **Figure 22-28.** This type of axle is sometimes referred to as a **swing axle.** The solid axle is shown in **Figure 22-29.**

The manner in how the axle retains the differential assembly determines many service procedures. The **integral** carrier, **Figure 22-29,** is installed in the housing, and is serviced by removing an **inspection cover** (43). The **removable carrier** contains the ring and pinion and differential assembly and is removed from the housing for service, **Figure 22-30.**

Solid Axles

On solid axle housings, two steel axles are placed inside the housing. Their inner ends almost touch. The outer ends protrude out of the housing and form a base upon which the wheels and hubs are attached. The inner ends are splined and are supported by the differential assembly. The outer ends are supported in straight roller, tapered roller, or ball bearings, **Figure 22-31.**

Solid Axle Retention Methods

The axles are held in the housing by **retainer plates** mounted on the outside of the axle, under the brake components, as shown in **Figure 22-31.** On other rear axle assem-

Figure 22-28. Overall view of one type of independent rear suspension and axles which use constant velocity (CV) joints on both the inboard and outboard ends of the axles. The differential assembly is fastened to the frame members, and does not move with the axles or suspension. (Nissan Motor Co.)

Figure 22-29. An exploded view of a semi-floating, hypoid type, rear axle assembly. This unit has an integral ring and pinion carrier (differential) housing. A—Exploded view of the differential assembly. B—Exploded view of the optional disc brake assembly. 1—Differential drive pinion gear nut. 2—Differential drive pinion gear washer. 3—Differential drive pinion gear yoke. 5—Differential drive pinion gear dirt deflector. 6—Differential drive pinion gear seal. 7—Differential drive pinion gear outer bearing assembly. 9—Rear axle housing drain plug. 15—Differential drive pinion gear spacer. 16—Rear axle housing assembly. 17—Rear axle vent. 18—Differential drive pinion bearing assembly. 19—Shim differential drive pinion gear. 20—Gear differential ring. 22—Differential carrier bearing cap. 23—Differential drive pinion mounting gear. 24—Differential bearing shim. 25—Differential bearing spacer. 26—Differential bearing cap bolt/screw. 28—Differential ring gear bolt/screw. 29—Differential pinion gear shaft bolt/screw. 32—Differential bearing assembly. 33—Differential case. 34—Rear axle housing chip collecting magnet. 35—Differential pinion gear shaft. 36—Differential pinion gear. 37—Differential pinion gear thrust washer. 38—Differential side gear thrust washer. 39—Rear wheel speed sensor reluctor wheel. 40—Differential side gear. 41—Rear axle housing bolt/screw. 43—Rear axle housing cover. 44—Rear axle shaft bearing assembly. 45—Rear axle housing cover gasket. 46—Rear brake backing plate. 48—Rear axle housing bolt/screw. 49—Rear axle shaft bearing seal. 54—Rear axle shaft lock. 58—Rear brake drum. 59—Rear brake assembly. 61—Rear wheel bolt/screw. 63—Rear axle (drum brake assemblies) shaft. 64—Rear brake backing plate nut. 65—Rear brake caliper assembly plate. 66—Caliper assembly mounting bolt/screw. 67—Axle tube flange shim. 68—Rear brake caliper mounting plate nut. 69—Rear brake caliper assembly. 70—Rear axle (disc brake assemblies) shaft. 71—Rear brake rotor. 72—Rear brake backing plate bolt/screw. 73—Sensor plug mounting bolt/screw. 75—Wheel speed sensor assembly. (Pontiac)

Figure 22-30. An exploded view of a removable ring and pinion carrier assembly. This unit can be removed from the rear axle housing. 1—Rear-wheel anti-lock brake speed sensor. 2—Rear-wheel anti-lock speed sensor bolt. 3—Pinion flange nut. 4—Pinion flange. 5—Pinion seal. 6—Outer pinion bearing. 7—Inner pinion bearing. 8—Differential carrier. 9—Differential carrier nuts. 10—Side bearing cap. 11—Side bearing cap bolt. 12—Collapsible spacer. 13— Pinion selective shim. 14—Pinion gear. 15—Ring gear. 16—Right differential case. 17—Left differential case. 18—Rear-wheel anti-lock (RWAL) excitor ring. 19—Side gear. 20—Side bearing. 21—Ring gear bolt. 22—Right side bearing adjuster. 23—Left side bearing adjuster. 24—Side bearing lock plate. 25—Side bearing lock plate bolt. 26—Differential pinion gear. 27—Side gear washer. 28—Side gear spring washer. 29—Pinion washer. 30—Pinion cross shaft—short. 31—Pinion cross shaft—long. 32—Cross shaft roll pin. 33—Cross shaft joint. (Geo)

Figure 22-31. A cross-sectional view of a rear axle shaft, bearing, housing, seal, brake backing plate, and the bearing retainer. (Geo)

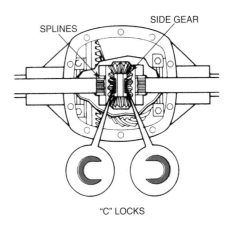

Figure 22-32. Axle shafts are retained in some differentials with "C" locks. The "C" lock is held in position by a groove cut in the side gear. The "C" lock cannot be removed until it is free of the side gear groove. (Chrysler)

blies, the axles are held in place by *C-locks* in the differential assembly, **Figure 22-32.**

Independent Axles

On independent rear suspensions, the axles resemble the front wheel CV axle shafts. These axles are usually equipped with CV joints at their inner and outer ends, **Figure 22-33.** The differential housing is bolted to the frame. The outer axle shafts are supported by bearing assemblies that are attached to the rear suspension.

The axles are held in place by nuts which tighten the outer CV axle shaft to the rear bearing assembly. The independent suspension allows the rear wheels to be individually sprung, improving vehicle handling. A variation of this axle

setup is used on front- and four-wheel drive vehicles with the engine conventionally placed (engine facing forward).

Attaching Wheel Hubs

The wheel hub is welded to the axle. The axle end is formed into a flange upon which the wheel is bolted. The wheel lugs are pressed into drilled holes in the hub. The flange may have a hole to reach the backing plate nuts, **Figure 22-34.**

Types of Axles

Axles that turn with the wheels are called live axles. The two basic types include the **full-floating axle** and **semi-floating axle**. The full-floating axle transmits engine power, but does not carry any of the vehicle weight. All weight is supported through the outer bearing assembly.

The semi-floating axle delivers power and supports the vehicle weight through the shaft bearing in the axle housing. Most cars utilize the semi-floating axle. Most heavy trucks

Figure 22-39. Differential action during straight ahead driving. Note that the pinion gears do not rotate and they drive both side gears at the same speed. (Chrysler)

Figure 22-40. Differential action during a turn. The pinion gears rotate in opposite directions and "walk" around in the side gear. This allows the gears to turn (drive) the axles in the same direction, but at different speeds. (Chrysler)

called **differential** or **carrier bearings**. In some applications, the carrier is made as a solid part of the axle housing. An assembled view of a differential is shown in **Figure 22-41**.

Limited-Slip Differential

To avoid the loss of driving force that occurs when one wheel begins to slip, **limited-slip differentials** contain internal components that automatically transfer the torque to the wheel that is not slipping. This enables the vehicle to continue its forward motion. This type of differential will provide better traction than the standard differential. It is particularly useful when roads are slippery. It is also valuable by producing faster acceleration in high performance vehicles. A high horsepower engine will often cause one wheel to spin during heavy acceleration if a standard differential is used.

Figure 22-41. Cutaway view of an assembled front differential assembly that is used with a four-wheel drive vehicle. Note the vacuum motor which shifts the front axle into and out of engagement. (Toyota)

Most limited-slip differentials employ the principle of friction to provide some resistance to normal differential action. Some systems use worm and wheel gears. These are discussed in the following sections.

Clutch Plate Limited-Slip Differential

The *clutch plate limited-slip differential*, sometimes called a Sure-Grip, Positraction, or Traction-Lok differential, is typical of friction limited-slip differentials. It resembles the standard differential, but with several important additions. The axle side gears are driven by four differential pinions. This requires two separate pinion shafts. The two shafts cross, but are free to move independently of each other. The shaft outer ends are not round, but have two flat surfaces that form a shallow V. These ramp-like surfaces engage similar ramps cut in the differential case, **Figure 22-42.**

Figure 22-43. Cross-section of a Sure-Grip differential. This differential uses clutch plates by the pinion gears. Pinion thrust members are moved against the clutch plates by pinion gears.

Figure 22-42. Pinion shafts and case ramps. Notice that the shafts fit together but are free to move outward. A—End view of a pinion shaft at rest in the bottom of case ramp. B—When the case pulls on the pinion shaft, the pinion end slides up the ramp. This forces the pinion shaft in an outward direction and moves the pinion gear outward, locking the clutch. Both shafts react but in opposite directions.

A series of four clutch discs are placed behind each axle side gear thrust member. Two of these discs are splined to the differential case and two are splined to the thrust member. The thrust member is splined to the axle. When the thrust members push outward, the clutch discs are forced together, locking the axle to the case, **Figure 22-43.**

Clutch Plate Operation

When the drive shaft drives the pinion gear, the torque thrust is transmitted to the ring gear. As the ring gear drives the differential case, the pinion shafts are forced to rotate with the case.

The differential pinions encounter resistance when they attempt to turn the axle side gears. **See Figure 22-44.** This resistance is transferred to the pinion shafts that are driving

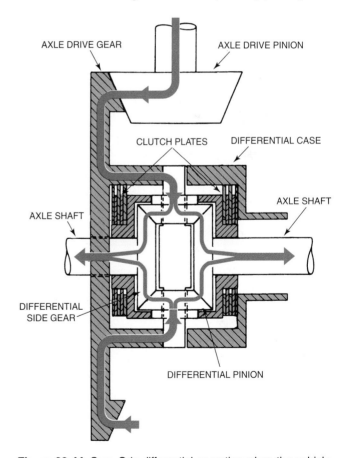

Figure 22-44. Sure-Grip differential operation when the vehicle is moving in a straight line. Both pinion shafts are in the outer positions, locking up the clutch plates. The differential pinions are not walking and both shafts are receiving equal torque. (Chrysler)

the pinions. As both ends of each pinion shaft are seated in tapered ramps, this forces the shafts to slide up the ramp surfaces. This sliding movement forces both shafts in an outward direction. As each shaft moves outward, it moves its pinions in the same direction. The pinions press against the side gears, forcing them to lock up the clutches. This is the action when the vehicle is traveling in a straight line.

When the vehicle turns a corner, the inner shaft slows down. When this happens, the pinion gears will start turning on their shafts. They will walk around the slower shaft and speed up the other shaft. This walking causes the outer shaft to rotate faster than the differential case, allowing the pinion shaft on the outer side to slide down its ramp. This releases the pressure on the outer clutches and lets the differential unit operate much like the standard model. **Figure 22-45** shows differential action when one axle is moving faster than the other. Note that the slower moving axle is receiving most of the torque since it remains clutched to the case.

Figure 22-45. Sure-Grip differential operation when the vehicle is moving around a corner. The left axle has slowed down, which allows the pinions to walk and release pressure on the outer or right-hand clutch plate assembly. This causes the differential to transfer a greater amount of driving torque to the left-hand, or inner axle.

Cone Clutch Differential Operation

The *cone clutch limited-slip differential* operates in the same manner as the clutch plate differential, but uses cone clutches to provide the friction surface. The assembly shown in **Figure 22-46** uses cone clutches under coil spring pressure. The pressure of the coil springs forces the clutch cones into tight engagement with the case. This action tends to lock the axles to the case. In order for differential action to occur, the cones must be forced to slip. If one wheel slips, the other will still receive some driving force via the cone.

Torsen® Differential

The *Torsen differential*, **Figure 22-47**, uses *worm gears* and *wheels* or *spur gears* to provide traction under all conditions. The operation of the Torsen differential depends on the fact that the worm gears can turn the wheels easily, but the wheels have a hard time turning the worm gears. This allows the Torsen differential to transmit power to the wheel with the most traction.

Hypoid Gearing

To facilitate lowering the drive shaft tunnel in the floor of the car and to allow lowering the body of the car, pinion gears enter and drive the ring gear somewhat below the centerline of the axles. This gearing setup is referred to as *hypoid gearing*. A special hypoid lubricant is necessary to prevent premature wear due to the sliding and wiping action that takes place between the ring and pinion gear teeth, **Figure 22-48.**

Study the construction used in the pinion shaft assembly in **Figure 22-48.** Note that two tapered roller bearings are used to support the shaft. This type of bearing withstands both *radial load* (forces working at right angles to the shaft) and *thrust load* (lengthwise).

Ring and Pinion Adjustments

The ring and pinion adjustment in relation to each other are of critical importance to quiet operation and durability. The tooth contact position, as well as *clearance* and *backlash* (distance one gear will move back and forth without moving the other gear), is of critical importance. Ring and pinions are always matched and must be installed as a pair. Never replace one without the other. **Figure 22-49** illustrates tooth clearance, backlash, and other gear tooth nomenclature.

Correct and incorrect ring and pinion tooth contact patterns are shown in **Figure 22-50.** The correct contact pattern is very important for strength, wear, and quiet operation. After cleaning, these patterns are brought out by coating the teeth with ferric oxide or other suitable compounds. These compounds are included with many replacement ring and pinion sets. The gears are revolved in both directions and the contact pattern becomes visible. The drive side is the side that contacts when the pinion is driving the ring. The coast pattern is when the ring is driving the pinion.

Figure 22-46. The cone clutch limited-slip differential operates in the same manner as the disc clutch types. Spring and side gear force push the cones into a machined surface on the differential case, driving both axles. A and B illustrate two different styles of cone clutch construction. (General Motors)

Gear Ratio

The engine speed must be reduced to provide sufficient power to move the vehicle. This reduction is accomplished by making the ring gear with several times the number of teeth as that of the pinion. The difference is expressed as a ***gear ratio***. The gear ratio of the ring and pinion is sometimes called the ***final drive ratio***. Gear ratios vary but commonly cover a range of around 2.56:1 to nearly 4.11:1. Higher gear ratios are used on large trucks.

When gear ratios are even, such as 3:1 or 4:1, the same teeth on the pinion would contact the same teeth on the ring

every third or fourth revolution of the pinion. Any tooth damage or imperfection would then tend to be transferred to the constantly mating tooth, reducing service life. To avoid this, most ratios are uneven. For example, 2.56:1 and 3.27:1 are two commonly used gear ratios. The uneven ratio prevents frequent contact between the same teeth, providing a varying contact wear pattern.

Lower number final drive ratios will reduce engine speed and increase fuel economy, but will produce poorer acceleration. The correct ratio is determined by a careful consideration of the vehicle weight, the type of service it will have, the

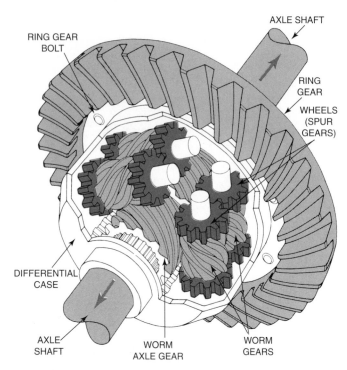

Figure 22-47. A cutaway view of a Torsen®/Gleason No-Spin gear and wheel positive traction differential unit. This differential will transmit power (torque) to the wheel with the best traction. (Torsen/Gleason Co.)

Figure 22-48. Cross-section of a typical hypoid gearset. Note how the pinion gear engages the ring gear below the axle centerline. (General Motors)

engine horsepower, and whether the transmission has an overdrive gear. See **Figure 22-51.**

Calculating Final Gear Ratio

To calculate the final gear ratio, remember that the pinion gear (drive gear) always has fewer teeth than the ring gear (driven gear). Count the number of teeth on the ring and pinion and divide the number of ring gear teeth by the number of pinion gear teeth.

If a pinion gear with 9 teeth is used with a ring gear with 27 teeth, for example, the drive ratio is 27 divided by 9, or 3:1.

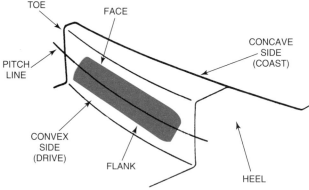

Figure 22-49. Gear tooth nomenclature. The toe is the small part of the gear that faces inward. (Chevrolet)

The final drive ratio is usually not a whole number. A more realistic situation would be a pinion gear with 11 teeth and a ring gear with 40 teeth. The final drive ratio would be 3.636363:1. For easier reading, such a number is rounded to two decimal places, or 3.64:1.

Common final gear ratios today range from 1.8:1 to 3.2:1. This permits better fuel economy. In older cars, factory gear ratios were usually lower (as much as 4.11:1) for greater pulling power and acceleration. Aftermarket high performance rear axles can have gear ratios as low as 8:1.

Axle Lubrication

A heavy viscosity oil, either petroleum-based or synthetic, is normally used with hypoid gears in rear axle housings. The viscosity rating for oil used in most rear axle assemblies is between SAE 80 and SAE 120. Special additives are required for limited-slip differentials.

In operation, oil is thrown over all the parts by the ring gear. Some installations make use of troughs to guide the returning lubricant to specific spots, such as the ring and pinion contact area and the pinion bearings. The lubricant is retained by gaskets or sealers and oil seals. A drain plug is provided at the bottom of some housings. A filler plug is located on the side of the housing or on the access cover.

NORMAL OR DESIRABLE PATTERN. THE DRIVE PATTERN SHOULD BE CENTERED ON THE TOOTH. THE COAST PATTERN SHOULD BE CENTERED ON THE TOOTH, BUT MAY BE SLIGHTLY TOWARD THE TOE. THERE SHOULD BE SOME CLEARENCE BETWEEN THE PATTERN AND THE TOP OF THE TOOTH.

BACKLASH CORRECT.   THINNER PINION POSITION SHIM REQUIRED.

BACKLASH CORRECT.   THICKER PINION POSITION SHIM REQUIRED.

PINION POSITION SHIM CORRECT.   DECREASE BACKLASH.

PINION POSITION SHIM CORRECT.   INCREASE BACKLASH.

Figure 22-50. Ring and pinion gear tooth contact patterns. Pinion and backlash adjustments will be reversed on removable carrier differentials. (Chevrolet)

HIGH NUMERICAL ("LOW RATIO")	MIDRANGE	LOW NUMERICAL ("HIGH RATIO")
4.10	3.54	3.21
MORE PULLING POWER, FASTER ACCELERATION, LOWER FUEL ECONOMY, HIGHER ENGINE RPM/NOISE, MORE ENGINE FAN COOLING, LESS PRONE TO "LUG," SLOWER TOP ROAD SPEED		LESS PULLING POWER, SLOWER ACCELERATION, HIGHER FUEL ECONOMY, LOWER ENGINE RPM/NOISE, LESS ENGINE FAN COOLING, MORE PRONE TO "LUG," FASTER TOP ROAD SPEED
STEEP GRADES	VARIED TERRAIN	FLAT TERRAIN
MAXIMUM TOWING MAXIMUM LOADS	MODERATE TOWING MODERATE LOADS	LIGHT TOWING LIGHT LOADS

Figure 22-51. An axle ratio versus power and fuel economy chart. As the axle ratios increase in number, power increases, but fuel economy decreases. As the number decreases, fuel economy increases, but there is less power. (Dodge)

Transaxle Differential Assembly

The front-wheel drive transaxle contains the differential assembly and some means of reducing engine speed. The differential assembly used with longitudinal engines is identical internally with the rear-wheel drive system. The differential assembly used with transverse engines is different in appearance, but accomplishes the same objectives.

In either type of transaxle, the operation of the differential assembly is the same as differentials used in rear-wheel drive axles. Front-wheel drive systems do not use limited-slip differentials, since the engine weight over the driving wheels usually provides sufficient traction in most conditions.

The transaxle final drive ratio may be accomplished by using a separate planetary gearset, such as the one shown in **Figure 22-52.** This planetary gearset is locked in one gear ratio at all times. Other transaxles provide the final drive ratio by varying the gear ratios inside the transaxle.

Transaxle Operation

Power (torque) is fed to the transaxle input shaft, via the clutch or torque converter. It then travels through the transaxle and is carried to the differential assembly by gears or a drive chain. The torque then passes through the differential gears, through the axles, onto the wheels, **Figure 22-53.** Transaxle parts and operation were discussed in Chapter 21.

Figure 22-52. The final drive ratio in this automatic transaxle is accomplished by using a planetary gearset. (Cadillac)

Figure 22-53. Power (torque) flow through one particular four-speed automatic transaxle in 4th gear. (Honda)

Four-Wheel Drive Front Drive Axles

Vehicles equipped with four-wheel drive use a front drive axle that is similar in construction to rear-wheel drive axles. Torque is supplied to the front axle by the transfer case, discussed in Chapter 20, and a front drive shaft. These axle assemblies can be either a one-piece housing setup, **Figure 22-54**, or an independent suspension type with CV axles that resemble the ones used on front-wheel drive vehicles. This type of front drive axle unit is illustrated in **Figure 22-55**.

Figure 22-54. A four-wheel drive, solid one-piece front axle and differential assembly. This system uses a four link coil spring-type front suspension. An axle disconnect is used instead of manual or automatic hubs. (Dodge)

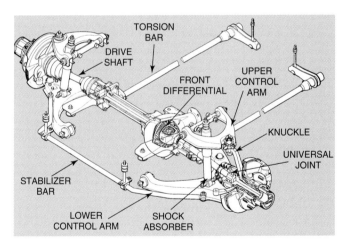

Figure 22-55. Cutaway view of a four-wheel drive, independent front suspension. Note the position of the torsion bars.

Front Axle Steering Provision

The differential assembly and other internal parts of the four-wheel drive front axle are identical to those used in the rear drive axle. However, the front axle assembly must allow the wheels to be turned as well as driven. To accomplish this, a yoke or strut and steering knuckle assembly is added to the solid front axle.

The wheel components are attached to the yoke, which is welded into place on the axle housing. To allow the drive axle to be turned with the steering knuckle, a universal joint is used. On the independent suspension front drive axle, the CV joints allow the outer axle to be turned with the wheels, **Figure 22-55**. Operation is similar to that of the front-wheel drive CV axle discussed earlier in this chapter.

Summary

Drivelines must operate at high speeds. Therefore, they must be accurately constructed and carefully balanced. The driveline must flex to accommodate movement in the rear suspension. Universal joints are used to allow this movement without damaging the drive shaft. The rear-wheel drive universal joint is called a cross and roller or Cardan joint. Some universal joints are lubricated upon construction and are sealed for life. Other types utilize a grease fitting for periodic lubrication.

To prevent speed fluctuation transfer to the pinion shaft, it is essential that both front and rear drive shaft yokes be in the same plane. As driveline length changes, it is necessary to use a slip joint to allow movement of the drive shaft. Constant velocity universal joints are used to provide smooth torque transfer without speed fluctuations.

The Hotchkiss drive is the most widely used driveline. When the rear axle housing drive thrust is carried by the springs or control arms, an open shaft Hotchkiss drive may be used. The Hotchkiss driveline uses two or more universal joints. The drive shaft may be of two-piece design. On some older cars, the torque tube system was employed.

CV axles are used on front-wheel drive vehicles and on some rear-wheel drive systems with independent rear suspensions. Most CV axle shafts are single solid shafts, although a few are hollow tubes. Some CV shafts are two-piece units with a center support bearing. The two basic CV joint types are the tripod and Rzeppa joints. Some two-piece shafts may use a cross and roller universal joint.

The rear axle assembly provides a base for springs, holds the vehicle up, provides a foundation for the brakes, holds the wheels in line, and drives the rear wheels while allowing them to turn at different speeds. The rear axle assembly is divided into several major sections: housing, axles, ring and pinion, and differential. Axles are of two types: semi-floating and full-floating. The differential unit contains axle side gears, pinions, a pinion shaft, and the case itself. The differential drives both axles while allowing their speeds to vary. Limited-slip differentials improve the performance of the differential under wet or icy conditions.

The differential unit is supported by the differential carrier and it revolves in tapered roller bearings. The ring gear is bolted to the differential case. The pinion gear, supported on a shaft in the carrier, drives the ring gear. The rear axle assembly is lubricated by a heavy hypoid gear oil. Limited-slip differentials require a special lubricant additive. Follow the manufacturer's specifications for proper lubricant type and viscosity.

Transaxle differentials use the same principles as the rear drive systems, but house all parts in the transaxle case. The differential assembly used with longitudinal engines is identical internally with the rear-wheel drive system. The differential assembly used with transverse engines is different in appearance, but works in the same manner.

On vehicles equipped with four-wheel drive, a front drive axle must be used. This enables the vehicle to go over rough and soft terrain such as rocks, mud, and sand. The four-wheel drive front axle must have a provision for steering. Four-wheel drive vehicles with solid front axles use universal joints, while independent front suspensions use CV joints.

Know These Terms

Drive shaft	C-locks
Universal joint	Full-floating axle
Cross and roller	Semi-floating axle
Cardan universal joint	Differential
Center cross	Side gear
Yokes	Differential case
Bearing caps	Pinion shaft
Trunnions	Differential pinion gears
Slip yoke	Ring gear
Hotchkiss drive	Pinion gear
Two-piece Hotchkiss drive	Differential carrier
Center support bearing	Carrier bearings
Constant velocity universal joint	Limited-slip differential
Constant velocity axle	Clutch plate limited-slip differential
CV axle	Cone clutch limited-slip differential
CV joint	Torsen differential
Tripod joint	Worm gears
Rzeppa joint	Wheels
CV joint boot	Spur gears
Axle housing	Hypoid gearing
Solid axle	Radial load
Independent axle	Thrust load
Swing axle	Clearance
Integral carrier	Backlash
Inspection cover	Gear ratio
Removable carrier	Final drive ratio
Retainer plate	

Review Questions—Chapter 22

Do not write in this book. Write your answers on a separate sheet of paper.

1. The cross and roller universal joint allows the driveline _____ to change without damaging the drive shaft.
   - (A) length
   - (B) angle
   - (C) shape
   - (D) speed

2. Technician A says that the most common type of driveline arrangement is the torque tube drive. Technician B says that the torque tube drive uses two universal joints. Who is right?
   - (A) A only.
   - (B) B only.
   - (C) Both A & B.
   - (D) Neither A nor B.

3. A center support bearing is used on the _____ driveline.

4. When the drive thrust is carried by the rear springs or control arms, the _____ drive must be used.

5. When the cross and roller universal joint is used, it is necessary to incorporate a _____ in the drive system.

6. Technician A says that most CV axle shafts are solid. Technician B says that two-piece CV axle shafts use a center support bearing. Who is right?
   - (A) A only.
   - (B) B only.
   - (C) Both A & B.
   - (D) Neither A nor B.

7. All of the following statements about rear-wheel drivelines are true, EXCEPT:
   - (A) if a universal joint is at an angle and the driving shaft speed is constant, the driven shaft speed will rise and fall twice during each revolution.
   - (B) if the angle of drive is not equally divided between two shafts, the speed of the driven shaft will be constant.
   - (C) with a universal joint on each end of a drive shaft, shaft speed fluctuation can be reduced if both universal joint yokes are in the same plane.
   - (D) two universal joints in a single housing will produce an even transfer of torque without speed fluctuations.

8. Universal joint friction is reduced by using roller bearings between the bearing caps and _____.

9. If a universal joint does not have a grease fitting, how can it be lubricated?

10. Technician A says that an integral carrier has an inspection cover to gain access to the internal components. Technician B says that C-locks are used to hold the axles in place on an independent rear suspension. Who is right?
    - (A) A only.
    - (B) B only.
    - (C) Both A & B.
    - (D) Neither A nor B.

11. Name the two different types of axles.

12. Of the above axle types, which one is primarily used on automobiles and light trucks?

13. Of the above axle types, which one carries no vehicle weight?

14. When must the rear wheels of a vehicle turn at different speeds?

    (A) When rounding a corner.

    (B) When accelerating in a straight line.

    (C) When braking on wet or icy pavement.

    (D) Both A & C.

15. The differential _____ gears are splined to the axles.

16. All of the following statements about standard (non limited-slip) differential units are true, EXCEPT:

    (A) when the differential case turns, the differential pinion shaft turns with it.

    (B) the turning differential pinion gears will pull the axle side gears along with them.

    (C) during a turn, the differential pinion gears begin to rotate on the pinion shaft.

    (D) if one wheel begins to slip, the differential pinion gears will walk around the spinning side gear and drive the stopped side gear.

17. A clutch plate limited-slip differential will drive the _____ when one wheel begins to slip.

    (A) turning side gear

    (B) stationary side gear

    (C) turning pinion gear

    (D) differential carrier

18. What is the reason for using hypoid gears in the rear axle?

    (A) Quieter operation.

    (B) Longer gear life.

    (C) Using lighter lubricant.

    (D) Lowering the vehicle body.

19. If a pinion has 13 teeth, and the matching ring gear has 39 teeth, what is the gear ratio?

20. If a pinion has 11 teeth, and the matching ring gear has 40 teeth, what is the gear ratio?

21. If a pinion has 9 teeth, and the matching ring gear has 42 teeth, what is the gear ratio?

22. Technician A says that a good quality SAE 40 engine oil is satisfactory as a rear axle lubricant. Technician B says that limited-slip differentials must have a special type of gear oil. Who is right?

    (A) A only.

    (B) B only.

    (C) Both A & B.

    (D) Neither A nor B.

23. Technician A says that a transaxle differential is identical in operation to a rear-wheel drive differential. Technician B says that final drive ratio in a transaxle is sometimes obtained by using an extra planetary gearset. Who is right?

    (A) A only.

    (B) B only

    (C) Both A & B.

    (D) Neither A nor B.

24. What extra function must be provided for the front drive axle of a four-wheel drive vehicle?

25. Four-wheel drive vehicles can use both _____ or _____ front axle setups.

Rear disc brakes are becoming more common on new vehicles. (Chrysler)

23

Brakes

After studying this chapter, you will be able to:
- Identify the basic parts of the brake hydraulic system.
- Describe the principles used for brake hydraulic system operation.
- Identify the basic parts of the brake friction system.
- Describe the principles used for brake friction system operation.
- Explain the differences between drum and disc brakes.
- Describe the principles and components of the vacuum power brake system.
- Describe the principles and components of the hydraulic power brake system.
- Describe the principles and components of anti-lock brake systems.
- List the safety hazards and precautions involved in brake system repairs.

This chapter covers the components and operation of modern disc and drum brake systems. The brake system is subdivided into the hydraulic system (master cylinder, wheel cylinders, calipers, lines and hoses, and valves), and friction system (brake shoes and drums, disc brake rotors and pads). This chapter also covers drum and disc parking brakes, vacuum and hydraulic power brake assists, and anti-lock brake and traction control systems. After studying this chapter, you will understand the operating principles and components of modern brake systems.

STOP **Warning: Brake friction materials contain *asbestos*—a known carcinogen. Brake assemblies can produce small airborne particles of asbestos during cleaning, which are easily inhaled. Breathing these particles may cause emphysema or cancer. The following safety rules should be observed at all times:**

- Never use compressed air to blow brake assemblies clean. Use a contained vacuum cleaning system or flush with cleaner or water.
- When some exposure might be unavoidable, wear an approved filter mask.

Hydraulic Basics

Early cars used complex linkages to operate the brakes. Modern vehicles use the principles of *hydraulics* to transfer power to the brakes. Hydraulics is the practical application of the principles of liquids in motion.

Liquids can include water, oil, transmission fluid, and for our purposes in this chapter, brake fluid. Brake fluid, confined in a *hydraulic system*, is used to transmit both motion and pressure from the brake pedal to the wheels. A liquid under confinement can be used to:
- Transmit pressure
- Increase pressure
- Decrease pressure
- Transmit motion

Air Is Compressible, Liquids Are Not

Air confined under pressure will compress, thereby reducing its volume, **Figure 23-1.** When a liquid is confined and placed under pressure, it cannot be compressed. **Figure 23-2A** shows a cylinder filled with oil. A leakproof piston is placed on top of the oil. When a downward force is applied, as shown in **Figure 23-2B**, the force will not compress the oil.

Pascal's Law

A French scientist, Blaise Pascal, discovered that when pressure was exerted on a confined fluid, the pressure was transmitted undiminished throughout the fluid. **Figure 23-3** illustrates *Pascal's law*. Notice that the original pressure (force) placed on the liquid is the same at all outlets.

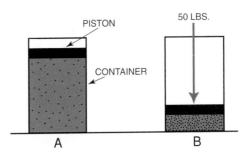

Figure 23-1. Air is compressible. A—There is no pressure on the piston. B—Pressure has forced the piston down, compressing the air trapped in the container.

419

Figure 23-2. Liquids cannot be compressed. When pressure is applied to the piston in B, it does not compress the liquid.

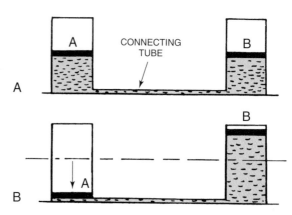

Figure 23-4. Liquids can transmit motion. A—Both pistons are at rest. B—Piston in left cylinder has been forced down. When one piston travels down, it forces liquid into the other cylinder. Since the other cylinder is the same size, the distance that the piston will be raised is equal to the distance that the other piston was lowered.

Figure 23-3. When pressure is exerted on a confined liquid, it is transmitted undiminished. Force on the piston has created a pressure of 50 psi (pounds per square inch), upon the liquid in the pressure cylinder. Notice that all gauges read the same throughout the system. Pressure is transmitted undiminished to all parts of the system. If gauge A reads 50 psi, gauges B, C, D, and E will also read 50 psi.

Figure 23-5. Using a liquid to transmit force. A 200 lb. force on piston A is transmitted, via liquid, to piston B.

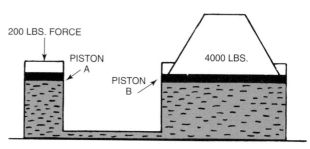

Figure 23-6. Liquids can be used to increase force. A 200 lb. force on piston A with an area of 1 in^2 is increased to 4000 lbs. on piston B with an area of 20 in^2.

Liquids Can Transmit Motion and Force

In **Figure 23-4,** you will see that any movement of piston A will cause piston B to move an equal amount. This is a transmission of motion through a liquid. If a 200 lb. force is placed on piston A in **Figure 23-5,** piston B will support 200 lbs. Both pistons are the same size. In a hydraulic system, this force is usually expressed as **hydraulic pressure**.

Liquids Can Increase Force

When a force is applied to piston A in **Figure 23-6,** it can be increased if it is transmitted to a larger piston B. If piston A has a surface area of 1 in^2, the 200 lb. force on piston A represents a pressure of 200 pounds per square inch (psi). According to Pascal's Law, this 200 psi force will be transmitted undiminished.

If piston B has a surface area of 20 in^2, piston A will exert a 200 lb. force on each square inch of piston B. This would produce a mechanical advantage (MA) of twenty, and the original 200 lb. force would be increased to 4000 lbs. The force may be further increased by either making piston A smaller or piston B larger.

Liquids Can Decrease Force

If a force is applied to piston B, the original force of 200 lbs. would have to be raised to 80,000 lbs. to produce a pressure of 4000 lbs. on piston A. By applying the force to the large piston, the force increase has been reversed and the original force, as applied to the smaller piston, will be diminished.

This force's ability to produce pressure can be increased or decreased by applying it to a larger or smaller area. Notice in **Figure 23-7** that pressures in the pump and lifting pistons are the same. However, the force applied to the pump piston has been increased many times on the head of the lift.

A Hydraulic Jack

Figure 23-7 shows how a fluid can be used to produce a powerful lifting force using the principles of hydraulics. When the jack handle raises piston A, piston A will form a vacuum. This will draw check valve 1 open and close check valve 2. When the handle is depressed with a force that exerts 200 lbs. pressure (or any force) on piston A, check valve 1 will close, check valve 2 will open and 200 psi will be transmitted to piston B. If piston B has a surface area one hundred times greater than the 1 in² area of A, piston B will raise a weight of 20,000 lbs.

Figure 23-7. Simple hydraulic jack. If piston B has an area 100 times greater than piston A, the ram will lift 100 times more than the pressure generated by piston A.

Hydraulic Principles in Vehicle Brake Systems

When the driver depresses the brake pedal, the force is transmitted undiminished to each caliper or wheel cylinder. The caliper pistons or wheel cylinders transfer this force (increased or decreased, depending on piston area) to the friction linings.

When the master cylinder piston moves, the caliper pistons or wheel cylinders will move until the brake friction components are engaged. Further movement is impossible as any attempt to depress the master cylinder piston beyond this point will transmit additional pressure, not motion.

Brake Fluid

Brake fluid is used to transmit motion and pressure through the hydraulic system. Not any fluid can be used in a brake system. Some of the more important characteristics of quality brake fluid are:

- Maintains even viscosity throughout a wide temperature variation.

- Does not freeze at the coldest possible temperature that the vehicle may encounter.

- Boiling point is above the highest operating temperature of the brake system parts.

- Is hygroscopic (has the ability to absorb and retain moisture) to prevent internal freezing of parts.

- Acts as a lubricant for pistons, seals, and cups to reduce internal wear and friction.

- Must not corrode the brake system's metal parts.

- Must not swell or deteriorate the brake system's plastic and rubber parts.

Many brake fluids contain alcohol, glycerin, and other non-petroleum ingredients. Some heavy duty commercial and high performance vehicles use **silicone brake fluid**. This fluid offers extended service life and top performance under a wide range of operating conditions.

Although most modern brake fluids are designed to be interchanged, do not mix different fluids without checking the manufacturer's service manual. Use high quality brake fluid only. It should meet or exceed current SAE recommendations and conform to the latest DOT (Department of Transportation) standards.

Under no circumstances put anything but brake fluid into the brake system. Any mineral or petroleum-based oils such as motor oil, transmission fluid, power steering fluid, kerosene, or gasoline in even the smallest amounts will swell and destroy the rubber cups and seals in the system.

 Warning: Brake fluid is poison. Keep it away from skin and eyes. Do not allow brake fluid to splash on painted surfaces.

Master Cylinder

The **master cylinder** is the central unit in which hydraulic pressure is developed. Pressure from the driver's foot pressing on the brake pedal is transmitted to the master cylinder piston. As the piston is forced forward in the cylinder, it pushes brake fluid ahead of it. Since the system is airtight, the piston is acting upon a solid column of fluid.

When the friction members have moved far enough to fully apply, the fluid movement ceases and pressure rises in response to the amount of force on the master cylinder piston. **Figure 23-8** illustrates brake pedal linkage, master cylinder, hydraulic valves, lines, and brake assemblies. All of these components will be discussed later in this chapter.

Master Cylinder Construction

Most master cylinders are manufactured of cast iron or aluminum. The master cylinder has a drilled bracket as part of the casting for mounting. Modern master cylinders are installed on a vacuum or hydraulic power booster mounted to the vehicle's firewall, **Figure 23-9.** With the master cylinder in this location, it can be inspected and serviced easily and reduces the chances of contamination by water, oil, or dirt. It is operated by a suspended pedal.

A

METERING VALVE

AIR VENT

SLIGHT DAMPNESS MAY APPEAR HERE

PLUG THREADS

SWITCH STEM ON SHOULDER

PISTON OFF-CENTER TO LEFT

PROPORTIONING VALVE & SECTION

B

RESERVOIR CAP

RESERVOIR CAP DIAPHRAGM

RESERVOIR BODY

SCREW

FLUID LEVEL SWITCH

SECONDARY SPRING RETAINER

RESERVOIR O-RINGS

CENTER VALVE SPRING

SECONDARY RETURN SPRING

CYLINDER BODY

CENTER VALVE PLUNGER

SECONDARY PISTON

"L" TYPE CUP SEAL

PISTON PIN STOP

"L" TYPE CUP SEAL

PRESSURE DIFFERENTIAL WARNING SWITCH

RETAINING RING

PRIMARY CUP RETAINING RING

RECUPERATING TYPE CUP SEAL

END PLUG

"L" TYPE CUP SEAL

PRIMARY PISTON

END PLUG O-RING
ELECTRICAL BIAS SPRING

PROPORTIONING VALVE O-RING

RECUPERATING GUIDE

PROPORTIONING VALVE

PROPORTIONING VALVE SPACER

Figure 23-22. Proportioning valves. A—A proportioning valve inside a three-function combination valve assembly. B—An exploded view of a dual master cylinder that houses an internal proportioning valve in its cylinder body. Note the brake fluid level warning light switch. (Allied-Signal and General Motors)

The three function valve houses the metering valve, the proportioning valve, and the brake warning light switch. These valves cannot be adjusted or repaired. If they are defective, the entire valve must be replaced.

Brake Lines

The master cylinder is connected to the wheel cylinders by **brake lines** made of high quality, double-walled, steel tubing. The tubing is copper-plated and lead-coated to prevent

Figure 23-32. Simplified wheel cylinder action. Fluid under pressure enters the wheel cylinder and forces the pistons and push rods outward by pressing on the rubber cups.

Figure 23-33. Hydraulic failures can be disastrous. With the dual hydraulic system, some braking force can be maintained. A—A line failure in the front brakes will allow fluid to escape, however, the rear brakes retains its supply of fluid and braking action is maintained at a reduced level. B—The rear brakes are affected, but the principles explained earlier still apply.

fluid. As the air leaves the end of the submerged hose, bubbles rise in the fluid. Air cannot be drawn back into the system.

Hydraulic System Vapor Lock

Fresh, quality brake fluid will remain liquid at any brake system temperature. Old, low quality brake fluid or fluid that is

Figure 23-34. A—Cutaway of bleeder screw. B—Wheel cylinder showing bleeder screw.

contaminated can boil at normal braking temperatures. Boiling brake fluid becomes a gas, which can be compressed.

Since the brake hydraulic system depends on having noncompressible fluid, vaporized brake fluid will make it impossible to transmit the proper braking force from the brake pedal to the wheels. Many accidents have been caused by boiling brake fluid. After the accident, the fluid will cool off and recondense, making it impossible to locate as the problem. This is why high quality brake fluid should always be used.

Brake Friction Members

The purpose of the brake *friction members* is to physically stop the vehicle. These units, including disc brake pads and rotors and brake shoes and drums, change physical movement into heat by the use of friction. Every wheel contains either a disc or drum brake assembly.

The *kinetic energy* (energy in a moving object) in the moving vehicle is converted into heat by the brakes. A fast-moving vehicle has tremendous energy. To bring it to a stop will produce a great amount of heat. Most of the heat is given off by the friction members to the surrounding air. The components and function of each type of friction member is covered below.

Coefficient of Friction

As you learned in Chapter 3, friction is created whenever two objects are rubbed together. The ability of materials to slide across each other is called the *coefficient of friction*. The coefficient of friction is calculated by dividing the force needed to push a load across a given surface.

For example, if it takes 5 pounds (2.25 kg) of force to move a 10 pound (4.5 kg) block across a smooth surface, the coefficient of friction between the two surfaces is 5 divided by 10 or .5. If it takes 20 pounds (9 kg) of pressure to move the same block across another surface, then the coefficient of friction is 20 divided by 10 or 2. This system is used to determine how various friction materials will act in combination with a brake rotor or drum to stop a vehicle.

Figure 23-35. Bleeding hydraulic system with a pressurized bleeder tool. Note air bubbles appearing in the glass jar as fluid forces air from the lines. (Bendix)

Friction Linings

Brake linings are made from materials which will produce friction with the rotor or drum and withstand the high temperatures developed during braking. In the past, brake linings were made from ground asbestos fibers pressed into shape. Since asbestos has been shown to cause respiratory problems and cancer, most modern brake pads and shoes are made without asbestos.

Current linings are made from synthetic and steel fibers, and iron, ceramic, and metallic powders. Linings made from these materials are usually referred to as **semi-metallic**. For heavy duty braking, special metallic linings, which are very resistant to brake fade, are used.

Brake Fade

Each time the brake friction members slow or stop vehicle movement, tremendous heat is created. If some method was not incorporated to dissipate this heat, the brake components would become so hot that they would cause other parts to catch fire. Therefore, brake friction materials are designed to melt at a certain temperature. When heat causes the friction material to melt, the rotor or drum slides over the melted friction material. No more friction is available to produce more heat. This is called **brake fade**.

With no friction, braking is reduced, or even vanishes entirely. Even hard pedal pressure will not produce fast, even stops. If the brakes fade under normal driving, the cause must be found and corrected. Vehicles used in high speed and heavy duty applications have metallic linings that have great resistance to fade.

Disc Brake Assembly

The disc brake uses a **rotor** as its friction surface. The rotor is bolted to and revolves with the wheel hub. **Disc brake pads** are installed in the caliper which surrounds the rotor. The rotor is stopped when the brake pads are pressed against it by the caliper piston (discussed earlier). Most calipers are single piston types.

Older designs allowed the brake pads to drag very lightly against the rotor at all times. To reduce drag and improve fuel economy, modern disc brake systems operate with only a

minimal pad to disc clearance (about .005″ or 0.13 mm). The disc brake pads are self-centering and press on each side of the rotor with equal pressure.

Disc brakes resist brake fade because the rotor's larger surface area is exposed to the open air. The rotor may be solid or have fins and/or drilled holes for cooling, **Figure 23-36.** Despite the fact that the rotor is exposed to water and dirt, the disc brakes work well during wet or dry operation without grabbing. Due to the relatively small friction area and the lack of servo or self-energizing action common in drum brakes, disc brakes require a higher operating hydraulic pressure.

Brake Pad Construction

Brake pads consist of friction materials **bonded** or **riveted** (glued) to a metal plate. Past friction materials included asbestos, which has been replaced with various high temperature compounds. These compounds are mixed with metallic compounds into a matrix to make a semi-metallic friction material. Some heavy duty high temperature brake applications use friction materials made up almost entirely of various metals. Sometimes, a metal wear sensor is riveted to the metal plate. When the pads are worn sufficiently, the wear sensor will contact the rotor, producing a high pitched squeal.

Braking Ratio

When a vehicle is stopped, there is a transfer of weight to the front of the vehicle due to its inertia. This forces the vehicle's weight against the front tires while it relieves weight off the rear tires somewhat.

To compensate for, and to take advantage of, this effect, the front brakes usually are designed to produce more stopping power than the rear. This is called the vehicle's **braking ratio**. An average ratio would be: Front brakes—55% to 60%. Rear brakes—40% to 45% of the stopping force. This ratio will vary depending on the type and size of vehicle, vehicle loading, and whether the vehicle uses front- or rear-wheel drive. The hydraulic system may also be designed to modify the braking ratio for increased braking efficiency.

Backing Plate

A round, stamped sheet metal or steel plate is bolted to the front spindle, or to the end of the rear axle housing. This

Figure 23-36. A disc brake assembly from a front-wheel drive vehicle which uses finned brake rotors. Air passing between the rotor fins while the vehicle is moving, helps to dissipate the heat. (Bendix/Chrysler)

backing plate, when used for disc brakes, serves as a shield for the caliper and rotor. When it is used for drum brakes, it serves as the foundation upon which the wheel cylinder and brake shoe assembly is fastened. The backing plate is rigid and cannot move in any direction, **Figure 23-37.**

Drum Brake Assembly

Each *drum brake assembly* consists of the brake backing plate, a set of brake shoes, shoe retainer clips and return springs, and a brake drum. These components are covered in the following sections.

Figure 23-37. Typical brake backing plate. The backing plate forms a foundation for the brake shoes and wheel cylinder. Disc brakes use a similar plate to shield against debris. (Hyundai)

Brake Shoe Assembly

All drum brake assemblies use two *brake shoes*. These shoes are made of stamped steel and have brake linings either riveted or bonded to the outer surface. Although of similar design, there are some minor differences in the shapes of the shoes. All utilize a T-shape cross-section, **Figure 23-38.** A web is used to give the shoe rigidity. When forced against the drum, it will exert braking pressure over the full lining width and length.

The brake shoes ends may be free-floating or they may have one end fastened to an anchor. The *primary* (front or leading) *brake shoe* faces toward the front of the vehicle. It often has a different size lining than the other shoe. The *secondary* (rear or trailing) *brake shoe* faces the rear of the vehicle. Some newer drum brake assemblies use brake shoes that can be mounted in either position.

Brake return or retracting springs are used to pull the shoes together when hydraulic pressure is released. Small

Figure 23-38. Two brake shoe designs. (Dodge)

spring clips of various designs are used to keep the shoes against the backing plate to ensure shoe alignment and prevent rattle. Study the arrangement of parts shown in the exploded view of a drum brake assembly in **Figure 23-39.**

Brake Drum

The **brake drum** fits between the wheel and hub and completely surrounds the brake shoe assembly. It comes very close to the backing plate so that water and dust cannot enter easily. The center section is constructed of stamped steel, with an outer cast iron braking rim. An aluminum outer rim is sometimes used to aid in cooling. When aluminum is used, a cast iron braking surface is fused to the aluminum rim.

The heavy casting enables the drum to absorb and dissipate heat from the braking process without distorting. Cooling fins are often cast into the rim to assist in heat dissipation, **Figure 23-40.** The braking area of the drum must be smooth, round, and parallel to the shoe surface. When the wheels turn, the drum revolves around the stationary brake shoes.

Drum Brake Operation

When hydraulic system operation creates pressure in the wheel cylinder, the wheel cylinder pistons and links move the brake shoes outward into contact with the revolving brake drum. Since the shoes cannot revolve, they will stop the drum and wheel.

Drum Brake Arrangement

There are many arrangements used in mounting drum brakes. Several popular ones are illustrated in this chapter.

Most utilize **servo action** (one shoe helps to apply the other), as well as **self-energizing** (using frictional force to increase shoe-to-drum pressure).

Servo Action, Self-Energizing Brakes

Servo and self-energizing action is produced by hooking the heel of the primary shoe to the toe of the secondary shoe. When the wheel cylinder forces the top ends of the shoes against the revolving brake drum, it will try to carry the forward shoe around. As the primary shoe attempts to revolve, it will jam the secondary shoe against the single anchor pin. This stops both shoes and produces a binding effect that actually helps the shoes apply themselves. This servo and self-energizing action reduces the amount of needed pedal pressure.

Figure 23-40. Cross-sections of cast iron and aluminum brake drums. Note the cast iron inner liner when aluminum is used to facilitate cooling.

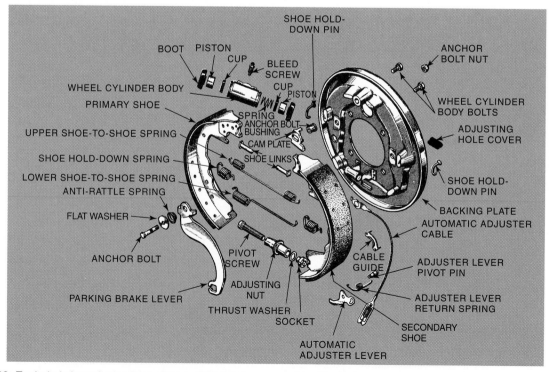

Figure 23-39. Exploded view of a backing plate and brake shoe assembly. (Dodge)

Note how the primary shoe in **Figure 23-41** attempts to rotate in the direction of the drum. Since the adjusting screw connects it to the toe of the secondary shoe, the heel of the secondary shoe is jammed against the anchor pin. The arrows illustrate the braking force direction. When the vehicle is traveling in reverse, the secondary shoe applies the primary shoe.

The primary shoe lining on self-energizing brakes generally is smaller and of a different composition. The secondary shoe does more of the braking, so less lining material is needed on the primary shoe. A servo action, self-energizing brake assembly is shown in **Figure 23-42.** Note that the primary shoe has less lining. The star wheel at the bottom is used to adjust the shoes to keep them close to the drum.

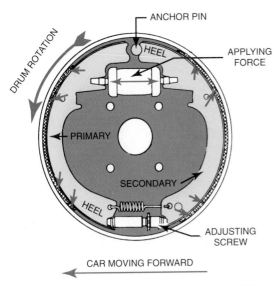

Figure 23-41. Servo action, self-energizing brake. When actuated, the primary shoe starts to move with the drum and in so doing, applies the secondary shoe. (Buick)

Figure 23-42. Servo action, self-energizing drum brake. The primary shoe (left) has a short lining when used in this setup (Wagner Electric Corp.).

Self-Adjusting Brakes

Modern drum brake systems are *self-adjusting*. Each utilizes a series of springs, levers, and cables that automatically adjusts the drum-to-lining clearance as the linings wear down. Manual adjustment is provided by turning the star wheel with a special adjusting tool.

The adjustment systems are of three general types, which are identified below. Some systems operate only when braking in reverse, others in a forward direction, or braking in either direction.

Lever Adjuster

An *adjustment lever* is attached to one of the brake shoes in such a manner that it is free to pivot back and forth. One end engages the teeth in the star wheel, while the other is attached to a link, as in **Figure 23-43.** The link is attached either to the anchor (adjustment will take place when braking in one direction only) or to the other brake shoe (will function when braking in either direction).

Figure 23-43. Lever type automatic brake adjuster. This unit functions only when braking in reverse.

A spring holds the adjustment lever in a downward position. Since the actuating link is attached to the anchor, it will operate only in one direction. On brake assemblies where the lever is pivoted to the secondary shoe, it will function only during reverse braking.

Cable Adjuster

Study the construction of the *cable adjuster* in **Figure 23-44.** This particular unit passes the actuating cable up over the anchor and attaches it to the secondary shoe, causing it to function when braking in either direction.

When the brakes are applied, the shoes move out until they contact the rotating drum. They will then move around with the drum until the secondary shoe heel engages the anchor. The small out and around movement tightens the

Figure 23-44. Cable type automatic brake adjuster. This specific drum brake setup works when braking in either direction.

actuating cable and pulls it upward on the adjustment lever a small amount. When the brakes are released, the shoes are retracted, causing the actuating cable to become slack and the return spring pulls the adjustment lever back down. This action is repeated during each brake application.

Since the amount of lever movement is very small, the cable will not normally draw the lever up far enough to engage a new tooth on the star wheel. However, when sufficient lining wear has taken place, the cable movement will be enough to draw the lever up to the next tooth on the star wheel. When the brakes are released, the return spring will draw the lever down, forcing it to rotate the star wheel one tooth. This adjustment action will take place during the entire life of the lining.

Link Adjuster

The **link adjuster** is very similar to the cable type. Instead of using a cable, it uses two separate links which perform the same task. The utilization of links instead of the cable is the basic difference, **Figure 23-45.**

Figure 23-45. Link type automatic brake adjuster. This type of adjuster functions during reverse braking.

Parking Brakes

On most modern vehicles, the **parking brakes**, sometimes called the **emergency brakes**, is part of the rear brake assembly. This basic system is used with both drum and disc rear brakes. In most parking brakes, a foot pedal or hand-operated lever is connected through linkage and cables to both rear brake assemblies. When the emergency brake is applied, the cables pull a lever in each rear brake assembly.

Drum Parking Brake Operation

The top of the lever is bolted to one shoe and one end of a strut (steel bar) is notched into the lever below the top bolt. The other end of the strut is notched into the opposite shoe. The emergency brake cable is attached to the lower end of the lever. See **Figure 23-46.**

Figure 23-46. Rear-wheel parking brake assembly. Rear cable pulls on brake lever, thus causing strut to spread and apply the brake shoes. (Bendix)

When the cable pulls the bottom of the lever toward the left, the lever forces the strut to the left until it presses the shoe against the drum. At this point, continued movement of the lever causes it to pivot on the strut. This moves the lever and shoe to which it is bolted to the right until it engages the drum. Any further lever movement will now apply force to both shoes.

Caliper Parking Brake Operation

Vehicles equipped with rear disc brakes incorporate an integral thrust screw mechanism in the caliper piston. This caliper is similar to the front caliper in design and operation. The parking brake is actuated by a lever located on the inboard side of the caliper. The lever is moved by the parking brake cable.

As the lever is applied, it rotates the thrust screw which forces the piston assembly against the shoe and lining. Continued application moves the caliper, bringing the outboard shoe and lining into contact with the rotor, firmly holding it in position. An exploded view of this caliper setup is shown in **Figure 23-47.**

Figure 23-47. Exploded view of a rear disc caliper assembly. Note that this unit incorporates an integral parking brake setup. Study all part names and locations. 1—Nut. 2—Park brake level. 3—Return spring. 4—Damper. 5—Bolt. 6—Bracket. 7—Lever seal. 8—Anti-friction washer. 9—Mounting bolt. 10—Outboard shoe and lining. 11—Inboard shoe and lining. 12—Shoe retainer. 13—Insulator. 14—Bolt boot. 15—Support bushing. 16—Bushing. 17—Caliper piston boot. 18—Two-way check valve. 19—Piston assembly. 20—Retainer. 21—Piston locator. 22—Piston seal. 23—Actuator screw. 24—Balance spring and retainer. 25—Thrust washer. 26—Shaft seal. 27—Cap. 28—Bleeder valve. 29—Caliper housing. 30—Bracket. 31—Wear sensor. 32—Retaining clip.

Power Brake Systems

Most modern vehicles are equipped with *power brakes* as standard equipment. The power brake unit is an additional part that operates with the hydraulic system. Power brakes reduce the amount of pedal pressure necessary to stop the vehicle. Pedal travel (distance from release position to full brake application) can also be shortened. Power brakes can be vacuum or hydraulically assisted.

Vacuum-Assisted Power Booster

The *vacuum power brake booster* is a closed cylinder with a piston inside. One side of the piston is connected to the master cylinder piston. The other side is connected to the brake pedal. A *vacuum control valve* is placed between the brake and the piston.

Vacuum Power Booster Construction

A power brake booster operates from the vacuum produced in a gasoline engine. If the vehicle has a diesel engine, an engine- or electrically-driven vacuum pump is used, as diesel engines do not provide sufficient vacuum for efficient brake booster operation.

The vacuum control valve admits vacuum to one side of the piston, while the normal atmospheric pressure is allowed

to exist on the other. This valve can also allow atmospheric pressure to reach both sides of the piston, **Figure 23-48.**

Vacuum and Atmospheric Suspended Booster

The *vacuum suspended booster* has a vacuum on both sides of the diaphragm or piston when the booster is in the released position. When the booster is applied, atmospheric pressure is admitted to one side to cause the necessary movement of the piston. See the schematic in **Figure 23-49A.** An *atmospheric suspended booster* has atmospheric pressure on each side of the piston in the released position. To cause booster action, vacuum is admitted to one side, **Figure 23-49B.** Most modern brake systems use the vacuum suspended booster.

Vacuum Power Booster Operation

When the driver presses the brake pedal down, the vacuum control valve closes off the atmospheric pressure to the brake cylinder side of the piston. Further movement of the brake pedal opens a vacuum inlet passage to this same side. As there is atmospheric pressure on one side of the piston and a partial vacuum on the other, the piston will be forced toward the vacuum side. Since the piston is connected to the master cylinder piston, it will apply pressure to the brake system. The vacuum power brake has four stages of operation:

Figure 23-48. Schematic of a simplified power brake booster. Engine vacuum is admitted through the vacuum inlet. Control valve A can apply either vacuum or atmospheric pressure to the B section of the booster cylinder. When the brake pedal is being applied, the pedal linkage causes control valve A to cut off atmospheric pressure and to apply vacuum to the B side. Atmospheric pressure is forcing the piston and push rod to the right, which builds pressure in the master cylinder.

Figure 23-49. Power boosters. A–Vacuum suspended. B–Atmospheric (air) suspended type. Study the differences. (Wagner)

- Released position (brake pedal not being depressed).
- Applied position (brake pedal being depressed).
- Holding position (brake pedal with driver applying constant pressure).
- Releasing position (brake pedal being released).

These stages of operation are discussed in the following sections. Refer to the sectional view in **Figure 23-50**, and the operational cross-sections in **Figure 23-51**.

Released Position

With the engine running and the brake pedal fully released, the valve operating rod and plunger are moved to

Figure 23-50. Cutaway of a typical vacuum power booster. 1—Master cylinder. 2—Vacuum check valve. 3—Grommet. 4—Diaphragm. 5—Diaphragm plate. 6—Rear shell. 7—Diaphragm spring. 8—Reaction plate. 9—Valve plunger. 10—Bearing seal. 11—Poppet valve. 12—Poppet valve spring. 13—Poppet retainer. 14—Dust boot. 15—Valve operating rod. 16—Filter and silencers. 17—Valve rod and plunger return spring. 18—Mounting stud. 19—Air valve lock plate. 20—Diaphragm. 21—Front shell. 22—Push rod seal. 23—Cylinder-to-shell seal. 24—Hydraulic push rod. 25—Adjusting screw. (GMC)

the right by the return spring, **Figure 23-51A**. This presses the right end of the valve plunger against the face of the poppet valve, closing off the atmospheric port. The vacuum port is open, which allows vacuum to form on both sides of the diaphragm plate. The left side of the diaphragm is subjected to constant vacuum, regardless of plunger position. With a vacuum on both sides, the diaphragm return spring moves the diaphragm plate to the right, releasing all pressure on the master cylinder.

Applied Position

When the driver depresses the brake pedal, the valve operating rod is moved to the left, **Figure 23-51B**. This causes the valve plunger to move to the left. As the plunger moves, it will compress the return spring and move the poppet valve into contact with the vacuum port seat in the valve housing. This closes the vacuum port leading to the right side of the diaphragm.

Further application of the brake pedal will cause the valve rod to force the valve plunger away from the poppet, opening the atmospheric port. As the port is opened, atmospheric air will rush into the right side of the diaphragm (control vacuum area) and force the diaphragm plate to the left. This applies pressure to the master cylinder push rod.

Providing Brake Feel

Note in **Figure 23-51A** how the rubber reaction disc is compressed when the brakes are applied. As the master

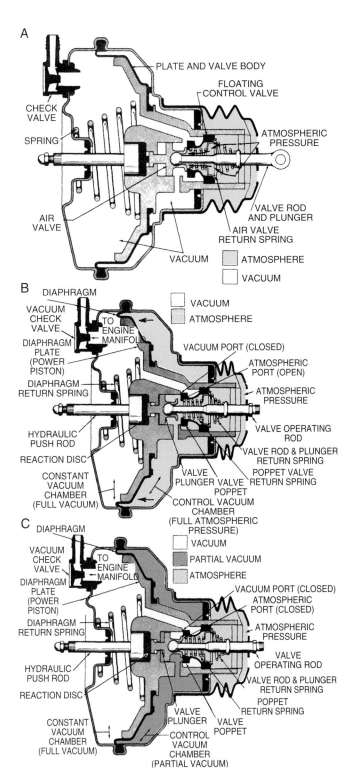

Figure 23-51. Typical vacuum power booster action.
A–Released position. Vacuum is on both sides of the diaphragm. The spring moves the diaphragm to the right. Pressure is not applied to the master cylinder. B–Applied position. The poppet valve closes the vacuum port and the valve plunger moves to the left, opening the port. Atmospheric pressure forces the diaphragm plate toward the vacuum side. C–Holding position. Both vacuum and atmospheric ports are closed. This will retain the desired amount of braking. (GMC)

cylinder piston builds up hydraulic pressure in the brake system, a reaction pressure is transmitted back through the master cylinder push rod. The compressed rubber reaction disc transmits this pressure to both the diaphragm plate and the valve plunger. The pressure on the plunger valve tends to force it to the right (without moving the diaphragm plate), causing the valve to close off the atmospheric port.

The movement of the valve plunger is transmitted to the valve operating rod and on to the brake pedal. This provides the driver with **brake feel** to determine the amount of braking effort being exerted. This reaction force is directly proportional to pressure created within the master cylinder. Some power boosters use a reaction plate, levers, and diaphragms instead of the rubber disc. Note that the reaction disc in **Figure 23-51A** is not compressed and that a portion engages the valve plunger. Compare this with the compressed reaction disc shown in **Figure 23-51B**.

Vacuum Runout Point

The **vacuum runout point** occurs when vacuum has built up the maximum pressure possible on the power piston or diaphragm plate. If more pressure than full vacuum can produce is desired, additional pressure must be exerted by the driver on the pedal. This will hold the vacuum port wide open and transmit all of the driver's effort directly to the master cylinder piston. Wheel lockup (tires will stop revolving and slide) or anti-lock cycling will usually occur before the vacuum runout point is reached.

Holding Position

As long as the driver increases pedal pressure, the valve plunger will move to the left. When the driver exerts the desired amount of pressure, plunger movement will cease. The reaction force, transmitted to the reaction disc, will move the valve plunger (without moving the diaphragm plate) a slight amount to the right. This shuts off the atmospheric port. The vacuum port also remains shut.

When this balanced condition occurs, the right side of the diaphragm plate will be subjected to a specific and unchanging amount of atmospheric pressure. This maintains a constant pressure in the brake system. If more pedal force is applied, the atmospheric valve is reopened, causing the diaphragm plate to exert additional pressure on the master cylinder. It will maintain this pressure until pedal and reaction forces are again balanced.

Figure 23-51C shows a power booster in the holding position. Both vacuum and atmospheric ports are closed. Note how the reaction disc has moved the valve plunger a little to the right (in relation to diaphragm plate), as compared with the applied position in **Figure 23-51B**. This action closes the atmospheric port.

Released Position

If the pedal is released, the atmospheric port closes and the vacuum port opens, exposing both sides of the diaphragm plate to vacuum. As the force is removed from the plate, the diaphragm return spring will push the plate and valve assembly to the right of the booster cylinder.

Other Vacuum Booster Types

There are many variations in booster design, however, the basic operating principles are much the same. The paragraphs below briefly discuss some of the vacuum power booster designs used in the past, and on some vehicles today.

Tandem Booster

The **tandem booster**, shown in **Figure 23-52**, uses two diaphragm plates to increase booster-to-master cylinder pressure. This has the effect of doubling the force of the vacuum in the same size booster. Tandem boosters are often found on larger cars, vans, and light trucks.

Vacuum Reservoir

As long as the engine is running, vacuum is available for the booster. When the engine stops, vacuum is gone. To provide several brake applications without engine vacuum, the booster is designed to maintain a **vacuum reservoir**. Even though engine vacuum may be lost, enough vacuum will be retained in the booster body to provide one or more power-assisted stops.

Most modern vacuum booster systems have a check valve in the booster body itself. Carefully study the check valve arrangement in **Figure 23-52**. A separate reservoir, with a vacuum check valve, may be found on some cars and a few large trucks. One type is shown in **Figure 23-53**.

Booster Failure

In the event the booster or the vacuum supply fails, the brakes may still be applied by foot pressure alone. It will require somewhat more pressure than when the booster is

Figure 23-53. Vacuum reservoir tank. Reservoir allows one or two brake applications after engine vacuum is gone. (Wagner Div. of Cooper Industries)

working, but the system will still function. Stopping distance will be greatly increased. Engine performance may also be affected if the failure is due to the loss of vacuum.

Hydraulic Pressure-Operated Power Booster

The **hydraulic power booster** (also called a Hydro-Boost) is used on some vehicles, usually those with diesel engines. The hydraulic booster is operated by hydraulic pressure developed by the power steering pump. Power steering

Figure 23-52. A cross-sectional view of a dual (tandem) vacuum power booster unit with attached master cylinder. Study the overall construction carefully. (Bendix)

pump pressure is delivered to the booster by high pressure hoses. Some heavy duty trucks employ an electro-hydraulic emergency pump as a backup source if the power steering pump becomes inoperative.

The hydraulic power booster system consists of a hydraulic pressure source and the hydraulic booster. **Figure 23-54** shows a typical pressure supply from the power steering pump. As with the vacuum booster, the hydraulic booster is coupled directly to the master cylinder. Movement of the brake pedal operates the booster valve, causing the booster to exert pressure on the master cylinder primary piston. The paragraphs below discuss the operation of the hydraulic booster in the released and applied positions.

Figure 23-54. Hydraulic booster system. The pressurized fluid from the power steering pump is directed to the steering gear and then to the master cylinder. The brake and power steering fluid are separate from each other.

Hydraulic Power Booster Operation

In the fully released position, **Figure 23-55A**, power steering fluid flows through the booster power section on to the steering gearbox. No pressure is built up by the booster.

As the brake pedal is depressed, **Figure 23-55B**, the input rod and piston are forced forward. This action causes the lever to move the spool valve forward (towards the master cylinder), admitting more fluid into the space behind the power piston. As pressure builds, the power piston is forced forward, actuating the master cylinder.

The amount of pressure exerted by the booster (up to its maximum output) is proportional to the pressure exerted on the brake pedal. Brake feel is provided by fluid pressure generated in the space between the inboard end of the input rod and the power piston. This fluid pressure attempts to force the input rod back against pedal pressure. This gives the driver the needed pedal feel so that correct foot pressure may be exerted. Excess hydraulic fluid pressure is first vented to the accumulator; any remaining pressure goes back to the power steering pump reservoir.

Hydraulic Accumulator

All hydraulic *accumulators* are either spring-loaded or contain gas under pressure. The accumulator is filled with fluid by the power steering pump, and is pressurized whenever the brakes are applied. If the engine stalls or a problem occurs, such as a power steering pump failure or leak, or the drive belt breaks, the accumulator will contain enough pressurized fluid to provide between one and three power-assisted brake applications.

Even after the accumulator charge has been depleted, the brakes can still be operated by using pedal pressure only. As with all boosters that become inoperative, pedal resistance and stopping distance will be noticeably increased. **Figure 23-56** shows an exploded view of a hydraulic power booster unit. Note the accumulator.

STOP **Warning: Accumulators contain strong springs or pressurized gas and can fly apart with lethal force. Special training is recommended before servicing these units. Do not apply heat to an accumulator. For proper disposal, follow manufacturer's instructions.**

Figure 23-55. A—Cross-sectional view of one Hydro-Boost design. This booster is in the fully released position. B—Hydraulic booster in applied position. The lever has moved the spool forward, raising the fluid pressure behind the power piston. The piston moves forward to exert pressure on the master cylinder piston. (Bendix)

Figure 23-56. Exploded view of a hydraulic power booster. Note the accumulator that retains pressure for one or more brake applications in the event pump pressure is lost. (Chevrolet)

Anti-Lock Brake Systems (ABS)

Many vehicles are now being equipped with *anti-lock brake systems*, usually called *ABS*. Most ABS systems used on automobiles are similar to the one shown in **Figure 23-57** and control all four wheels. The ABS systems used on some light trucks operate only the rear wheels (rear-wheel anti-lock or RWAL), **Figure 23-58.** These systems, whether two- or four-wheel, use electronic and hydraulic components to help prevent wheel lockup during hard braking.

Anti-lock brakes allow the driver to maintain directional control while providing maximum braking efficiency. The ABS system does this by *pulsing* (applying and releasing) the brakes much more quickly than the driver could. This keeps any of the wheels from locking and causing a skid.

Figure 23-57. Overall view of a vehicle which is equipped with a four-wheel anti-lock braking system. (Honda)

Figure 23-58. This pickup truck is equipped with a rear-wheel anti-lock (RWAL) braking system. A transmission mounted vehicle speed sensor is used in place of sensors being located at each rear wheel. (Chevrolet)

Anti-Lock Brake System Components

Anti-lock brake systems use an electronic control system to modify the operation of the brake hydraulic system. The electronic and hydraulic components work together to prevent wheel lockup during periods of hard braking. Most anti-lock brake systems, no matter who manufacturers them, contain several common components. These components, shown in **Figure 23-59**, include *wheel speed sensors*, a *control module*, and a *hydraulic modulator*. Some vehicles also use G-force sensors and a pedal travel switch. Some anti-lock brake systems use an accumulator that is pressurized with brake fluid automatically by an electric pump. Most modern anti-lock brake systems have self-diagnostic capabilities.

Note that the brake friction components and most of the hydraulic components, such as wheel cylinders, caliper pistons, master cylinder, hydraulic lines, and power brake system components, are the same as those used on vehicles without ABS. When discussing ABS systems, the other friction and hydraulic components are referred to as the *foundation brakes*, or the *base brakes*.

Anti-Lock Brake Operation

Under normal braking conditions, the anti-lock portion of the brake system does not operate. The sensors continuously monitor wheel rotation and send signals to the anti-lock controller. When the brake pedal is pressed, fluid flows from the master cylinder, through the hydraulic modulator, and into the wheel cylinder or caliper, **Figure 23-60.** The wheel speed sensors monitor wheel speed to determine whether any of the wheels are ceasing to turn (locking).

If a wheel begins to lock up, the speed sensor reading alerts the ABS electronic control unit. When the ABS controller senses that a wheel is nearing lockup, it signals the appropriate solenoid valve in the hydraulic modulator to block the fluid

passage between the master cylinder and the locking wheel assembly. When this occurs, pressure is trapped between the brake and the hydraulic modulator. Master cylinder fluid pressure cannot flow through the solenoid valve and the brake pressure at the affected wheel is held constant, **Figure 23-60.**

If the control module detects further lockup on the affected wheel, it will command the hydraulic modulator to decrease brake pressure to the appropriate wheel, **Figure 23-61.** To accomplish this, the solenoid valve in the modulator moves to cut off fluid pressure from the master cylinder and allows brake fluid at the caliper to flow back into the accumulator, master cylinder reservoir, or pump intake. When this occurs, pressure at the wheel is decreased.

With the piston type hydraulic modulator, the solenoid valves isolate the circuit from the master cylinder, and the pistons are moved to reduce pressure. **Figure 23-62** is a cutaway of one particular unit used to control fluid pressure to the front and rear brakes.

After reducing pressure, the wheel will accelerate. When the wheel accelerates to a preset level, the control module will signal the hydraulic modulator to increase pressure. This causes wheel deceleration and the cycle begins again.

When all the wheels are rotating normally, the solenoid valves in the modulator return to their original position and the foundation braking system takes over. At the same time, the modulator pump delivers any excess fluid back into the accumulator or master cylinder. Most anti-lock brake systems can repeat this cycle up to 15 times a second.

Traction Control Systems

To reduce wheel spin when accelerating on slippery surfaces, some vehicles are equipped with *traction control systems*, also called acceleration slip regulation. These systems are able to reduce engine power and operate the brake

Figure 23-59. Schematics of four wheel anti-lock braking systems during normal (non-anti-lock mode) braking. A–Illustrates normal brake pressure traveling to the wheels. B–Fluid flow through the various valves of the system. Note that this system also includes an electronic traction control module. (Chevrolet)

Figure 23-60. Schematic of an anti-lock brake system. When the brake pedal force is excessively heavy, wheel lockup can occur. When lockup is detected, the ABS control unit operates the solenoid valve, the outlet valve is closed, and the inlet valve is opened. High fluid pressure is sent into chamber C, and the piston is pushed up, causing the slide piston to travel upward and the cut-off valve to close. As the cut-off valve begins to close, fluid flow from the master cylinder to the brake caliper is interrupted. At the same time, the volume of chamber B increases and the fluid pressure in the brake caliper decreases. When both inlet and outlet valves are closed, caliper pressure is constant. When wheel lockup ceases, normal fluid pressure is resumed to the brake caliper. The outlet valve is open, the inlet valve is closed, and the solenoid valve is turned off. (Honda)

Figure 23-61. This schematic illustrates the brake fluid flow away from the brake caliper, decreasing braking ability of that wheel. This is part of normal ABS cycling. (Honda)

Figure 23-62. A cross-sectional view of a piston type modulator assembly which controls the fluid pressure to both the front and rear wheel brakes. (Honda)

system to increase vehicle acceleration and stability on wet, icy, or uneven road surfaces. Traction control systems also provide higher levels of cornering performance.

The traction control system can apply the brakes on the drive axles. On a two-wheel drive system, it will control only the driving wheels. On a full-time four-wheel drive system, it can apply any one of the four brakes. If the system detects one drive wheel spinning at a faster rate than the others, it will apply the appropriate amount of braking force to slow the wheel to the correct speed.

If the system determines that one or more drive wheels are spinning excessively, it can close the throttle or briefly retard ignition timing to prevent further spinning. Most vehicles with traction control also have an anti-lock brake system and are usually controlled by a single electronic control unit, **Figure 23-63.**

Brake Lights

The vehicle brake lights are operated either by a hydraulically operated switch placed somewhere in the brake line, or by a mechanically operated switch actuated by the brake pedal. The mechanical switch is the most common switch on newer vehicles. Brake lights use dual filament bulbs, one filament for the tail lights, and a brighter filament for the brake lights. Brake lights and switches are covered in more detail in Chapter 17.

Summary

Brake lining dust contains minute particles of asbestos, which can cause cancer. When cleaning brake assemblies, use care to avoid breathing the dust. Have proper ventilation. Have a dust disposal system and when needed, wear a suitable respirator.

Liquids, under confinement, can be used to transmit motion and to increase or decrease pressure. Air is compressible, liquids are not. Pascal's law states that when pressure is exerted on a confined liquid, it is transmitted undiminished throughout the liquid.

The brake system can be divided into two principal parts, the hydraulic system and the friction members. When the brake pedal is depressed, the master cylinder piston compresses brake fluid in the master cylinder. This causes fluid to move in the brake lines. This fluid movement will expand the wheel cylinders and calipers, causing them to apply the brake pads and shoes to the brake rotors and drums. Both movement and pressure are used in the hydraulic system.

Almost all vehicles use a double-piston or dual master cylinder, which provides a brake fluid source to the front and rear brakes. The front brakes generally provide somewhat more braking force than the rear brakes. This is to compensate for the transfer of weight to the front during stops. Hydraulic control valves are used to provide maximum braking power under all conditions. These valves are the metering

Figure 23-63. One particular traction control system and components. This traction control system manages the engine torque and braking of the drive wheels. Tire slippage (spinning) during takeoff on slippery road surfaces is carefully controlled. The system eliminates the need for the driver to control the accelerator pedal when starting off, turning, or accelerating on slick roads. The traction control and anti-lock brake electronic control units are combined into one control unit on this system. (Lexus)

valve, proportioning valve, and pressure differential switch. Two or more of these valves can be combined into a combination valve.

All air must be expelled from a hydraulic system. The removal of this air is termed bleeding. Never use any fluid other than high quality brake fluid in the system. Anything else will quickly ruin the rubber cups and seals, making the brakes inoperative.

Brake lines are made of double-walled steel tubing. Flexible hoses are used in both the front and in the rear. There are two types of wheel cylinders, single and double-piston.

The disc brake provides high resistance to both brake fade and grabbing. A caliper attached to the spindle or axle tightens and presses the brake pads against the rotor to stop it from turning. Disc brakes stay cooler, but require higher pedal pressure.

The drum brake assembly consists of a backing plate, brake shoes and springs, and a brake drum. The brake shoes are attached to the backing plate. The shoes are arranged so they may be expanded by the wheel cylinders. As the shoes expand, they will stop the brake drum and wheel. There is one primary shoe and one secondary shoe per wheel.

Some shoes are arranged so that servo action assists in applying the brakes. Brake shoe servo action is when one shoe helps apply the other. Self-energizing shoes are arranged so that shoe-to-drum friction helps apply the shoe. Some shoes are self-adjusting; others may be adjusted periodically to compensate for shoe lining wear.

There are two types of emergency or parking brakes in general use. One operates the regular service brake shoes on the rear axle, while the other operates rear brake pads on the rear axle. An older parking brake system uses a drive line brake.

Power brakes are used on almost all vehicles today. The power brake is essentially the regular brake system with a vacuum or hydraulic power booster added to reduce the braking effort by the driver. A vacuum reservoir is provided so that one or two brake applications can be made after the engine stops. Some systems used with diesel engines provide an engine- or electrically-driven pump to produce sufficient vacuum for brake application.

The diaphragm type vacuum power booster is in common use today. They may be either vacuum or atmospheric suspended. All work in essentially the same manner.

Atmospheric pressure can be applied to one side of the piston, upon application of the brake pedal. With atmospheric pressure on one side and vacuum on the other, the piston is forced to move in the direction of the vacuum. As it moves, it applies force either to the master cylinder piston or to the brake pedal itself.

A valve is used to control the admission of atmospheric pressure and the application of the vacuum. The booster works in four stages: released, being applied, holding, releasing. The power booster is designed to provide a braking "feel" for the driver, which is essential in controlling the amount of brake pressure. The vacuum runout point for a booster is when full vacuum is applied and the booster has exerted all possible pressure on the system.

Hydraulic power boosters are also used, especially on vehicles with diesel engines. They employ pressure from the power steering pump. The hydraulic booster system has an accumulator to provide reserve braking power if the hydraulic system fails.

Anti-lock brake systems use electronic and hydraulic components to help prevent wheel lockup during hard braking. The anti-lock brake system is a combination of electronic and hydraulic components which pulse the brakes quickly to prevent wheel lockup. Many anti-lock brake systems also provide for traction control to help with acceleration on slippery roads.

Know These Terms

Asbestos
Hydraulics
Hydraulic system
Pascal's Law
Hydraulic pressure
Brake fluid
Silicone brake fluid
Master cylinder
Reservoir
Low fluid warning switch
Pistons
Piston return springs
Primary cup
Secondary cup
Bleeder ports
Push rod
Dual brake system
Dual master cylinder
Diagonal split brake system
Quick take-up master
    cylinder
Quick take-up valve
Pumping
Proportioning valve
Metering valve
Pressure differential switch
Combination valve
Dual proportioning valve

Height sensing proportioning
    valve
Brake lines
Brake hoses
Disc brake caliper
Caliper pistons
Seal ring
Floating calipers
Wheel cylinder
Wheel cylinder pistons
Cups
Cup expanders
Dust boots
Single-piston cylinders
Stepped wheel cylinder
Bleeder screw
Friction members
Kinetic energy
Coefficient of friction
Semi-metallic
Brake fade
Rotor
Disc brake pads
Bonded
Riveted
Braking ratio
Backing plate
Drum brake assembly

Brake shoes
Primary brake shoe
Secondary brake shoe
Brake drum
Servo action
Self-energizing brakes
Self-adjusting brakes
Adjustment lever
Cable adjuster
Link adjuster
Parking brakes
Emergency brakes
Power brakes
Vacuum power brake
    booster
Vacuum control valve
Vacuum suspended booster

Atmospheric suspended
    booster
Brake feel
Vacuum runout point
Tandem booster
Vacuum reservoir
Hydraulic power booster
Accumulator
Anti-lock brake system
    (ABS)
Pulsing
Wheel speed sensors
Control module
Hydraulic modulator
Foundation brakes
Base brake
Traction control system

Review Questions—Chapter 23

Do not write in this text. Write your answers on a separate sheet of paper.

1. Technician A says that air is not compressible. Technician B says that liquids can transmit both pressure and motion. Who is right?

    (A) A only.

    (B) B only.

    (C) Both A & B.

    (D) Neither A nor B.

2. According to Pascal's law, the original pressure placed on a confined liquid is _____ throughout the liquid.

    (A) transferred with increased pressure

    (B) transferred with decreased pressure

    (C) transferred undiminished

    (D) transferred increase or decrease, depending on the shape of the container.

3. If a 100 lb. (46 kg) force is applied to a piston with 1 in^2 (6.5 mm^2)of area, how much pressure would a piston with an area of 10 in^2 (65 mm^2) exert, if both of these pistons rested with an airtight seal on a column of oil? Assume that both cylinders or columns are connected via a pipe.

4. How many pistons does the modern master cylinder have? _____

5. A dual master cylinder _____.

    (A) provides greater braking power

    (B) applies pressure to separate front and rear brake hydraulic systems

    (C) works the clutch also

    (D) has two cylinders, one on top of the other

6. The master cylinder reservoir must be filled to within about _____ of the reservoir cover or covers.

7. Technician A says that the reservoir cover must be vented. Technician B says that the reservoir cover must always be removed to check the fluid level. Who is right?
   (A) A only.
   (B) B only.
   (C) Both A & B.
   (D) Neither A nor B.

8. The reservoir provides extra fluid to _____.
   (A) replace losses due to seepage
   (B) provide extra fluid to compensate for lining wear
   (C) absorb heat from the master cylinder
   (D) Both A & B.

9. Brake lines must be made of _____.
   (A) double-walled steel
   (B) flared copper
   (C) double-walled brass
   (D) Any of the above.

10. Brake lines, where connections are made, must have a _____ flare.

11. Name three parts of a wheel cylinder.

12. Technician A says that a small amount of air in the brake system is permissible. Technician B says that automatic transmission fluid is a satisfactory substitute for brake fluid. Who is right?
    (A) A only.
    (B) B only.
    (C) Both A & B.
    (D) Neither A nor B.

13. Which of the following valves controls pressure to the rear wheels?
    (A) Proportioning valve.
    (B) Master cylinder check valve.
    (C) Pressure differential switch.
    (D) Metering valve.

14. Which of the following valves warns the driver that one side of the split hydraulic system has failed?
    (A) Proportioning valve.
    (B) Master cylinder check valve.
    (C) Pressure differential switch.
    (D) Metering valve.

15. Wheel cylinders are fastened to the _____.
    (A) brake drum
    (B) backing plate
    (C) spindle
    (D) All of the above.

16. How many single wheel cylinders would be used on a single brake drum assembly?

17. The secondary brake shoe faces _____.
    (A) the back of the vehicle
    (B) the front of the vehicle
    (C) to the front on the left side, to the rear on the right side
    (D) in either direction, depending on the manufacturer

18. The brake shoe configuration (design) commonly used today is the _____.
    (A) duo-servo, fixed anchor, self-adjusting
    (B) non-servo, single adjustable anchor
    (C) self-energizing, duo-anchor, self-centering
    (D) single servo

19. Technician A says that front and rear brake shoe return springs push the wheel cylinder pistons inward when hydraulic pressure is removed. Technician B says that the brakes produce a lot of heat and the brake drums and rotors should be thick to absorb it. Who is right?
    (A) A only.
    (B) B only.
    (C) Both A & B.
    (D) Neither A nor B.

20. All of the following statements are true, EXCEPT:
    (A) the backing plate holds the wheel cylinder and brake shoes in position.
    (B) the backing plate keeps water out of the shoe and drum assembly.
    (C) the caliper is the mounting surface for the rotor.
    (D) the caliper holds the pads in position.

21. The _____ valve closes off pressure to the front disc brakes until the hydraulic system pressure can overcome rear brake shoe retracting spring pressure.

22. Explain servo action.

23. What is meant by self-energizing?

24. Brake shoe self adjusters are used on _____ vehicles.
    (A) very old
    (B) off-road
    (C) disc brake
    (D) all modern

25. Why do disc brakes require higher hydraulic pressures as compared to drum brakes?

26. A type of parking brake that is not used much any more is the _____ brake.
    (A) rear drum
    (B) rear disc
    (C) transmission
    (D) None of the above.

27. The vacuum power brake requires a vacuum source other than the intake manifold on _____ engines.

28. The vacuum power brake vacuum control valve is operated by _____.
    (A) manifold vacuum
    (B) engine speed
    (C) master cylinder hydraulic pressure
    (D) movement of the brake pedal

29. What does vacuum suspended mean when referring to the power booster?

30. What type of power booster is in popular use today?
    (A) Bellows.
    (B) Diaphragm.
    (C) Piston.
    (D) All of the above.

31. A _____ prevents loss of vacuum when the engine stops running.

32. The hydraulic brake booster utilizes pressure generated by the _____ system.

33. The hydraulic brake booster uses a _____ to provide reserve pressure in case the regular hydraulic system fails.
    (A) motor driven pump
    (B) vacuum pump
    (C) accumulator
    (D) vacuum back-up booster

34. Name the three main components of an anti-lock braking system.

35. Most anti-lock brake systems have _____ capabilities.

The modern engine compartment is tightly packed, however fluid fill and check points are clearly marked. Can you find all of the fluid fill points for this engine? (Ford Motor Co.)

24

Suspension Systems

After studying this chapter, you will be able to:
- Identify the purpose of the suspension system.
- Explain the difference between sprung and unsprung weight.
- Name the different types of vehicle frames.
- Describe the function and operation of chassis springs.
- Describe the function of control arms and struts.
- Describe the function and operation of ball joints.
- Describe the function and operation of shock absorbers.
- Explain the differences between conventional and MacPherson strut suspensions.
- Explain the operation of front suspension components.
- Explain the operation of rear suspension components.
- Explain the operation of automatic level controls.

This chapter will cover the principles and components of the suspension system. There are many variations in the design of modern suspension systems. In addition, there are many variations between front and rear suspensions. However, they all operate on basic principles and have the same basic purpose—reducing road shock transferred to the passenger compartment and improving handling. After studying this chapter, you will be familiar with the purposes and designs of modern suspension systems.

The Need for a Suspension System

If a vehicle's axles were bolted directly to its frame or body, every rough spot in the road would transmit a jarring force throughout the vehicle. Riding would be uncomfortable, and handling at freeway speeds would be impossible. The fact that the modern vehicle rides and handles well is a direct result of a *suspension system*.

Even though the tires and wheels must follow the road contour, the body should be influenced as little as possible. The purpose of any suspension system is to allow the body of the vehicle to travel forward with a minimum amount of up-and-down movement. The suspension should also permit the vehicle to make turns without excessive body roll or tire skidding. See **Figure 24-1.**

Sprung Weight

Sprung weight refers to the weight of all vehicle parts that are supported by the suspension system. The frame, engine, drive train, body, and all parts mounted on the body make up the sprung weight.

Figure 24-1. The vehicle body must be insulated against road shock. The blue dotted line shows how the vehicle body moves forward smoothly despite the rapid up-and-down motion of the suspension and wheels.

Unsprung Weight

Unsprung weight refers to all parts of the vehicle that are not supported by the suspension system, such as the wheels, tires, steering knuckles, and rear axle. The ideal situation is to have as little unsprung weight as possible in relation to the sprung weight. The unsprung weight will then have a minimal effect on the riding characteristics of the vehicle.

Suspension System Components

The following sections cover the various parts of the modern suspension system and discusses the relationship between them.

Vehicle Frames

A vehicle's frame or body must form a rigid structural foundation and provide solid anchorage points for the suspension system. There are two types of vehicle construction in common use today: *body-over-frame construction*, **Figure 24-2,** which uses a separate steel frame to which the body is bolted at various points and *unibody construction*, **Figure 24-3,** in which the body sections serve as structural members. Unibody construction is the most common, but

Figure 24-2. A steel pickup truck channel type frame which is welded and riveted together. They may be coated with paint and/or wax to resist corrosion. (Dodge)

Figure 24-3. Unibody construction. By using the body sections as strength members, great rigidity is obtained. This type of body construction generally does not use a frame. All the sections are welded together. (Chevrolet)

body-over-frame construction is still used on pickup trucks and large cars.

Springs

The **springs** are the most obvious part of the suspension system. Every vehicle has a spring of some kind between the frame or body and the axles. There are three types of springs in general use today: leaf, coil, and torsion bar. Two different types of springs can be used on one vehicle. Air springs were once used in place of the other types of springs, but are now obsolete. Many modern vehicles have air-operated suspensions, but they are used to supplement the springs.

Leaf Springs

Leaf springs are usually used on the rear axles of large cars and pickup trucks. The most common leaf spring configuration consists of a number of flat steel leaves of varying lengths that are bolted together to form a single unit. This design is called the semi-elliptical leaf spring.

The spring is fastened to the axle by U-bolts, **Figure 24-4.** Notice the use of rubber isolators to eliminate spring vibration transfer. The ends of the spring are shackled to the frame. The ends of the top leaf, or main leaf, are curled around to form the spring eyes. See **Figure 24-5.** On some springs, the ends of the second leaf are curled around the eye to provide additional strength. The spring center bolt passes through the spring, keeping the leaves properly spaced in a lengthwise position. The top of the center bolt fits into a depression in the mounting pad, pinning the spring firmly to the axle mounting pad when the U-bolts are tightened.

When the spring is bent downward, the leaves slide against each other. The same action takes place on the rebound (springs snapping back to their original shape). To prevent squeaks and to ease spring action, neoprene or nylon pads are often used between the ends of the leaves. The

Figure 24-4. Spring to axle housing mounting. Note the use of rubber isolator blocks. (Dodge)

springs then flex these small rubber pads. Several rebound clips are placed around the spring leaves at various points. These clips prevent the leaves from separating when the spring rebounds upward. Note the rebound clips and the leaf rubber pads shown in **Figure 24-5.**

Figure 24-5. Partial view of a semi-elliptical leaf spring. The center bolt keeps the leaves in line and properly spaced.

Spring Shackles

The leaf spring is held in place by two **spring shackles.** One end of the spring is mounted on a pivot shackle that will not allow fore-and-aft movement. The other end of the spring is mounted on a hinge-type shackle that allows the spring to shorten and lengthen as it flexes up and down. See **Figure 24-6.**

Figure 24-6. Flexing causes a variation in spring length. 1—Stationary spring hanger. 2—Hinge-type shackle. In A, normal load may produce this spring shape. In B, the spring has been compressed. End 1 has merely pivoted, but end 2 has moved out as the spring lengthens. The difference in length is shown at C.

Modern spring shackles use rubber bushings between the spring eye and the spring eye bolt. See **Figure 24-7.** The spring and bolt do not touch. The pivoting motion is absorbed by the flexible rubber bushing. The bushings require no lubrication. A complete semi-elliptical spring is shown in **Figure 24-8.** The left end pivots in a spring hanger. The right end is supported on a hinge shackle. Rubber bushings are used in both ends.

Figure 24-7. Rubber-bushed spring shackle. Bushings are in two parts. A metal sleeve fits inside the bushings and a shackle bolt passes through this sleeve. When the shackle bolts are tightened, the rubber bushings are somewhat compressed, causing them to expand and grip both the spring eye and the bushing sleeve tightly. All movement is taken within the rubber bushings.

Figure 24-8. A semi-elliptical leaf spring rear suspension. The center bolt holds the leaves in line and properly spaced. (Toyota)

Chapter 24 Suspension Systems 457

Single Leaf Spring

A single-leaf, semi-elliptical spring is shown in **Figure 24-9.** The spring is long and wide, is made of steel or fiberglass, and is relatively thin. The entire spring consists of one leaf.

Figure 24-9. Single leaf spring. Long, wide, and quite thin. Entire spring is made up of one leaf.

Coil Springs

Coil springs are used in many modern vehicles as part of conventional or MacPherson strut suspensions. They can be installed at the front or rear axle. Coil springs are made of special spring steel rods that are heated and wound in the shape of a spiral coil. Coil springs are carefully tempered to achieve the proper tension.

One end of the coil spring is secured to the frame or body, and the other is fastened to the axle or another suspension device. Pads are used on the ends to prevent vibration transfer and squeaks. See **Figure 24-10.**

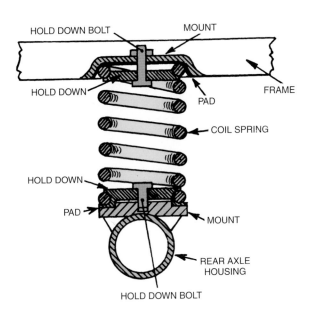

Figure 24-10. Coil spring. Each end is bolted to mount. Rubber or fabric pads are used at ends.

Torsion Bar

The **torsion bar** is a long spring-steel bar. One end is mounted to the vehicle's frame or body. The other end is free to turn. A lever arm, which is at right angles to the bar, is secured to the free end of the bar. This lever arm is fastened to the suspension device. When the wheel strikes a bump and the lever arm is pushed upward, it will twist the bar. The bar will have a resistance to twisting that has been carefully calibrated to the load forces it is designed to bear. **Figure 24-11** shows a typical torsion bar. **Figure 24-12** illustrates the operation of a simplified front torsion bar suspension.

Shock Absorbers

When the vehicle is traveling forward on a level surface and the wheels strike a bump, the spring is rapidly compressed (coil springs) or twisted (leaf springs and torsion bars). The spring will attempt to return to its normal loaded length. In so doing, it will rebound, causing the body of the vehicle to be lifted. Since the spring has stored energy, it will rebound past its normal length. The upward movement of the vehicle also assists in rebounding past the spring's normal length.

The weight of the vehicle then pushes the spring down after the spring rebounds. The weight of the vehicle will push the spring down, but since the vehicle is traveling downward, the energy built up by the descending body will push the spring below its normal loaded height. This causes the spring to rebound again. This process, called **spring oscillation**, gradually diminishes until the vehicle is finally still. **Figure 24-13.** Spring oscillation can affect handling and ride quality and must be controlled.

Shock Absorber Control Action

To control spring oscillation, a dampening device called a **shock absorber** is used. Many types of shock absorbers have been used in the past. Modern vehicles use the **telescoping shock absorber**. See **Figure 24-14.** One end of the shock is mounted to the frame, the other end is attached to the axle. Rubber bushings are used to fasten the shock. When the spring attempts to compress or rebound, its action is hindered by the shock absorber.

As the body attempts to rise and fall in relation to the axle, the shock must telescope out and in. The shock's resistance to the telescopic movement hinders this up-and-down motion. Instead of a long series of uncontrolled oscillations, spring action is smoothed out, and the vehicle will quickly return to its normal loaded level.

Shock Absorber Construction

The telescoping shock absorber consists of an inner cylinder, an outer cylinder, a piston and piston rod, and, in some cases, an outer dust and rock shield. A series of valves in the piston and at the bottom of the inner cylinder control the movement of the hydraulic fluid within the shock.

Shock Absorber Operation

Figure 24-15 illustrates a typical telescoping shock absorber in three positions. The left-hand illustration shows the shock at rest with the vehicle at normal loaded height. Notice that the inner cylinder (pressure tube) is completely

Figure 24-11. Operation of a longitudinal (parallel with vehicle) torsion bar. A—A simple torsion bar mounted to a vehicle frame. B—Torsion bar at rest and bar movement (twist) from the vehicle suspension jounce and/or rebound. The elasticity of the spring steel tries to return the torsion bar to its rest position. (FMC Corp.)

Figure 24-12. Simplified torsion bar front suspension. When the wheel spindle moves up or down, the torsion bar must be twisted. The torsion bar anchor is bolted to frame. Both lower control arm support and upper control arm pivot support are fastened to the frame by using support brackets.

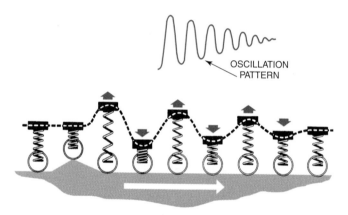

Figure 24-13. Spring oscillation. When the wheel strikes a bump, the spring is compressed. Even though the wheel returns to the level roadway, the spring oscillates. Oscillation gradually diminishes and finally stops. (Ford)

filled with fluid, while the outer cylinder (reservoir tube) is only partially filled. The piston is near the midpoint of its travel in order to allow up-and-down movement.

The middle illustration, **Figure 24-15,** shows the action of the shock during spring compression. Note that the piston and piston rod have moved down in the inner cylinder, forcing the fluid to pass through the piston valve into the upper section of the cylinder. Since the piston rod occupies space formerly filled with fluid, some fluid must be displaced through the base

valve into the outer cylinder. The valves are calibrated to cause a certain resistance to the passage of fluid. Although the fluid passes through the valves quite easily when the shock is compressed slowly, any increase in compression speed causes a rapid buildup of resistance. The shock thus cushions the violent force of the spring compression.

The right-hand illustration, **Figure 24-15,** shows shock action during spring rebound. The piston is forced upward in the inner cylinder and the fluid trapped above the piston

UPPER RUBBER MOUNT

COVER PLATE

DUST SHIELD

KONI

PISTON ROD

TOP PLUG

OIL SEAL

RESERVOIR TUBE

INNER PRESSURE TUBE (CYLINDER)

PISTON

SPRING

ADJUSTING NUT

FOOT OR BASE VALVE

LOWER RUBBER MOUNT

Figure 24-14. A cutaway of a typical shock absorber showing construction. (Koni)

moves down through the piston via a different valve. To compensate for the reduced amount of piston rod now in the pressure tube, additional fluid is pulled in from the outer cylinder through the base valve. Some shock valves are calibrated to provide more resistance on rebound than on compression.

Figure 24-16 shows a typical mounting setup for a telescoping shock absorber. The top end is fastened by rubber bushings to the frame. The bottom is bolted to the lower arm of the front suspension system. The up-and-down movement of the suspension arm will operate the shock. Some shock absorbers can be set to provide a soft, normal or a firm action, others provide this feature automatically. Many modern shock absorbers are gas-filled to improve rebound control without stiffening the ride. One is shown on a rear suspension system in **Figure 24-17.**

Air Shock Absorbers

Some suspension systems incorporate two adjustable *air shock absorbers* that are attached to the rear suspension and connected to an air valve with flexible tubing.

Air operated shock absorbers have hydraulic dampening systems which operate in the same manner as those on conventional shocks. In addition, they contain a sealed air chamber, which is acted on by pressure from a height control sensor. Varying the pressure to the air chamber causes the air shock to increase or decrease its length or operating range.

Air pressure is delivered to the air shocks through plastic tubing. The tubing connects the shocks to an air valve. Air pressure for raising the shocks is generally obtained from an outside source, such as a service station compressor, and is admitted through the air valve. To deplete the shocks of unwanted air (lower vehicle curb height), the air valve core is depressed, allowing air to escape.

Control Arms and Struts

All vehicles have either *control arms* or *struts* to keep the wheel assembly in the proper position. The control arms and struts allow the wheel to move up and down while preventing it from moving in any other direction. The wheel will tend to move in undesirable directions whenever the vehicle is accelerated, braked, or turned. Vehicle suspensions may have control arms only or a combination of control arms and struts.

Figure 24-18 shows a typical control arm used on many front-wheel drive vehicles. The front and rear attachment points pivot on rubber bushings. The attachment points absorb the tendency of the control arm to move forward and rearward as the wheel moves. The control arm design keeps the wheel from moving inward or outward.

By designing the upper and lower control arms carefully, it is possible to have a suspension that allows the wheel to move up and down while causing it to remain in the straight up and down position. The upper and lower control arms

SHOCK ABSORBER
AT REST

COMPRESSION STROKE

EXTENSION STROKE

DUST SHIELD

PISTON ROD

OIL
SEAL

TOP
PLUG

INNER
CYLINDER

OUTER
CYLINDER

PISTON
VALVE

BASE
VALVE

FLUID
ESCAPES
THROUGH PISTON
VALVE INTO
UPPER PART OF
PRESSURE TUBE

FLUID
UNDER
PRESSURE

EXCESS FLUID WHICH
CANNOT BE
ACCOMMODATED IN
UPPER PART OF
PRESSURE TUBE DUE
TO DISPLACEMENT OF
PISTON ROD IS FORCED
THROUGH BASE VALVE
INTO RESERVOIR TUBE

FLUID
UNDER
PRESSURE

FLUID ESCAPES
THROUGH PISTON
VALVE INTO
LOWER PART OF
PRESSURE TUBE

ADDITIONAL FLUID
DRAWN IN THROUGH
BASE VALVE FROM
RESERVOIR TUBE TO
COMPENSATE FOR
DISPLACEMENT OF
PISTON ROD

Figure 24-15. Shock absorber action—at rest, compression, extension. Study each illustration and determine shock action shown in each.

Figure 24-16. Shock absorber mounting. (Dodge)

Figure 24-18. An exploded view of a front-wheel drive suspension assembly showing a typical control arm (lower), mounting bushings and locations. 1—Stabilizer nut. 2—Link assembly. 3—Stabilizer bolt. 4—Washer. 5—Bolt. 6—Bolt. 7—Nut. 8—Washer. 9—Lower arm rubber bushing. 10—Nut. 11—Bolt. 12—Lower arm ball joint. 13—Ball joint dust boot. 14—Lower arm rubber bushing. 15—Lower control arm. 16—Frame/body. (Kia Motors)

Figure 24-17. A gas-filled shock absorber mounted to a coil spring rear suspension system. (Geo)

Figure 24-19. Upper and lower arm pivot arcs of individual front wheel suspension system.

move through different arcs, keeping the outer pivot points in alignment. See **Figure 24-19.** This improves handling over bumps.

Figure 24-20 shows a typical control arm and strut assembly. All contact points with the frame are mounted through rubber bushings. The strut rod (also called the tension strut or the strut bar) keeps the control arm from moving forward and rearward. The control arm itself keeps the wheel from moving inward or outward.

Ball Joints

All modern vehicles use *ball joints*, **Figure 24-21.** The function of the ball joint is to carry the vehicle load to the wheels while allowing relative movement between the wheel assembly and the body. The ball joint that carries the majority

of the vehicle weight is called the *load-carrying ball joint*. The other joint is called the *follower joint*. Depending on the suspension arrangement, ball joints can be placed under either *tension loading* (forces attempt to pull joint apart) or

Figure 24-20. A control arm and strut type front suspension system. (Chrysler Corp.)

Figure 24-21. Load carrying ball joints. A—The location of the spring will determine which joint will be the load carrier. B—The different styles of load carrying ball joints—compression loaded and tension loaded. Study the construction, road and load force. (Moog)

compression loading (forces attempt to compress joint). **Figure 24-22** shows one that is *preloaded* by a coil spring. Preloading will keep the joint bearing surfaces in constant contact. One arrangement (coil spring placed between the upper control arm and body) places the main joint at the top. In this setup, the main joint is compression loaded. The follower joint is tension loaded.

Figure 24-22. Cross-sectional view of a four-wheel drive front suspension system which uses a tension spring loaded upper ball joint. Study the layout. (Isuzu)

Figure 24-23 illustrates one basic arrangement in which both joints are tension loaded. Note that the lower joint is the load-carrying joint. Another arrangement tension loads the follower joint and compression loads the load-carrying joint.

Stabilizer Bars

To overcome the tendency of a vehicle's body to lean on corners, a *stabilizer bar* is incorporated into the suspension system. Made of spring steel, the stabilizer bar passes across the frame and is secured to the frame in two places. The outer ends of the stabilizer bar are fastened to the lower control arms (when used in front) through short linkage arms. Stabilizer bars can be used on both the front and rear suspensions.

Figure 24-23 illustrates a stabilizer bar and its location on the front cradle. The two bushing brackets are used to fasten the bar to the frame. A short linkage (spacer) connects the stabilizer bar to the control arms. **Figure 24-24** shows one side of a stabilizer bar. Notice how it is connected directly to the lower control arm, eliminating additional linkage.

Stabilizer Bar Action

As long as the body dips up and down in a level manner, the stabilizer bar does not affect its action. When the body attempts to tip to one side, one end of the bar bends down and the other end bends up. This imparts a twisting force to the bar. The bar resists this twisting force. In so doing, it helps to keep the vehicle level. See **Figure 24-25.**

Figure 24-23. Cutaway view of an independent suspension as used on a front-wheel drive vehicle. Study the entire suspension layout. (Audi)

Figure 24-24. Stabilizer bar connectors. Other end of bar (not shown) is mounted in the same manner. (Chevrolet)

Front Suspension Systems

Almost all modern front suspension systems are independent. With an independent suspension, each front wheel is free to move up and down with a minimum effect on the other wheel. In an independent suspension system, there is also far less twisting motion imposed on the frame than in a system with a solid axle. Nevertheless, a few off-road, four-wheel drive vehicles and large trucks continue to use a solid axle front suspension. The two major types of independent front suspension are the *conventional front suspension* and the *MacPherson strut front suspension*.

Conventional Independent Front Suspension

In the conventional front suspension system, one or two control arms are used at each wheel. In most systems, the coil springs are mounted between the vehicle's frame and the lower control arm. See **Figure 24-26**. In older systems, coil springs are mounted between the upper control arm and vehicle body, **Figure 24-27**.

A torsion bar front suspension system is shown in **Figure 24-28**. When the lower arm moves upward, it twists the torsion bar. A transverse-mounted torsion bar arrangement is illustrated in **Figure 24-29**.

Figure 24-25. Stabilizer bar action. In A, the frame is moving up and down, but is not tipping. The bar offers no torsional resistance. In B, the frame is tipping to the right, pressing down on 1 and lifting up on 2. The bar must be twisted to allow this action. Resistance to twisting will minimize rolling or tipping motion of frame

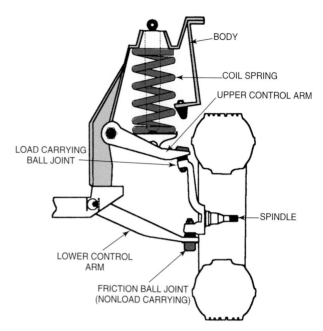

Figure 24-27. Coil spring mounted above the upper control arm. Note the narrow lower control arm. (FMC)

Figure 24-26. Independent front wheel suspension, using long and short control arms and coil springs. Note stabilizer bar. (General Motors)

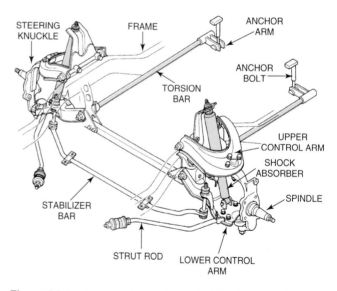

Figure 24-28. A torsion bar, independent front suspension system as used on a rear-wheel drive truck. (Mazda)

Coil Spring Front Suspension

Figure 24-30 shows a typical independent front suspension that uses rubber bushing control arm pivots. The top of the coil spring rests in a cup-like spot against the frame. The bottom of the coil spring is supported by a pad on the lower control arm. The top of each shock absorber is fastened to the frame; the bottom is attached to the lower control arm.

When the wheel strikes a bump, it is driven upward. This causes arms to pivot upward, compressing the spring and shock. Rubber bumpers limit control arm travel and soften the blow when the limit is reached. For steering, the front wheel steering knuckle pivots on ball joints.

A current front suspension system (one side) is shown in **Figure 24-31.** The spindle, or steering knuckle, pivots on ball joints. Rubber bushings are used for the control arms. In **Figure 24-32,** the coil spring is mounted on top of the upper control arm, with the upper end supported in a tall housing that is an integral part of the body and frame.

Torsion Bar Front Suspension

A torsion bar is located on each side of the frame in the front of the vehicle. The lower control arm is attached to the

Figure 24-29. A transverse torsion bar front suspension assembly. The torsion bar runs across the width of the chassis. This setup also eliminates the need for strut rods. (Moog)

free end of the torsion bar. When the wheel is driven upward, the lower control arm moves upward, twisting the long spring-steel bar. **Figure 24-33** shows a view of a complete torsion bar suspension. **Figure 24-34** illustrates a similar setup for hinging the lower control arm. Notice that the arm pivots on a stub shaft. The torsion bar fits into the end and does not support the arm. It merely produces spring resistance to up-and-down movement.

Figure 24-30. Exploded view of long and short arm suspension setup. (Chrysler)

Figure 24-31. One side of a front suspension system that is used on a two-wheel drive truck. Study the construction. (Dodge)

Figure 24-34. A torsion bar with lower control arm. The control arm is supported on the inner stub shaft, not on the torsion bar itself. (Moog)

Figure 24-32. A coil spring mounted on top of the upper control arm and attached to the body. (Moog)

Figure 24-33. A torsion bar front suspension for a rear-wheel drive vehicle. The torsion bar is fastened to the lower control arm in this setup. Some four-wheel drive vehicles, with torsion bars, have them connected to the upper control arm. This provides increased ground clearance. (Nissan)

Figure 24-35. Cutaway view of a MacPherson strut front suspension assembly that is mounted to the vehicle subframe. This setup is used with a front-wheel drive car. (Ford Motor Company)

MacPherson Strut Front Suspension

Most modern vehicles, especially those with front-wheel drive, use the MacPherson strut front suspension systems, **Figure 24-35.** Note that the MacPherson strut contains a coil spring, which is mounted on top of the heavy strut-and-pedestal assembly. Rubber pads at the top and bottom of the coil spring cushion spring application and reduce squeaks, **Figure 24-36.** The entire MacPherson strut assembly is attached to the steering knuckle at the

lower part of the pedestal, **Figure 24-37.** The bottom of the MacPherson strut assembly is attached to the single control arm through a ball joint.

The entire strut assembly turns when the wheel is turned. A bearing or thrust plate at the top of the strut assembly allows relative movement between the assembly and the vehicle body. The ball joint allows the strut assembly to turn in relation to the control arm. The strut contains a *damper*, which operates in the same manner as a conventional shock absorber. Most damper assemblies have a protective cover that keeps dirt and water away from the damper piston rod.

Figure 24-36. Exploded view of a MacPherson strut assembly. (Pontiac)

Figure 24-37. A MacPherson strut attached to the steering knuckle. Note the stabilizer bar. (Ford Motor Company)

Solid Axle Front Suspension

The use of the solid axle front suspension is generally confined to trucks and off-road vehicles. This system uses a solid steel dead axle (does not turn with wheels) with a leaf spring at each side. Pivot arrangements between the axle and the wheel spindles allow the wheels to swivel on each end, **Figure 24-38.** A solid axle, four-wheel drive setup is shown in **Figure 24-39.**

Any up or down movement of either front wheel causes a vertical tipping effect of both wheels because they share a common axle. This effect upsets the steering geometry and

Figure 24-38. A solid front axle, leaf spring, suspension assembly. (Moog)

The advantage of the MacPherson strut is its compact design, which allows more room for service on small car bodies. In addition to the common MacPherson strut coil spring arrangement discussed above, a slightly different design places the coil spring between the frame or body and the lower control arm. While this design is not common, it does qualify as a MacPherson strut suspension.

Figure 24-39. A solid front axle, link and coil spring front suspension as used with one particular four-wheel drive truck. (Dodge)

imposes a twisting motion to the frame. See **Figure 24-40.** One exception to this is the Twin-I-beam front axle used in some light trucks. In this setup, two beams are used. Each beam pivots independently, **Figure 24-41.** Coil springs are placed between the I-beam axles and the vehicle's frame.

Figure 24-40. Tipping effect of solid front axle.

Figure 24-41. Ford Twin I-Beam front suspension as used on light duty (1/2, 3/4, and 1 ton) trucks. A coil spring rides between each individual I-beam and the frame. Each axle is free to pivot up and down without affecting the other. (Ford)

Rear Suspension Systems

Rear suspensions on vehicles with a solid rear axle housing generally utilize coil springs or leaf springs. When the vehicle has an independent rear suspension system, coil springs, MacPherson struts, a single transverse leaf spring, or even torsion bars can be used.

Solid Rear Axle Suspensions

Figure 24-42 illustrates a typical suspension system utilizing coil springs. The rear axle housing is mounted on

Figure 24-42. View of a rear suspension system that uses coil springs, with upper and lower control arms. This setup is also termed a four-link suspension. (Cadillac)

springs and is attached to a set of upper and lower control arms (also called control links or control struts) to provide proper rear axle housing alignment. The control arm pivot points are insulated by rubber bushings. One end of the arm is connected to the housing; the other end is connected to the frame. The arm arrangement allows the rear axle housing to move up and down but prevents excessive front-to-back and side-to-side movement.

The shock absorbers in **Figure 24-43** are straddle mounted (shocks are closer together at the top than the bottom). In addition to controlling oscillation, straddle mounting assists in controlling side movement between the frame and the axle housing and helps resist tipping on turns. Another type of solid rear suspension is shown in **Figure 24-44.** This type is used with the solid rear axles found on many front-wheel drive vehicles.

Independent Rear Suspensions

Some rear end designs have differential housing attached to the vehicle's frame and drive the rear wheels through open (or enclosed) axles, using universal joints to allow flexibility. These assemblies were discussed in more detail in Chapter 22. The independent rear suspension system in **Figure 24-45** uses a MacPherson strut assembly for each rear wheel. These strut assemblies are mounted to the spindles. Suspension movement is controlled with lateral links and trailing arms. A stabilizer bar is also used.

Coil springs and MacPherson struts are also widely used. There are other variations in the use of control arms. **Figure 24-46** illustrates a semi-independent rear suspension that incorporates a twisting cross beam axle setup. The axle connects to the vehicle's underbody and holds the wheels in correct alignment.

Suspension Lubrication

Chassis grease is compounded to enter fittings readily, lubricate well, stay flexible at low temperatures, adhere to the moving parts, and resist water. Where chassis grease is needed for the suspension system, *grease fittings* are provided. Grease fittings are often used on the ball joints. Some vehicles have fittings on the control arm bushings. Some suspension parts have *plugs* instead of fittings. If plugs are installed, the technician must replace them with grease fittings. After greasing is completed, the plugs can be replaced or the fittings can be left in place for the next lubrication.

Figure 24-43. Leaf spring rear suspension system. Springs control axle housing rotation, fore-and-aft and side-to-side movement. Strattle mounted (angled) shock absorbers also help control side-to-side movement. (Toyota)

Figure 24-44. A solid rear axle assembly as used with one particular front-wheel drive car. This axle is used on standard, as well as with electronic level control (ELC) suspensions. (Pontiac)

Figure 24-52. Level control system dryer unit. Note the use of silica as a drying agent. (Oldsmobile)

Figure 24-53. Automatic level control valve is actuated by over-travel level. (Pontiac)

valve to admit more air to the shocks. When the air shocks have raised the vehicle to the distance that the vehicle was at before the load was added, the lever will cause the valve to close. To prevent bumps from actuating the control valve, a time delay mechanism is built into the sensor.

From the control unit, air passes to the shock absorbers or struts. These operate in the same manner as the air shock absorbers discussed earlier in this chapter. The only difference is that varying air pressures are controlled by the sensor instead of an outside air pressure source. A typical air shock is illustrated in **Figure 24-55.**

Computerized Ride Control Systems

Computerized ride control systems, also called *active suspensions*, are computer-controlled electronic suspension systems that can adapt to specific driving conditions. See **Figure 24-56.**

Typical ride control systems contain steering sensors, which monitor the direction and speed of steering wheel rotation; brake sensors, which monitor brake system applications; and an acceleration signal sensor, which monitors the rate of acceleration. A control module receives signals from these sensors and uses them to determine output signals to the actuators. The actuators control the flow of hydraulic fluid to adjustable shock absorbers. Many systems have a mode select switch, which allows the driver to adjust the ride control system.

Under normal driving conditions, a driver can pick the ride best suited for handling and comfort. For example, if a vehicle is being driven on a winding road, the driver can pick a firm setting. In this mode, the ride control module will signal actuators to close valves on the adjustable shocks. This will produce a stiff ride and the vehicle will corner well. If the

Figure 24-55. Special air shock absorber used with an automatic level control system. Note rubber boot. (Buick)

Figure 24-54. Control sensor action when a load is added to the vehicle. Vehicle curb height is decreased, causing the over-travel lever to move upward to open the intake valve and pass compressed air to the shock absorbers. (Buick)

Figure 24-56. A computerized, Continuously Variable Road Sensing Suspension (CV-RSS) system. These suspensions adjust automatically to the ever changing road conditions—smooth, rough, corners, etc. (Cadillac)

vehicle is being driven on a highway, however, the driver can switch to a soft mode. In this mode, the valves in the adjustable shocks are opened and a soft, comfortable ride is produced.

Under certain driving conditions, the control module can override the driver's selection. During periods of hard braking, for example, a brake sensor signals the control module to close the valves on the adjustable front shocks or struts. This stiffens front shocks and minimizes front-end diving. Under heavy acceleration, the acceleration sensor signals the control module to stiffen the adjustable rear shocks or strut, preventing rear-end squatting. A road-sensing suspension system is shown in **Figure 24-57.** System design and operation vary from manufacturer to manufacturer.

STEERING
SENSOR

SPEED
SENSITIVE
STEERING
SOLENOID

STRUT

ROTARY
COMBINATION
SENSOR

ROAD SENSING
SUSPENSION MODULE

ELECTRONIC LEVEL
CONTROL COMPRESSOR

SHOCK
ABSORBER

ROTARY
COMBINATION
SENSOR

Figure 24-57. A schematic of a road sensing suspension (RSS) system, which controls shock absorber and strut damping forces, in relation to changing road and driving conditions. This system is able to make these changes in 15-20 milliseconds (thousandths of a second). Speed sensitive steering on this vehicle is also controlled by this system. (Cadillac)

When the driver steers the vehicle into a sharp turn, a steering sensor sends an appropriate signal to the control module. The module signals the actuators to increase shock pressure on the outside of the vehicle. This action decreases vehicle leaning in turns. Other systems also provide programmed ride control. The degree of stiffness and handling can be programmed into the system by the driver. Modern systems are usually computer-controlled, with a control pad or switch in the passenger compartment.

Summary

Vehicle bodies must be suspended on some type of spring devices to isolate them from the irregularities of the road. The body and frame unit must be rigid and strong to provide secure anchorage for the suspension system and to provide alignment and the securing of all parts.

Some cars use separate frames, while others use unibody construction. Where the separate frame is used, it is constructed of steel channels or square tubing and welded together. It has various crossmembers to provide mounting and bracing points.

There are three types of springs used to suspend the car: leaf springs, coil springs, and torsion bars. The suspension system depends on these springs, as well as control arms and strut rods, to control suspension operation. Stabilizer bars help prevent tipping or rolling on corners. All modern vehicles use ball joints to provide for movement between the spindle and the control arm. Hydraulic shock absorbers are used to control spring oscillation. Most vehicles have independent wheel suspensions on the front. This is accomplished by mounting the wheel assembly on the ends of pivoting control arms. Any of the three springs can be used in this system.

The rear axle can be independent or solid. Common springs used in the rear axle assembly are the coil spring, leaf spring, or torsion bar. Various combinations of control arms or stabilizer bars are used, depending on the type of drive. Many modern rear suspensions make use of MacPherson strut assemblies.

Some air shocks are manually pumped up by the driver. Ride control systems are usually air powered. They may be controlled by a leveling valve or by an on-board computer.

Know These Terms

Suspension system
Sprung weight
Unsprung weight
Body-over-frame construction
Unibody construction
Spring
Leaf spring
Spring shackles
Coil spring
Torsion bar
Spring oscillation
Shock absorber
Telescoping shock absorber
Air shock absorber
Control arm
Strut
Ball joint
Load-carrying ball joint
Follower joint
Tension loading
Compression loading
Preloaded
Stabilizer bar
Conventional front suspension
MacPherson strut front suspension
Damper
Rear suspension
Grease fitting
Plugs
Automatic level control system
Air compressor
Height control sensor
Computerized ride control system
Active suspension

Review Questions—Chapter 24

Do not write in this book. Write your answers on a separate sheet of paper.

1. Technician A says that the wheels, tires, and rear axle are part of the vehicle's unsprung weight. Technician B says the parts of the vehicle that are supported by the suspension system are the unsprung weight. Who is right?
   (A) A only.
   (B) B only.
   (C) Both A & B.
   (D) Neither A nor B.

2. In _____ construction, the body sections serve as structural members.
   (A) stub
   (B) unibody
   (C) conventional
   (D) None of the above.

3. The hinge shackle used with a leaf spring allows it to change _____ as it moves up and down.

4. All the following statements about coil springs are true, EXCEPT:
   (A) coil springs can be part of a conventional suspension.
   (B) coil springs are not used as part of a MacPherson strut suspension.
   (C) coil springs can be installed at the front axle.
   (D) coil springs can be installed at the rear axle.

5. A torsion bar absorbs shocks by _____ .
   (A) compressing
   (B) expanding
   (C) twisting
   (D) bending

6. Technician A says that both ends of the torsion bar are anchored to the frame. Technician B says that air springs are obsolete. Who is right?
   (A) A only.
   (B) B only.
   (C) Both A & B.
   (D) Neither A nor B.

7. The coil spring can be mounted in all of the following ways, EXCEPT:

    (A) between the frame and the rear axle.

    (B) between the frame and the lower control arm.

    (C) between the body and the upper control arm.

    (D) between the upper and lower control arms.

8. If the shock absorber did not control spring oscillation, what would happen to the oscillations?

9. How does the shock absorber control spring oscillation?

10. Technician A says that some ball joints are tension loaded. Technician B says that some ball joints are compression loaded. Who is right?

    (A) A only.

    (B) B only.

    (C) Both A & B.

    (D) Neither A nor B.

11. When the solid front axle is used, it is generally used on _____ .

    (A) older trucks

    (B) large cars

    (C) four-wheel drive vehicles

    (D) Both A & C.

12. What is the greatest advantage of the independent front wheel suspension system?

13. What does a stabilizer bar prevent?

14. Name the two types of loading that ball joints can be placed under.

15. Which of the following statements about a load-carrying ball joint is true?

    (A) It may be tension or compression loaded.

    (B) It carries the majority of the vehicle weight.

    (C) It does not swivel as well as move up and down.

    (D) It is the only ball joint on a MacPherson strut assembly.

16. Name the major internal parts of the telescoping shock absorber.

17. Technician A says that some of the newer suspension joints can forego greasing for periods up to 30,000 miles (48 270 km). Technician B says that rubber bushed shackles should be oiled every 5000 miles (8000 km). Who is right?

    (A) A only.

    (B) B only.

    (C) Both A & B.

    (D) Neither A nor B.

18. What kind of springs can be used on rear axle assemblies?

    (A) Leaf.

    (B) Coil.

    (C) Torsion bar.

    (D) All of the above.

19. All of the following statements about the automatic level control height control valve are true, EXCEPT:

    (A) the valve is attached to the vehicle frame.

    (B) the valve is connected to a suspension arm or rear axle housing.

    (C) the valve senses any distance changes between the frame and drivetrain.

    (D) the valve is operated by an overtravel lever.

20. An active suspension system can be controlled by _____.

    (A) a computer

    (B) the driver through a control pad or switch

    (C) the engine control computer

    (D) Both A & B.

Cutaway of a power rack-and-pinion spool valve assembly that uses an electromagnet to vary the steering effort required in response to vehicle speed and road conditions. (General Motors)

25

Steering Systems

After studying this chapter, you will be able to:

- Identify the major parts of a parallelogram steering system.
- Identify the major parts of a rack-and-pinion steering system.
- Compare the parallelogram and rack-and-pinion steering systems.
- Explain the operation of a parallelogram power steering gear.
- Explain the operation of a rack-and-pinion power steering gear.
- Describe the different types of power steering pumps.

This chapter is concerned with the principles and components of the steering system. Modern steering systems are either parallelogram systems or rack-and-pinion systems.

Both are available in manual and power-assisted versions. Studying this chapter will prepare you for Chapter 27, which discusses wheel alignment.

Steering System

The steering system is designed to allow the driver to move the front wheels to the right or left with a minimum of effort and without excessive movement of the steering wheel. Although the driver can move the wheels easily, road shocks are not transmitted to the driver. This absence of road shock transfer is referred to as the nonreversible feature of steering systems.

Many types of steering systems have been used in the past, **Figure 25-1**. This chapter will cover the steering systems currently used. Although there are some variations, all steering systems have some principles and components in

Figure 25-1. One particular conventional steering linkage arrangement as used with a rear-wheel drive pickup truck. The truck has been raised on a single-post lift to expose the steering linkage. (Dodge)

common. The basic steering system can be divided into three main assemblies:

- The spindle and steering arm assemblies.
- The linkage assembly connecting the steering arms and steering gear.
- The steering wheel, steering shaft, and steering gear assembly.

These assemblies are used in all steering systems. The principles and components of each assembly are discussed in the following sections.

Spindle and Steering Arm Assembly

When the front wheels are turned, the *spindle assembly* units (sometimes called the steering knuckles) swivel on the ball joints of a conventional suspension system or on the ball joint and upper bearing assembly of a MacPherson strut assembly. The ball joints and other suspension system components were discussed in Chapter 24. **Figure 25-2** illustrates a MacPherson strut suspension.

Spindle

The spindle is attached to the wheel rim and tire, as well as the brake drum or rotor. These parts rotate on the spindle.

The spindle is also the mounting surface for the stationary brake components, such as the caliper and pads or the backing plate, wheel cylinder, and shoes. A typical spindle assembly is shown in **Figure 25-3.**

Steering Arms

The *steering arms* are either bolted to the spindle or forged as an integral part of the spindle. The outer ends of the steering arms have a tapered hole to which the tie rod end ball sockets are attached. When the steering arms are moved to the right or left, they force the spindle to pivot on the ball joints or on the ball joint and strut top bearing, depending on system design. See **Figure 25-4.**

Steering Linkage

Linkage is necessary to connect the steering gear pitman arm to the steering arms. The two linkages most commonly used today are the *parallelogram linkage* and the *rack-and-pinion linkage*. The parallelogram linkage was the most common arrangement for many years and is still used on large cars and pickup trucks. The rack-and-pinion has been used on most small and mid-size vehicles for the past 15 years. The two types of linkage are discussed in the following sections.

RACK AND PINION ASSEMBLY

MACPHERSON STRUT

Figure 25-2. An overall view of a MacPherson strut steering setup. (Toyota Motor Corporation)

Figure 25-3. A ball joint steering knuckle assembly as used with a four-wheel drive vehicle. No kingpin is used. The steering knuckle swivels on the upper and lower ball joints. Note the centerline drawn through the ball joints. (Isuzu)

Figure 25-4. A —A steering arm, which is bolted to the spindle on a four-wheel drive front axle. B—This steering arm is forged as an integral part of the steering knuckle and spindle. Note the location of the tie rod connection. (General Motors)

Parallelogram Linkage

When viewed from the top, the parallelogram linkage is arranged in the shape of a parallelogram, **Figure 25-5.** Movement at the connecting points of the linkage pieces is handled by ***ball-and-socket connections***, such as those shown in **Figures 25-6** and **25-7.** The parts of the parallelogram linkage include the pitman arm, the center link, the idler arm, and the tie rods.

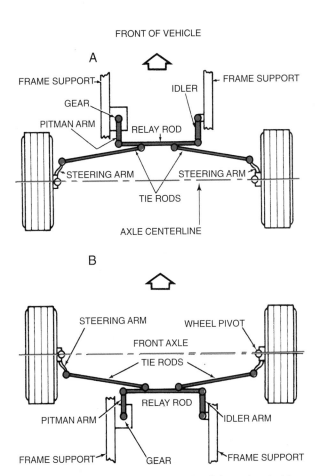

Figure 25-5. A—A parallelogram steering linkage located in front of the axle centerline. B—This parallelogram linkage is placed behind the axle centerline. These different linkage setups will help to maintain the suspension geometry as the steering and suspension move, keeping all parts in proper relationship to one another. (General Motors)

Pitman Arm

The ***pitman arm*** (also called the steering gear arm) is attached to the output shaft of the steering gear. The pitman arm is usually splined to the output shaft and is held in place by a large nut. See **Figure 25-8.** Movement of the steering gear causes the pitman arm to swing from side to side. The pitman arm may be equipped with a ball joint connection where it is attached to the center link, or it may have a hole to accept a ball stud.

Figure 25-8. A pitman arm which is removed from the steering gear. The pitman arm is fastened to the steering gear shaft with a nut and lock washer. (Chevrolet)

Figure 25-6. Two styles of ball-and-socket connections. If the tension spring on the side of the ball stud seat breaks on either type, it cannot collapse far enough to permit the socket seats to spread apart and drop the ball stud. Seat spreading is controlled by the steel block or bumper inside the spring. (Toyota)

Center Link

The *center link* (also called a relay rod, or drag link) is a long bar that transfers movement from the pitman arm to the other parts of the steering linkage. The pitman arm is attached to one end of the center link by means of a ball joint connection, **Figure 25-9.**

Idler Arm

The end of the center link opposite the pitman arm is attached to an *idler arm* with a ball joint connection. The idler arm pivots on metal bushings or bearings that are placed on a solid shaft that is bolted to the frame. Some idler arms pivot on rubber bushings. The idler arm is arranged so it is parallel to the pitman arm. The purpose of the idler arm is to keep the center link in alignment as it is moved by the pitman arm. Two idler arms used in one particular steering setup are shown in **Figure 25-9.**

Tie Rods

Tie rods, **Figure 25-10,** are used to connect the steering arms to the center link. The parallelogram steering system has two inner tie rods and two outer tie rods. One end of each tie rod has a ball joint socket, which is used to connect the rod to the steering arms or center link. The ball sockets are commonly called the tie rod ends. The other end of each rod is threaded.

A threaded *tie rod sleeve* is installed between the tie rods to form a tie rod assembly. The threads on one side of the assembly are left-hand threads, while the threads on the other side are right-hand threads. Therefore, turning the sleeve will change the length of the assembly. Tie rod assembly length can be changed to adjust toe. This is discussed in more detail in Chapter 26. One type of adjustable tie rod end is shown in **Figure 25-11.** A typical tie rod adjustment procedure is shown in **Figure 25-12.**

Figure 25-7. Different types of ball socket tie rod ends. B uses a nylon bearing, while A and C employ a metal-to-metal bearing surface.

Figure 25-9. A center link with other related steering linkage parts. (Chevrolet)

Figure 25-10. Tie rods connecting steering arms (knuckles) to the center link (relay rod). (Geo)

Figure 25-11. Adjustable tie rod end. The ball socket can be screwed in or out of tie rod. When proper adjustment is achieved, it is retained by tightening the clamp on the tie rod. This will bind the tie rod threads against those on the ball socket end.

Tie rod assemblies are usually equal length and about the same length as the lower control arms. As the frame (to which the center link is fastened via the pitman arm and idler arm) moves up and down in relation to the spindle, there will

TURN DOWNWARD TO INCREASE ROD LENGTH

TURN UPWARD TO DECREASE ROD LENGTH

LEFT-HAND SLEEVE

TURN DOWNWARD TO DECREASE ROD LENGTH

TURN UPWARD TO INCREASE ROD LENGTH

RIGHT-HAND SLEEVE

Figure 25-12. Tie rod adjustment. This type uses a double-end sleeve with two clamps. (Mercury)

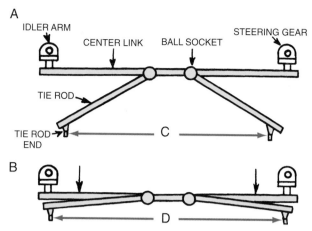

A

IDLER ARM   CENTER LINK   BALL SOCKET   STEERING GEAR

TIE ROD

TIE ROD END   C

B

D

Figure 25-13. The center link and tie rods should be nearly parallel. A—Setup with the tie rods and center link not parallel (front view). Notice distance C between tie rod ends. B—When the body of the vehicle dips downward, the center link is carried down with the frame. The tie rod ends are fastened to the steering arms and cannot move down. As the center link travels down, the angle between the link and the rods narrows. The tie rods must spread out (distance D), forcing the steering arms out and toeing the wheels in. When a vehicle is at normal curb height, the link and rods should be almost parallel, as in B. In this position, the link can move up and down with a minimal effect on toe-in and toe-out.

be minimum disturbance in toe-in and toe-out, since the control arm and tie rod assemblies will be moving through almost identical arcs. This similarity of arcs keeps the tie rods and spindle in the same relative position when driving over rough roads.

Parallelogram Component Arrangement

The center link and the tie rods should be as close to parallel as possible (when viewed from front). This will help eliminate toe-in and toe-out changes as the frame moves up and down, **Figure 25-13.** A complete parallelogram linkage system is shown in **Figure 25-14.**

Another type of linkage arrangement used on trucks with a solid front axle is shown in **Figure 25-15.** Notice that the tie rod is one piece and is connected at each end to the steering arms. A drag link, working fore and aft, connects the pitman arm (sometimes referred to as the steering sector shaft arm) to an extension on the spindle. When the drag link swivels this spindle, the action is transferred to the steering arms by the tie rod.

Rack-and-Pinion Linkage

The rack-and-pinion steering system contains fewer linkage components than the parallelogram system. There is no pitman arm, idler arm, or center link. The steering column shaft is connected directly to the pinion, or sector shaft. The pinion operates the rack section, which operates the tie rods and, therefore, the steering knuckles. See **Figure 25-16.**

The only rack-and-pinion linkage parts are inner and outer tie rods. The outer tie rod ends resemble those discussed earlier in this chapter. The inner tie rod ends are a simple ball socket arrangement that is covered with a bellows or boot to keep out water and dirt. The inner tie rod can turn

TIE ROD ASSEMBLY (LH)   RELAY ROD   TIE ROD ASSEMBLY (RH)

CLAMP POSITIONER

PITMAN ARM

IDLER ARM AND SUPPORT ASSEMBLY

Figure 25-14. Top view of a parallelogram linkage. Each tie rod can be adjusted without changing toe-in or toe-out of the opposite wheel. This allows a proper setting and leaves the steering wheel in the straight ahead position. (Oldsmobile)

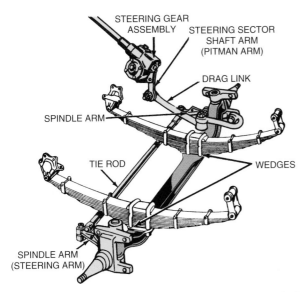

Figure 25-15. Steering linkage. This drawing shows a typical linkage setup on a solid axle, light truck application. The steering arm (spindle arm) on the driver's side acts as a bell crank. (Ford)

Figure 25-16. Exploded view of a rack-and-pinion steering gearbox assembly. Both ends of the rack are attached to the steering arms (not shown) by means of the tie rods. (General Motors)

in its socket, and toe adjustments are made by loosening a locknut and turning the inner tie rod in the outer tie rod. A few rack-and-pinion units have adjustment sleeves that are similar to those used in parallelogram linkage systems.

Steering Wheel, Steering Shaft, and Steering Gear

The *steering wheel*, *steering shaft*, and *steering gear* are important parts of the steering system. Steering effort begins at the steering wheel and shaft. The steering gear transforms the turning motion of the shaft to the linear movement of the linkage.

Steering Wheel

Besides the steering wheel's obvious job of allowing the driver to input steering motion, it contributes to steering ease by its size. The larger the steering wheel, the less effort required to make turns. This is important on vehicles without power steering.

Steering Shaft

The steering shaft connects the steering wheel and the steering gear. In the past, it consisted of an upper shaft made of hardened steel, a flexible coupling, and a lower, or stub, shaft splined to match the input shaft of the steering gear. The modern steering shaft has a two-piece upper shaft, which is designed to collapse if the driver is thrown against the steering wheel during an accident. The steering shaft often has a flexible joint to allow steering effort to be transmitted through at an angle. A modern steering shaft is shown in **Figure 25-17.**

Steering Shaft Coupling

The *steering coupling* absorbs road vibrations that get past the other steering system linkage. It consists of a rubber disc and is connected between the upper and lower steering shafts. The disc is firm enough to accurately transmit steering effort between the shafts. Vibrations and road shocks transmitted from the lower shaft twist the rubber instead of traveling to the upper shaft. A typical steering shaft coupling assembly is shown in **Figure 25-18A.**

Steering Shaft Universal Joint

Many steering shafts have one or more *universal joints,* which allow the shaft to be located at various convenient angles without moving the steering gear. Universal joints also relieve the mounting stresses and deflecting (bending) forces sometimes encountered in a solid shaft. In addition, the universal joint dampens steering shock and vibration transfer to the steering wheel. See **Figure 25-18B.**

Steering Gear

The steering gear is designed to multiply the driver's turning torque so the front wheels may be turned easily. When the parallelogram linkage is used, the torque developed by the driver is multiplied through gears and is then transmitted to the wheel spindle assemblies through the linkage. On the rack-and-pinion steering system, the steering column shaft is

Figure 25-17. An exploded view of a standard (non-tilt) steering column assembly used with an airbag. Columns vary in design and construction. 1—Locking hex nut. 2—Retaining ring. 3—Airbag coil assembly. 4—Wave washer. 5—Connector shroud. 7—Shaft lock spacer. 8—Retaining ring. 9—Shaft lock. 10—Turn signal cancel cam assembly. 11—Upper bearing spring. 12—Binding HD cross recess screw. 13—RD wash HD screw. 14—Switch actuator arm. 15—Turn signal switch assembly. 16—HD Screw. 17—Thrust washer. 18—Buzzer switch assembly. 19—Lock retaining screw. 20—Steering column housing assembly. 21—Sector. 22—Steering column lock cylinder set. 25—Rack preload spring. 26—Switch actuator rack. 27—Solenoid cable assembly. 28—Connector clip. 29—Switch actuator rod. 30—Upper bearing retainer. 31—Bearing retaining bushing. 32—Bearing assembly. 33—Spring thrust washer. 34—Spring and bolt assembly. 35—Horn circuit contact. 36—Flathead cross recess screw. 37—Shift lever gate. 38—Switch actuator pivot pin. 39—Binding HD cross recess screw. 40—Housing cover. 41—Pivot and pulse switch assembly. 42—Buzzer switch retaining clip. 43—Wiring protector. 45—Retaining ring. 46—Steering shaft assembly. 48—Shift lever spring. 49—Gearshift lever bowl assembly. 50—Gearshift bowl shroud. 51—Bowl lower bearing. 52—Steering column jacket assembly. 54—Wash HD screw. 55—Dimmer and ignition switch mounting stud. 56—Connector body bracket assembly. 57—Hexagon nut. 58—Solenoid bracket. 59—Adjuster housing assembly. 60—Ball joint cap. 61—Solenoid protector. 62—Hex washer head screw. 63—Interlock solenoid assembly. 66—Cable retainer. 67—Flat HD screw. 68—Ignition switch assembly. 69—Hex washer HD tapping screw. 70—Dimmer switch assembly. 71—Dimmer switch actuator rod. 73—Shift tube assembly. 74—Spring thrust washer. 75—Shift tube return spring. 76—Adapter and bearing assembly. 77—Bearing retainer. 78—Lower bearing adapter clip. 79—Bearing preload washer. 80—Lower spring retainer. 81—Shaft sleeve.

Figure 25-18. Two different types of steering shaft flexible coupling designs. Compare A and B. Note the protective coupling shield used in B. This shield protects the joint from rocks, mud, etc. (General Motors)

connected directly to the pinion shaft. Turning the pinion moves the rack section, which moves the linkage. Late-model vehicles use either manual steering gears or power steering gears.

Manual Parallelogram Linkage Steering Gear

The simplest form of the manual steering gear used with parallelogram steering systems is the *conventional steering gear*, **Figure 25-19.** It consists of a steel shaft with a *worm*

1-TOP COVER.	8-ADJUSTING SCREW STOP.	15-DUST EXCLUDER.	22-GASKET.
2-CAPSCREW.	9-FOLLOWER PEG SCREW.	16-PITMAN ARM.	23-ADJUSTING SHIMS.
3-ADJUSTING SCREW.	10-FOLLOWER PEG.	17-WASHER.	24-END COVER.
4-LOCKNUT.	11-STEERING BOX.	18-CASTELLATED NUT AND COTTER PIN.	25-SEAL.
5-FILLER PLUG.	12-INNER COLUMN.	19-WORM GEAR.	26-NUT.
6-WASHER.	13-STEERING BOX BRACKET.	20-BEARINGS.	27-CAPSCREW.
7-GASKET.	14-OIL SEAL.	21-RACES.	

Figure 25-19. Exploded view of a worm and tapered pin (follower peg) type steering box.

gear on one end. The other end is attached to the steering shaft. A *pitman arm shaft* passes at right angles to the worm gear. The inner end of the pitman shaft (also called cross shaft, roller shaft, sector shaft, or gear shaft) engages the worm gear either through gear teeth, a round steel peg, a roller gear, or a notched arm that passes around a peg affixed to a ball nut that rides on the worm.

In **Figure 25-19**, a tapered peg, (10), rides in the worm grooves. When the worm is revolved, it causes the peg to follow along the worm grooves, imparting a turning motion to the pitman shaft assembly. Splines in the pitman arm attach it securely to the pitman shaft.

The worm gear end of the steering shaft is supported by ball or roller bearings located on each side of the worm. These bearings remove end and side play in the worm. Bearing adjustment is provided by shims. The pitman arm shaft operates in bushings or needle bearings. There is an adjustment screw to control worm and pitman shaft clearance.

A cast housing surrounds and holds all parts in alignment. The housing is partially filled with gear oil for lubrication. Seals prevent the escape of lubricant and keep out dust and dirt. The housing is bolted to the frame or some other rigid area of the vehicle. The steering shaft passes up through a steering column to the steering wheel.

Recirculating Ball Steering Gear

Figure 25-20 is a cross-section of the *recirculating ball steering gear.* Instead of a tapered peg riding in the worm grooves, this steering gear uses a ball nut that rides up and down the worm. Ball bearings ride half in the worm and half in the nut. When the worm is turned, the ball bearings impart an axial (lengthwise of shaft) thrust to the ball nut. Because the

Figure 25-20. Recirculating ball worm and nut steering gear. A—A simple steering gear action produced from a screw and nut. By turning the screw, the nut (ball nut) will travel up or down the threads of the screw (worm shaft). This turns the steering wheel rotary (around-and-around) motion into a lateral (side-to-side) movement of the steering linkage. B—Cross-sections of the recirculating ball worm and nut steering gear. Study part names, locations, and functions. (Dodge and FMC Corp.)

nut is prevented from turning, it will travel up or down, depending on the worm direction.

As the ball bearings roll, they reach the end of the groove in the nut and are forced through a return tube. Eventually, they re-enter the nut groove at the opposite end. This process accounts for the name recirculating ball steering gear.

One side of the nut has gear teeth cut into it. The pitman arm sector gear teeth engage the nut teeth. When the nut travels up or down, the pitman shaft is forced to rotate. The recirculating ball worm and nut steering gear reduces friction to a very low level, making it a very popular design.

Worm-and-Roller Steering Gear

A *worm-and-roller steering gear* is shown in **Figure 25-21.** The pitman shaft engages the worm by means of a

Figure 25-21. Cross-sections of a worm and roller manual steering gear. (Toyota)

roller with gear teeth cut around it. The roller is mounted on antifriction bearings. Because the roller is free to turn, the friction developed in a wiping gear action is bypassed. When the worm is rotated, the roller teeth follow the worm and impart a rotary motion to the pitman shaft.

Manual Rack-and-Pinion Steering Gear

A manual rack-and-pinion steering gear is shown in **Figures 25-22** and **25-23.** A steering shaft from the steering wheel fastens to the *pinion shaft*, usually through a universal joint. The teeth on the pinion are meshed with the teeth on the *rack.* When the pinion is turned, it forces the rack to move, either to the right or left. The ends of the rack are connected to the steering arms by flexible joints and short tie rods. All gear rack movement is transferred directly to the steering arms.

Steering Gear Reduction

The amount of *gear reduction* in steering gears depends on the vehicle type and weight, the steering characteristics (fast or slow) desired, and the ultimate use of the vehicle. Steering gear ratios will vary from 15:1 to 24:1. Steering wheel movement will average from 4 to 6 turns to move the wheels from full left to full right for standard manual steering gears. The more turns needed to move from full left to full right, the easier the steering. The modern steering gear ratio is a compromise between steering ease and handling.

Power Steering

Power steering is designed to reduce the effort needed to turn the steering wheel by utilizing hydraulic pressure to bolster (strengthen) the normal torque developed by the steering gear. Power steering systems should ease steering wheel manipulation and, at the same time, offer enough resistance that the driver can retain some road feel. Power steering is used with both conventional and rack-and-pinion systems. Both types of power steering systems are discussed in the following sections.

Figure 25-22. Cutaway view of a rack-and-pinion assembly. Note how the rack-and-pinion gears mesh.

Figure 25-23. An exploded view of a manual rack-and-pinion steering assembly. Study the overall construction and part layout carefully. (Subaru)

Road Feel

Road feel is the feeling imparted to the steering wheel by the wheels of a vehicle in motion. This feeling is very important to the driver in sensing and predetermining vehicle steering response.

A good driver can tell when the front wheels are approaching the walk (slipping sideways) point and if more or less turning effort is required to stabilize the vehicle body on turns or when driving in windy conditions. Complete and effortless power steering would rob the driver of valuable road feel. To maintain road feel, power steering systems require

some wheel effort. Wheel effort of approximately 1 to 9 lbs. pull on the steering wheel rim is acceptable.

Power Steering Components

All modern power steering systems are integral systems. These systems use control and use the hydraulic pressure directly within the steering gear housing. The steering gear housings used in integral systems are known as **self-contained power steering gears**. Pressure is provided by a hydraulic pump, usually belt driven by the engine, to produce the necessary hydraulic pressure. A few are driven by an electric motor. A typical integral power steering system is shown in **Figure 25-24.**

Figure 25-24. Integral power steering system. Note the gearbox and oil pump cutaways. (Chrysler)

In all self-contained power steering gears, a **control valve** is actuated by the driver's steering effort. This valve admits oil, under pressure, to one side of a **hydraulic piston** or the other. The pressure the oil creates against the piston is transferred to the pitman shaft, assisting the driver in turning the front wheels.

Self-Contained Power Steering Gear Components

The self-contained steering gear contains the control valve mechanism, the power piston, and the gears. Pressure developed by the unit is applied to the pitman shaft. All modern conventional power steering gears are **inline** units. **Figure 25-25** shows a basic inline unit. Notice that all the basic elements of the conventional manual steering gear are used. A pitman shaft (steering gear cross shaft) engages a recirculating ball nut that rides on a typical worm gear or shaft. The basic differences include the utilization of the ball nut as a hydraulic power piston and the addition of a **reaction unit**, a **pivot lever**, and a valve body containing a **spool valve.**

Unit Operation

In operation, oil under pressure from the pump enters the valve body through the inlet passage. When no effort (above 1 to 9 lb.) is being applied to the steering wheel, the reaction unit is centered and the pivot lever is straight up and down. This keeps the spool valve in a neutral position.

Two round washer-like reaction springs hold the center thrust bearing race in a neutral position, **Figure 25-25.** The center thrust bearing is attached to the worm shaft and secured between two thrust bearings. These bearings are, in turn, affixed to the worm shaft by a shoulder on the left end and a locknut on the right end. The bearings revolve with the

worm shaft, but the center thrust bearing remains stationary. The center thrust bearing can move back and forth with the worm shaft, but it cannot move around with it.

The lower end of the pivot lever rests in a cutout in the center thrust bearing. When the center thrust bearing is in the neutral position, the pivot lever is straight up and holds the spool valve in the neutral position, **Figure 25-26A.** With the spool valve in the neutral position, oil is fed to both sides of the power piston and to both reaction rings.

Oil also works its way around the balls between the power piston and the worm shaft. This oil collects in the hollow formed between the left end of the worm shaft and the left end of the power piston. Pressure created on the worm shaft end is counterbalanced by pressure created on the worm shaft balancing ring. In the neutral position, oil pressure is equalized on all sides and no hydraulic pressure is applied to the pitman shaft by the power piston.

Left Turn

When the steering wheel is turned to the left, the worm shaft attempts to impart motion to the power piston. Because the power piston has teeth that engage the pitman arm teeth, the resistance to turning offered by the wheels holds the power piston stationary.

Because the power piston does not want to move, the worm shaft (which has some lateral play) will start to screw out of the power piston. As it screws out just a few thousandths of an inch, it moves the center thrust bearing race with it. The center thrust bearing race will then move the bottom of the pivot lever to the right. This causes the top of the pivot lever to move the spool valve to the left.

When the spool valve moves to the left turn position, **Figure 25-26B,** it opens the left turn oil passageway and oil

Figure 25-25. Cross-section of a power steering unit. This is a self-contained, inline unit.

Figure 25-26. A—A spool valve in the neutral position. Note that the spool valve is centrally located and that pressurized oil passes to the power piston through both piston outlets. B—Spool valve in the left turn position. The valve has moved to the left. The right piston outlet is cut off from the source of pressurized oil. Return flow will now pass up through the right-side piston outlet. (Plymouth)

travels to the left turn power chamber. The right turn passageway can no longer receive pressurized oil, but it has opened to allow the oil to be returned from the right turn power chamber.

As soon as the spool valve is moved to the left, oil flows to the left turn power chamber and exerts a force on the power piston. Since the right turn power chamber oil is no longer pressurized, the power piston will be forced to the left. This squeezes the right turn power chamber oil out through the oil return passageways and back to the pump reservoir. Look at **Figure 25-27.**

As the oil pressurizes the left turn power chamber, it also flows to the right side reaction ring. This creates pressure that attempts to return the center thrust bearing to the neutral position. The round reaction springs also try to force the center thrust bearing back to the neutral position. These two forces on the center thrust bearing fight against the driver's turning force on the wheel, producing the essential road feel.

When the driver's turning force no longer exceeds the reaction ring pressure, the center thrust bearing will be forced back to the neutral position. This pivots the spool valve to neutral and equalizes the pressure on each side of the power piston.

Right Turn

A right turn produces the same action as a left turn, but the spool valve moves to the right and oil pressure is applied to the right turn power chamber. The worm shaft is connected to the steering shaft by a flexible connector. This connector allows the necessary worm shaft end movement. Maximum pump pressure for this unit is around 950 psi (6550 kPa). Oil leakage is prevented by neoprene O-rings that ride in grooves. Study **Figures 25-25** through **25-27.** Trace the oil flow patterns. Study the various parts and their actions.

Inline Unit with Torsion Bar and Rotating Spool Valve

A popular variation of the inline, self-contained power steering unit is shown in **Figure 25-28.** It employs a spool valve, but instead of sliding back and forth, the spool rotates a small amount inside the valve body. This type of power steering unit is referred to as an open-center, rotary-type, three-way valve or simply a **rotary spool valve**. The rotary spool valve is a very close fit in the valve body.

The steering shaft is connected to a coupling, which, in turn, is splined to the lower stub shaft. The stub shaft passes through and is pinned to the spool valve. The outer end of the stub shaft is pinned to a torsion bar (tempered steel bar designed to twist a certain amount when a turning force is applied). The inner end of the stub shaft floats (is free) on the bar.

The inner end of the torsion bar is pinned to the valve body cap. The valve body cap, in turn, is pinned to the worm shaft. A pressure line and return line from the steering pump are attached to the gear valve housing.

Oil pressure in the pressure cylinder will run approximately 125 psi (861.87 kPa) for normal driving, 400 psi (2758 kPa) for cornering, and up to 1200 psi (8274 kPa) for parking.

Figure 25-27. Oil flow during a left turn. Study the oil flow for this turn position. A right turn is merely a reversal of this when the spool valve is moved to the right by the valve-actuating lever.

Figure 25-41. Overall view of a power rack-and-pinion steering system showing hose and tubing routing. Note the power steering fluid cooler. This is an oil-to-air type unit. (Honda)

Power Steering Systems Can Be Operated Manually

In the event of pump pressure failure, power steering systems can be operated manually with somewhat more effort than required with a conventional manual steering gear. This is because there is always a mechanical connection through the gears, even when no hydraulic pressure is available. Extra effort is required to move the hydraulic fluid in the gearbox, as well as turn the wheels.

Power Steering Fluids

The fluid level in the power steering pump should be checked frequently. Check the level when the fluid is at its normal operating temperature. Most pumps have a dipstick for checking the fluid level, **Figure 25-42.** Fluid should be between the add and full marks. If the fluid level is low, inspect the entire system for leaks. If fluid must be added, always use the power steering fluid intended for the system. Most modern vehicles are designed to use special power steering fluid, not automatic transmission fluid. Always check manufacturer's specifications before adding fluid.

Electronic Steering Control

Electronic steering control systems are sometimes used on vehicles equipped with power steering. These systems reduce power steering assist at cruising speeds to increase control and road feel, and increase assist at low speeds to facilitate parking. If the electronic system fails, the power steering system operates normally.

Electronic steering systems are operated by a control module that relies on inputs from the vehicle speed sensor and a steering wheel rotation sensor. The control module uses information on steering wheel movement and vehicle speed to determine the amount of power steering assist provided by a flow control solenoid. The flow control solenoid is mounted in the high-pressure side of the power steering system, usually in the pump output passage. In some systems, a magnetic rack-and-pinion spool valve assembly is used instead of a flow control solenoid to vary steering assist.

In the near future, some vehicles will be equipped with fully electronic steering. With fully electronic steering, there will be no mechanical connection between the steering wheel and the steering gear. Sensors in the steering wheel will operate motors that turn the wheels.

Summary

Steering linkage is provided to transfer the force from the pitman arm to the steering arms. The two most popular linkage arrangements are the parallelogram arrangement and the rack-and-pinion arrangement. The various linkage parts are connected by ball-and-socket connections, which allow swiveling movement without end play.

The steering wheel and steering shaft deliver the turning effort to the steering gear. Vehicles can use either a manual steering gear or a power steering unit. Some popular types of gearing used in both manual and power systems include the recirculating ball, worm-and-sector, worm-and-taper pin, and worm-and-roller steering gears. Most new cars use rack-and-pinion steering.

Both conventional and rack-and-pinion steering gears can be power assisted. Both types of power steering systems are actuated by oil pressure. The pressurized oil is admitted to either side of the power cylinder as controlled by a valving setup.

Figure 25-42. Power steering fluid reservoir. A—Power steering pump reservoir and dipstick location on one engine. B—Dipstick showing the full cold side and the full hot side fluid levels. (Ford Motor Co.)

Road feel is maintained by the use of a torsion bar, balanced oil pressure, and return springs. The power steering system uses oil pressure to assist the driver only when the pull on the steering wheel exceeds 1 to 9 lbs. When the turning effort on the steering wheel falls below this amount, oil pressure is equalized on both sides of the power piston.

Oil pressure is provided by a high-pressure oil pump. The system can use the vane, rotor, roller-vane, or slipper-vane pump unit. The pump is connected to the power unit by high-pressure hoses. The correct fluid must always be used in the power steering system.

Know These Terms

Spindle assembly
Steering arm
Parallelogram linkage
Rack-and-pinion linkage
Ball and socket connections
Pitman arm
Center link
Idler arm
Tie rod
Tie rod sleeve
Steering wheel
Steering shaft
Steering gear
Steering coupling
Universal joint
Conventional steering gear
Worm gear
Pitman arm shaft
Recirculating ball
    steering gear
Worm and roller
    steering gear
Pinion shaft
Rack
Gear reduction
Power steering
Road feel
Self-contained power
    steering gear
Control valve
Hydraulic piston
Inline
Reaction unit
Pivot lever
Spool valve
Rotary spool valve
Power steering pump
Vane pump
Rotor pump
Roller vane pump
Slipper vane pump
Gear pump
Electronic steering control
    systems

Review Questions—Chapter 25

Do not write in this book. Write your answers on a separate sheet of paper.

1. The front wheels swivel on one or two _____ .
   - (A) bearings
   - (B) ball joints
   - (C) rubber bushings
   - (D) Both A & B.

2. Name four major components of the parallelogram steering linkage.

3. The steering arms are attached to the _____ .
   - (A) tie rod ends
   - (B) spindles
   - (C) center link
   - (D) Both A & B.

4. Technician A says that a ball-and-socket connection is used to attach the pitman arm to the center link. Technician B says that a ball-and-socket connection is used to attach the idler arm to the frame. Who is right?
   - (A) A only.
   - (B) B only.
   - (C) Both A & B.
   - (D) Neither A nor B.

5. Why does the modern steering shaft have a two-piece upper shaft?

6. The side of the idler arm opposite the center link is bolted to the _____.
   - (A) frame
   - (B) steering gear
   - (C) spindle
   - (D) None of the above.

7. The modern steering gear ratio is a compromise between _____ and _____ .

8. A self-contained power steering gear contains all the following hydraulic units, EXCEPT:
   - (A) control valve.
   - (B) hydraulic piston.
   - (C) pump.
   - (D) worm gear.

9. What part serves as the hydraulic power piston on a parallelogram steering gear?

10. What part serves as the hydraulic power piston on a rack-and-pinion steering gear?

11. Name three types of power steering pumps.

12. Power steering pressures on older vehicles could be as high as _____ pounds or _____ kPa.

13. Technician A says that automatic transmission fluid can be used to top off any power steering system. Technician B says that the power steering fluid level should only be checked when there is evidence of a leak. Who is right?
    - (A) A only.
    - (B) B only.
    - (C) Both A & B.
    - (D) Neither A nor B.

14. Why is a flexible coupling installed between the upper and lower steering shaft?

15. Technician A says that rack-and-pinion steering makes use of a worm and roller assembly to assist rapid rotation. Technician B says that recirculating balls are used in some steering gears to reduce friction. Who is right?
    - (A) A only.
    - (B) B only.
    - (C) Both A & B.
    - (D) Neither A nor B.

26

Wheels and Tires

After studying this chapter, you will be able to:
- Describe basic wheel rim design and construction.
- Describe various types of wheel hubs and bearings.
- Explain the methods of modern tire construction.
- Explain different tire construction and size designations.
- Identify tire and wheel size designations.
- Select appropriate tire inflation and rotation procedures.

This chapter will cover wheel rims, wheel hubs and bearings, and tires. While these items are common to all vehicles, enough variations exist to make a thorough understanding of these parts necessary. Upon completion of this chapter, you will be able to identify the major types of wheel rims, identify the differences in wheel hubs and bearings used in both front- and rear-wheel drive vehicles, and how to use the most current tire rating system.

Wheels

In the past, almost all factory supplied *wheel rims* (the assembly on which the tire is mounted) were made of *stamped steel*, either painted to match the vehicle's color or simply painted black. In the past, the only way to obtain any other type of wheel was from an aftermarket supplier. Today, *custom wheels* made of aluminum, magnesium, graphite, and other materials are available not only from the aftermarket, but as original equipment from vehicle manufacturers. These two major types of wheels are discussed in the following two sections.

Steel Wheels

Most stamped steel wheels are *drop center* types, as shown in **Figure 26-1**. It is made in two sections. The outer part forms the rim. The center section (sometimes called the spider) is spot welded to the rim. The center portion has four, five, or sometimes six holes used in mounting the wheel to the vehicle.

The center section of the rim is recessed or "dropped" to allow the tire to be removed easily. When one bead of the tire is placed in the dropped area, it is then possible to pull the opposite bead off the rim. Some wheels have *safety ridges* near the lips of the rim. In the event of a blowout, the safety

Figure 26-1. Typical drop center wheel. Center section (spider) can be riveted or welded to the rim. Note the drop center section to permit tire removal. Lightweight cast or forged aluminum wheels are finding increased use. (Chrysler)

ridges tend to keep the tire from moving into the dropped center, then coming off the wheel, **Figure 26-2**. The wheel must be manufactured to relatively close tolerances so that no vibration results when it is mounted, **Figure 26-3**.

Custom Wheels

Custom wheels made of aluminum, aluminum alloy, composite (graphite or plastic), or chromed steel are available as original equipment from many vehicle and aftermarket manufacturers. Some wheels are solid aluminum, while others have a steel core covered with aluminum. Alloy wheels are usually a mixture of aluminum and magnesium. Wire wheels are also available. **Figure 26-4** shows one particular original equipment custom wheel.

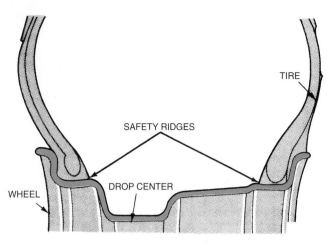

Figure 26-2. The safety rim has a ridge on each side of the wheel which retains the tire in case of a flat or blowout (ruptured tire). (Chrysler)

Figure 26-4. With improvements in materials and manufacturing, many vehicle manufacturers are offering aluminum custom wheels as standard equipment. One type of aluminum wheel used on a luxury sedan is shown here. (Oldsmobile)

Figure 26-3. All wheels must be true. In the upper illustration, left-handed arrow indicates the surface to be checked to determine side movement; right-hand arrow indicates area checked for out-of-roundness. The wheel is spun and a dial indicator is used to read any movement in .001″ (0.025 mm) increments. Runout should not exceed 1/16 or .0625″ (1.59 mm). (Chrysler)

Wheel Rim Size

Rim size is determined by three measurements: rim width, rim diameter, and flange height. Rim width and diameter are measured in inches. A letter (J, K, and so on) is used to indicate a definite flange height. For example, a K rim flange is 0.77″ (19.5 mm) high. See **Figure 26-5**. These measurements apply to rims made of any material.

Figure 26-5. Measuring points used to determine rim size. These numbers are sometimes cast on the inner side of the rim. (Jaguar)

Wheel Lug Bolts and Nuts

The wheel is bolted to the hub either by **lug bolts** that pass through the wheel and thread into the hub, or by threaded studs, called **wheel lugs**, that protrude from the hub. In the case of threaded studs, special tapered nuts called **lug nuts** are required. The lug nut taper matches the taper of the wheel rim mounting holes.

Most vehicles use right-hand thread wheel lugs on both sides. A few vehicles use left-hand threads (nut or bolt turns counterclockwise to tighten) on the driver's side, and right-hand threads (turn clockwise to tighten) on the passenger's side.

Torquing Wheel Nuts

When the wheel rims are made of aluminum, or a composite of aluminum and steel, proper **wheel nut torque** is critical. Always torque to the manufacturers' specifications. Although correct torque is not as important with steel rims, most modern vehicles have front disc brakes with thin rotors that can be deformed by overtorquing. A complete wheel, tire, and hub assembly is shown in **Figure 26-6**.

Do not use an impact wrench on any aluminum or alloy wheel, unless it is equipped with a **torque stick**. Torque sticks are flexible extensions which limit the output of the impact wrench to a preset value. When a certain torque value is reached, the stick will flex instead of transmitting further torque. A torque wrench should be used to tighten the rim if torque sticks are not available.

Wheel Hubs and Bearings

The **wheel hubs** form the mounting surface for the wheel and tire. Front-wheel hubs revolve about the steering knuckle spindle on either ball or tapered roller bearings. Rear-wheel hubs are usually part of the axle assembly on solid axle rear-wheel drive vehicles. Front-wheel drive vehicles, and vehicles with independent rear suspensions have separate hubs containing the wheel bearings.

Wheel Bearings

The drive and non-drive axles of a vehicle are supported by bearings. Two main types of bearings are used on modern vehicles:

- **Tapered roller bearings**, **Figure 26-7**.
- **Straight roller** and **ball bearings**, **Figure 26-8**.

Tapered roller bearings can be cleaned, regreased, and adjusted. The straight roller and ball bearings used on most modern front-wheel drive vehicles cannot be adjusted and cleaned, and are replaced as a unit. Wheel bearings use a quality, high temperature grease. **Figure 26-9** shows the location of this grease in a typical tapered roller bearing assembly. Notice that the hollow hub is not completely filled. The bearings, however, are thoroughly **packed**.

Figure 26-6. Front wheel and tire assembly. Safety ridges are used to prevent the tire from leaving the wheel when flat. (Toyota)

Figure 26-7. Exploded view of a front hub assembly which uses tapered roller bearings. 1—Steering knuckle. 2—Splash shield. 3—Grease seal. 4—Hub bolt. 5—Outer tapered roller bearing assembly. 6—Washer. 7—Castellated nut. 8—Dust cap. 9—Cotter pin. 10—Brake rotor assembly. 11—Inner tapered roller bearing assembly. 12—Bolt. 13—Lock washer. 14—Gasket. (Chevrolet)

Bearing Retaining Devices

Some method of holding the bearing on the wheels must be used. On front and rear wheels with tapered roller bearings, a **castellated nut** (slotted) is used on the end of the

Figure 26-8. Cross-sectional view of a rear hub assembly which uses inner and outer ball bearings. (Daihatsu)

Figure 26-9. Front hub showing placement of wheel bearing grease. (Dodge)

spindle to remove excessive play between the bearings and hub. A **safety washer** is used between the nut and the bearing. It has a metal tab that rides in a groove in the threaded area of the spindle.

When the hub and bearing spin, the rotating motion is not transferred to the nut, since the washer tab prevents it from turning. A new **cotter pin** is installed through the holes in the nut and spindle to keep the nut from turning. **Figure 26-10** shows the spindle nut, cotter pin and safety washer.

Figure 26-10. Exploded view of a front suspension and spindle assembly showing the spindle nut (5), cotter pin (3), safety washer (6), and fine adjustment nut set cover (4). 1—Brake caliper. 2—Hub cap. 3—Cotter pin. 4—Fine adjustment nut cover. 5—Spindle nut. 6—Safety washer. 7—Brake disc. 8—Outer bearing. 9—Wheel hub. 10—Oil seal. 11—Inner bearing 12—Dust cover. 13—Tie-rod end. 14—Lower control arm ball joint. 15—Knuckle spindle. (Mazda Motor Corp.)

Some adjusting nuts are staked into position by denting a thin lip on the nut itself. The lip is forced into a special groove in the spindle thread area. This is called a **staked nut**. The method allows for near zero play bearing adjustment. A new nut must be used each time bearing service is performed. **Figure 26-11** illustrates a staked nut.

A hub and bearing arrangement for one type of front-wheel drive is shown in **Figure 26-12**. The hub is splined to the outer drive shaft and is held in place by a locknut. The shaft (and hub) revolve in a special double-row ball bearing. Most bearings used on front-wheel drive axles are pressed onto the hub. The rear bearings of many front-wheel drive vehicles use a similar design.

Tires

Tires serve two main functions. They provide a cushioning action that softens the jolts caused by road irregularities. In this respect, they are actually serving as part of the suspension system. They also provide proper **traction**. Traction enables the vehicle to drive itself forward, provides a means of steering, and allows reasonably fast stopping. Therefore, quality tires are essential to safe vehicle operation.

Tire Construction

Tire treads and sidewalls are constructed of various types of natural and synthetic rubber (neoprene). The tire cords, which support the tread, can be made of rayon, nylon,

Figure 26-11. Staking a hub nut. A—A chisel is struck with a hammer, causing the nut lip to be bent into the spindle groove. B—Length and depth of proper stake. C—Finished staked nut. (Plymouth)

Figure 26-12. Cross-sectional view of a front-wheel drive front hub showing part arrangement. Study carefully. (Saab)

polyester, aramid, Kevlar, and fiberglass. Steel wire is often used in the belt section of tires. **Figure 26-13** shows typical tire construction.

The fabric casing uses layers of interwoven cord material to provide the tire with shape and strength. The cord material is wrapped around steel wires located at the point where the tire attaches to the rim. This contact point is called the **bead**. The beads provide strength to prevent the tire from opening up and leaving the wheel. Filler strips reinforce the bead section. The bead also provides the air seal between the rim and tire.

Many older tires were constructed with two or four layers, or **plies** of cord material, at an angle to the tire centerline.

Figure 26-13. Typical bias belted tire construction. This specific tire uses four sidewall plies (bias arrangement) and two belts beneath the tread. (BF Goodrich)

Look at **Figure 26-14A**. This is termed **bias construction**. Another method of arranging the plies is illustrated in **Figure 26-14B**. This is called **bias-belted tire construction**. Note the difference in cord angles between A and B.

The third type of construction is **radial tire construction**, in which the body cords cross the tire centerline almost at right angles to the belts, **Figure 26-14C**. Radial tires may also be belted. Today, radial tires are used for almost all applications, including retrofitting older vehicles that originally came with bias ply tires.

Tire Rating Information

Tire ratings are determined by a system which uses a series of letters and numbers molded on the side of the tire, or listed in the vehicle owners manual. The rating system identifies the tire size, rim size, and type of construction, as well as the maximum speed and load handling capabilities. A typical modern tire might have the series of letters and numbers shown in **Figure 26-15** on its sidewall.

The letter **P** indicates the tire is designed for a passenger vehicle, such as a car or light truck. Other possible tire designations are **T** for temporary, such as a space saver tire, **LT** for light truck, and **C** for commercial vehicles, such as large trucks. This letter may be absent on some tires.

The number **205** represents the tire's section width (width of the tread) in millimeters, measured at its widest point. This is the actual tire size. Sizes range from 145 to 315, with most sizes from about 185 to 235. The higher the number, the larger the tire.

The number **55** is the aspect ratio (relationship of a tire's cross-sectional height to its width). This means that this tire's height is 55 percent of its width, **Figure 26-15**. Other common aspect ratios are 50, 60, 65, 70, 75, and 80. The higher the aspect ratio, the taller the tire. Low aspect ratios provide more traction, while high aspect ratios give better mileage.

Figure 26-14. Typical tire construction. A—Bias ply (sidewall plies crisscrossed, no belts). B—Bias-belted (sidewall plies criss-crossed, belts beneath tread area). C—Radial construction. (BF Goodrich)

Figure 26-15. A typical metric tire size breakdown. Size (P 205/55VR16 for example) will be molded into the tire sidewall area. (Chevrolet)

The letter **V** is the *speed rating*. The speed rating gives the maximum speed at which the tire can be operated. This ranges from B (31 mph or 50 kmh) to Z (over 149 mph or 240 kmh). The letter **R** indicates radial ply construction. A bias ply tire will be marked **B**. Almost all passenger car and light truck tires made today are radial tires.

The number **16** is the rim diameter in inches. Modern wheel rims range from 12 inches to 17 inches. The most common rim sizes are 13, 14, and 15 inches. Other rim dimensions are discussed in the section on wheel rims.

Tire Quality Grading

All passenger and light truck vehicle tires currently produced are graded by the US Department of Transportation's (DOT) *uniform tire quality grading system*. The quality grading system is applicable to the three areas shown below.

The *temperature resistance rating* uses three letter grades: A, B, and C. While A offers the greatest resistance to heat generation, C provides the least. All tires must meet the C rating. Tire *traction rating* is also graded A, B, and C. A offers the best traction (wet roads), while C offers the minimum amount.

Tire *tread wear rating* is graded by using a set of numbers ranging from 100 to about 500. A tire that has a tread wear grade of 150 should supply approximately 50% more mileage than a tire with a tread wear rating of 100.

Other Tire Rating Numbers and Letters

Some tires have a number, such as 80, which indicates the tire's load index. The load index is the load carrying capacity of a tire. This particular number means that the tire would have a load carrying capacity of 992 pounds (450 kg). Therefore four of these tires could be installed on a vehicle which weighs, fully loaded, no more than 3968 pounds (1800 kg). Many tires have the speed rating letter after the load index number.

Some tires have the letters **M & S** on their sidewalls. This designates that it is an all-season tire. The letters M & S stand for mud and snow. Tires with this designation can be used on wet, muddy, or icy roads and will give a reasonable amount of traction in these conditions.

Special Service Tires

Many safety and high speed tires are available. High speed tires generally use steel wires which resist expansion from centrifugal force in the outer ply and tread areas. Steel, which helps to control distortion, also resists punctures better than fabric belts.

Most vehicles are now equipped with a compact, or *space saver spare tire*. It is designed to take up less cargo space and is lighter than a normal tire. The compact spare tire is for temporary use only. Use it to replace a flat until it is repaired or replaced. Do not rotate a compact spare in with the other tires. When replacing this tire, mount only on a special wheel designed for its use. Do not use hub caps or wheel covers on the rim as possible tire damage could result. Keep the space saver tire inflated to recommended pressure. A space saver spare tire is shown in **Figure 26-16**.

Determining the Correct Tire for a Vehicle

When replacing original equipment tires, the technician should take into consideration vehicle weight, type of suspension system, and horsepower. A tire that is too small will be overloaded. A tire that is too large will add to the vehicle's unsprung weight, upsetting the suspension system balance.

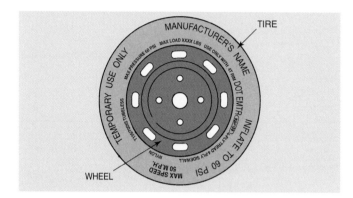

Figure 26-16. A compact spare tire is designed to be light, small, and most importantly, used only as a temporary tire.

A tire load information label can be found on most vehicles. It is generally located on the driver's door, on the door pillar, or inside the glove box. The load information label contains specific information on maximum vehicle load, tire size (including spare tire), and inflation pressures. Speed rated tires should be replaced with tires that have an equal or higher speed rating. Older vehicles with bias or bias-belted tires can be equipped with radial tires by the use of interchange charts, such as the one in **Figure 26-17**.

Tire Valves

The *tire valve*, or *valve stem*, **Figure 26-18**, is the means of adding air to the tire and wheel assembly. The tire valve is a rubber and metal assembly with a small *valve core* threaded into the center. The valve core contains the actual valve mechanism. Depressing the valve allows air to enter or leave the tire. Tire valves are always installed in the wheel rim.

Tire Pressure is Important

Vehicle manufacturers determine the proper tire and *inflation pressure* after extensive research. Tires must be inflated to recommended pressures. Proper inflation pressure is important for proper traction, riding comfort, fuel mileage, and tire wear. Note the effects of over, under, and proper inflation in **Figure 26-19**. Note how the full tread width of the correctly inflated tire (center illustration in **Figure 26-19**) contacts the surface of the road.

Overinflation will make the tire ride hard and more susceptible to casing (ply) breakage. Note how the overinflated tire bulges in the center, pulling the edges of the tire away

from the road. This produces rapid wear in the center and will not allow all of the tread to contact the road for best traction.

Underinflation will cause tire heating, produce mushy steering, and will not properly present the full tread area for traction. An underinflated tire will cause the sidewalls to flex excessively and will quickly generate damaging heat. In addition, the center of the tread will buckle up away from the road and cause rapid wear on the tire's outer edges.

Figure 26-20 shows an inflation pressure conversion chart. To provide proper steering, ride, wear, and dependability, keep the tire pressures within the manufacturer's recommended range. Inflate tires to recommended pressure when cold (preferably after the vehicle has been sitting overnight). A tire may be considered cold after standing out of direct sunlight for three or four hours.

When the vehicle is driven, the tire temperature rises. The rise will depend upon speed, load, road smoothness, and prevailing temperature. A cold tire at 24 psi (165 kPa) will build up pressure to about 29 psi (200 kPa) after four miles (6.4 km) at speeds over 40 mph (64.4 kmh).

When checking hot tires, the pressure will exceed cold specifications. Never let air out of a hot tire to get the specified cold inflation pressure. For heavy loads or sustained high speed driving, some tire manufacturers recommend increasing cold pressure 4 psi (25 kPa). Do not increase tire pressure above this.

Tire Rotation

Tire life can be extended by *tire rotation* at regular intervals. The front tires are placed at the rear before any front wheel misalignment can cause serious tire imbalance or tire wear. Tire rotation should be done about every 5000 miles (8000 km). **Figure 26-21** shows some popular methods of rotation, using both conventional and radial tires. Some tire manufacturers recommend that radial tires be rotated so they always turn in the same direction, as in the right hand illustration in **Figure 26-21**. The compact space saver spare tire should never be rotated.

Tire Runout and Balance

Tires must run reasonably true to prevent vibrations. **Figure 26-22** shows one set of *tire runout* measurements. Notice that tire runout is not as critical as wheel runout. As the tire is flexible, it can absorb some of its own inaccuracy. Wheels should also be checked for radial and lateral runout, **Figure 26-23**.

To operate smoothly, it is essential that a tire and wheel be properly *balanced*. Tire imbalance will cause poor ride, excessive tire wear, and steering and suspension component wear. The two major effects of imbalance are *wheel tramp* (tire and wheel hopping up and down), and *wheel shimmy* (shaking from side to side). For maximum tire wear and ride quality, all tires must be in static and dynamic balance.

Static Balance

When a tire is in proper *static balance*, the weight mass will be evenly distributed around the axis of rotation. If the wheel is raised from the floor and spun several times and it

CONSTRUCTION TYPES

DIAGONAL	DIAGONAL AND BELTED BIAS				RADIAL				
	78 Series	70 Series	60 Series	50 Series	Metric	78 Series	70 Series	60 Series	50 Series
6.15/155-13									
					155R13				
6.00-13					165R13				
	A78-13	A70-13	A60-13			AR78-13	AR70-13	AR60-13	
6.50-13	B78-13	B70-13	B60-13	B50-13	175R13	BR78-13	BR70-13	BR60-13	BR50-13
	C78-13	C70-13	C60-13	C50-13		CR78-13	CR70-13		CR50-13
7.00-13					185R13				
	D78-13	D70-13	D60-13	D50-13		DR78-13	DR70-13		
					195R13	ER78-13	195/70R-13	ER60-13	
					155R14				
	A78-14					AR78-14		AR60-14	
6.45-14	B78-14		B60-14		165R14	BR78-14			
6.95-14	C78-14	C70-14	C60-14		175R14	CR78-14	CR70-14		
	D78-14	D70-14	D60-14			DR78-14	DR70-14		
7.35-14	E78-14	E70-14	E60-14		185R14	ER78-14	ER70-14	ER60-14	
7.75-14	F78-14	F70-14	F60-14	F50-14	195R14	FR78-14	FR70-14	FR60-14	
8.25-14	G78-14	G70-14	G60-14	G50-14	205R14	GR78-14	GR70-14	GR60-14	GR50-14
8.55-14	H78-14	H70-14	H60-14	H50-14	215R14	HR78-14	HR70-14	HR60-14	
8.85-14	J78-14	J70-14	J60-14		225R14	JR78-14	JR70-14	JR60-14	JR50-14
		L70-14	L60-14				LR70-14	LR60-14	
				M50-14					
				N50-14					
	A78-15	A70-15				AR78-15			
	B78-15		B60-15	B50-15	165R15	BR78-15	BR70-15		
6.85-15	C78-15	C70-15	C60-15		175R15	CR78-15	CR70-15		
	D78-15	D70-15				DR78-15	DR70-15		
7.35-15	E78-15	E70-15	E60-15	E50-15	185R15	ER78-15	ER70-15	ER60-15	
7.75-15	F78-15	F70-15	F60-15		195R15	FR78-15	FR70-15	FR60-15	
8.25-15	G78-15	G70-15	G60-15	G50-15	205R15	GR78-15	GR70-15	GR60-15	GR50-15
8.55-15	H78-15	H70-15	H60-15	H50-15	215R15	HR78-15	HR70-15	HR60-15	HR50-15
8.85-15	J78-15	J70-15	J60-15		225R15	JR78-15	JR70-15	JR60-15	JR50-15
9.00-15		K70-15				KR78-15	KR70-15		
9.15-15	L78-15	L70-15	L60-15	L50-15	235R15	LR78-15	LR70-15	LR60-15	LR50-15
	M78-15					MR78-15	MR70-15		
8.90-15									
	N78-15			N50-15		NR78-15			
7.00-15									
6.00-16									

Figure 26-17. A tire size and construction "interchangeability" chart. There are a number of different charts used, listing almost any interchange that may be needed. (Rubber Manufacturers Assoc.)

Figure 26-18. A—In typical valve stem construction, the rubber body or stem houses the core. B—Valve core action. Note that the valve cap acts as second seal against air leakage, as well as preventing entry of dust. (Cadillac)

PSI	kPa	PSI	kPa
20	140	31	215
21	145	32	220
22	155	33	230
23	160	34	235
24	165	35	240
25	170	36	250
26	180	40	275
27	185	45	310
28	190	50	345
29	200	55	380
30	205	60	415
Conversion: 6.9 kPa = 1 psi			

Figure 26-20. Typical tire pressure conversion chart: psi = pounds per square inch and kPa = kilopascals (metric pressure measurement). You should also see the "Useful Conversion Tables" in the back of this text for exact conversion figures. (Chevrolet)

Figure 26-19. Inflation effect on tire and tread contact. Proper road contact can only be obtained with correct inflation. Notice the slight difference in sidewall bulge between the properly and improperly inflated radial tire. (Chevrolet and Ford)

Figure 26-21. Tire rotation recommendations as used by one manufacturer. Note that radial tires are only moved from front-to-back or back-to-front on the same side. Cross-switching (which reverses tire rotation) should not be done on radials. (Chevrolet)

always stops in a different place, it is statically balanced, **Figure 26-24**.

If the wheel revolves until one side is down, it is obvious that this side is heavier than the opposite side. The tire and wheel is statically imbalanced. Static imbalance is corrected by clipping lead weights to the rim edge opposite the heavy side.

Dynamic Balance

Dynamic balance is achieved when the weight mass is in the same plane as the centerline of the wheel. Note in **Figure 26-25** that the centerline of the weight mass is not in the same plane as the centerline of the wheel. When the wheel spins, centrifugal force will attempt to bring the weight mass centerline into the wheel centerline plane.

Weight mass 2 will attempt to move to the left. Weight mass 3 will attempt to move to the right. As the wheel revolves, the weight masses will reverse their positions, 2 will move to the right, 3 to the left. Each half turn of the wheel will

A

TIRE

DIAL INDICATOR

B

WHEEL

Figure 26-22. The wheel and tire runout must be within specific limits as set by the manufacturer. These limits will vary by manufacturer, and will differ depending on the material used for wheel construction—steel, aluminum, etc. Note the use of a dial indicator to obtain precise readings. (Honda)

A   B

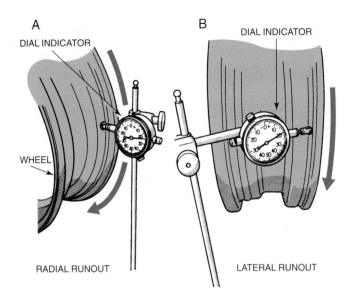

DIAL INDICATOR

DIAL INDICATOR

WHEEL

RADIAL RUNOUT   LATERAL RUNOUT

Figure 26-23. A—Checking a wheel for radial runout with a dial indicator. B—Checking the same wheel for excessive lateral runout. Wheels should be checked before the tire is mounted. (Chrysler)

BALANCE WEIGHT   TIRE   LIGHT AREA

WHEEL

A   B   C

Figure 26-24. A—Static balance weight. B and C—If more than one weight is necessary, it is essential that they be evenly distributed on each side of the light area (indicated by small vertical line). (Plymouth)

reverse the position of the weight masses., As each weight mass attempts to enter the wheel centerline plane, the opposing weight mass will pull it back, causing shimmy or wobble. This will cause tire, suspension, and steering wear.

Dynamic imbalance is corrected by adding lead wheel-weights to both sides of the rim, until the weight mass centerline is in the same plane as the wheel centerline, **Figure 26-26**. When this happens, the assembly is now dynamically balanced.

High Speeds and Overloading Produce Heat and Excessive Wear

The relationship between vehicle speed, overloading, and tire temperature is shown in **Figure 26-27**. Note how the heat goes up faster when a given tire is subjected to a 20% overload as opposed to the normal load. When tires operate at 250°-275°F (121°-135°C), they lose a great deal of strength and wear resistance.

High speed driving also affects tire tread wear. Higher speeds result in higher tire temperatures and increased tread

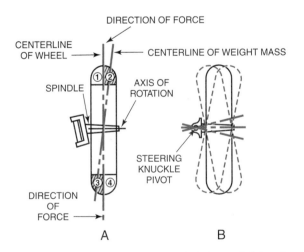

DIRECTION OF FORCE

CENTERLINE OF WHEEL   CENTERLINE OF WEIGHT MASS

SPINDLE

AXIS OF ROTATION

STEERING KNUCKLE PIVOT

DIRECTION OF FORCE

A   B

Figure 26-25. This tire is dynamically imbalanced. A is a front view and B is a top view. The weights on each side try to pull the tire into the centerline. As the tire approaches its centerline, the opposing weight pulls it away, creating wheel shimmy. (Plymouth)

wear. At 80 miles per hour, (128 kph) for example, tire temperatures build to the critical level, even under normal load. See **Figure 26-27**.

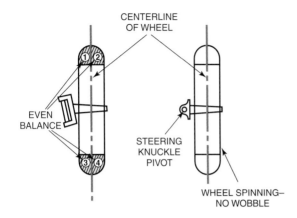

Figure 26-26. Dynamic balance. Note the absence of wheel wobble when dynamic balance is achieved.

Figure 26-27. Tire speed, load, and temperature graph. At high speeds, a small speed increase causes a large increase in the temperature. Note how overload raises temperature and reduces tire life. (Rubber Manufacturers Assoc.)

Summary

Wheel rims can be made of stamped steel, or custom wheels made of various materials. The wheel rims are fastened to the wheel hub using four to six lug nuts or bolts.

The wheel hubs rotate on tapered roller, straight roller, or ball bearings, and are lubricated by wheel bearing grease. Most front wheels use tapered roller bearings. Rear wheels are bolted to integral or detachable hubs.

Tires are an important part of the suspension system. They provide a cushioning effect to absorb some road shocks and supply the traction necessary for driving and braking. Rubber, fabric, and steel wires are used in tire construction. Special safety type tires are available. A wide variety of tread designs are manufactured. Most tires are the radial type.

Newly manufactured tires are graded using the Uniform Tire Quality Grading System. Tires and wheels must run true, and be balanced statically and dynamically. Lead wheel weights are used in balancing a tire and wheel assembly. Proper tire inflation is vital to good steering, riding quality, and tire life.

High speeds can ruin a tire. Excessive speed promotes heating resulting in a loss of tire strength and wear quality. Safe vehicle operation is also drastically reduced. Tires should be rotated every 5000 miles (8 046 km). Always double check when mounting wheels on a vehicle to make certain they are bolted on securely.

Know These Terms

Wheel rim	Bias-belted tire construction
Stamped steel	Radial tire construction
Custom wheel	Tire rating
Drop center	Speed rating
Safety ridges	Uniform tire quality grading system
Lug bolts	
Wheel lugs	Temperature resistance rating
Lug nuts	
Wheel nut torque	Traction rating
Torque stick	Tread wear rating
Wheel hub	Space saver spare tire
Tapered roller bearing	Tire valve
Straight roller bearing	Valve stem
Ball bearing	Valve core
Packed	Inflation pressure
Castellated nut	Overinflation
Safety washer	Underinflation
Cotter pin	Tire rotation
Staked nut	Tire runout
Traction	Tire balance
Bead	Wheel tramp
Plies	Wheel shimmy
Bias tire construction	Static balance
	Dynamic balance

Review Questions—Chapter 26

Do not write in this book. Write your answers on a separate sheet of paper.

1. Custom wheel rims can be made from _____ .
    (A) aluminum
    (B) magnesium
    (C) steel and aluminum
    (D) All of the above.

2. All of the following statements about wheel bearings are true, EXCEPT:
   (A) tapered roller bearings can be cleaned, regreased, and adjusted.
   (B) most newer vehicles use greasable ball bearings.
   (C) straight roller bearings used on front-wheel drive vehicles are replaced as a unit.
   (D) wheel bearings must be packed with quality, high temperature grease.

3. Air is sealed in the tire by the rim and tire _____ .

4. Which of the following parts should be replaced when tapered roller bearings are greased?
   (A) Safety washer.
   (B) Slotted nut.
   (C) Cotter pin.
   (D) Both A & C.

5. What is the advantage of the drop center steel wheel?

6. What are the two main functions of vehicle tires?

7. Technician A says that air is injected into the tire through a valve stem and core assembly. Technician B says that the valve core contains the actual valve mechanism. Who is right?
   (A) A only.
   (B) B only.
   (C) Both A & B.
   (D) Neither A nor B.

8. If an older vehicle was originally equipped with bias ply tires, what kind of replacement tires are usually available?
   (A) Bias tires only.
   (B) Bias or belted tires only.
   (C) Bias, belted, or radial tires.
   (D) Radial tires.

9. Technician A says that a tire in dynamic balance will also be in static balance. Technician B says that static balancing a tire will correct shimmy. Who is right?
   (A) A only.
   (B) B only.
   (C) Both A & B.
   (D) Neither A nor B.

10. Extreme wear on the outside on both sides of the tire tread indicates _____ .
    (A) overinflation
    (B) underinflation
    (C) incorrect toe
    (D) a bent wheel rim

11. The most commonly used tire construction type is the _____ .
    (A) radial
    (B) bias
    (C) bias belted
    (D) biased radial

12. List the three different Uniform Tire Quality Grading System categories.

13. Draw a diagram showing how radial tires should be rotated.

14. When rotating tires, the compact (space saver) spare must be used _____ .
    (A) in the front
    (B) in the back
    (C) for emergencies only
    (D) Either A or B.

15. How does high speed affect tire life?

16. Tires should be rotated every _____ miles/kilometers.
    (A) 5000/8000
    (B) 7500/12 000
    (C) 10,000/16 000
    (D) 15,000/32 000

17. Proper tire inflation pressure is important in four ways. Name them.

18. All of the following statements about tire inflation are true, EXCEPT:
    (A) a tire is considered cold after standing out of direct sunlight for four hours.
    (B) when the vehicle is driven, the temperature of its tires rises.
    (C) always let air out of hot tires to get specified cold pressure.
    (D) for heavy loads or sustained high speed driving, tire pressure can be increased by 4 psi (25 kPa).

19. Draw a cross section of a typical tire and name the various parts.

20. What part of the tire tread will wear out when a tire is underinflated?

27

Wheel Alignment

After studying this chapter, you will be able to:
- Explain the purpose of wheel alignment.
- Identify the major wheel alignment angles.
- Identify the most common related wheel alignment angles.
- Identify vehicle alignment adjustment devices.
- Identify suspension, steering, and tire factors which could affect alignment.

In Chapters 24 through 26, you learned about the design and components of the vehicle suspension system, steering system, and wheels and tires. This chapter discusses the principles of aligning all of these parts to provide optimum handling and tire wear. Although this process involves almost all of the steering and suspension components, it is commonly known as wheel alignment. After completion of this chapter, you will be able to explain wheel alignment angles and be familiar with the devices used to measure these angles.

Purpose of Wheel Alignment

It is not enough to merely place the front wheels on hubs, stand them up straight and devise a method of turning them from left to right. The vehicle could be driven, but it would steer poorly. At higher speeds, it would become dangerous to handle and tire life would be short. For good steering, handling, and smooth operation, the wheels must be precisely aligned.

Wheel Alignment Angles

Wheel alignment is the process of measuring and correcting the various angles formed by the front and rear wheels, spindles, and steering arms. Correct alignment is vital. Improper alignment can cause hard steering, pulling to one side, wandering, noise, and rapid tire wear.

Types of Wheel Alignment

Rear-wheel drive vehicles require a *two-wheel alignment*, or front-wheel alignment only. The rear wheels are attached to a solid rear axle assembly which cannot be adjusted, and generally stays in alignment throughout the life of the vehicle.

Today, most front-wheel drive vehicles have provisions for adjusting the rear wheels. In addition, many rear-wheel drive vehicles are equipped with independent rear

suspensions, which also must be adjusted. Also, modern solid rear axles and suspension systems are lightweight and can become misaligned. Therefore, the *four-wheel alignment*, in which the front and rear wheel alignment angles are checked and adjusted, is commonly performed.

Adjustable front wheel settings on most modern vehicles are caster, camber, and toe. Nonadjustable settings are steering axis inclination and toe-out on turns. Rear wheel settings that can be made on many modern vehicles are camber and toe. Modern practice is to check both front and rear wheel alignment. Note that the various alignment angles are all related. A change in one can alter the others.

Alignment Measurement Values

All alignment values, except for toe, are measured in degrees. Degrees is the unit of measurement for angles. One degree is 1/360 of a circle. Toe is measured in fractions of an inch or millimeters.

Caster

Everyone is familiar with the common caster used on some furniture. You may have wondered why the little wheel always swivels around and trails almost obediently behind a chair or dresser leg. The reason is simple.

Referring to **Figure 27-1**, you will see that the centerline about which the caster wheel swivels strikes the floor ahead of it. If the caster attempts to move to either side, the point of resistance between the caster and the floor will be to the side of the swivel centerline.

Figure 27-1. A chair leg caster. The centerline of the swivel axis contacts the floor ahead of the caster wheel contact point.

Since the caster is encountering some resistance to forward motion, it will not move until the moving weight mass actually drags it forward. However, it cannot be dragged forward until all the slack is taken up. In this case, it will not move straight forward until it is directly in back of the swivel centerline. **Figure 27-2** illustrates how resistance to forward motion forces a trailing object (caster wheel) to line up behind the moving swivel line.

Figure 27-2. To demonstrate the caster effect, as the table leg B starts to move to the right, the caster wheel, which is off to one side encounters a tooling resistance. This resistance forces the wheel to line up and trail directly behind the table leg in C.

The application of the caster principle to vehicles involves the placement of the *steering axis*. The steering axis is formed by the upper and lower ball joints, strut mount, etc., **Figure 27-3**. This creates *caster*, which can be either positive or negative.

Positive Caster

By tilting the top of the steering knuckle toward the rear of the car, the centerline of the axis, or steering point, will be in front of the point at which the tire encounters the road. As this places the point of resistance to forward motion behind the steering centerline, the wheel is forced to track behind, automatically lining up with the moving car. This is referred to as *positive caster*, **Figure 27-4**.

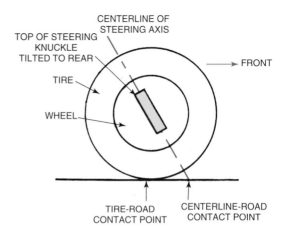

Figure 27-4. Positive caster. Steering axis (swivel axis) strikes the road in front of the tire-to-road contact point. The wheel will trail behind the steering axis centerline-to-road contact point. (Tilt shown is exaggerated.)

Positive caster tends to force the wheels to travel in a straight ahead position. It also assists in recovery (wheels turning back to straight ahead position) after making a turn. On late model cars, there is often little or no positive caster. Positive caster makes it more difficult to turn the wheels from the straight ahead position than when no caster angle is present.

Another aspect of positive caster is a mild tipping effect when cornering. When making a right turn, the right wheel will cause the steering knuckle to raise slightly, while the left wheel will allow the knuckle to lower, creating the tipping effect. If the left side of the vehicle was allowed to rise during a right turn, it would have an adverse effect on the vehicle's cornering ability. When the wheels are turned to the left, the left side raises and the right side drops.

Negative Caster

To ease turning, many cars employ a *negative caster* angle, which angles the top of the steering knuckle to front of

Figure 27-3. The steering axis is formed by the ball joint and strut position. A—Negative caster. B—Postive caster. (Hunter Engineering Company.)